Conceptual Physical Science

Explorations

Paul G. Hewitt
John Suchocki
Leslie A. Hewitt

Teacher's Guide
to Text and Laboratory Manual

Addison
Wesley

San Francisco Boston New York
Capetown Hong Kong London Madrid Mexico City
Montreal Munich Paris Singapore Sydney Tokyo Toronto

Cover Credit: "Primal Motion"
Michael T. Stewart ©/Molten Images.com

ISBN: 0-321-05170-X

3 4 5 6 7 8 9 10 - MAL - 04 03

www.aw.com/physics

To Science Editor Ben Roberts

who initiated *Conceptual Physical Science—Explorations*

Table of Contents
Conceptual Physical Science—*Explorations*
Teaching Guide

Part 8 Astronomy

Appendices

Laboratory Suggestions, with Answers to Lab Manual Questions

Introduction

This guide describes a way to teach physical science conceptually. People with a conceptual understanding of physical science are more alive to the world, just as a botanist taking a stroll through a wooded park is more alive than most of us to the trees, plants, flora, and the life that teems in them. The richness of life is not only seeing the world with wide open eyes, but knowing what to look for. This puts the physical science teacher in a very nice role—being the one who points out the connections of nature. Such a teacher is in a good position to add meaning to students' lives.

Your influence goes beyond the students you face in class, for it is passed on to others through them. Many of your students will become teachers in elementary school, where they must feel good about science as they impart science to their students. In our profession, we can never tell where our influence stops. It will touch younger people in their precious years, when the world "out there" is wonderful and exciting. It will touch kids who wonder about stars, clouds, wind, rocks, electronic and mechanical gadgets, plants, animals, and food. What must be turned around is the finding of recent studies that the more science a student has in school, the *less* likely the student is to opt for a career in science. Science courses, too often, are the "killer courses" in schools. Let *Conceptual Physical Science—Explorations* not be one of them! The rigor in tilling a field has more to do with the depth of the plow setting than the field itself. *Conceptual Physical Science—Explorations*, with the plow not too deep and not too shallow, can be a favorite and meaningful course for both you and your students.

Teaching

Knowledge is acquired layers at a time, each layer supported by the layer beneath. Students don't learn science concepts unless they tie to something they already understand—hence the emphasis on *analogies* in this guide and the textbook. Use analogies in your teaching whenever possible. You may find that your students are an excellent source of new analogies and examples to supplement those in the text. A productive class assignment is:

> Choose one (or more) of the concepts presented in the reading assignment and cite any illustrative analogies or examples that *you* can think of.

This exercise not only prompts your students to make connections between their own experience and the concepts being learned, but adds to your future teaching material.

We can paraphrase William James, who stated that "wisdom is knowing what to overlook," and say that good teaching is knowing what to omit. It is important to distinguish between what to skim over and what to concentrate on. Too often a teacher will spend precious class time digging into non-central and non-essential material. How nice for the student when class time is stimulating and the material covered is central and relevant.

This text begins with physics, with its supply of equations. These are important in a conceptual course—not as a recipe for plugging in numerical values, but as a guide to thinking. The equation tells the student what variables to consider in treating an idea. In physics, for example, how much an object accelerates depends not only on the net force, but on mass as well. The formula $a = F/m$ reminds one to consider both quantities. Does gravitation depend on an object's speed? Consideration of $F \sim mM/d^2$ shows that it doesn't, and so forth. The problems at the ends of many chapters involve computations that help to illustrate concepts rather than to challenge your students' mathematical abilities. The number of problems are intentionally few to avoid overload. Please do not turn this course into a number-crunching one.

There are no answers to exercises and problems in the textbook, which will perplex students who expect answers at the end of the book. Because of the variety of philosophies that teachers have about when and whether to provide answers, all solutions to exercises and problems, in student-oriented detail, are included at the end of each chapter discussion in this guide. So you decide whether you wish to copy, post, distribute, or whatever. It's your course.

Before moving on to new material in class, provide your students with a self check after important ideas and concepts are presented. After presenting an idea and supporting it with examples, state: "If you understand this—if you really do—then you can answer the following question." Then pose a question slowly and clearly, best in multiple-choice form or such that a short answer is called for. Ask the class to make a response—perhaps written. Then ask them to compare their answers to their neighbors' papers, and depending on the importance of the question, ask them to briefly discuss it with their neighbors. Several of this type questions in class brings the students into an active role. It mainly clears misconceptions before they are carried along into new material. We call these questions, CONCEPT CHECKS, in the textbook and in the suggested discussions on the following pages of this guide. The concept-check procedure may also be used to *introduce* ideas. A discussion of the question, the answer, and some of the misconceptions associated with it, will get more attention than the same idea presented as a statement of fact. And one of the neat features of asking for neighbor participation is that it gives you pause to reflect on your delivery. Such reflections can be very worthwhile!

We strongly recommend lecture notes. Even quite abbreviated notes will remind you of points you wish to cover in your presentation—which can be scanned during your check-your-neighbor interludes. Such notes insure you don't forget main points, and a mark or two lets you know next time what you missed or where you stopped.

Most suggested presentations in this guide require more than one class period, depending on your pace of instruction and what you add or omit. Teachers have their own teaching styles, and we present our lecture discussions only to show what works for us (more question asking and less professing—we pose many more check questions than the samples in this guide). Whatever your teaching style, you may find these suggested lectures quite useful, and a means to jump off and develop your own non-computational way of teaching.

IN YOUR TEACHING, BETTER TO BE A GUIDE ON THE SIDE THAN A SAGE ON THE STAGE!

Ancillaries

Make use of the **NEXT-TIME QUESTIONS** book, which has challenging questions for every chapter and appendix of the text. They should be presented after your students have finished covering a concept. Select pages can be photocopied and used on display boards to capture attention and provoke discussion. They can also be made into transparencies to be used as a brain teaser for homework and for class discussion. So conclude your lessons with them in class as bridges to the next class meeting, or post them in the hallway for all to ponder. They are best used when there is a few-day gap between question and posted answer.

The student book, **Conceptual Physical Science EXPLORATIONS PRACTICE BOOK**, can serve as a tutor on the side. The book is chock full of insightful and interesting activities called EXPLORATIONS for every chapter, and for Appendices C and D. They prompt your students to engage their minds and DO physical science. Reduced answered pages are at the back of the book, allowing students feedback to their own work. This is done knowing that a few students will simply look at the answers before trying their own. You'll have a good class if most avoid this shortcut. The Practice Pages should not be graded, which encourages peeking at the back. They are what the name implies—practice. Assessment can be made with questions from the Test Bank, not the Practice Book.

The **Test Bank** is a compilation of questions by the authors, available in book form and on Test Gen software CD-ROM (PC and Macintosh compatible).

There is a booklet of blackline masters, **Assessment Masters: Pre Tests and Semester Tests**, that are questions by the authors that are not in the Test Bank. Each chapter has a test of true-false, multiple choice, and short answer questions. There are also tests of 20 multiple-choice questions for each of the eight parts of the book.

LABORATORY MANUAL: The laboratory manual, by Hewitt, Suchocki, Hewitt, and Baird, includes simple activities to precede the coverage of course material as well as experiments that are a follow through to course material. Instructions and answers to most of the lab questions are included at the end of this guide.

VIDEOTAPES: For the physics part of your course is a video lecture series of 34 lessons, *Conceptual Physics Alive!* These are on videotapes or DVDs. They feature Paul Hewitt's classroom lectures while teaching Conceptual Physics at the University of Hawaii in 1989-1990. Although the setting was a university, high school students overwhelmingly make up the viewers of these taped lessons. They are as entertaining as they are informative. If you're not familiar with them, get a sample DVD or videotape from Conceptual Productions, www.conprod.com. For the chemistry part of this course, John Suchocki has made videos that focus on demonstrations in chemistry. Contact Conceptual Productions for information on obtaining any of these lessons.

Please bring to our attention any errors you find in this manual, in the textbook, or its ancillaries. We welcome correspondence suggesting improvements in the presentation of physical science, and we answer mail [Pghewitt@aol.com; Lahewitt@aol.com; Jasuchocki @aol.com]. Good luck in your course!

Some Teaching Tips

• Attitude toward students and attitude about science in general is of utmost importance: Consider yourself not the master in your classroom, but the main resource person, the pace setter, and the guide. Consider yourself a bridge between your students' ignorance and some of the information you've acquired in your study. Guide their study—steer them away from the dead ends you encountered, and keep them on essentials and away from time-draining peripherals. You are there to help them. If they see you so, they'll appreciate your efforts. This is a matter of self-interest. An appreciated teacher has an altogether richer teaching experience than an under-appreciated teacher.

• Don't be a "know-it-all." When you don't know the answer to a question, don't pretend you do. You'll lose more respect faking knowledge, than not having it. If you're new to teaching, students will understand you're still pulling it together, and will respect you nonetheless. But if you fake it, and some of your students CAN tell, whatever respect you've earned plummets.

• Be firm, and expect good work of your students. But be fair and get papers graded and returned quickly. Be sure the bell curve of grades reflects a reasonable average. If you have excellent students, some should score 100% or near 100% on exams. The least respected teacher in this author's memory was one who made exams so difficult that the class average was near the noise level, where the highest marks were some 50%.

• Be sure that the knowledge you want your students to acquire is reflected by your test items. The student question, "Will that be on the test?" is a *good* question. What is important—by definition—is what's on the test. If you consider a topic important, include it so you allow your students credit for their feedback on it.

• Consider having students repeat work that you judge to be poor—before it gets a final grade. A note on a paper saying you'd rather not grade it until they've given it another try is the mark of a concerned and caring teacher.

• Do less professing and more questioning. Information that is of value ought to be the answer to a question. "Check your neighbor" should be an important feature of your class. Beware of the pitfall of too quickly answering your own questions.

• Show respect for your students. Although all your students are more ignorant of science than you are, some are more intelligent than you are. Underestimating their intelligence is likely overestimating your own. Respect is a two-way street.

Classroom Drawing Techniques

I vividly remember as a student how annoyed I was with a professor who couldn't draw a simple cube in his lectures. He'd make an attempt, step back and look at it, wipe part of it from the board and patch it here and there with little improvement. He always ended up with a "cube" with non-parallel sides. I thought, "He's forever overloading us with homework assignments that take up entire weekends and he won't take a few minutes of his own time to learn how to draw a simple cube." Teachers have a responsibility to improve their art skills if that art is part of their presentation. Only a small amount of practice is needed.

A step-by-step method for drawing a cube is shown at the right. The important key is keeping the vertical lines vertical, and the other two sets of lines parallel to one another. Simply draw a "square" tilted for perspective, draw its twin slightly displaced, then connect the two with parallel lines. For a finishing touch, wipe away part of the lines to indicate which lines are behind.

Copy your favorite comic strip characters a few times, and you'll have developed enough skill to show improved drawing with your classes. The added respect you'll get from your students is well worth the effort. Stick figures are easiest to draw. If you learn to draw a few of these, you can go a step further and use double lines for a full figure, as shown. Either way has merit. The number of individual drawings you'll do in class is likely small in number—perhaps a dozen or so. Variations on a few basic drawings results in many drawings. For example, a person running along the street can be easily changed to a person pitching a ball. This and others are shown on the following three pages, step by step. I suggest you try your hand at these on your chalkboard or overhead transparencies. Take your time doing these, and after the motor skill is programmed in you, work on speed. You're highly successful when you can casually draw an illustration at about the pace you write a formula on the board. So give these a try, then try copying your favorite comic strip characters. Good Energy!

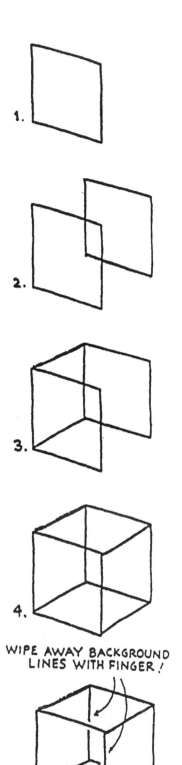

WIPE AWAY BACKGROUND LINES WITH FINGER !

Draw Me ... Step by step!

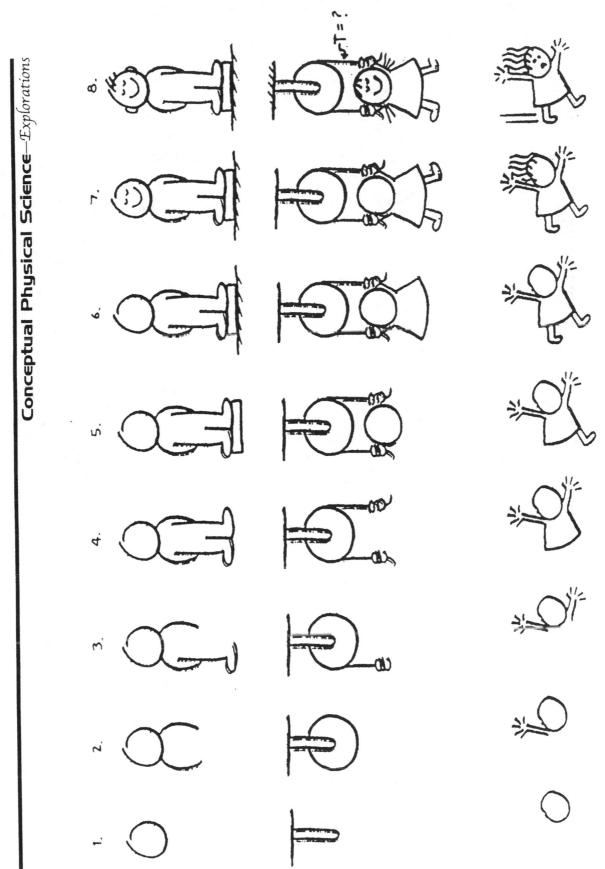

7

Draw Me ... Step by step!

1.

2.

3.

4.

5.

6.

7.

8.

9.

10.

Draw Me ... Step by step!

I About Science

Learning Objectives
After studying Chapter 1, students will be able to:
• Outline the 5 steps of the scientific method.
• Distinguish between an observation and a fact.
• Distinguish between a fact and a hypothesis.
• Distinguish between a hypothesis and a law or principle.
• Distinguish between the everyday meaning and the scientific meaning of theory.
• Explain why the refinement of theories is a strength in science.
• Distinguish between science and technology.

Possible Misconceptions to Correct
• **Not so!** Physics is applied mathematics.
• **Not so!** Facts are unchangeable.
• **Not so!** A theory is a scientific word for guess.
• **Not so!** It is bad science to change your mind.
• **Not so!** Science and technology are the same.
• **Not so!** Hypothesis and theory are two words for the same thing.

Unlike other texts that begin with the customary treatment of measurements, significant figures, and system of measurements (that are anything but exciting to most students) the goal of this chapter is to introduce the scientific process. This is captured in the cartooned statements. The authors don't lecture on this chapter, and instead assign it as reading. The boxes on pseudoscience and risk assessment should be excellent for student discussions.

In the **Explorations Practice Book:**
• Making Hypotheses

In the **Next-Time Questions** book:
• Hypotheses

In the **Lab Manual:**
• Tuning the Senses (enhancing perception)
• Making Cents (introduces the mass balance and the making of a simple graph)

1.1 A Brief History of Advances in Science

The roots of science are found in every culture. The Chinese discovered printing, the compass, and rockets; Islam cultures developed algebra and lenses; mathematicians in India developed the concept of zero and infinity. This text, nevertheless, emphasizes western science. Science did advance faster in western rather than eastern cultures, largely because of the different social and political climates. While early Greeks in an era of experimental democracy and freethinking were questioning their speculations about the world, their counterparts in the more authoritarian eastern parts of the world were largely occupied in absorbing the knowledge of their forebears. In regions like China, absorbing this knowledge was the key to personal success. So scientific progress in eastern cultures was without the early period of questioning that accelerated the scientific advances of Europe and Eurasia. In any event, it is important to emphasize throughout your course that all **science is a human endeavor**. It is a human activity that answers questions of human interest. It is done by and for humans.

You may consider elaborating the idea that the test of correctness in science is experiment. As Einstein once said, "many experiments may show that I'm right, but it takes only one experiment (that can be repeated) to show that I'm wrong." Ideas must be verifiable by other scientists. In this way science tends to be self-correcting.

1.2 Mathematics and Conceptual Physical Science

The mathematical structure of physical science is evident in this book by the many equations. These are shorthand notations of the connections and relationships of nature. They are seen as guides to thinking, and only secondarily as recipes for solving problems.

1.3 The Scientific Method—A Classic Tool

The scientific method is given in a 5-step form. We say that science is structured common sense. The scientific method is an example. The scientific method is to be seen as a sensible way to go about investigating nature. Although the five steps are useful, they don't merit your students memorizing them.

1.4 Scientific Hypotheses

Distinguish between *hypothesis, theory, fact,* and *concept.* Point out that theory and hypothesis are not the same. A **theory** applies to a synthesis of a large body of information. The criterion of a theory is not whether it is true or untrue, but rather whether it is useful or nonuseful. It is useful even though the ultimate causes of the phenomena it encompasses are unknown. For example, we accept the theory of gravitation as a useful synthesis of available knowledge that relates to the mutual attraction of bodies. The theory can be refined, or with new information it can take on a new direction. It is important to acknowledge the common misunderstanding of what a scientific theory is, as revealed by those who say, "But it is not a fact; it is *only* a theory." Many people have the mistaken notion that a theory is tentative or speculative, while a fact is absolute.

Impress upon your class that a **fact** is not immutable and absolute, but is generally a close agreement by competent observers of a series of observations of the same phenomena. The observations must be testable. Since the activity of science is the determination of the most probable, there are no absolutes. Facts that were held to be absolute in the past are seen altogether differently in the light of present-day knowledge.

By **concept**, we mean the intellectual framework that is part of a theory. We speak of the concept of time, the concept of energy, or the concept of a force field. Time is related to motion in space and is the substance of the Theory of Special Relativity. We find that energy exists in tiny grains, or quanta, which is a central concept in the Quantum Theory. An important concept in Newton's Theory of Universal Gravitation is the idea of a force field that surrounds a material body. A concept envelops the overriding idea that underlies various phenomena. Thus, when we think "conceptually" we envelop a generalized way of looking at things.

Prediction in science is different from prediction in other areas. In the everyday sense, one speaks of predicting what has not yet occurred, like whether or not it will rain next weekend. In science, however, prediction is not so much about what *will* happen, but about what *is* happening and is not yet noticed, like what the properties of a hypothetical particle are and are not. A scientist predicts what can and cannot happen, rather than what will or will not happen.

1.5 A Scientific Attitude Underlies Good Science
Expand on the idea that honesty in science is not only a matter of public interest, but is a matter of self-interest. Any scientist who misrepresents or fudges data, or is caught lying about scientific information, is ostracized by the scientific community. There are no second chances. The high standards for acceptable performance in science, unfortunately, do not extend to other fields that are as important to the human condition. For example, consider the standards of performance required of politicians.

1.6 Science Has Limitations
Just as a great strength of a democracy is its openness to criticism, likewise with science. This is in sharp contrast to dogma, which is seen as absolute. The limitations of science, like those of democracy, are open for improvement. The world has suffered enormously from those who have felt their views were beyond question.

1.7 The Search For Order—Science, Art, and Religion
Einstein said "Science without religion is deaf; religion without science is blind." The topic of religion in a science text is rare. We treat it briefly only to address what is foremost on many students' minds. Do religion and science contradict each other? Must one choose between them? We hope our very brief treatment presents a satisfactory answer to these questions. Since September 11, 2001, the footnote in this section of the textbook should be in bold letters: "Of course this doesn't apply to certain fundamentalists, Christian, Moslem, or otherwise, who steadfastly assert that one cannot embrace both their brand of religion and science". As was horribly shown at the WTC, September 11, 2001, religious (and political) extremists certainly do have a conflict with science and rational thinking in general.

1.8 Technology—Practical Use of The Findings Of Science
In discussions of science and technology and their side effects, a useful statement is: *You can never do just one thing*. Doing *this* affects *that*. This is similar to "there is never just one force" in discussions of Newton's third law.

1.9 The Physical Sciences: Physics, Chemistry, Geology, and Astronomy
With regard to science courses and liberal arts courses, there is a central factor that makes it difficult for liberal arts students to delve into science courses the way that science students can delve into liberal arts courses—and that's the **vertical nature of science courses.** They build upon each other, as noted by their prerequisites. A science student can take an intermediate course in literature, poetry, or history at any time, and in any order. But in no way can a humanities student take an intermediate physics or chemistry course without first having a foundation in elementary physics and mathematics. Hence the importance of this conceptual course.

Chapter 1 Answers and Solutions

Key Terms and Matching Definitions

__4__ fact
__5__ law
__3__ hypothesis
__7__ pseudoscience
__1__ science
__2__ scientific method
__8__ technology
__6__ theory

Review Questions

1. What is science? (Name the two major aspects of science which are discussed in the first paragraphs of this chapter.)
   First: organized common sense, thinking, and observation that forms a body of knowledge; second: a process of discovering and organizing data about nature.

2. What discovery in the 15th century greatly advanced progress in science?
   The discovery of the printing press.

3. Throughout the ages, has acceptance or resistance usually been the general reaction to new ideas about established "truths"?
   Resistance.

4. When was the mathematical structure of science discovered?
   In the 16th century.

5. Why is mathematical problem solving not a major feature of this book?
   Too much emphasis on math diminishes the focus on what this book is about—learning concepts.

6. Outline the steps of the scientific method.
   1. **Recognize a question or a problem.**
   2. **Make an educated guess—a hypothesis—to answer the question.**
   3. **Predict consequences that can be observed if the hypothesis is correct. The consequences should be *absent* if the hypothesis is not correct.**
   4. **Do experiments to see if the consequences you predicted are present.**
   5. **Formulate the simplest general rule that organizes the three ingredients—hypothesis, predicted effects, and experimental findings.**

7. Distinguish among a scientific fact, a hypothesis, a law, and a theory.
   Whereas a *fact* is generally a close agreement by competent observers of a series of observations of the same phenomenon, a *hypothesis* is an educated guess, which when verified may become a *law*. A scientific *theory* is a synthesis of a large body of information that encompasses well-tested and verified hypotheses.

8. What is the hallmark of a scientific hypothesis?
   That it be testable.

9. How many experiments are necessary to invalidate a scientific hypothesis?
   Only one, providing it is repeatable.

10. In science, what kind of ideas are generally accepted?
Those that are testable.

11. Why is honesty a matter of self-interest to a scientist?
The scientist is in an arena where falsehood will sooner or later be found, and discredit that scientist.

12. What is meant by the term supernatural, and why does science not deal with it?
Supernatural is "above nature," not in the domain of science which deals only with the domain of nature.

13. How are science and the arts similar?
They both predict experiences.

14. Why are students of the arts encouraged to learn about science and science students encouraged to learn about the arts?
Learning both provides a fuller and more rounded education.

15. Why do many people believe they must choose between science and religion?
Because they assume they address the same realms, which they normally don't.

16. How do scientists regard "not knowing" in general?
Not knowing is a part of the study of science, so scientists are used to it and accept it (while some people fight it).

17. Clearly distinguish between science and technology.
Science has to do with gathering and organizing knowledge; technology puts that knowledge into practice and provides the tools needed for finding more.

18. Cite at least two examples of the physical sciences, and two from the life sciences.
Physics, chemistry, earth science, meteorology, and astronomy fall into the physical sciences. Botany, zoology, and biology fall into the category of the life sciences.

19. Of physics, chemistry, and biology, which science is the least complex? The most complex? (At your school, which of these is the "easiest" and which is the "hardest" as a science course?)
Science wise, physics is the least complex, with chemistry next, then biology as the most complex of all. (Often a biology course demands less mastery than a physics course, and may be easier.)

20. How does material in this section relate to the opening photo on page 1 of this book?
The perspective of this section is condensed in little Sarah's question.

Solutions to Chapter 1 Exercises

1. In daily life people are often praised for maintaining some particular point of view, for the "courage of their convictions." A change of mind is seen as a sign of weakness. How is this different in science?
   A change of mind is a strength of science, enabling refinements in theories.

2. In daily life we see many cases of people who are caught misrepresenting things and who soon thereafter are excused and accepted by their contemporaries. How is this different in science?
   There are no second chances in the scientific community for scientists who misrepresent or lie about experimental data.

3. Which of the following are scientific hypotheses?
   (a) Chlorophyll makes grass green. (b) The Earth rotates about its axis because living things need an alternation of light and darkness. (c) Tides are caused by the moon.
   a. **This is a scientific hypothesis, for it can be tested. For example, you can extract chlorophyll for grass and note its color.** *b.* **This statement is an assertion with no test for validity.** *c.* **The test of observation and correlation of tidal movements with that of the moon makes this a scientific hypothesis.**

4. In answer to the question, "When a plant grows, where does the material come from?" Aristotle hypothesized by logic that all material came from the soil. Do you consider his hypothesis to be correct, incorrect, or partially correct? What experiments do you propose to support your choice?
   Aristotle's hypothesis was partially correct, for material that makes up the plant comes partly from the soil, but mainly from the air and water. An experiment would be to weigh a pot of soil with a small seedling, then weigh the potted plant later after it has grown. The fact that the grown plant will weigh more is evidence that the plant is composed of more material than the soil offers. By keeping a record of the weight of water used to water the plant, and covering the soil with plastic wrap to minimize evaporation losses, the weight of the grown plant can be compared to the weight of water it absorbs. How can the weight of air taken in by the plant be estimated?

5. What is probably being misunderstood by a person who says, "But that's only a scientific theory"?
   What is likely being misunderstood is the distinction between theory and hypothesis. In common usage, "theory" may mean a guess or hypothesis, something that is tentative or speculative. But in science a theory is a synthesis of a large body of validated information (e.g., cell theory or quantum theory). The value of a theory is its usefulness (not its "truth").

6. a. Make an argument for bringing to a halt the advances of technology.

   b. Make an argument that advances in technology should continue.

   c. Contrast your two arguments.
   The answers to these are open ended.

2 Newton's First Law of Motion — Inertia

Learning Objectives

After studying Chapter 2, students will be able to:
• Distinguish between Aristotle's classifications of natural and unnatural motion.
• State the difference between Aristotle's focus on classification and Galileo's focus on experimentation.
• Describe Galileo's contribution to the science of motion.
• Distinguish between speed and velocity.
• Define inertia.
• State Newton's first law of motion.
• Distinguish between force and net force.
• Explain what the Equilibrium Rule, $\Sigma F = 0$, means.
• Define support force.
• Distinguish between static equilibrium and dynamic equilibrium.
• Explain how an object not connected to the ground continues moving with the moving Earth.

Possible Misconceptions to Correct

• **Not so!** Speed and velocity are two words for the same concept.
• **Not so!** Constant motion requires a force.
• **Not so!** Inertia is a force.
• **Not so!** The sun moves around the stationary Earth.

Demonstration Equipment

• Coat hanger and clay blobs (pictured on the next page)
• Wooden block stapled to a piece of cloth (to simulate table-cloth pull)
• Tablecloth (without a hem) and a few dishes (for the table-cloth pull)

Kinematics is the study of motion without regard to the forces that produce it. When forces are considered, the study is then of dynamics. One of the great follies of physics instruction is overtime on kinematics. Whereas many physics and physical science books begin with a chapter on kinematics, such is avoided in this book. The amount of kinematics that is needed is blended into this and the following chapter. As such, please do not focus undue attention to the concepts of speed, velocity, and acceleration. And please spare your students graphical analysis of these topics, which is better left to a math class or a follow-up physics course. Mastering motion graphs is more of an uphill task than getting a grip on the concepts themselves (but try telling that to a teacher who has a passion for graphical analysis!). The concepts of speed, velocity, and acceleration are nicely treated in the following mechanics chapters anyway, when your students are better prepared. Beginning with these topics can bog a course down at the outset. So lightly treat the sections on speed and velocity, and then move as smoothly as you can to where the meat is—Newton's first law.

Of particular interest to me (PG Hewitt) is the Personal Essay in the chapter, which relates to events that inspired me to pursue a life in physics—my meeting with Burl Grey on the sign-painting stages of Miami, Florida. Relative tensions in supporting cables is what first caught my interest in physics, and I hope to instill the same interest with your students with this chapter. It begins with a historical perspective, so if you're a history buff, you may want to expand on this.

Note that in introducing force I first use pounds—most familiar to your students. A quick transition, without fanfare, introduces the newton. I don't make units a big deal and don't get into the laborious task of unit conversions, which is more appropriate for physics majors.

The distinction between mass and weight will await the following chapter, when it's needed in Newton's second law. I see the key to good instruction as treating somewhat difficult topics only when they are required. For example, I see as pedagogical folly spending the first week on unit conversions, vector notation, graphical analysis, and scientific notation. How much better if the first week is a hook to promote class interest, with these things introduced later if or when they are needed.

A brief treatment of units and systems of measurement are provided in Appendix A.

In the **Explorations Practice Book**:
• Inertia
• The Equilibrium Rule: $\Sigma F = 0$
• The Equilibrium Rule: $\Sigma F = 0$
• Free Fall Speed

In the **Next-Time Questions** Book:
• Pellet in the Spiral
• Ball Swing

In the **Lab Manual**:
If you get into motion you can consider the Sonic Ranger lab, which uses a sonar ranging device to plot in real time the motion of students, rolling ball, or whatever. The lab is scheduled, however, for the following chapter where students will learn about acceleration. This lab can be intriguing, so be careful that it doesn't swallow too much time. Again, overtime on kinematics is the black hole of physics teaching!

There is no **OHT** (Overhead Transparency) for this chapter.

SUGGESTED PRESENTATION

Your first question: What means of motion has done more to change the way cities are built than any other? Answer: The elevator!

2.1 Aristotle's Classification of Motion
Briefly discuss Aristotle's views on motion. His views were a good beginning for his time. They were flawed from the point of view of what we know today, but his efforts to classify all things, motion being one of them, was a boost in human thinking. Perhaps we remember him too much for his errors, when in total, he did much to shape good thinking in his time.

2.2 Galileo's Concept of Inertia
Acknowledge the chief difference with Aristotle's approach and that of Galileo. The big difference between these two giant intellects, was **the role of experiment**—emphasized by Galileo. The legendary experiment at the Leaning Tower of Pisa is a good example. Interestingly, legend has it that many people who saw the falling objects fall together continued to teach otherwise. Seeing is not always believing. Ideas that are firmly established in one's thinking are difficult to change. People in science must be prepared to have their thinking challenged often.

2.3 Galileo Formulated the Concepts of Speed and Velocity
Speed and Velocity
Define speed, writing its equation in longhand form on the board while giving examples—automobile speedometers, etc. Similarly define velocity, citing how a racecar driver is interested in his *speed*, whereas an airplane pilot is interested in her *velocity*—speed and direction. Tell your class that you're not going to make a big deal about distinguishing between speed and velocity, but you are going to make a big deal of distinguishing between speed or velocity and another concept—*acceleration* (next chapter).

2.4 Motion Is Relative
Acknowledge that motion is relative to a frame of reference. When walking down the aisle of a train at 1 m/s, your speed relative to the floor of the train is different than your speed relative to the ground. If the train is moving at 50 m/s, then your speed relative to the ground is 51 m/s if you're walking forward, or 49 m/s if you're walking toward the rear of the train. Common sense.

2.5 Newton's First Law of Motion—The Law of Inertia
Begin by pointing to an object in the room and stating that if it started moving, one would reasonably look for a cause for its motion. We would say that a force of some kind was responsible, and that would seem reasonable. Tie this idea to the notion of force maintaining motion as Aristotle saw it. State that a cannonball remains at rest in the cannon until a force is applied, and that the force of expanding gases drives the ball out of the barrel when it is fired. (I have a 10-cm-diameter solid steel sphere, actually a huge ball bearing, that I use in this lecture. Use one, or a bowling ball, if available.) But what keeps the cannonball moving when the gases no longer act on it? This leads you into a discussion of inertia. In the everyday sense, inertia refers to a habit or a rut. In physics it's another word for laziness, or the resistance to change as far as the state of motion of an object is concerned. I roll the ball along the lecture table to show its tendency to keep rolling. Inertia was first introduced not by Newton, but by Galileo as a result of his inclined-plane experiments.

> DEMONSTRATION: Show that inertia refers also to objects at rest with the classic *tablecloth-and-dishes demonstration*. [Be sure to pull the tablecloth slightly downward so there is no upward component of force on the dishes!] I precede this demo with a simpler

version, a simple block of wood on a piece of cloth—but with a twist. I ask what the block will do when I suddenly whip the cloth toward me. After a neighbor check, I surprise the class when they see that the block has been stapled to the cloth! This illustrates Newton's zeroth law—be skeptical. Then I follow up with the classic tablecloth demo. Don't think the classic demo is too corny, for your students will really love it.

Of course when we show a demonstration to illustrate a particular concept, there is almost always more than one concept involved. The tablecloth demo is no exception, which also illustrates impulse and momentum (Chapter 5 material). The plates experience two impulses: friction between the cloth and the dishes, and friction between the sliding dishes and the table. The first impulse moves the dishes slightly toward you. It is brief and very little momentum builds up. Once the dishes are no longer on the cloth, the second impulse acts in a direction away from you and prevents continued sliding toward you, bringing the dishes to rest. Done quickly, the brief displacement of the dishes is hardly noticed. Is inertia really at work here? Yes, for if there were no friction in the demo, the dishes would strictly remain at rest.

DEMONSTRATION: Continuing with inertia, do as Jim Szeszol does and fashion a wire coat hanger into an "m" shape as shown. Two globs of clay are stuck to each end. Balance it on your head, with one glob in front of your face. State you wish to view the other blob and ask how you can do so without touching the apparatus. Then simply turn around and look at it. It's like rotating the bowl of soup only to find the soup remains put. Inertia in action! (Of course, like the tablecloth demo, there is more physics here than inertia; this demo can also be used to illustrate rotational inertia and the conservation of angular momentum.)

A useful way to impart the idea of mass and inertia is to place two objects, say a pencil and a piece of chalk, in the hands of a student and ask for a judgment of which is heavier. The student will likely respond by shaking them, one in each hand. Point out that in so doing the student is really comparing their inertias, and is making use of the intuitive knowledge that weight and inertia are directly proportional to each other. In the next chapter you'll focus more on the distinction between mass and weight, and between mass and volume.

CHECK YOUR NEIGHBOR: How does the law of inertia account for removing dirt from your shoes by stamping on the porch before entering a house, or snow from your shoes by doing the same. Or removing dust from a coat by shaking it?

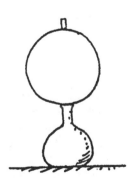

DEMONSTRATION: Do as Marshall Ellenstein does and place a metal hoop atop a narrow jar. On top of the hoop balance a piece of chalk. Then whisk the hoop away and the chalk falls neatly into the narrow opening. The key here is grabbing the hoop on the inside, on the side farthest from your sweep. This elongates the hoop horizontally and the part that supports the chalk drops from beneath the chalk. (If you grab the hoop on the nearer side, the elongation will be vertical and pop the chalk up into the air!)

Units of Force—Newtons
I suggest not making a big deal about the unfamiliar unit of force—the newton. I simply state it is the unit of force used by physicists, and if students find themselves uncomfortable with

it, simply think of "pounds" in its place. Relative magnitudes, rather than actual magnitudes, are the emphasis of conceptual physical science anyway. Do as my mentor Burl Grey does in Figure 2.12 and suspend a familiar mass from a spring scale. If the mass is a kilogram and the scale is calibrated in newtons, it will read 9.8 N. If the scale is calibrated in pounds it will read 2.2 pounds. State that you're not going to waste valued time in unit conversions (students can do enough of that in one of those dull physics courses they've heard about).

CHECK YOUR NEIGHBOR: Which has more mass, a 1-kg stone or a 1-lb stone? [A 1-kg stone has more mass, for it weighs 2.2 lb. But we're not going to make a fuss about such conversions. If the units newtons bug you, think of it as a unit of force or weight in a foreign language for now!]

2.6 Net Force—The Combination of All Forces That Act on an Object
Discuss the idea of more than one force acting on something, and the resulting net force. Figure 2.10 captures the essence.

2.7 Equilibrium For Objects At Rest
Cite other *static* examples, where the net force is zero as evidenced by no changes in motion. Hold the 1-kg mass at rest in your hand and ask how much net force acts on it. Be sure they distinguish between the 9.8 N gravitational force on the object and the zero net force on it—as evidenced by its state of rest. (The concept of acceleration is introduced in the next chapter.) When suspended by the spring scale, point out that the scale is pulling up on the object, with just as much force as the Earth pulls down on it. Pretend to step on a bathroom scale. Ask how much gravity is pulling on you. This is evident by the scale reading. Then ask what the net force is that acts on you. This is evident by your absence of and motion change. Consider two scales, one foot on each, and ask how each scale would read. Then ask how the scales would read if you shifted your weight more on one scale than the other. Ask if there is a rule to guide the answers to these questions. There is: $\Sigma F = 0$. For any object in equilibrium, the net force on it must be zero. Before answering, consider the skit in PG Hewitt Personal Essay.

Signpainter Skit: Draw on the board the sketch below, which shows two painters on a painting rig suspended by two ropes.

Step 1: If both painters have the same weight and each stands next to a rope, the supporting force in the ropes will be equal. If spring scales were used, one on each rope, the forces in the ropes would be evident. Ask what the scale readings in each rope would be in this case. [The answer is each rope will support the weight of one man + half the weight of the rig—both scales will show equal readings.]

Step 2: Suppose one painter walks toward the other as shown in the sketch, which you draw on the chalkboard (or show via overhead projector). Will the reading in the left rope increase? Will the reading in the right rope decrease? Grand question: Will the reading in the left rope increase exactly as much as the decrease in tension in the right rope? And if so, how does either rope "know" about the change in the other rope? After neighbor discussion,

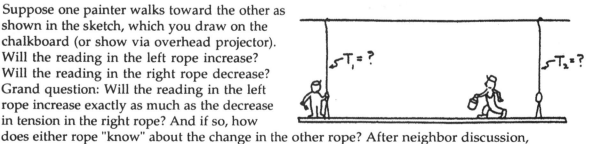

be sure to emphasize that the answers to these questions lie in the framework of the Equilibrium Rule: $\Sigma F = 0$. Since there is no change in motion, the net force must be zero, which means the upward support forces supplied by the ropes must add up to the downward force of gravity on the two men and the rig. So a decrease in one rope must necessarily be met with a corresponding increase in the other. (This example is dear to my heart [PGH]. Both Burl and I didn't know the answer way back then—because neither he nor I had a model for analyzing the problem. We didn't know about Newton's first law and the Equilibrium Rule. How different one's thinking is depends on whether there is a model or guidance. If Burl and I had been mystical in our thinking, we might have been more concerned with how each rope "knows" about the condition of the other. This is the approach that intrigues many people with a nonscientific view of the world.)

2.8 The Support Force—Why We Don't Fall Through the Floor
Ask what forces act on a book at rest on your lecture table. Then discuss Figure 2.8, explaining that the atoms in the table behave like tiny springs. This upward support force is equal and opposite to the weight of the book, as evidenced by the book's state of rest. The support force is a very real force. Because it is always perpendicular to the surface, it is called a *normal force*. Without it, the book would be in a state of free fall.

2.9 Equilibrium for Moving Objects
If you're in the car of a smoothly moving train and you balance a deck of cards on a table, they are in equilibrium whether the train is in motion or not. If there is no change in motion (acceleration), the cards don't "know the difference."

2.10 The Earth Moves Around the Sun
Stand facing a wall and jump up. Then ask why the wall does not smash into you as the Earth rotates under you while you're airborne. Relate this to the idea of a helicopter ascending over San Francisco, waiting motionless for 3 hours and waiting until Washington DC appears below, then descending. Hooray, this would be a neat way to fly cross-country! Except, of course, for the fact that the "stationary" helicopter remains in motion with the ground below. "Stationary" relative to the stars means it would have to fly as fast as the Earth turns (what jets attempt to do!).

Tell your students that humankind struggled for nearly 2000 years in developing the ideas of this chapter. With this in mind, remind them that they should be patient with themselves (and you of them) if it takes a few days or weeks to achieve as much.

We teachers learned our physics when we started teaching it -- when we *talked* about it. Your students can learn this way also, right in your class. Become proficient at the Check-Your-Neighbor way of teaching. Learn to ask good questions that promote peer discussions. More questioning, more student interaction, and less professing!

Chapter 2 Answers and Solutions

Key Terms and Matching Definitions

__9__ equilibrium rule
__6__ force
__1__ inertia
__7__ net force
__8__ newton
__5__ Newton's First Law of Motion—The Law of Inertia
__2__ speed
_10__ support force
__4__ vector quantity
__3__ velocity

Review Questions

1. According to Aristotle, what tendency of moving objects governed their motions?
   The tendency of moving objects was to seek their natural resting places.

2. According to Aristotle, what kinds of motion required no forces?
   Natural motion on Earth and heavenly motion required no force for their motions.

3. What two main ideas of Aristotle did Galileo discredit?
   Galileo discredited the idea that heavy objects fall faster than light ones, and that a force is necessary to maintain motion.

4. What is the name of the property of objects to maintain their states of motion?
   Inertia.

5. Distinguish between speed and velocity.
   Speed is magnitude (how much) and velocity is speed with direction (how much and which way).

6. Why do we say velocity is a vector and speed is not?
   Velocity involves both magnitude (speed) and direction. Speed involves only magnitude.

7. How can you be both at rest and also moving at 100,000 km/h at the same time?
   You can be at rest relative to the Earth, but moving at 100,000 km/h relative to the sun.

8. Between Aristotle and Galileo, who relied on experiments?
   Galileo.

9. Who was the first to discover the concept of inertia, Galileo or Newton?
   Galileo. Newton advanced it to a fundamental law that underlies all motion.

10. What is the tendency of a moving object when no forces act on it?
    To move in a straight line at constant velocity.

11. When only a pair of equal and opposite forces act on an object, what is the net force acting on it?
    Zero.

12. We've learned that velocity is a vector quantity. Is force also a vector quantity? Why or why not?
    Yes, because like velocity, it has magnitude and direction.

13. What is the name given to the force that occurs in a rope when both ends are pulled in opposite directions?
    Tension.

14. How much tension is there in a rope that holds a 20-N bag of apples at rest?
    20 N.

15. What does $\Sigma F = 0$ mean?
    It means that the vector sum of all the forces that act on an object in equilibrium equals zero. Forces cancel.

16. Why is the support force on an object often called the normal force?
    Because it acts at right angles to the surface. Normal is another term for "right angle."

17. When you weigh yourself, are you actually reading the support force acting on you, or are you really reading your weight?
    You actually read the support force acting on you, which is the same as your weight when the scale is stationary.

18. Give an example of something moving when a net force of zero acts on it?
    A bowling ball rolling down the lane (until it hits the pins).

19. If we push a crate at constant velocity, how do we know how much friction acts on the crate compared to our pushing force?
    Since it slides in equilibrium (constant velocity), we know the friction must be equal and opposite to our push. That way they cancel and the crate slides without changing speed.

20. If you're in a smooth-riding bus that is going at 50 km/h and you flip a coin vertically, what is the horizontal velocity of the coin in midair?
    The coin's horizontal velocity is same as the bus speed, 50 km/h.

Solutions to Chapter 2 Exercises

1. Galileo found that a ball rolling down one incline will pick up enough speed to roll up another. How high will it roll compared to its initial height?
   Ideally it will roll to its initial height. In practice, the effects of friction prevent it from reaching its exact initial height. (If it did, it would roll down and up indefinitely.)

2. Correct your friend who says, "The race-car driver rounded the curve at a constant velocity of 100 km/h."
   Constant velocity along a curve is a contradiction. The statement should say constant speed of 100 km/h.

3. If the speedometer of a car reads a constant speed of 50 km/h, can you say that the car has a constant velocity? Why or why not?
   You can say the car has a constant speed, but not constant velocity—unless you know the car is moving in a straight-line path. If it's going around a curve, for example, its velocity is changing.

4. If a huge bear were chasing you, its enormous mass would be very threatening. But if you run in a zigzag pattern, the bear's mass would be to your advantage. Why?
   Because of the bear's huge inertia, its tendency to move in a straight line would enable you to get out of its way.

5. A space probe may be carried by a rocket into outer space. What keeps the probe going after the rocket no longer pushes it?
   Nothing keeps the probe moving. In the absence of a propelling force it would continue moving in a straight line.

6. Consider a ball at rest in the middle of a toy wagon. When the wagon is pulled forward, the ball rolls against the back of the wagon. Interpret this observation in terms of Newton's first law.
   The tendency of the ball is to remain at rest. From a point of view outside the wagon, the ball stays in place as the back of the wagon moves toward it. (Because of friction the ball rolls along the cart surface—without friction the surface would slide beneath the ball.)

7. Why do you lurch forward in a bus that suddenly slows? Why do you lurch backward when it picks up speed? What law applies here?
   The law of inertia applies in both cases. When the bus slows, you tend to keep moving at the previous speed and lurch forward. When the bus picks up speed, you tend to keep moving at the previous (lower) speed and you lurch backward.

8. Push a shopping cart and it moves. When you stop pushing, it comes to rest. Does this violate Newton's law of inertia? Defend your answer.
   If there were no friction acting on the shopping cart it would continue in motion when you stop pushing. But friction does act, and the shopping cart slows. This doesn't violate the law of inertia because an external force indeed acts.

9. When a car moves along the highway at constant velocity, the net force on it is zero. Why, then, do you continue running your engine?
   You run your engine to provide a force to counter friction.

10. Roll a bowling ball down a lane and you'll find it moves slightly slower with time. Does this violate Newton's law of inertia? Defend your answer.
    If there were no force acting on the ball it would continue in motion without slowing. But air drag does act, along with slight friction with the lane, and the ball slows. This doesn't violate the law of inertia because external forces indeed act.

11. Consider a pair of forces, one having a magnitude of 20 N, and the other 12 N. What maximum net force is possible for these two forces? What is the minimum net force possible?

The maximum resultant occurs when the forces are parallel in the same direction—32 N.
The minimum occurs when they oppose each other—8 N.

12. Can an object be in mechanical equilibrium when only a single force acts on it? Explain.
If only a single nonzero force acts on an object, it will not be in mechanical equilibrium.
There would have to be another or other forces to result in a zero net force for equilibrium.

13. The sketch shows a painting staging in mechanical equilibrium. The person in the middle weighs 250 N, and the tensions in each rope are 200 N. What is the weight of the staging?
From the equilibrium rule, $\Sigma F = 0$, the upward forces are 400 N, and the downward forces are 250 N + the weight of the staging. So the staging must weigh 400 N – 250 N = 150 N.

14. A different staging that weighs 300 N supports two painters, one 250 N and the other 300 N. The reading in the left scale is 400 N. What is the reading in the right hand scale?
From the equilibrium rule, $\Sigma F = 0$, the upward forces are 400 N + tension in the right scale. This sum must equal the downward forces 250 N + 300 N + 300 N. Arithmetic shows the reading on the right scale is 850 N – 400 N = 450N.

15. Nellie Newton hangs at rest from the ends of the rope as shown. How does the reading on the scale compare to her weight?
The scale will read half her weight. Then $\Sigma F = 0$. (Upward pull of left rope + upward pull of right rope - weight) = 0.

16. Harry the painter swings year after year from his bosun's chair. His weight is 500 N and the rope, unknown to him, has a breaking point of 300 N. Why doesn't the rope break when he is supported as shown at the left? One day Harry is painting near a flagpole, and, for a change, he ties the free end of the rope to the flagpole instead of to his chair, as shown at the right. Why did Harry end up taking his vacation early?
In the left figure, Harry is supported by two strands of rope that share his weight (like the little girl in the previous exercise). So each strand supports only 250 N, which is below the breaking point. Total force up supplied by ropes equals weight acting downward, giving a net force of zero. Harry is in equilibrium. In the right figure, Harry is now supported by one strand, which for Harry's well-being requires that the tension be 500 N. Since this is above the breaking point of the rope, it breaks. The net force on Harry is then only his weight, with no other to keep him in equilibrium. His unfortunate fall changes his vacation plans.

17. As you stand at rest on a floor, does the floor exert an upward force against your feet? If so, what exactly is this force?
Yes, the floor is being squeezed and pushes upward against your feet with a force equal to that of your weight. This upward support force (called the *normal force*) and your weight are oppositely directed, so the net force on you is zero. Hence you're in equilibrium.

18. A child learns in school that the Earth is traveling faster than 100,000 kilometers per hour around the sun, and in a frightened tone asks why we aren't swept off. What is your explanation?
We aren't swept off because we are traveling just as fast as the Earth, just as in a fast-moving vehicle you move along with the vehicle. Also, there is no atmosphere through which the Earth moves, which would do more than blow our hats off!

19. If you toss a coin straight upward while riding in a train, where does the coin land when the motion of the train is uniform along a straight-line track? When the train slows while the coin is in the air? When the train is turning?
The coin is moving along with you when you toss it, maintaining the same forward motion you have. So the coin lands in your hand. If the train slows while the coin is in the air, it will land in front of you. If the train makes a turn while the coin is in the air, it will land off to the side of you. The coin continues in its horizontal motion, in accord with the law of inertia.

20. As the Earth rotates about its axis, it takes three hours for the United States to pass beneath a point above the Earth that is stationary relative to the sun. What is wrong with the following scheme? To travel from Washington D.C. to San Francisco and use very little fuel, simply ascend in a helicopter high over Washington D.C. and wait three hours until San Francisco passes below.

This plan ignores the concept of inertia. Like the flipped coin of Exercise 19, the motion of the hovering helicopter is not zero relative to the Earth's axis, but remains at the speed of the Earth's turning surface at that point. To remain motionless above Washington D.C., it would have to thrust through the air at the same and opposite speed of the turning Earth below. This is what jet planes attempt to do.

Solutions to Chapter 2 Problems

1. What is your average speed if you run 50 meters in 10 seconds?
   Average speed = distance/time = 50 m/10 s = 5 m/s.

2. A tennis ball travels the full length of the court, 24 meters, in 0.5 second. What is its average speed?
   Average speed = distance/time = 24 m/0.5 s = 48 m/s.

3. Find the net force produced by a 30-N and 20-N force in each of the following cases:
   a. Both forces act in the same direction.
   30 N + 20 N = 50 N in the same direction.
   b. Both forces act in opposite directions.
   30 N − 20 N = 10 N in the direction of the 30-N force.

4. A horizontal force of 100 N is required to push a box across a floor at a constant speed.
   a. What is the net force acting on the box?
   Zero, because it moves steadily (in moving equilibrium).
   b. What is the force of friction acting on the box?
   The friction force is −100 N, equal and opposite to the 100-N push.

5. Phil Physicer weighs 600 N (132 lb) and stands on two bathroom scales. He stands so one scale reads twice as much as the other. What are the scale readings?
   Let the reading on one scale be x. Then the reading on the other is $2x$. That's $3x$ combined, which add up to 600 N. So $x = 200$ N. So one side reads 200 N and the other reads twice this, 400 N.

3 Newton's Second Law of Motion

Conceptual Physical Science—Explorations

3.1 Galileo Developed the Concept of Acceleration
3.2 Force Causes Acceleration
3.3 Mass is a Measure of Inertia
      Mass is Not Volume
      Mass is Not Weight
      One Kilogram Weighs 9.8 Newtons
3.4 Mass Resists Acceleration
3.5 Newton's Second Law Links Force, Acceleration, and Mass
3.6 Friction is a Force That Affects Motion
3.7 Objects in Free Fall Have Equal Acceleration
3.8 Newton's Second Law Explains Why Objects in Free Fall Have Equal Acceleration
3.9 Acceleration of Fall is Less When Air Drag Acts

Learning Objectives

After studying Chapter 3, students will be able to:
• Define acceleration, and distinguish it from velocity.
• State the relationship between acceleration and net force.
• Distinguish between volume, weight, and inertia.
• State the relationship between acceleration and mass.
• Distinguish between the concepts of directly proportional and inversely proportional to.
• State Newton's second law of motion.
• Explain how friction affects motion.
• Apply Newton's second law to explain why the acceleration of an object in free fall does not depend on the mass of the object.
• Describe what happens to the acceleration and the velocity of a falling object in the presence of air drag.

Possible Misconceptions to Correct

• **Not so!** If an object has zero acceleration, then it must be at rest.
• **Not so!** Constant velocity requires a force.
• **Not so!** Even if no force acts on it, a moving object will eventually stop.
• **Not so!** Mass and weight are two names for the same thing.
• **Not so!** Mass and volume are two names for the same thing.
• **Not so!** Heavy objects always fall faster than light objects.
• **Not so!** Objects have no weight in a vacuum.

Demonstration Equipment

• Spring balance and wood block (that you'll pull across the table at constant speed)
• Iron ball, about 1 kilogram, with hooks for attached strings (mass vs weight demo)
• Hammer and heavy weight (or sledge hammer and blacksmith anvil)

We extend the brief treatment of speed and velocity of the previous chapter to acceleration in this chapter. The acceleration of free fall provides a good example of acceleration. Once the distinction between velocity and acceleration is made, you move into Newton's second law. In this chapter we also distinguish between mass and weight without making a big deal about

28   Conceptual Physical Science—Explorations **Teaching Guide**

their units of measurement (because we're convinced that time is better spent on physics concepts.) A brief treatment of units and systems of measurement is provided in Appendix A. It is useful to represent magnitudes with numerical quantities from time to time. An option that sometimes better makes the point is the exaggerated symbol technique that is shown in the textbook.

Overhead Transparency (1) available for:
Figure 3.4

In the **Explorations Practice Book**:
• Action and Reaction Pairs

In the **Next-Time Questions** Book:
• Vehicle Collision
• Scale Reading
• Leaning Tower of Pisa Drop
• Interactions
• Tug of War

In the **Lab Manual**:
• Go Go Go (experiment)
• Sonic Ranger (activity)
• Reaction Time (activity)
• Pulled Over (activity)
• The Weight (experiment)

SUGGESTED PRESENTATION

In Chapter 2 the concept of inertia was introduced—the property of matter wherein changes in motion are resisted. Things at rest tend to remain at rest; things moving tend to remain moving—if no forces are exerted. Now we learn about acceleration—the change in velocity that objects experience when a force *is* exerted.

3.1 Galileo Developed the Concept of Acceleration
Define acceleration, identifying it as a vector quantity, and cite the importance of CHANGE. That's change in speed, or change in direction. Hence both are acknowledged by defining acceleration as a rate of change in velocity rather than speed. Ask your students to identify the three controls in an automobile that enable the auto to *change* its state of motion—that produce *acceleration* (accelerator, brakes, and steering wheel). State how one lurches in a vehicle that is undergoing acceleration, especially for circular motion, and state why the definition of velocity includes direction to make the definition of acceleration all-encompassing. Talk of how without lurching one cannot sense motion, giving examples of coin flipping in a high-speed aircraft versus doing the same when the same aircraft is at rest on the runway.

Units for Acceleration
Give numerical examples of acceleration in units of kilometers/hour per second to establish the idea of acceleration. Be sure that your students are working on the examples with you. For example, ask them to find the acceleration of a car that goes from rest to 100 km/h in 10 seconds. It is important that you not use examples involving seconds twice until they taste success with the easier kilometers/hour per second examples. Have them check their work with their neighbors as you go along. Only after they get the hang of it, introduce meters/second/second in your examples to develop a sense for the units m/s^2.

Falling Objects

Round off 9.8 m/s^2 to 10 m/s^2 in your discussions and you'll more easily establish the relationships between velocity and distance. Later you can then move to the more precise 9.8 m/s^2, when more precision is wanted.

> CHECK YOUR NEIGHBOR: If an object is dropped from an initial position of rest from the top of a cliff, how *fast* will it be traveling at the end of one second? (You might add, "Write the answer on your notepaper." And then, "Look at your neighbor's paper—if your neighbor doesn't have the right answer, reach over and help him or her—talk about it.")

After explaining the answer when class discussion dies down, repeat the process asking for the speed at the end of 2 seconds, and then for 10 seconds. This leads you into stating the relationship $v = gt$, which by now you can express in shorthand notation. After any questions, discussion, and examples, state that you are going to pose a different question—not asking for how *fast*, but for how *far*. Ask how far the object falls in one second.

Ask for a written response and then ask if the students could explain to their neighbors *why* the distance is only 5 m rather than 10 m. After they've discussed this for almost a minute or so, ask "If you maintain a speed of 60 km/h for one hour, how far do you go?"—then, "If you maintain a speed of 10 m/s for one second, how far do you go?" Important point: You'll appreciably improve your instruction if you allow some thinking time after you ask a question. Not doing so is the folly of too many teachers. Then continue, "Then why is the answer to the first question not 10 meters?" After a suitable time, stress the idea of *average* velocity and the relation $d = vt$.

For accelerating objects that start from a rest position, the average velocity is half the final velocity (average velocity = [initial velocity + final velocity]/2).

> CHECK YOUR NEIGHBOR: How far will a freely falling object that is released from rest fall in 2 seconds? In 10 seconds? (When your class is comfortable with this, then ask how far in 1/2 second.)

Investigate Figure 3.4 and have students complete the speed readings. Ask what odometer readings (that measure distance) would be for the speeds shown. To avoid information overload, we restrict all numerical examples of free fall to cases that begin at rest. Why? Because it's simpler that way. (We prefer our students understand simple physics than be confused about not-so-simple physics!) We do go this far with them:

> CHECK YOUR NEIGHBOR: Consider a rifle fired straight downward from a high-altitude balloon. If the muzzle velocity is 100 m/s and air resistance can be neglected, what is the *acceleration* of the bullet after one second? (If most of your class say that it's *g*, you're on!)

I suggest *not* asking for the time of fall for a freely-falling object, given the distance. Why? Unless the distance given is the familiar 5 meters, algebraic manipulation is called for. If one of our teaching objectives were to teach algebra, this would be a nice place to do it. But we don't have time to present this stumbling block and then teach how to overcome it. We'd rather put our energy *and theirs* into straight physical science!

Please beware: Kinematics can be rich with puzzles, graphical analysis, ticker timers, photogates, and algebraic problems. Our strong suggestion is to resist these and move quickly into the rest of mechanics, and then into other interesting areas of physics. Getting bogged down with kinematics, with so much material ahead, is a widespread practice. Please do your class a favor and hurry on to the following material. If at the end of your course you have time (ha ha), *then* bring out the kinematics toys and have a go at them.

3.2 Force Causes Acceleration

State that acceleration is produced by an imposed force. Write this as $a \sim F$ and give examples of doubling the force and the resulting doubling of the acceleration, etc. Introduce the idea of net force, with appropriate examples—like applying twice the force to a stalled car gives it twice as much acceleration—three times the force, three times the acceleration.

> CHECK YOUR NEIGHBOR: If one were able to produce and maintain a constant net force of only 1 newton on the Queen Mary ocean liner, what would be its maximum speed? [Give multiple choices for an answer: a) 0 m/s; b) 1 m/s; c) less than 1 m/s; d) about 10 m/s; e) almost the speed of light!] In the following discussion, the key concept is *net force*. Point out the enormous applied forces necessary to overcome the enormous water resistance at high speeds, to yield a net force of 1 newton; and the meaning of acceleration—that every succeeding second the ship moves a bit faster than the second before. This would go on seemingly without limit, except for relativistic effects which result in (e) being the correct answer.

3.3 Mass is a Measure of Inertia

Mass is Not Volume

Comparing an overstuffed fluffy pillow to a small automobile battery should convince anyone that mass and volume are different. The unit of mass is the kilogram, and the unit of volume is cubic meters or liters. Decidedly different.

Mass is not Weight

To distinguish between mass and weight compare the efforts of pushing horizontally on a block of slippery ice on a frozen pond versus lifting it. Or consider the weightlessness of a massive anvil in outer space and how it would be difficult to shake. And if moving toward you, it would be harmful to be in its way because of its great tendency to remain in motion. The following demo (often used to illustrate impulse and momentum) makes the distinction nicely:

DEMONSTRATION: Hang a massive ball by a string and show that the top string breaks when the bottom is pulled with gradually more force, but the bottom string breaks when the string is jerked. Ask which of these cases illustrates weight [Interestingly enough, it's the weight of the ball that makes for the greater tension in the top string.] Then ask which of these cases illustrates inertia. [When jerked, the tendency of the ball to resist the sudden downward acceleration, its inertia, is responsible for the lower string breaking.] This is the best demo we know of for showing the different effects of weight and mass.

One Kilogram Weighs 9.8 Newtons

Suspend a 1-kilogram mass from a spring scale and show that it weighs 9.8 N. We can round this off to 10 N for precision is not needed.

3.4 Mass Resists Acceleration

The property of massive objects to resist changes is nicely shown with this follow-up demonstration.

DEMONSTRATION: Lie on your back and have an assistant place a blacksmith's anvil on your stomach. Have the assistant strike the anvil rather hard with a sledge hammer. The principles here are the same as the ball and string demo. Both the inertia of the ball and the inertia of the anvil resist the changes in motion they would otherwise undergo. So the string doesn't break, and your body is not squashed. (Be sure that your assistant is skillful with the hammer. When I began teaching I used to trust students to the task. In my fourth year the student who volunteered was extra nervous in front of the class and missed the anvil entirely—but not me. The hammer smashed into my hand breaking two fingers. I was lucky I was not seriously injured.)

Relate the idea of tightening a hammerhead by slamming the opposite end of the handle on a firm surface, with the bones of the human spine after jogging or even walking around. Interestingly, we are similarly a bit shorter at night. Ask your students to find a place in their homes that they can't quite reach before going to bed—a place that is one or two centimeters higher than their reach. Then tell them to try again when they awake the next morning. Unforgettable, for you are likely instructing them to discover something about themselves they were not aware of!

3.5 Newton's Second Law Links Force, Acceleration, and Mass
Point out that although Galileo introduced the idea of inertia, discussed the role of forces, and defined acceleration, he never made the connections to these ideas as Newton did with his second law. Although Galileo is credited as the first to demonstrate that in the absence of air resistance, falling objects fall with equal accelerations, he was unable to say why this is so. The answer is given by Newton's 2nd law.

SKIT: Hold a heavy object like a kilogram weight and a piece of chalk with outstretched hands, ready to drop them. Ask your class which will strike the ground first if you drop them simultaneously. They know. Ask them to imagine you ask the same of a bright child, who responds by asking to handle the two objects before giving an answer. Pretend you are the child judging the lifting of the two objects. "The metal object is heavier than the chalk, which means there is more gravity force acting on it, which means it will accelerate to the ground before the chalk does." Write the child's argument in symbol notation on the board, $a \sim F$. Then go through the motions of asking the same of another child, who responds with a good argument that takes inertia rather than weight into account. This child says, after shaking the metal and chalk back and forth in his or her hands, "The piece of metal is more massive than the chalk, which means it has more inertia than the chalk, which means it will be harder to get moving than the chalk. So the chalk will race to the ground first, while the inertia of the metal causes it to lag behind." Write this kid's argument with, $a \sim 1/m$. State that the beauty of science is that such speculations can be ascertained by experiment. Drop the weight and the chalk to show that however sound each child's argument seemed to be, the results do not support either. Then bring both arguments together with $a \sim F/m$, Newton's 2nd Law.

3.6 Friction is a Force That Affects Motion
Drag a block at constant velocity across your lecture table. Acknowledge the force of friction, and how it must exactly counter your pulling force. Show the pulling force with a spring balance. Now since the block moves without accelerating, ask for the magnitude of the friction force. It must be equal and opposite to your scale reading. Then the net force is zero. While sliding, the block is in dynamic equilibrium. That is, $\Sigma F = 0$.

CHECK YOUR NEIGHBOR (similar to one in the text): Suppose in a high-flying airplane the captain announces over the cabin public address system that the plane is flying at a constant 900 km/h and the thrust of the engines is a constant 80,000 newtons. What is the acceleration of the airplane? [Answer: Zero, because velocity is constant.] What is the combined force of air resistance that acts all over the plane's outside surface? [Answer: 80,000 N. If it were less, the plane would speed up; if it were more, the plane would slow down.]

Show what happens when you pull harder on the block. Your students see that when the pulling force is greater than the friction force, there is a net force greater than zero, as evidenced by the observed acceleration. Show different constant speeds across the table with the same applied force, which shows that friction is not dependent on speed. Distinguish between static and sliding friction, and show how a greater force is needed to get the block moving from a rest position. Show all this as you discuss these ideas. Cite the example in the book about skidding with locked brakes in a car [where the distance of skid for sliding friction is greater than static friction, where lower braking application results in nonsliding tires and shorter sliding distance]. Discuss the new automatic braking systems (ABS) now available on cars.

The box on page 43, **Practicing Physics**, nicely treats friction in some detail.

3.7 Objects in Free Fall Have Equal Acceleration
The falling speedometers of Figure 3.4 show that acceleration of free fall is constant. Speed picks up, and distance of fall increases, but acceleration remains a constant 10 m/s^2.

3.8 Newton's Second Law Explains Why Objects in Free Fall Have Equal Acceleration
Relate your skit to the case of the falling boulder and feather, Figure 3.15. Once these concepts are clear, ask how the bricks would slide on a frictionless inclined plane, then illustrate with examples such as the time required for a fully loaded roller coaster and an empty roller coaster to make a complete run. In the absence of friction effects, the times are the same. Cite the case of a Cadillac limousine and Volkswagen moving downhill in the absence of friction. By now you are fielding questions having to do with air resistance and friction.

3.9 Acceleration of Fall is Less When Air Drag Acts

DEMONSTRATION: After you have made clear the cases with no friction, then make a transition to practical examples that involve friction—leading off with the dropping of sheets of paper, one crumpled and one flat. Point out that the masses and weights are the same, and the only variable is air resistance. Bring in the idea of net force again, asking what the net force is when the paper falls at constant speed. (If you left the Chapter 2 demo of the falling book and paper on top of it unexplained, reintroduce it here.)

CHECK YOUR NEIGHBOR: What is the acceleration of a feather that "floats" slowly to the ground? The net force acting on the feather? If the feather weighs 0.01 N, how much air resistance acts upward against it?

These questions lead into a discussion of the parachutists in Figure 3.17. When the decrease of acceleration that builds up to terminal velocity is clear, return to the point earlier about the Cadillac and Volkswagen moving down an incline, only this time in the presence of air resistance. Then ask whether or not it would be advantageous to have a heavy cart or a light cart in a soap-box-derby race. Ask which would reach the finish line first if they were dropped through the air from a high-flying balloon. Then consider the carts on an inclined plane.

For your information, the terminal velocity of a falling baseball is about 150 km/h (95 mi/h), and for a falling Ping-Pong ball about 32 km/h (20 mi/h).

So far we have regarded a force as a push or a pull. We will consider a broader definition of force in the next chapter. Onward!

> Do you want your students to read chapter material *before* coming to class? Then reward them for doing so! Give them a quickie quiz at the outset of each class — or if not every class, then frequently at unannounced times. My students know they'll be quizzed on the chapter-end *Review Questions* of the assigned chapters. They *do* come to class prepared. Common sense — reward the behavior you want!

Chapter 3 Answers and Solutions

Key Terms and Matching Definitions

__1__ acceleration
_11__ air drag
_10__ free fall
__9__ friction
__2__ inertia
__4__ inversely
__7__ kilogram
__8__ Newton's second law
__3__ mass
_12__ terminal speed
_13__ terminal velocity
__5__ volume
__6__ weight

Review Questions

1. Distinguish between velocity and acceleration.
   Velocity is speed in a given direction, and acceleration is the time rate of change of velocity. The change can be in speed, direction, or both.

2. When are you most aware of motion in a moving vehicle—when it is moving steadily in a straight line or when it is accelerating?
   When the vehicle is accelerating, because then you feel a lurching sensation.

3. What is the acceleration of free fall?
   The acceleration of free fall is that provided only by gravity. On Earth it has the value 10 m/s².

4. Is acceleration proportional to net force or does acceleration equal net force?
   Acceleration is proportional to net force, meaning a change in one produces the same kind of change in the other. We'll see soon that acceleration is equal to the ratio of net force/mass.

5. What relationship does mass have with inertia?
   Mass is a measure of inertia. The greater the mass, the greater the resistance to changes in motion.

6. What relationship does mass have with weight?
   Weight and mass are directly proportional to each other. A change in one is the same kind of change in the other.

7. Fill in the blanks: Shake something to-and-fro and you're measuring its _____. Lift it against gravity and you're measuring its _____.
   Mass; weight.

8. What is the weight of a 1-kilogram brick?
   About 10 newtons (more precisely, 9.8 newtons).

9. Is acceleration *directly* proportional to mass, or is it *inversely* proportional to mass? Give an example.
   Acceleration is inversely proportional to mass, which means that acceleration and mass change in opposite directions. Large mass means small acceleration, for example.

10. If the net force acting on a sliding block is somehow tripled, by how much does the acceleration increase?
Acceleration also triples.

11. If the mass of a sliding block is somehow tripled at the same time the net force on it is tripled, how does the resulting acceleration compare to the original acceleration?
If you triple the force acting on three times the mass, there's no change in acceleration. Acceleration remains the same.

12. Suppose you exert a horizontal push on a crate that rests on a level floor, and it doesn't move. How much friction acts compared with your push?
The same, oppositely directed, resulting in a zero net force.

13. As you increase your push, will friction on the crate increase also?
Yes, until your push is hard enough to get the crate sliding.

14. Once the crate is sliding, how hard do you push to keep it moving at constant velocity?
You push with a force that equals that of friction (then the net force = 0).

15. What is meant by *free fall*?
Free fall is the state of an object when only the force of gravity is acting on it—no other forces.

16. Why doesn't a heavy object accelerate more than a light object when both are freely falling?
Acceleration is the ratio of force/mass. A heavy body has the same ratio as a light body, hence both accelerate equally in free fall.

17. The ratio of circumference/diameter for all circles is π. What is the ratio of force/mass for freely-falling bodies?
g, the acceleration of free fall.

18. What two principal factors affect the force of air resistance on a falling object?
Frontal area of fall and speed.

19. What is the acceleration of a falling object that has reached its terminal velocity?
Zero.

20. If two objects of the same size fall through air at different speeds, which encounters the greater air resistance?
The faster one encounters greater air resistance.

Hands-On Explorations

1. Drop a sheet of paper and a coin at the same time. Which reaches the ground first? Why? Now crumple the paper into a small, tight wad and again drop it with the coin. Explain the difference observed. Will they fall together if dropped from a second-, third-, or fourth-story window? Try it and explain your observations.
For small speeds and distances things appear to fall together when released at the same time. When dropped for longer distances, a crumpled piece of paper encounters more air drag compared with its weight than a coin, and the coin falls faster. From a four-story building the coin doesn't reach its terminal speed whereas the paper easily does.

2. Drop a book and a sheet of paper and note that the book has a greater acceleration; g. Place the paper beneath the book and it is forced against the book as both fall, so both fall at g. How do the accelerations compare if you place the paper on top of the raised book and then drop both? You may be surprised, so try it and see. Then explain your observation.
When the paper is on top of the falling book, air is pushed out of the way by the book so the paper encounters NO air drag. Hence it accelerates along with the book!

3. Drop two balls of different weight from the same height, and at small speeds they practically fall together. Will they roll together down the same inclined plane? If each is suspended from an equal length of string, making a pair of pendulums, and displaced through the same angle, will they swing back and forth in unison? Try it and see; then explain using Newton's laws.

They will fall together, roll together, and swing together, for the accelerating force is gravity. Compared with mass, the same ratio results. Each case is a version of $a = F/m$, so like the falling feather and boulder, acceleration is the same for each.

4. The net force acting on an object and the resulting acceleration are always in the same direction. You can demonstrate this with a spool. If the spool is pulled horizontally to the right, in which direction will it roll?

The spool will roll in the direction of the force that acts on it—in the same direction it is pulled. So when pulled to the right it rolls to the right. When pulled at an angle, however, it may roll to the left if the angle of the string is great enough.

Solutions to Chapter 3 Exercises

1. What is the net force on a bright red Mercedes convertible traveling along a straight road at a steady speed of 100 km/h?

The net force is zero because the car is traveling at constant velocity, which means with zero acceleration. (The acceleration would be the same no matter what the color!)

2. On a long alley a bowling ball slows down as it rolls. Is any horizontal force acting on the ball? How do you know?

Yes, if the ball slows down, a force opposite to its motion is acting—likely air drag and friction between the ball and alley.

3. In the orbiting space shuttle you are handed two identical boxes, one filled with sand and the other filled with feathers. How can you tell which is which without opening the boxes?

Shake the boxes. The box that offers the greater resistance to acceleration is the more massive box, the one containing the sand.

4. Your empty hand is not hurt when it bangs lightly against a wall. Why is it hurt if it does so while carrying a heavy load? Which of Newton's laws is most applicable here?

When carrying a heavy load there is more mass involved; more tendency to remain moving. If a load in your hand moves toward a wall, its tendency is to remain moving when contact is made. This tends to squash your hand if it's between the load and the wall—an unfortunate example of Newton's first law in action.

5. What happens to your weight when your mass increases?

Weight and mass are directly proportional. Therefore in any locality, when your mass increases your weight also increases.

6. When a junked car is crushed into a compact cube, does its mass change? Its weight? Its volume? Explain.

Neither the mass nor the weight of a junked car changes when it is crushed. What does change is its volume, not to be confused with mass and weight. Once crushed, the same mass and weight occupy less space.

7. What is the net force on a 1-N apple when you hold it at rest above your head? What is the net force on it after you release it?

When held at rest the upward support force equals the gravitational force on the apple and the net force is zero. When released, the upward support force is no longer there and the net force is the gravitational force, 1 N. (If the apple falls fast enough for air resistance to be important, then the net force will be less than 1 N, and eventually can reach zero if air resistance builds up to 1 N.)

8. Does a stick of dynamite contain force?

Neither a stick of dynamite nor anything else "contains" force. We will see later that a stick of dynamite contains *energy*, which is capable of producing forces when an interaction of some kind occurs.

9. If it takes 1 N to push horizontally on your book to make it slide at constant velocity, how much force of friction acts on the book?
   At constant velocity the net force is zero, so friction also equals 1 N.

10. A bear that weighs 4000 N grasps a vertical tree and slides down at constant velocity. What is the friction force that acts on the bear?
    Sliding down at constant velocity means acceleration is zero and the net force is zero. This can occur if friction equals the bear's weight, which is 4000 N.

11. A crate remains at rest on a factory floor while you push on it with a horizontal force F. How big is the friction force exerted on the crate by the floor? Explain.
    The force of friction on the crate must be $-F$. Then the net force on it is zero, which accounts for the state of rest.

12. Aristotle claimed the speed of a falling object depends on its weight. We now know that objects in free fall, whatever their weights, undergo the same gain in speed. Why does weight not affect acceleration?
    Rate of gain in speed (acceleration), is the ratio force/mass (Newton's second law), which in free fall is just weight/mass. Since weight is proportional to mass, the ratio weight/mass is the same whatever the weight of a body. So all freely falling bodies undergo the same gain in speed—g (illustrated in Figure 3.15). Although weight doesn't affect speed in free fall, weight does affect falling speed when air resistance is present (nonfree fall).

13. Two basketballs are dropped from a high building through the air. One ball is hollow and the other filled with rocks. Which accelerates more? Defend your answer.
    Here the balls fall in *air*, so they are not in free fall. Like the parachutists, the heavier ball will have to fall faster before air drag builds up to weight, so will fall faster through the air. Even if terminal velocity isn't reached, the heavier one will accelerate more than the light one.

14. A parachutist, after opening the chute, finds herself gently floating downward, no longer gaining speed. She feels the upward pull of the harness, while gravity pulls her down. Which of these two forces is greater? Or are they equal in magnitude?
    Both forces have the same magnitude. This is easier to understand if you visualize the parachutist at rest in a strong updraft—static equilibrium. Whether equilibrium is static or dynamic, the net force is zero.

15. Why will a sheet of paper fall slower than one that is wadded into a ball?
    A sheet of paper presents more surface area to the air in falling, and therefore has a smaller terminal speed. A wadded piece presents less area and therefore falls faster before reaching terminal speed.

16. Upon which will air resistance be greater; a sheet of falling paper or the same paper wadded into a ball that falls at a faster terminal speed? (Careful!)
    The same on each! In each case the paper reaches terminal speed, which means air drag equals the weight of the paper. Note that the wadded paper falls faster for air resistance to equal its weight. So although air drag is more pronounced for the paper in sheet form, the question asks for the amount—not the effect.

17. How does the force of gravity on a raindrop compare with the air drag it encounters when it falls at constant velocity?
    When anything falls at constant velocity, air drag and gravitational force are equal in magnitude. Raindrops are merely one example.

18. How does the terminal speed of a parachutist before opening a parachute compare to terminal speed after? Why is there a difference?

There are usually two terminal speeds, one before the parachute opens, which is faster, and one after, which is slower. The difference has mainly to do with the different areas presented to the air in falling. The large area presented by the open chute results in a slower terminal speed, slow enough for a safe landing.

19. How does the gravitational force on a falling body compare with the air resistance it encounters before it reaches terminal velocity? After?

Just before a falling body attains terminal velocity, there is still a downward acceleration because gravitational force is still greater than air resistance. When the air resistance builds up to equal the gravitational force, terminal velocity is reached. Then air resistance is equal and opposite to gravitational force.

20. Why is it that a cat that accidentally falls from the top of a 50-story building hits the ground no faster than if it fell from the 20th story?

The terminal speed attained by the falling cat is the same whether it falls from 50 stories or 20 stories. Once terminal speed is reached, falling extra distance does not affect the speed. (The low terminal velocities of small creatures enables them to fall without harm from heights that would kill larger creatures.)

Solutions to Chapter 3 Problems

1. One pound is the same as 4.45 newtons. What is the weight in pounds of 1 newton?

   1 N × 1 lb/4.45 N = 0.22 lb.

2. What is your own mass in kilograms? Your weight in newtons?

   1 kg weighs 10 N, which is the same as 2.2 lb. If you start with your weight in pounds, divide by 2.2 and you have your mass in kilograms. Then multiply that by 10 for your weight in newtons.

   That is, (your weight in lb) × (1 kg/2.2 lb) × (10 N/1 kg) = your weight in N.

3. What is the acceleration of a 40-kg block of cement when pulled sideways with a net force of 200 N?

   $a = F/m = 200 \text{ N}/40 \text{ kg} = 5 \text{ m/s}^2$.

4. If a mass of 1 kg is accelerated 1 m/s² by a force of 1 N, what would be the acceleration of 2 kg acted on by a force of 2 N?

   The acceleration of each is the same: $a = F/m = 2 \text{ N}/2 \text{ kg} = 1 \text{ N}/1 \text{ kg} = 1 \text{ m/s}^2$.

   (Incidentally, from the definition that 1 N = 1 kg·m/s², you can see that 1 N/kg is the same as 1 m/s².)

5. How much acceleration does a 747 jumbo jet of mass 30,000 kg experience in takeoff when the thrust for each of four engines is 30,000 N?

   For the jumbo jet: $a = F/m = 4(30{,}000 \text{ N})/30{,}000 \text{ kg} = 4 \text{ m/s}^2$.

6. Gravity on the surface of the moon is only 1/6 as strong as gravity on the Earth. What is the weight in newtons of a 10-kg object on the moon and on the Earth? What is its mass on each?

   Ten kilograms weighs about 100 N on the Earth (weight = mg = 10 kg × 10 m/s² = 100 N, or 98 N if g = 9.8 m/s² is used). On the moon the weight would be 1/6 of 100 N = 16.7 N (or 16.3 N if g = 9.8 m/s² is used). The mass would be 10 kg everywhere.

4 Newton's Third Law of Motion

Learning Objectives
After studying Chapter 4, students will be able to:
• Define force in terms of interaction.
• Explain why at least two objects are involved whenever a force acts.
• State Newton's third law of motion.
• Explain why the accelerations caused by an action force and by a reaction force do not have to be equal.
• Explain why action and reaction forces don't cancel.

Possible Misconceptions to Correct
• **Not so!** Pushes and pulls are applied only by living things.
• **Not so!** Things such as high-speed projectiles contain force.
• **Not so!** A reaction force occurs slightly after action force is applied.
• **Not so!** Action and reaction forces are equal and opposite only under certain conditions.

Demonstration Equipment
• Piece of rope for a classroom tug-of-war

Up to here a force is seen as a push or a pull. Newton's third law defines it better—as part of an interaction between one body and another. I like to say that you cannot exert a force on something—unless, and I pause, that something exerts an equal and opposite force on you. So you can't hit a ball *unless* the ball hits back. You can't exert a force on the floor when you walk, *unless* the floor exerts the same amount of force back on you, et cetera.

In discussing action and reaction emphasize the word "between." The forces *between* the Earth and moon, for example.

This is the shortest of the three chapters on Newton's laws.

In the **Practice Book**:
• Action and Reaction Pairs
• Interactions
• Vectors and the Parallelogram Rule
• Velocity Vectors and Components
• Force and Velocity Vectors
• Force Vectors and the Parallelogram Rule
• Force-Vector Diagrams

In the **Next-Time Questions** Book:
- Reaction Forces
- Apple on a Table
- Scale Reading
- Tug of War
- Tug of War 2
- Leaning Tower of Pisa Drop
- Apple on Table
- Atwood Pulley
- Airplane in the Wind

Overhead Transparency (1) available for:
Figure 4.6

SUGGESTED PRESENTATION

4.1 A Force is Part of an Interaction

Hold a piece of tissue paper at arm's length and ask if the heavyweight champion of the world could hit the paper with 50 pounds of force. Ask your class to check their answer with their neighbors. Then don't give your answer. Instead, continue with your lecture.

Reach out to your class and state, "I can't touch you, without you touching me in return—I can't nudge this chair without the chair in turn nudging me—I can't exert a force on a body without that body in turn exerting a force on me. In all these cases of contact there is a *single* interaction between *two* things—contact requires a *pair* of forces, whether they be slight nudges or great impacts, between *two* things. This is Newton's 3rd Law of motion. Call attention to the examples of Figure 4.6.

4.2 Newton's Third Law—Action and Reaction

Extend your arm horizontally and show the class that you can bend your fingers upward only very little. Show that if you push with your other hand, and thereby apply a force to them, or have a student do the same, they will bend appreciably more. Then walk over to the wall and show that the inanimate wall does the same (as you push against the wall). State that everybody will acknowledge that you are pushing on the wall, but only a few realize the fundamental fact that the wall is simultaneously pushing on you also—as evidenced by your bent fingers!

Do as Linda E. Roach does and place a sheet of paper between the wall and your hand. When you push on the paper, it doesn't accelerate—evidence of a zero net force on the paper. You can explain that in addition to your push, the wall must be pushing just as hard in the opposite direction on the paper to produce the zero net force. Linda recommends doing the same with an inflated balloon, whereupon your class can easily see that both sides of the balloon are squashed.

CHECK YOUR NEIGHBOR: Identify the action and reaction forces for the case of a bat striking the ball. [Ball strikes bat.]

4.3 A Simple Rule Helps Identify Action and Reaction

When body A acts on body B, body B reacts on body A. It makes no difference which is called action and which is called reaction. Figure 4.6 captures the essence.

Discuss walking on the floor in terms of the single interaction between you and the floor, and the pair of action and reaction forces that comprise this interaction. Contrast this to walking on frictionless ice, where no interaction occurs. Ask how one could leave a pond of frictionless ice. Make the answer easy by saying one has a massive brick in hand. By throwing the brick there is an interaction between the thrower and the brick. The reaction to the force on the brick, the recoiling force, sends one to shore. Or without such a convenient brick, one has clothing. Or if no clothing, one has air in the lungs. One could blow air in jet fashion. Exhale with the mouth facing away from shore, but be sure to inhale with the mouth facing toward shore.

CHECK YOUR NEIGHBOR: Identify the force that pushes a car along the road. [Interestingly enough, the force that pushes cars is provided by the road. Why? The tires push on the road (action) and the road pushes on the tires (reaction). So roads push cars along. A somewhat different viewpoint!]

4.4 Action and Reaction on Objects of Different Masses
Most people say that the moon is attracted to the Earth by gravity. Ask most people if the Earth is also attracted to the moon, and if so, which pulls harder, the Earth or the moon? You'll get mixed answers. Physicists think differently than most people on this topic: Rather than saying the moon is attracted to the Earth by gravity, a physicist would say there is an attractive force between the Earth and the moon. There is an important difference here.

Asking if the moon pulls as hard on the Earth as the Earth pulls on the moon is similar to asking if the distance between New York and Los Angeles is the same as the distance between Los Angeles and New York. Rather than thinking in terms of two distances, we think of a single distance *between* New York and Los Angeles. Likewise there is a single gravitational interaction between the Earth and the moon.

4.5 Action and Reaction Forces Act on Different Objects
Show your outstretched hand where you have a stretched rubber band between your thumb and forefinger. Ask which is pulling with the greater force, the thumb or the finger. Or, as you increase the stretch, which is being pulled with more force toward the other—the thumb toward the finger or the finger toward the thumb. After neighbor discussion, stress the single interaction between things that pull on each other. The Earth and the moon are each pulling on each other. Their pulls on each other comprise a single interaction. This point of view makes a moot point of deciding which exerts the greater force, the moon on the Earth or the Earth on the moon, or the ball on the bat or the bat on the ball, et cetera. Pass a box of rubber bands to your class and have them do it.

DEMONSTRATION: Tug-of-war in class. Have a team of women engage in a tug-of-war with a team of men. If you do this on a smooth floor, with men wearing socks and women wearing rubber-soled shoes, the women will win. This illustrates that the team who wins in this game is the team who pushes harder on the floor.

Discuss the firing of a cannonball from a cannon, as treated in the chapter. Illustrate Newton's 3rd law with a skit about a man who is given one last wish before being shot, who states that his crime demands more punishment than being struck by a tiny bullet, who wishes instead that the mass of the bullet match the magnitude of his crime (being rational in a rigid totalitarian society), that the mass of the bullet be much much more massive than the gun from which it is fired—and that his antagonist pull the trigger!

Return to your question about whether a heavyweight boxer could hit a piece of tissue paper with a force of 50 pounds or so. Now your class understands (hopefully) that the fist can't produce any more force on the paper than the paper exerts on the fist. The paper doesn't have enough mass to do this, so the answer is no. The fighter can't hit the paper any harder than the paper can hit in return. Consider solving Problem 3 in the end matter here.

4.6 The Classic Horse-Cart Problem—A Mind Stumper

Here we consider "systems." In the system of only the cart, there is a net force—that provided by the pull of the horse minus the small friction of the wheels on the ground. In the system of only the horse, the net force is the ground pushing on it minus the reaction pull by the cart. In the system of the cart-horse, the net force is that of the ground pushing on the horse. This point is worth developing.

Consider the three systems below: pool ball A, pool ball B, and balls A + B. Only in the two-ball system, A + B, is the net force zero.

System A

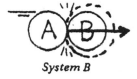

System B

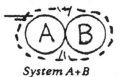

System A+B

4.7 Action Equals Reaction

Philosophically we know that if you try to do one thing, something else happens as a result. So we say you can never do only one thing. In this chapter we similarly see that you can never have only one force.

Chapter 4 Answers and Solutions

Key Terms and Matching Definitions

__2__ force pair
__1__ interaction
__3__ Newton's third law

Review Questions

1. In the simplest sense, a force is a push or a pull. In a deeper sense, what is a force?
   A force is an interaction between one thing and another.

2. How many forces are required for an interaction?
   Two.

3. When you push against a wall with your fingers, they bend because they experience a force. Identify this force.
   When you push on the wall, the wall pushes on you. It is the force of the wall on your fingers that bends them.

4. Why do we say a speeding object doesn't have force?
   Force is not a thing in itself, but something that a speeding object can *exert* on something else. A force is not a thing in itself like mass.

5. State Newton's third law of motion.
   Whenever one object exerts a force on a second object, the second object exerts an equal and opposite force on the first.

6. Consider hitting a baseball with a bat. If we call the force on the bat against the ball the *action* force, identify the *reaction* force.
   The reaction force is the ball hitting the bat.

7. If a bat hits a ball with 1000 N of force, how much force does the ball hit back on the bat?
   1000 N. Action and reaction forces are equal in magnitude.

8. If the world pulls you downward, what is the reaction force?
   The reaction is you pulling the world upward.

9. If the forces that act on a cannonball and the recoiling cannon from which it is fired are equal in magnitude, why do the cannonball and cannon have very different accelerations?
   Equal forces on unequal masses produce unequal accelerations, in accord with Newton's second law.

10. Identify the force that propels a rocket.
    The force that propels a rocket is the reaction to the force the rocket exerts on the exhaust gases.

11. How can the net force on the ball be zero when you kick it?
    Only if there is another external force on the ball, like someone kicking it in the opposite direction.

12. Why does a push on the dashboard of a stalled car not accelerate the car?
    Your push is internal to the car. To accelerate, an external force is needed.

13. Referring to Figure 4.12, how many forces are exerted on the cart? What is the horizontal net force on the cart?
Two, P and f. The net force is P - f.

14. How many forces are exerted on the horse? What is the net force on the horse?
Two, F, and P. The net force on the horse is F – P.

15. How many forces are exerted on the horse-cart system? What is the net force on the horse-cart system?
Two, F and f. The net force is F – f.

16. Who wins in a tug-of-war, those pulling harder on the rope, or pushing harder against the floor?
Both pull equally on the rope, so the winning team is the one that pushes harder on the floor.

17. How does a helicopter get its lifting force?
The helicopter blades force air downward, and in doing so the air forces the blades upward. The upward force provides lift.

18. A boxer can hit a heavy bag with great force. Why can't he hit a sheet of newspaper in midair with the same amount of force?
He can't exert any more force on the tissue paper than the tissue paper can exert on him. The tissue paper has insufficient inertia for a great force.

19. Can you physically touch another person without that person touching you with the same magnitude of force?
No, touching requires a two-ness; the toucher and the touchee.

20. Fill in the blanks: Newton's first law is often called the law of _____; Newton's second law highlights the concept of _____; and Newton's third law is the law of _____ and _____.
Inertia; acceleration; action; reaction.

Solutions to Chapter 4 Exercises

1. The photo shows Steve Hewitt and daughter Gretchen. Is Gretchen touching her dad, or is dad touching her? Explain.
In accord with Newton's third law, Steve and Gretchen are touching each other. One may initiate the touch, but the physical interaction can't occur without contact between both Steve and Gretchen. Indeed, you cannot touch without being touched!

2. For each of the following interactions, identify action and reaction forces. (a) A hammer hits a nail. (b) Earth gravity pulls down on you. (c) A helicopter blade pushes air downward.
Action; hammer hits nail. Reaction; nail hits hammer. (b) Action; Earth pulls down on you. Reaction; you pull up on the Earth. (c) Action; helicopter blade pushes air downward. Reaction; air pushes helicopter blade upward. (In these examples, action and reaction may be reversed—which is called which doesn't matter.)

3. You hold an apple over your head. (a) Identify all the forces acting on the apple and their reaction forces. (b) When you drop the apple, identify all the forces acting on it as it falls and the corresponding reaction forces. Neglect air drag.
(a) Two force pairs act; Earth's pull on the apple (action), and the apple's pull on the Earth (reaction). Hand pushes apple upward (action), and apple pushes hand downward (reaction). (b) If air drag can be neglected, one force pair acts; Earth's pull on apple, and apple's pull on Earth. If air drag counts, then air pushes upward on apple (action) and apple pushes downward on air (reaction).

4. Identify the action-reaction pairs of forces for the following situations: (a) You step off a curb. (b) You pat your tutor on the back. (c) A wave hits a rocky shore.

(a) Action; your foot pushes curb. Reaction; the curb pushes your foot. (b) Action; your hand pats tutor's back. Reaction; your tutor's back "pats" your hand. (c) Action; waves exert forces on rocky shore. Reaction; rocky shore exerts forces on waves.

5. Consider a tennis player hitting a ball. (a) Identify the action-reaction pairs when the ball is being hit, and (b) while the ball is in flight.
    (a) Action; racquet hits ball. Reaction; ball hits racquet. (b) While in flight there are two interactions, one with the Earth's gravity and the other with the air. Action; Earth pulls down on ball (weight). Reaction; ball pulls up on Earth. And, action; air pushes ball, and reaction; ball pushes air.

6. When you drop a rubber ball on the floor it bounces almost to its original height. What causes the ball to bounce?
    When the ball strikes the floor, the floor simultaneously strikes the ball. The strike of the floor on the ball causes it to bounce upward.

7. Within a book on a desk there are billions of forces pushing and pulling on all the molecules. Why is it that these forces never by chance add up to a net force in one direction, causing the book to accelerate "spontaneously" across the desk?
    The billions of force pairs are internal to the book, and exert no net force on the book. An external net force is necessary to accelerate the book.

8. You push a heavy car by hand. The car, in turn, pushes back with an opposite but equal force on you. Doesn't this mean the forces cancel one another, making acceleration impossible? Why or why not?
    When you push the car, you exert a force on the car. When the car simultaneously pushes back on you, that force is on you—not the car. You don't cancel a force on the car with a force on you. For cancellation, the forces have to be equal and opposite and act on the same object.

9. A farmer urges his horse to pull a wagon. The horse refuses, saying to try would be futile for it would flout Newton's third law. The horse concludes that she can't exert a greater force on the wagon than the wagon exerts on her, and therefore won't be able to accelerate the wagon. What is your explanation to convince the horse to pull?
    The forces do not cancel because they act on different things—one acts on the horse, and the other acts on the wagon. It's true that the wagon pulls back on the horse, and this prevents the horse from running as fast as it could without the attached wagon. But the force acting on the wagon (the pull by the horse minus friction) divided by the mass of the wagon, produces the acceleration of the wagon. To accelerate, the horse must push against the ground with more force than it exerts on the wagon and the wagon exerts on it. So tell the horse to push backward on the ground.

10. Suppose two carts, one twice as massive as the other, fly apart when the compressed spring that joins them is released. How fast does the heavier cart roll compared with the lighter cart?
    As in the preceding exercise, the force on each cart will be the same. But since the masses are different, the accelerations will differ. The twice-as-massive cart will undergo only half the acceleration of the less massive cart and will gain only half the speed.

11. If you exert a horizontal force of 200 N to slide a crate across a factory floor at constant velocity, how much friction is exerted by the floor on the crate? Is the force of friction equal and oppositely directed to your 200-N push? If the force of friction isn't the reaction force to your push, what is?
    The friction on the crate is 200 N, which cancels your 200-N push on the crate to yield the zero net force that accounts for the constant velocity (zero acceleration). Although the friction force is equal and oppositely directed to the applied force, the two do *not* make an action-reaction pair of forces. That's because both forces *do* act on the same object—the crate. The reaction to your push on the crate is the crate's push back on you. The reaction to the frictional force of the floor on the crate is the opposite friction force of the crate on the floor.

12. If a massive truck and Honda Civic have a head-on collision, upon which vehicle is the impact force greater? Which vehicle experiences the greater acceleration? Explain your answers.
In accord with Newton's 3rd law, the force on each will be of the same magnitude. But the effect of the force (acceleration) will be different for each because of the different mass. The more massive truck undergoes less change in motion than the Civic.

13. Ken and Joanne are astronauts floating some distance apart in space. They are joined by a safety cord whose ends are tied around their waists. If Ken starts pulling on the cord, will he pull Joanne toward him, or will he pull himself toward Joanne, or will both astronauts move? Explain.
Both will move. Ken's pull on the rope is transmitted to Joanne, causing her to accelerate toward him. By Newton's third law, the rope pulls back on Ken, causing him to accelerate toward Joanne.

14. Which team wins in a tug-of-war; the team that pulls harder on the rope, or the team that pushes harder against the ground? Explain.
The winning team pushes harder against the ground. The ground then pushes harder on them, producing a net force in their favor.

15. In a tug-of-war between two physics types, each pulls on the rope with a force of 250 N. What is the tension in the rope? If both remain motionless, what horizontal force does each exert against the ground?
The tension in the rope is 250 N. Since they aren't accelerating, each must experience a 250-N force of friction via the ground. They get this by pushing against the ground with 250 N.

16. A stone is shown at rest on the ground. (a) The vector shows the weight of the stone. Complete the vector diagram showing another vector that results in zero net force on the stone. (b) What is the conventional name of the vector you have drawn?
(a) The other vector is upward as shown.
(b) It is called the normal force.

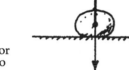

17. Here a stone is suspended at rest by a string. (a) Draw force vectors for all the forces that act on the stone. (b) Should your vectors have a zero resultant? (c) Why, or why not?
(a) As shown.
(b) Yes.
(c) Because the stone is in equilibrium.

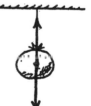

18. Here the same stone is being accelerated vertically upward. (a) Draw force vectors to some suitable scale showing relative forces acting on the stone. (b) Which is the longer vector, and why?
(a) As shown.
(b) Upward tension force is greater to result in upward net force.

19. Suppose the string in the preceding exercise breaks and the stone slows in its upward motion. Draw a force vector diagram of the stone when it reaches the top of its path.
As shown.

20. What is the acceleration of the stone in Exercise 19 at the top of its path?
The acceleration of the stone at the top of its path, or anywhere where the net force on the stone only that due to gravity is weight/mass = g. Or put another way, $a = F/m = mg/g = g$.

Solutions to Chapter 4 Problems

1. If you apply a net force of 5 N on an cart of mass 5 kg, what will be the acceleration?
From Newton's second law, $a = F/m$ = 5 N/5 kg = 1 m/s^2.

2. If you increase the speed of a 2.0-kg air puck by 3.0 m/s in 4.0 s, what force do you exert on it?
That's a very small acceleration. $F = ma = m\Delta v/\Delta t$ = (2.0 kg)(3.0 m/s)/(4.0 s) = 1.5 N, which is about 1/3 pound.

3. A boxer punches a sheet of paper in midair, and brings it from rest up to a speed of 25 m/s in 0.05 s. If the mass of the paper is 0.003 kg, what force does the boxer exert on it?
That's a very large acceleration. $F = ma = m\Delta v/\Delta t$ = (0.003 kg)(25 m/s)/(0.05 s) = 1.5 N, which also is about 1/3 pound.

4. If you stand next to a wall on a frictionless skateboard and push the wall with a force of 30 N, how hard does the wall push on you? If your mass is 60 kg, what's your acceleration?
The wall pushes on you with 30 N. $a = F/m$ = 30 N/60 kg = 0.5 m/s^2.

5 Momentum

5.1 Momentum is Inertia in Motion
5.2 Impulse Changes Momentum
      Case 1: Increasing Momentum—Increase Force, Time, or Both
      Case 2: Decreasing Momentum in a Long Time Means Less Force
      Case 3: Decreasing Momentum over a Short Time Means More Force
5.3 Momentum Change Is Greater When Bouncing Occurs
5.4 When No External Force Acts, Momentum Doesn't Change—It Is Conserved
5.5 Momentum Is Conserved In Collisions
      Elastic Collisions
      Inelastic Collisions

Learning Objectives

After studying Chapter 5, students will be able to:
• Define momentum.
• Calculate momentum given the mass and velocity in terms of *mv*.
• Define impulse and relate it to momentum.
• Give examples of how both the size of the force and the length of the time interval affect the change in momentum.
• State the law of conservation of momentum.
• Distinguish between an elastic collision and an inelastic collision.

Possible Misconceptions to Correct

• **Not so!** Impulse equals momentum rather than a change in momentum.
• **Not so!** Momentum is conserved only when a collision is elastic.
• **Not so!** Impact force and impulse are the same.

Demonstration Equipment

• Air track and carts of equal and unequal mass (if you're so fortunate!)

This chapter begins by continuing where chapter 4 leaves off. Newton's 2nd and 3rd Laws lead directly to momentum and its conservation. We emphasize the impulse-momentum relationship with applications to many examples that have been selected to grab the students' interest. In presenting your own, the exaggerated symbol technique as shown in Figures 5.4 - 5.7 is suggested. Draw a comparison between momentum conservation and Newton's 3rd Law in explaining examples such as rocket propulsion. You might point out that either of these is fundamental—i.e., momentum conservation may be regarded as a consequence of Newton's 3rd Law, or equally, Newton's 3rd Law may be regarded as a consequence of momentum conservation.

A system is not only isolated in space, but in time also. When we say that momentum is conserved when one pool ball strikes the other, we mean that momentum is conserved during the brief duration of interaction when outside forces can be neglected. After the interaction, friction quite soon brings both balls to a halt. So when we isolate a system for purposes of analysis, we isolate both in space and in time. System identification is developed on page 17 of Practice Book.

In the **Explorations Practice Book**:
• Changing Momentum
• Systems

In the **Next-Time Questions Book**:
• Long Cannon
• Momentum Conservation of Jocko the Clown
• Car-Truck Collision

There are two activities in the **Lab Manual**:
• Egg Drop
• Bouncy Board

Overhead Transparencies (2) available for:
Figures 5.4, 5.5, 5.7 and 5.12, 5.13

This chapter is important in its own right, and serves as a foundation for the concept of energy in the next chapter.

SUGGESTED PRESENTATION

5.1 Momentum is Inertia in Motion
Begin by stating that there is something different between a massive cement truck and a roller skate—they each have a different inertia. And that there is still something different about a moving cement truck and a moving roller skate—they have different momenta. Define and discuss momentum as inertia in motion.

> CHECK YOUR NEIGHBOR: After stating that a cement truck will always have more inertia than an ordinary roller skate, ask if a cement truck will always have more momentum than a roller skate.

Cite the case of the supertanker shown in Figure 5.1, and why such huge ships normally cut off their power when they are 25 or so kilometers from port. Because of their huge momentum (due mostly to their huge mass), about 25 kilometers of water resistance are needed to bring them to a halt.

5.2 Impulse Changes Momentum
Derive the impulse-momentum relationship. In Chapter 3 you defined acceleration as $a = \Delta v/t$ (really Δt, but you likely used t as the "time interval"). Then you defined acceleration in terms of the force needed, $a = F/m$. Now simply equate; $a = a$, or $F/m = \Delta v/t$, with simple rearrangement you have, $Ft = \Delta mv$ (as in the footnote at the beginning of the chapter).

Then choose your examples in careful sequence: First, those where the object is to increase momentum—pulling a slingshot or arrow in a bow all the way back, the effect of a long cannon for maximum range, driving a golf ball. Second, those examples where small forces are the object when decreasing momentum—pulling your hand backward when catching a ball, driving into a haystack versus a concrete wall, falling on a surface with give versus a rigid surface. Then lastly, those examples where the object is to obtain large forces when decreasing momentum—karate.

Point of confusion: In boxing, one "follows through" whereas in karate one "pulls back". But this is not so—a karate expert does not pull back upon striking his target. He or she strikes in such a way that the hand is made to bounce back, yielding up to twice the impulse to the target (just as a ball bouncing off a wall delivers nearly twice the impulse to the wall than if it stuck to the wall).

CHECK YOUR NEIGHBOR: Why is falling on a wooden floor in a roller rink less dangerous than falling on the concrete pavement? [Superficial answer: Because the wooden floor has more "give." Emphasize that this is the beginning of a complete answer—one that is prompted if the question is reworded as follows:] Why is falling on a floor with more give less dangerous than falling on a floor with less give? [Answer: Because the floor with more give allows a greater time for the impulse that reduces the momentum of fall to zero. A greater time for Δ momentum means less force.]

The loose coupling between railroad cars is a fascinating example of impulse-momentum. The loose coupling brings a long train initially at rest up to speed in a longer time. If the cars were tightly fastened, too much of a load would have to be moved in the same time. The looseness breaks the times of momentum change into segments. This is important in braking the train as well. (I compare this to taking school load in proper sequence, rather than all at once where for sure one's wheels would simply spin.)

5.3 Momentum Change Is Greater When Bouncing Occurs
Discuss bouncing and how Lester Pelton made a fortune from applying some simple physics to the old paddle wheels.

Bouncing does not necessarily increase impact force. That depends on impact time. Point out that bouncing involves some reversing of momentum, which means greater momentum change, and hence greater impulse. If the greater impulse is over an extended time (bouncing from a circus net), impact force is small. If over a short time (plant pot bouncing from your head), impact force is large. Damage from an object colliding with a person may depend more on energy transfer than on momentum change, so in some cases damage can be greater in an inelastic collision without bouncing.

DEMONSTRATION: Consider doing as Howie Brand does in Figure 5.9. The tip of a dart has half of a "happy ball" on its end. This end bounces well. The other end of the dart has half a "sad ball" that bounces poorly. You can arrange the displacement of the dart so that collision of the sad part doesn't topple the block. When you turn the dart around so the happy side makes contact with the block, toppling occurs. There is more impulse delivered by a bouncing dart than one that stops upon collision. Interesting.

5.4 When No External Force Acts, Momentum Doesn't Change—It Is Conserved
Distinguish between external and internal forces and lead into the conservation of momentum. Show from the impulse-momentum equation that no change in momentum can occur in the absence of an external net force.

System A

System B

System A+B

Defining Your System:
Momentum is not conserved in a system that experiences an external net force. Consider the simple case of a pool ball striking one at rest. If the system is the ball at rest, then an external force acts on it and momentum is increased. Momentum for this ball is not conserved. Or if the

system is the moving ball, then a reaction force acts on it when it strikes the ball at rest. This external force stops the ball in its tracks. Momentum for this ball is not conserved. Now consider the system of interest to be BOTH balls. For this system, no external force acts. The action and reaction forces occur within the system. For this system, net momentum doesn't change, and momentum IS conserved. (It is merely transferred from one part of the system to the other without net change.) How deeply you want to treat the notion of systems is your call. It can be glossed over for general students, or delved into in-depth with students who value further study in physics.

5.5 Momentum Is Conserved In Collisions

The numerical example of the air-track carts in the Calculation Corner box may clarify the vector nature of momentum—particularly for the case of the carts approaching each other. The emphasis you give to going over this will vary from class to class. It will be important if you are fortunate enough to have an air-track apparatus. Relate this to the exercises at the end of the chapter, particularly Exercises 4, 5, 6, and especially 7 (the lunching fish).

DEMONSTRATION: Show momentum conservation with an air-track performance.

Chapter 5 Answers and Solutions

Key Terms and Matching Definitions

__5__ elastic collision
__2__ impulse
__3__ impulse-momentum relationship
__6__ inelastic collision
__4__ law of conservation of momentum
__1__ momentum

Review Questions

1. Which has a greater momentum, a heavy truck at rest or a moving automobile?
   The truck at rest has no speed, hence no momentum. So the moving automobile has greater momentum.

2. How can a supertanker have a huge momentum when it moves relatively slowly?
   It has a huge momentum because its mass is so huge.

3. Why is it incorrect to say that impulse equals momentum?
   Impulse equals a *change* in momentum, not momentum itself.

4. To impart the greatest momentum to an object, what should you do in addition to exerting the largest force possible?
   Extend the time during which the force acts for more impulse.

5. For the same force, which cannon imparts the greater speed to a cannonball—a long cannon or a short one? Explain.
   A cannonball will have more momentum coming from the long cannon due to the force acting for more time.

6. If you're in a car that is going to hit something and stop, the momentum will change to zero whether you hit a brick wall or a haystack. So why is hitting a haystack a safer bet?
   Although the change in momentum, and therefore the impulse will be the same for both, hitting the haystack means a small force and long time (rather than a big force and short time hitting the wall).

7. Why is it less damaging if you fall on a mat than if you fall on a solid floor?
   The time to come to a stop will be longer on the mat. This means a longer time to stop and a smaller force.

8. Why is it a good idea to extend your hand forward when catching a fast-moving baseball with your bare hand?
   An extended hand has room to move backward when the ball is caught. This stretches the time, which results in less force.

9. In boxing, why is it advantageous to roll with the punch?
   The force of impact will be less if momentum changes over a long time. By making *t* long, *F* will be smaller.

10. In karate why is a short time of the applied force advantageous?
    The shorter time is accompanied by a greater force when the momentum of the arm is reduced.

11. Which is the greater change in momentum, a stop of something dead in its tracks, or a stop and then a reversal of direction?
Stopping and then reversing direction is a greater change in momentum.

12. Which requires the greater impulse, stopping something dead in its tracks, or stopping it and then reversing its direction?
Stopping and then reversing direction is a greater change in momentum and therefore requires a greater impulse.

13. When can the momentum of two moving objects be cancelled?
When their momentum is equal and opposite and they comprise the same system.

14. What does it mean to say that momentum (or any quantity) is *conserved*?
It means that in any interaction where external impulses don't occur, the momentum of a system remains the same before and after the interaction. In general it means that the magnitude of the quantity remains unchanged while other changes may take place.

15. When a cannonball is fired, its momentum does change! Is momentum conserved for the cannonball?
No, momentum is not conserved, for an impulse acts on the cannonball.

16. When a cannonball is fired, the cannon recoils. Is momentum conserved for the cannon?
No, momentum is not conserved, for an opposite impulse acts on the cannon.

17. When a cannonball is fired, is momentum conserved for the cannon-cannonball system as a whole? (Why is your answer different than in the previous two questions?)
Momentum *is* conserved for the cannon-cannonball system, where the forces are internal to the system. Both forces act within the system, whereas if the system in question is only the cannon (or cannonball), force is from outside the system.

18. Distinguish between an *elastic* collision and an *inelastic* collision. For which type of collision is momentum conserved?
An elastic collision is one where rebound is without lasting deformation or the generation of heat. An inelastic collision is one where deformation does occur, or heat is generated. Momentum is conserved for both types.

19. Railroad car A rolls at a certain speed and makes a perfectly elastic collision with car B of the same mass. After the collision, car A is observed to be at rest. How does the speed of car B compare with the initial speed of car A?
Like the balls in Figure 5.11, momentum is completely transferred from car A to car B. Since the masses are the same, the speed of Car B is equal to the initial speed of car A.

20. If the equally massive cars of the previous question stick together after colliding inelastically, how does their speed after the collision compare with the initial speed of car A?
Again, the momentum of car A is transferred, this time to both cars. Since twice the mass is moving after collision, the speed is half.

Solutions for Chapter 5 Exercises

1. When roller blading, why is a fall less harmful on a wooden floor than on a concrete floor with less give? Explain in terms of impulse and momentum.
The floor with less give means a shorter time for momentum to change, which means a greater force of contact. Ouch!

2. In terms of impulse and momentum, why do air bags in cars reduce the chances of injury in accidents?
Air bags lengthen the time of contact thereby reducing the force of contact.

3. In terms of impulse and momentum, why are nylon ropes, which stretch considerably under tension, favored by mountain climbers?

The time is extended while momentum decreases, thereby decreasing the jolting force of the rope. Note that in bringing a person to a stop more gently does *not* reduce the impulse. It only reduces the force.

4. If you throw an egg against a wall, the egg will break. But if you throw it at the same speed into a sagging sheet, it may not break. Why?
   Hitting the sagging sheet gives the egg more time to come to a stop. This means less force.

5. A lunar vehicle is tested on Earth at a speed of 10 km/h. When it travels as fast on the moon, is its momentum more, less, or the same?
   Its momentum is the same (its weight might change, but not its mass).

6. Which has the greater momentum when they move at the same speed—an automobile or a skateboard? Which requires the greatest stopping force?
   The automobile, for it has a greater mass. It also has more momentum and therefore requires more impulse to stop—and hence more force.

7. In answering the preceding exercise, perhaps you stated that the automobile requires more stopping force. Make an argument that the skateboard could require more stopping force, depending on how quickly you want to stop it.
   If you stop the auto in a very long time, and stop the skateboard very suddenly, more force may be required to stop the skateboard. For sake of argument, suppose the skateboard has mass *m*, and the auto has mass 1000 *m*. Suppose the time to stop the skateboard is *t*. Then if you take 1000 *t* to stop the car, the forces would be the same. Stop the auto in any time longer than this, and more force stops the skateboard.

8. Why is a punch more forceful with a bare fist than with a boxing glove?
   Impact with a boxing glove extends the time during which momentum of the fist is reduced, and lessens the force. A punch with a bare fist involves less time and therefore more force.

9. Why do 6-ounce boxing gloves hit harder than 16-ounce gloves?
   The lighter gloves have less padding, and less ability to extend the time of impact, and therefore result in greater forces of impact for a given punch.

10. Which undergoes the greatest change in momentum: (1) a baseball that is caught, (2) a baseball that is thrown, or (3) a baseball that is caught and then thrown back, if the baseballs have the same speed just before being caught and just after being thrown?
    (3) There is twice the momentum change for the baseball that is caught and then thrown back—change in stopping, and the same change in returning.

11. In the preceding question, in which case is the greatest impulse required?
    Greatest impulse also for (3) because of the greater change in momentum.

12. An apple gains momentum as it falls from a tree. Does this violate the conservation of momentum? Defend your answer.
    There is a net impulse on the apple, supplied by Earth gravity, so momentum changes and is not conserved.

13. In the preceding exercise, would momentum be conserved in the larger system apple-Earth? In this system, can it be said that the momentum of the falling apple is equal and opposite to the momentum of the Earth as it "races" up to meet the apple? What does this say about the upward speed of the Earth?
    Momentum is conserved in the apple-Earth system, for the forces are internal to the system. Momentum change of the apple is equal and opposite to momentum change of the Earth, and they cancel to zero. The massive Earth moves at an imperceptible speed—not noticed because its mass is so much larger than the apple's mass.

14. If only an external force can change the velocity of a body, how can the internal force of the brakes bring a car to rest?

The internal force of the brake brings the wheel to rest. But the wheel, after all, is attached to the tire which makes contact with the road surface. It is the force of the road on the tires that stops the car.

15. You are at the front of a floating canoe near a dock. You jump, expecting easily to land on the dock. Instead you land in the water. Explain.

In jumping, the momentum imparted to you is equal and opposite to the momentum of the canoe. This means you jump from a canoe that is moving away from the dock, reducing your speed relative to the dock, so you don't jump as far as you expected to.

16. A fully dressed person is at rest in the middle of a pond on perfectly frictionless ice and must get to shore. How can this be accomplished?

To get to shore, the person may throw keys or coins or an item of clothing. The momentum of what is thrown will be accompanied by the thrower's oppositely directed momentum. So one can recoil towards shore. (Or inhale facing the shore and exhale facing away.)

17. Two football players have a head-on collision and both stop short in their paths. If one player is twice as heavy as the other, how does his speed compare to the smaller player?

Momentum is the same for both, so the twice-as-heavy player would have to be moving at half the speed of the lighter player.

18. In the previous chapter, rocket propulsion was explained in terms of Newton's third law. That is, the force that propels a rocket is from the exhaust gases pushing against the rocket—the reaction to the force the rocket exerts on the exhaust gases. Explain rocket propulsion in terms of momentum conservation.

If the rocket and its exhaust gases are treated as a single system, the forces between rocket and exhaust gases are internal, and momentum in the rocket-gases system is conserved. So any momentum given to the gases is equal and opposite to momentum given to the rocket. A rocket attains momentum by giving momentum to the exhaust gases.

19. When you are traveling in your car at highway speed, the momentum of a bug is suddenly changed as it splatters onto your windshield. Compared to the change in momentum of the bug, by how much does the momentum of your car change?

By Newton's 3rd law, the force on the bug is equal in magnitude and opposite in direction to the force on the car windshield. The rest is logic: Since the time of impact is the same for both, the amount of impulse is the same for both, which means they both undergo the same change in momentum. The change in momentum of the bug is evident because of its large change in speed. The same change in momentum of the considerably more massive car is not evident, for the change in speed is correspondingly very small. Nevertheless, the magnitude of $m\Delta V$ for the bug is equal to $M\Delta v$ for the car!

20. If an 18-wheeler tractor-trailer and a sports car have a head-on collision, which vehicle will experience the greater force of impact? The greater impulse? The greater change in momentum? The greater acceleration?

The magnitude of force, impulse, and change in momentum will be the same for each. The sports car undergoes the greater acceleration because its mass is less.

Solutions for Chapter 5 Problems

1. What is the impulse needed to stop a 10-kg bowling ball moving at 6 m/s?

The bowling ball has a momentum of (10 kg)(6 m/s) = 60 kg·m/s, which has the magnitude of the impulse to stop it. That's 60 N·s. (Note that units N·s = kg·m/s.)

2. A car with a mass of 1000 kg moves at 20 m/s. What braking force is needed to bring the car to a halt in 10 s?

From $Ft = \Delta mv$, $F = \dfrac{\Delta mv}{t}$ = [(1000 kg)(20 m/s)]/10 s = 2000 N.

3. A car crashes into a wall at 25 m/s and is brought to rest in 0.1 s. Calculate the average force exerted on a 75-kg test dummy by the seat belt.

From $Ft = \Delta mv$, $F = \dfrac{\Delta mv}{t}$ = [(75 kg)(25 m/s)]/0.1 s = 18,750 N.

4. Lillian (mass 40.0 kg) standing on slippery ice catches her leaping dog (mass 15 kg) moving horizontally at 3.0 m/s. What is the speed of Lillian and her dog after the catch?

From the conservation of momentum,

$\text{Momentum}_{\text{dog}} = \text{momentum}_{\text{Lil + dog}}$

(15 kg)(3.0 m/s) = (40.0 kg + 15 kg)v

45 kg m/s = (55 kg) v

v = 0.8 m/s.

5. A 2-kg ball of putty moving to the right has a head-on inelastic collision with a 1-kg putty ball moving to the left. If the combined blob doesn't move just after the collision, what can you conclude about the relative speeds of the balls before they collided?

Momentum after collision is zero, which means the net momentum before collision must have been zero. So the 1-kg ball must be moving twice as fast as the 2-kg ball so that the magnitudes of their momenta are equal.

6. A railroad diesel engine weighs four times as much as a freight car. If the diesel engine coasts at 5 km/h into a freight car that is initially at rest, how fast do the two coast after they couple together?

The answer is 4 km/h. Let m be the mass of the freight car, and $4m$ the mass of the diesel engine, and v the speed after both have coupled together. Before collision, the total momentum is due only to the diesel engine, $4m$(5 km/h), because the momentum of the freight car is 0. After collision, the combined mass is ($4m + m$), and combined momentum is ($4m + m$)v. By the conservation of momentum equation:

$\text{Momentum}_{\text{before}} = \text{momentum}_{\text{after}}$

$4m$(5 km/h) + 0 = ($4m + m$)v

$v = \dfrac{(20m \cdot \text{km/h})}{5m}$ = 4 km/h.

(Note that you don't have to know m to solve the problem.)

7. A 5-kg fish swimming 1 m/s swallows an absent minded 1-kg fish swimming toward it at a velocity that brings both fish to a halt immediately after lunch. What is the velocity V of the smaller fish before lunch?

$\text{Momentum}_{\text{before}} = \text{momentum}_{\text{after}}$

(5kg)(1m/s) + (1kg)v = 0

5m/s + v = 0

v = -5 m/s

So if the little fish approaches the big fish at 5 m/s, the momentum after will be zero.

8. Can you run fast enough to have the same momentum as an automobile rolling at 1 mi/h? Make up reasonable figures to justify your answer.

Yes or no, depending on the masses of the runner and the car. A 200-lb person running 10 mi/h has as much momentum as a small 2000-lb car moving at 1 mi/h. On the other hand, consider a 100-lb person and a 4000-lb car. Running speed would have to be 40 mi/h (not possible) to match the car's momentum when moving at 1 mi/h. (Note that since weight and mass are directly proportional, we can express relative momenta via familiar weight units—pounds. The conversion factor relating mass and weight cancels out of any computation. Conversion factors for changing mi/h to m/s also cancel.)

6 Work and Energy

Conceptual Physical Science—Explorations

Learning Objectives
After studying Chapter 6, students will be able to:
• Determine the amount of work done when given the force and the distance moved.
• Determine the amount of power when work done and time are given.
• Calculate work as the product of force and distance.
• Calculate the amount of power when work done and time are given.
• Define work in terms of energy.
• Distinguish between potential and kinetic energy.
• Describe how the kinetic energy of an object depends on mass and speed.
• State the law of conservation of energy.
• Describe the function of a lever.
• Define efficiency in terms of work done and work input.

Possible Misconceptions to Correct
• **Not so!** Momentum and kinetic energy are much the same concept.
• **Not so!** Energy is conserved only under certain conditions.
• **Not so!** It is possible to get more energy out of a good machine than is put into it.

Demonstration Equipment
• A simple pendulum (any ball tied to a length of string)
• The swinging balls apparatus (optional)

This is an important chapter. The concept of energy is central to physics and is discussed in its various forms throughout the remainder of the text.

The bed-of-nails demo shown in Exercise 12 has been around for a long time. Since it is somewhat dangerous, many schools fearing litigation do not favor their teachers doing this in class. It is shown in the introduction to Conceptual Physics Alive!, both videotapes and DVDs. Quite impressive.

In the **Explorations Practice Book:**
• Work, Power, and Energy
• Conservation of Energy
• Machines

In the **Next-Time Questions** Book:
• Roller Coaster
• Ball Toss

In the **Laboratory Manual**:
• Rolling Stop (experiment)

Overhead Transparencies (1) available for:
Figures 7.4 and 7.8

A nice discussion to kick off a treatment of energy is presented by Feynman in the beginning of his Chapter 4, *The Feynman Lectures On Physics* (Addison-Wesley, 1963).

SUGGESTED PRESENTATION

Begin by standing on a chair against a wall with an extended heavy pendulum bob held at the tip of your nose. Say nothing. Release the bob and let it swing out, then back to your nose. Don't flinch. Then comment on your confidence in physical laws and lead into a distinction between potential and kinetic energy. That is, point out that where the bob is moving fastest, it is lowest, and where it is highest, it doesn't move at all. The bob transforms energy of motion to energy of position in cyclic fashion. Allow the pendulum to swing to-and-fro while you're talking. Its motion decays. Why? Then point out the transformation of energy from the moving bob to the molecules of air that are encountered, and to the molecules in the bending string or wire at the pivot point. The energy of the pendulum will end up as heat energy. I quip that on a very hot day, somebody, somewhere, is swinging a giant pendulum to-and-fro.

6.1 Work—Force × Distance
Define work and compare it to impulse of the previous chapter. In both cases, the effect of exerting a force on something depends on how long the force acts. In the previous chapter, how long was meant as time, and we spoke of impulse. In this chapter, how long is meant as distance, and we speak of work. Cite the examples of the drawn slingshot and the long barreled cannon, where the added length produces greater speed. We described this greater speed in terms of greater momentum: Now we describe this greater speed in terms of greater energy—that is, greater KE.

CHECK YOUR NEIGHBOR: Is work done when a weightlifter holds a barbell stationary above her head? [Yes and no. With each contraction of the weightlifter's heart, a force is exerted through a distance on her blood and so does work on the blood. But this work is not done on the barbell.]

6.2 Power—How Quickly Work Gets Done
A watt of power is the work done in vertically lifting a quarter-pound hamburger with cheese (approx. 1 N) one meter in one second.

6.3 Mechanical Energy
Cite the various forms of energy, and state that we'll consider only mechanical energy for now, which takes the form of potential energy and kinetic energy.

6.4 Potential Energy Is Stored Energy
Return to your pendulum: With the pendulum at equilibrium show how the force necessary to pull it sideways (which varies with the angle made by the string) is very small compared to the force necessary to lift it vertically (its weight). Point out that for equal elevations, the arced path is correspondingly longer than the vertical path—with the result that the

product of the applied force and distance traveled—the work done—is the same for both cases. (Without overdoing it, this is a good place to let your students know about integral calculus—how calculus is required to add up the work segments that continuously increase in a nonlinear way.) Then discuss the work needed to elevate the ball in Figure 6.8.

CHECK YOUR NEIGHBOR: Does a car hoisted for lubrication in a service station have PE? How much work will raise the car twice as high? Three times as high? How much more PE will it have in these cases?

You can give the example of dropping a bowling ball on your toe—first from a distance of 1 mm above your toe, then to various distances up to 1 m above your toe. Each time, the bowling ball would do more work on your toe, because it would possess more gravitational potential energy when released.

6.5 Kinetic Energy Is Energy Of Motion

Relate force × distance = Δ KE to examples of pushing a car, and then to braking a car as treated in the text. To a close approximation, skidding force is independent of speed. Hence change in KE is approximately equal to change in skidding distance. When the car's brakes are applied, the car's kinetic energy is changed into internal energy in the brake pads, tire, and road as they become warmer.

You may or may not at this point preview future material by relating the idea of the KE of molecules and the idea of temperature. State that molecules in a substance having the same temperature have the same average KE. If the masses of the molecules are the same, then it follows that the speeds of the molecules are the same. But what if the masses are different, for example in a sample of gas made up of light and heavy molecules at the same temperature? Which molecules would move faster? (If you shook a container of billiard balls mixed with Ping-Pong balls so that both kinds of balls had the same kinetic energy, which would move faster in the container?) (If an elephant and a mouse run with the same kinetic energy, which is to say both will do the same amount of work if they bump into the door of a barn, can you say which of the two is running faster?) You might consider the demonstration of inhaling helium and talking at this point—particularly if you are not including the chapters on sound in your course design. Relate the higher temperature due to the faster moving helium molecules to the higher temperature in a bugle when faster moving air is blown through it.

6.6 Work-Energy Theorem

When discussing whether or not work is done, be sure to specify *done on what*. If you push a stationary wall, you may be doing work on your muscles (that involve forces and distances in flexing), but you do no work *on the wall*. Key point: If work is done on something, then the energy of that something changes. Distinguish between the energy one expends in doing things, and the work that is actually done *on* something.

CHECK YOUR NEIGHBOR: When a car slows down due to air drag, does its KE decrease? [Most certainly!]

CHECK YOUR NEIGHBOR: Which is greater, 1 joule or 1 newton? [Whoops! The comparison is silly, for they're units of completely different things—work and force. An idea about the magnitude of 1 joule is that it is the work done in vertically lifting a quarter-pound hamburger with cheese (approx. 1 N) one meter.

6.7 Conservation of Energy

Discuss Figures 6.8 and 6.9 and then return to your pendulum. Explain how the kinetic energy and hence, the speed of the bob at the bottom of its swing is equal to the speed it would have if dropped vertically through the same height.

CHECK YOUR NEIGHBOR: Refer to Figure 6.8 in "inclines" a and b: How does the speed of the ball compare at ground level when released from equal elevations? [It is impressive that the speeds will be the same. The lesser acceleration down the sloped ramp is compensated by a longer time. But return to the situation and ask how the *times* to reach the bottom compare and be prepared for an incorrect response, "The same!" Quip and ask if the colors and temperatures will also be the same. Straightforward physics can be confusing enough!]

DEMONSTRATION: Preview electricity and magnetism and bring out the horseshoe magnet hand-cranked generator that lights up the lamp shown ahead in Figures 12.26 and 12.27. Have student volunteers attest to the fact that more work is needed to turn the crank when the lamp is connected than when it is not. Then relate this to the Concept Check about fuel consumption in an automobile when lights are on.

When gasoline combines with oxygen in a car's engine, the chemical potential energy stored in the fuel is converted mainly into molecular KE (thermal energy). Some of this energy in effect is transferred to the piston and some of this causes motion of the car.

Go over the Challenge Question in the text about fuel economy—very important. (I pose the same question on my exams, which to the student is the *definition* of what's important!) As a side point, gas economy is increased when tires are inflated to maximum pressures, where less flattening of the tire occurs as it turns. The very important point of this exercise is the upper limit possible.

I extend this idea of an upper limit to the supposed notion that certain gadgets attached to automobile engines will give phenomenal performance—so much in fact, (tongue in cheek) that the oil companies have gobbled up the patents and are keeping them off the market. Charlatans stand ready to benefit from this public perception, and offer the public a chance to invest in their energy producing machines. They prey on people who are ignorant of or do not understand the message of the energy conservation law. You can't get something for nothing. You can't even break even, because of the inevitable transformation of available energy to heat. For more on such charlatans, read Bob Park's book, *Voodoo Science*.

6.8 Machines—Devices To Multiply Forces

Show how a lever is a simple machine, obeying the work in = work out principle. And show that a pulley is an extension of a simple lever.

6.9 Efficiency—A Measure Of Work Done For Energy Spent

It should be enough that your students become acquainted with the idea of efficiency, so I don't recommend setting the plow setting too deep for this topic. The key idea to impart is that of useful energy. To say that an incandescent lamp is 10% efficient is to say that only 10% of the energy input is converted to the useful form of light. All the rest turns to heat. But even the light energy converts to heat upon absorption. So all the energy input to an incandescent lamp is converted to heat. This means that it is a 100% efficient *heater* (but not a 100% device for emitting light)!

6.10 Sources of Energy

It is important that students don't see electricity, steam, and other transporters of energy as energy sources. Sources include solar, geothermal, and nuclear. Electricity, for example, involves some source such as a waterfall (potential energy) or fuel to produce steam. Call attention to Figure 6.24, a sensible and future contender of power. Look ahead to Section 26.4 in the text for fascinating information on fuel cells.

6.11 Energy is Needed for Life
When biologists talk of energy in living systems, they're talking about the same energy discussed in this chapter. Our bodies obey the same principles that levers and other machines obey.

Dark Energy: Not discussed in the text is the current serious speculation of dark energy, which is postulated to be speeding up the expanding universe. You may want to discuss this current finding, which may be one of the most important discoveries in science in the past quarter century.

NEXT-TIME QUESTION: Exercise 17, when you've shown the swinging ball apparatus in class.

Sample Advanced Problem and Solution (that shows how an equation guides thinking! Note how each step dictates the next step.)

Problem: A car traveling along a level road at speed v slams on the brakes and skids to a stop. If the force of friction on the car is half the car's weight, how far does the car slide? (Hint: Use the work-energy theorem and solve for d.)

Solution: By the work-energy theorem,
$W = \Delta KE$

Work done on the car is Fd, so

$$Fd = \Delta(1/2\ mv^2)$$

The only force F that does work to reduce the kinetic energy is the force of friction. This force acts through d, the distance of skidding. The mass of the car is m, and its initial speed is v. In this problem the final speed of the car will be zero, so the change in kinetic energy is simply the initial kinetic energy at speed v. You're looking for distance, so write the equation in a "$d =$" form. It becomes

$$d = \frac{\Delta(1/2\ mv^2)}{F} \qquad = \frac{1/2\ mv^2}{f} \qquad = \frac{1/2\ mv^2}{mg/2} \qquad = \frac{v^2}{g}$$

where F is half the car's weight, $mg/2$.
    Note how the terms in the equation dictate subsequent steps and guide your thinking. The final expression tells you the stopping distance is proportional to speed squared, which is consistent with it being proportional to KE. It also tells you that if g were greater, the force of friction would be greater and skidding distance less—which is quite reasonable. Cancellation of mass tells you that the mass of the car doesn't matter. All cars skidding with the same initial speed, with friction equal to half their weights, will skid the same distance. And as for units, note that v^2/g has the unit $(m^2/s^2)/(m/s^2) = m$, a distance, as it should be. How nice that much can be learned by a thoughtful examination of a simple equation.

Chapter 6 Answers and Solutions

Key Terms and Matching Definitions

__8__ conservation of energy
_10__ efficiency
__4__ energy
__6__ kinetic energy
__9__ machine
__5__ potential energy
__2__ power
__3__ watt
__1__ work
__7__ work-energy theorem

Review Questions

1. A force sets an object in motion. When the force is multiplied by the time of its application, we call the quantity *impulse*, which changes the *momentum* of that object. What do we call the quantity *force × distance*?
   Work.

2. Cite an example where a force is exerted on an object without doing work on the object.
   A force is needed to hold a barbell overhead, but this force does no work on the barbell while the barbell is at rest.

3. Which requires more work—lifting a 50-kg sack a vertical distance of 2 m or lifting a 25-kg sack a vertical distance of 4 m?
   Both require the same work because the force × distance is the same for each.

4. If both sacks in the preceding question are lifted their respective distances in the same time, how does the power required for each compare? How about for the case where the lighter sack is moved its distance in half the time?
   Power for each is the same because the same work is done in the same time. Twice the power is required to do the same work on the lighter sack in half the time.

5. Exactly what is it that a body having energy is capable of doing?
   Work.

6. What are the two main forms of mechanical energy?
   Potential energy and kinetic energy.

7. A car is lifted a certain distance in a service station and therefore has potential energy relative to the floor. If it were lifted twice as high, how much potential energy would it have?
   Twice.

8. Two cars are lifted to the same elevation in a service station. If one car is twice as massive as the other, how do their potential energies compare?
   The twice-as-massive car has twice the PE.

9. How many joules of potential energy does a 1-N book gain when it is elevated 4 m? When it is elevated 8 m?
   PE = 1 N × 4 m = 40 J. At 8 m the PE = 80 J.

10. A moving car has kinetic energy. If it speeds up until it is going four times as fast, how much kinetic energy does it have in comparison?

A three-times as fast car has 4^2 or 16 times the KE.

11. Compared to some original speed, how much work must the brakes of a car supply to stop a four-times-as-fast car? How will the stopping distance compare?
A four-times-as-fast car has 16 times as much KE and will require 16 times as much work to stop, and 16 times as much stopping distance.

12. What will be the kinetic energy of pile driver ram when it undergoes a 10 kJ decrease in potential energy? (Assume no energy goes to heat.)
PE = KE = 10kJ.

13. Can a machine multiply input force? Input distance? Input energy? (If your three answers are the same, seek help, for the last question is especially important.)
Yes; yes; NO! (Machines are good at multiplying force or distance, but no machine can multiply energy—a conservation of energy no-no!

14. If a machine multiplies force by a factor of four, what other quantity is diminished, and how much?
Increasing force means decreasing distance, so the distance moved by the four-fold force is one-fourth as much.

15. If the man in Figure 7.15 pulls 1 m of rope downward with a force of 100 N, and the load rises 1/7 as high (about 14 cm), what is the maximum load that can be lifted?
Seven times as much, 700 N.

16. What is the efficiency of a machine that miraculously converts all the input energy to useful output energy?
100%—the efficiency of an *ideal* machine.

17. Is a machine physically possible that has an efficiency greater than 100 percent? Discuss.
Not in the world as we know it. Such a machine would clearly violate the conservation of energy, a law that has never been violated.

18. What is the ultimate source of energies for the burning of fossil fuels, dams, and windmills?
Solar energy.

19. What is the ultimate source of geothermal energy?
Nuclear energy from radioactive decay.

20. The energy we require for existence comes from the chemically stored potential energy in food, which is transformed into other forms when it is metabolized. What happens to a person whose work output is less than the energy he or she consumes? Whose work output is greater than the energy he or she consumes? Can an undernourished person perform extra work without extra food? Briefly discuss.
When work output is less than input energy, the person gains weight. When work output is more than input energy, weight loss results. An undernourished person performing extra work without extra food violates energy conservation—and perishes.

Solutions for Chapter 6 Exercises

1. When the mass of a moving object is doubled with no change in speed, by what factor is its momentum changed? Its kinetic energy?
   When the mass is doubled with no change in speed, both momentum and KE are doubled.

2. When the velocity of an object is doubled, by what factor is its momentum changed? Its kinetic energy?
   When the velocity is doubled, the momentum is doubled and the KE is increased by a factor of 4. Momentum is proportional to speed, KE to speed squared.

3. Consider a ball thrown straight up in the air. At what position is its kinetic energy a maximum? Where is its gravitational potential energy a maximum?
   Kinetic energy is a maximum as soon as the ball leaves the hand. Potential energy is a maximum when the ball has reached its zenith.

4. At what point in its motion is the KE of a pendulum bob a maximum? At what point is its PE a maximum? When its KE is half its maximum value, how much PE does it have?
   The KE of a pendulum bob is maximum where it moves fastest, at the lowest point; PE is maximum at the uppermost points. When the pendulum bob swings by the point that marks half its maximum height, it has half its maximum KE, and its PE is halfway between its minimum and maximum values. If we define PE = 0 at the bottom of the swing, the place where KE is half its maximum value is also the place where PE is half its maximum value, and KE = PE at this point. (In accordance with energy conservation: total energy = KE + PE).

5. A physical science teacher demonstrates energy conservation by releasing a heavy pendulum bob, as shown in the sketch, allowing it to swing to-and-fro. What would happen if in his exuberance he gave the bob a slight shove as it left his nose? Explain.
   If the ball is given an initial KE, it will return to its starting position with that KE (moving in the other direction!) and hit the instructor. (The usual classroom procedure is to release the ball from the nose at rest. Then when it returns it will have no KE and will stop short of bumping the nose.)

6. Discuss the design of the roller coaster shown in the sketch in terms of the conservation of energy.
   The design is impractical. Note that the summit of each hill on the roller coaster is the same height, so the PE of the car at the top of each hill would be the same. If no energy were spent in overcoming friction, the car would get to the second summit with as much energy as it starts with. But in practice there is considerable friction, and the car would not roll to its initial height and have the same energy. So the maximum height of succeeding summits should be lower to compensate for friction.

7. Suppose that you and two classmates are discussing the design of a roller coaster. One classmate says that each summit must be lower than the previous one. Your other classmate says this is nonsense, for as long as the first one is the highest, it doesn't matter what height the others are. What do you say?
   You agree with your second classmate. The coaster could just as well encounter a low summit before or after a higher one, so long as the higher one is enough lower than the initial summit to compensate for energy dissipation by friction.

8. Consider molecules of hydrogen (tiny ones) and oxygen (bigger ones) in a gas mixture. If they have the same average kinetic energy (they will at the same temperature), which molecules have the greatest average *speed*?
   For the same KE, the ones with less mass have higher speed.

9. On a slide a child has potential energy that decreases by 1000 J while her kinetic energy increases by 900 J. What other form of energy is involved, and how much?
   The 100 J of potential energy that doesn't go into increasing her kinetic energy goes into thermal energy—heating her bottom and the slide.

10. According to the work-energy theorem, in the absence of friction, if you do 100 J of work on a cart, how much will you increase its kinetic energy?
You'll increase its KE by 100 J.

11. Does speed affect the friction between a road and a skidding tire?
Speed doesn't affect the force of friction. Fast or slow, the friction force is the same.

12. The photo shows Paul Hewitt delivering a blow to a cement block that rests on a bed of nails. Sandwiched bravely between beds of nails is San Mateo High School physics teacher, Pablo Robinson. Since the blow is shared by many nails on Robinson's body, the force per nail won't puncture his skin. Discuss what Robinson's fate might be if the block were less massive and unbreakable, and the beds contained fewer nails.
Exaggeration makes the fate of teacher Pablo Robinson easier to assess: He would not be so calm if the cement block were replaced with the inertia of a small stone, for inertia plays a role in this demonstration. If the block were unbreakable, the energy that busts it up would instead be transferred to the beds of nails. So it is desirable to use a block that will break upon impact. If the bed consisted of a single nail, finding a successor to Pablo would be very difficult, so it is important that the bed have plenty of nails!

13. Consider the identical balls released from rest on Tracks A and B as shown. When they reach the right ends of the tracks, which will have the greater speed? (Hint: Will their KEs be the same at the end?) Which will get to the end in the shortest time? (Hint: Considering the extra speed in the lower part of track B, which ball has the greatest average speed on the ramps?)
Both will have the same speed at the end because both balls convert the same PE to KE. But since the average speed is greater on track B, that ball will get to the end first (but with the same speed as A). Note there is a difference between asking which has the greatest speed and which gets to the end in the shortest time.

14. You tell your friend that no machine can possibly put out more energy than is put into it, and your friend states that a nuclear reactor puts out more energy than is put into it. What do you say?
Your friend may not realize that mass itself is congealed energy, so you tell your friend that much more energy in its congealed form is put into the reactor than is taken out from the reactor. Almost 1% of the mass of fission fuel is converted to energy of other forms.

15. Two lumps of clay with equal and opposite momenta have a head-on collision and come to rest. Is momentum conserved? Is kinetic energy conserved? Why are your answers the same or different?
Net momentum before the lumps collide is zero, and is zero after collision. Momentum is indeed conserved. Kinetic energy after is zero, but was greater than zero before collision. The lumps are warmer after colliding because the initial kinetic energy of the lumps transforms into thermal energy. Momentum has only one form. There is no way to "transform" momentum from one form to another, so it is conserved. But energy comes in various forms and can easily be transformed. No single form of energy such as KE need be conserved.

16. Scissors for cutting paper have long blades and short handles, whereas metal-cutting shears have long handles and short blades. Bolt cutters have very long handles and very short blades. Why is this so?
Scissors and shears are levers. The applied force is normally exerted over a short distance for scissors so that the output force is exerted over a relatively long distance (except when you want a large cutting force like cutting a piece of tough rope, and you place the rope close to the "fulcrum" so you can multiply force). With metal-cutting shears, the handles are long so that a relatively small input force is exerted over a long distance to produce a large output force over a short distance.

17. Consider the swinging-balls apparatus. If two balls are lifted and released, momentum is conserved as two balls pop out the other side with the same speed as the released balls at impact. But momentum would also be conserved if one ball popped out at twice the speed. Can you explain why this never happens? (Hint: If the collision is perfectly elastic, what beside momentum would have to be conserved? Can you see why this exercise is here rather than in the previous chapter on momentum?)

There is more to the "swinging balls" problem than momentum conservation, which is why the problem wasn't posed in the previous chapter. Momentum is certainly conserved if two balls strike with momentum $2mv$ and one ball pops out with momentum $m(2v)$. That is, $2mv = m2v$. We must also consider KE. Two balls would strike with $2(1/2\ mv^2) = mv^2$. That means the single ball would pop out with twice the speed. Then it would carry away twice as much energy as was put in:

$$1/2\ m(2v)^2 = 1/2\ m(4v^2) = 2mv^2$$

This is clearly a conservation of energy no-no!

18. Does a high-efficiency machine degrade a relatively high or relatively low percentage of energy to thermal energy?
Relatively low. Low efficiencies degrade more energy to thermal energy.

19. If an automobile had a 100% efficient engine, transferring all of the fuel's energy to work, would the engine be warm to your touch? Would its exhaust heat the surrounding air? Would it make any noise? Would it vibrate? Would any of its fuel go unused?
An engine that is 100% efficient would not be warm to the touch, nor would its exhaust heat the air, nor would it make any noise, nor would it vibrate. This is because all these are transfers of energy, which cannot happen if all the energy given to the engine is transformed to useful work.

20. A friend says the energy of oil and coal is actually a form of solar energy. Is your friend correct, or mistaken?
Correct, for the energy found in oil and coal was at one time solar energy.

Solutions to Chapter 6 Problems

1. How many joules of work are done when a force of 1 N moves a book 2 m?
    Work = Fd = 1 N × 2 m = 2 Joules.

2. (a)How much work do you do when you push a crate horizontally with 100 N across a 10-m factory floor? (b) If the force of friction between the crate and floor is a steady 70 N, how much KE is gained by the crate after sliding 10 m? (c) How much of the work you do converts to heat?
    You do F × d = 100 N × 10 m = 1000 J of work. Because of friction, net work on the crate is less. ΔKE = Net work = net force × distance = (100 N – 70 N)(10 m) = 300 J. So the rest, 700 J, goes into heating the crate and floor.

3. This question is typical on some driver's license exams: A car moving at 50 km/h skids 15 m with locked brakes. How far will the car skid with locked brakes at 150 km/h?
    At three times the speed, it has 9 times (3^2) the KE and will skid 9 times as far—135 m. Since the frictional force is about the same in both cases, the distance has to be 9 times as great for 9 times as much work done by the pavement on the car.

4. A force of 50 N is applied to the end of a lever, which is moved a certain distance. If the other end of the lever moves one-third as far, how much force can it exert?
    From $F × d = F' × d/3$, we see F = 3F' = 150 N.

5. Consider an ideal pulley system. If you pull one end of the rope downward with 50 N a distance of 1 meter, how high will you lift a 200-N load?
    Your input work is 50 J, so 200-N × h = 50 J· h = 50/200 = 0.25 m.

6. In the hydraulic machine shown, it is observed that when the small piston is pushed down 10 cm, the large piston is raised 1 cm. If the small piston is pushed down with a force of 100 N, what is the most force that the large piston could exert?
    $(Fd)_{input} = (Fd)_{output}$
    $(100 N × 10 cm)_{input} = (? × 1 cm)_{output}$
    So we see that the output force is 1000 N (or less if the efficiency is less than 100%).

7. How many watts of power are expended when a force of 1 N moves a book 2 m in a time interval of 1 s?
    Power = Fd/t = 2J/1s = 2 watts.

8. Which produces the greater change in kinetic energy: Exerting a 10-N force for a distance of 5 m, or exerting a 20-N force over a distance of 2 m? (Assume that all of the work goes into KE.)
    The work done by 10 N over a distance of 5 m = 50 J. That by 20 N over 2 m = 40 J. So the 10-N force over 5 m does more work and could produce a greater change in KE.

9. Consider the inelastic collision between the two freight cars in the previous chapter (Figure 5.12). The momentum before and after the collision is the same. The KE, however, is less after the collision than before the collision. How much less, and what becomes of this energy?
    The freight cars have only half the KE possessed by the single car before collision. Here's how to figure it:
    $KE_{before} = 1/2\ mv^2$
    $KE_{after} = 1/2\ (2m)(v/2)^2 = 1/2\ (2m)\ v^2/4 = 1/4\ mv^2$
    What becomes of this energy? Most of it goes into nature's graveyard—thermal energy.

7 Gravity

Learning Objectives

After studying Chapter 7, students will be able to:
• Explain Newton's idea that the moon falls toward the Earth like an apple does.
• Explain why the moon does not fall into the Earth and the planets do not fall into the sun.
• State Newton's law of universal gravitation.
• Explain the significance of an inverse-square law.
• Explain how the moon causes ocean tides.

Possible Misconceptions to Correct

• **Not so!** Newton discovered gravity rather than discovering that gravity is universal.
• **Not so!** Above the atmosphere there is no gravity.
• **Not so!** The moon and planets are beyond the pull of Earth's gravity.
• **Not so!** Ocean tides are higher on the side of the Earth nearest the moon.
• **Not so!** The moon produces tides in the fluids of our body that affect our behavior.

Demonstration Equipment

None

This chapter begins and ends on an astronomical theme, and makes use of the historical approach. It is prerequisite to the following chapter on projectile and satellite motion.

This chapter offers a good place to reiterate the idea of a scientific theory, and comment on the all-too common and mistaken idea that because something has the status of scientific theory, it is somehow short of being valid. This view is evident in those who say, "But it's *only* a theory." Bring the essence of the first and last footnotes in the chapter into your discussion (about scientific homework and not being able to see radically new ways of looking at the world). The last chapter on *Cargo Cult Science* of Feynman's book, *Surely You're Joking, Mr. Feynman* (Norton, 1985), expands nicely on this.

You can compare the pull of the moon that is exerted on you with the pull exerted by more local masses, via the gravitational equation. Consider the ratio of the mass of the moon to its distance squared:

$$7.4 \times 10^{22} \text{kg}/(4 \times 10^5 \text{km})^2 = 5 \times 10^{12} \text{kg}/\text{km}^2$$

This is a sizable ratio, one that buildings in your vicinity cannot match (city buildings of greatest mass are typically on the order of 10^6 or 10^7 kilograms). However, if you stand 1 kilometer away from the foot of a mountain of mass 5×10^{12} kilograms (about the mass of Mt. Kilimanjaro), then the pull of the mountain and the pull of the moon are about the same on you. Simply put, with no friction you would tend to gravitate from your spot toward the mountain—but you experience no tendency at all to gravitate from your spot toward the moon! That's because the spot you stand on undergoes the same gravitational acceleration toward the moon as you do. Both you and the entire Earth are accelerating toward the moon. Whatever the lunar force on you, it has no tendency to pull you off a weighing scale.

Dark matter is mentioned at the end of the chapter. Dark matter greatly affects the behavior of the universe, which it seems, is accelerating outward, rather than slowing down. A different form of energy, referred to as the dark energy, apparently works against the force of gravity to accelerate the expansion of the universe. The concepts of dark matter and dark energy are at the forefront of physics at this point, and are quite mysterious.

In the **Exploration Practice Book:**
• Inverse-Square Law
• Force and Weight
• Our Ocean Tides

In the **Next-Time Questions** Book:
• Body Tides

Overhead Transparencies (5) available for:
Figures 9.4, 9.6, 9.13, 9.18, Figure 22.17 and Figure 24.1.

This is an interesting chapter, for the material is interesting in itself, is interesting historically, and is closely related to areas of space science that are currently in the public eye.

SUGGESTED PRESENTATION

Begin by briefly discussing the simple codes and patterns that underlie the complex things around us, whether musical compositions or DNA molecules, and then briefly describe the harmonious motion of the solar system, the Milky Way and other galaxies in the universe—stating that the shapes of the planets, stars, and galaxies, and their motions are all governed by an extremely simple code, or if you will, a pattern. Then write the gravitational equation on the board. Give examples of bodies pulling on each other to convey a clear idea of what the symbols in the equation mean and how they relate. (Acknowledge that many other texts and references use the symbol r instead of the d used in this text. The r is used to indicate the radial distance from a body's center of gravity, and to emphasize the center-to-center rather than surface-to-surface nature for distance. We don't set our plow that deep, however, and use d for distance.)

7.1 The Legend of the Falling Apple
The equation for gravitation begins with the legend of the falling apple. Seeing one event was wonderfully linked to another—the orbiting moon.

7.2 The Fact of the Falling Moon
It's true. The moon is falling. Always has been. Why doesn't it reach ground? Answer this by establishing what tangential velocity is. If this is not clear, then what follows will not be

7.3 Newton's Grandest Discovery—The Law of Universal Gravitation
Define and give examples of the terms in the equation for gravity. The equation to the physical science student should be what sheet music is to a musician.

CHECK YOUR NEIGHBOR: How is the gravitational force between a pair of planets altered when one of the planets is twice as massive? [Twice.] When both are twice as massive? [Four times as much.] When they are twice as far apart? [One-fourth as much.] When three times as far apart? [1/9 as much.] Ten times as far apart? [1/100 as much.]

CHECK YOUR NEIGHBOR: What do you say to a furniture mover who claims that gravity increases with increased distance from the Earth, as evident to him when he's carrying heavy loads up flights of stairs? [Make a distinction between how tired you get with time and the pull of gravity.]

7.4 Gravity and Distance: The Inverse-Square Law
Discuss the inverse-square law and go over Figures 7.4 and 7.5. Mention they could as well represent the intensity of radioactivity. Using OHT 6 can be helpful here.

CHECK YOUR NEIGHBOR: A sheet of photographic film is exposed to a point source of light that is a certain distance away. If the sheet were instead exposed to the same light four times as far away, how would the intensity on the film compare? [1/16 as much.] A radioactive detector registers a certain amount of radioactivity when it is a certain distance away from a small piece of uranium. If the detector is four times as far from the uranium, how will the radioactivity reading compare? [Again, 1/16 as much.]

7.5 The Universal Gravitational Constant, *G*
Don't make a big deal out of G. It serves to unite the unit of force with the other units of mass and distance.

7.6 The Mass of the Earth is Measured
What *is* interesting, however, is that finding *G* enabled science types to calculate the Earth's mass. This was a big deal to the general public back then (as indicated in the text with the cartoon newsboy).

7.7 Ocean Tides Are the Result of Differences in Gravitational Pulls
Begin your treatment of tides by asking the class to consider the consequences of someone pulling your coat. If they pulled only on the sleeve, for example, it would tear. But if every part of your coat were pulled equally, it and you would accelerate—but it wouldn't tear. It tears when one part is pulled harder than another—or it tears because of a *difference* in forces acting on the coat. In a similar way, the spherical Earth is "torn" into an elliptical shape by differences in gravitational forces by the moon and sun.

CHECK YOUR NEIGHBOR: Why do the tides not occur at the same time each day? [As the Earth takes 24 hours to rotate, the moon advances in its orbit one hour ahead of the Earth. If the moon didn't move in its orbit, the high-tide bulge would be at the same time daily as the Earth spins beneath the water.]

Explain tides via the accelerating ball of Jell-O as in the text. Equal pulls result in an undistorted ball as it accelerates, but unequal pulls cause a stretching. This stretching is evident in the Earth's oceans, where the side nearest the moon is appreciably closer to the moon than the side farthest away. A body close to the Earth has a greater difference in forces between its close and far parts than the same body farther away.

Below we see a sketch you might draw to show the tidal effect of the sun. Note the greater difference ΔF for the Earth when close to the sun, and less when farther away.

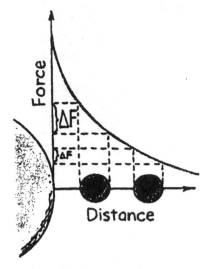

CHECK YOUR NEIGHBOR: Consider the tiny tidal forces that DO act on our bodies, as a result of parts of our bodies experiencing slightly different gravitational forces. What planetary body is most responsible for microtides in our bodies? [The Earth, by far. In standing, there is a greater difference in Earth gravity on our feet compared to our heads than the corresponding differences in gravity due to farther away planetary bodies.]

Explain why tides are greater when Earth, sun, and moon are aligned.

Saturn's rings are the result of the strong tides about Saturn. Such rings are the debris left over from bodies torn apart by Saturn's tidal forces. Such would occur for our moon if it comes closer to the Earth. Too close, and the Earth's tidal forces would tear the moon into a billion pieces, forming rings similar to those of Saturn.

Tidal forces reach an extreme in the case of a **black hole**. The unfortunate fate of an astronaut falling into a black hole is not encountering the singularity, but the tidal forces encountered far before getting that close. Approaching feet first, for example, his closer feet would be pulled with a greater force than his midsection, which in turn would be pulled with a greater force than his head. The tidal forces would stretch him and he would be killed before these forces literally pulled him apart. Black holes are discussed in Chapter 40.

7.8 Gravitation is Universal

Few theories have affected science and civilization as much as Newton's theory of gravitation. The successes of Newton's ideas ushered in the so-called Age of Enlightenment, for Newton had demonstrated that by observation and reason and by employing mechanical models and deducing mathematical laws, people could uncover the very workings of the physical universe. How profound that all the moons, planets, stars, and galaxies have such a beautifully simple rule to govern them; namely,

$$F = G \frac{m_1 m_2}{d^2}$$

The formulation of this simple rule is one of the major reasons for the success in science that followed, for it provided hope that other phenomena of the world might also be described by equally simple laws.

This hope nurtured the thinking of many scientists, artists, writers, and philosophers of the 1700s. One of these was the English philosopher John Locke, who argued that observation and reason, as demonstrated by Newton, should be our best judge and guide in all things and that all of nature and even society should be searched to discover any "natural laws" that might exist. Using Newtonian physics as a model of reason, Locke and his followers modeled a system of government that found adherents in the thirteen British colonies across the Atlantic. These ideas culminated in the Declaration of Independence and the Constitution of the United States of America.

Chapter 7 Answers and Solutions

Key Terms and Matching Definitions

__7__ Big Bang
__8__ dark matter
__2__ law of universal gravitation
__3__ inverse-square law
__6__ neap tide
__5__ spring tide
__1__ tangential velocity
__4__ universal constant of gravitation, G

Review Questions

1. What connection did Newton make between a falling apple and the moon?
   He realized they were both under the influence of Earth gravity.

2. What does it mean to say something moving in a curve has a tangential velocity?
   Tangential velocity is velocity that is parallel to (tangent) to the curve at every point.

3. In what sense does the moon "fall?"
   It falls beneath the straight-line path it would follow if there were no gravity.

4. State Newton's law of universal gravitation in words. Then do the same with one equation.
   Every mass attracts every other mass with a force that for any two masses is directly proportional to the product of the masses involved and inversely proportional to the square of the distance separating them.

$$F \sim \frac{m_1 m_2}{d^2}$$

5. How does the force of gravity between two bodies change when the distance between them is doubled?
   The force is 1/4 as much, in accord with the inverse-square law.

6. How does the thickness of paint sprayed on a surface change when the sprayer is held twice as far away?
   The paint is 1/4 as thick, in accord with the inverse-square law.

7. How does the brightness of light change when a point source of light is brought twice as far away?
   Brightness is 1/4 as much, in accord with the inverse-square law.

8. At what distance from Earth is the gravitational force on an object zero?
   At no distance away from the Earth. It approaches zero with great distances, but never actually reaches zero. (Interestingly, due to cancellation, it does equal zero the Earth's center!)

9. What is the magnitude of gravitational force between two 1-kilogram bodies that are 1 meter apart?
   6.67×10^{-11} N.

10. What is the magnitude of the gravitational force between the Earth and a 1-kilogram body?
    9.8 N.

11. What do we call the gravitational force between the Earth and your body?
    Your weight.

12. When G was first measured, the experiment was called the "weighing the Earth experiment." Why?
Because once G was known, it was a simple matter to calculate the mass of the Earth.

13. Do tides depend more on the strength of gravitational pull or on the *difference* in strengths? Explain.
Tides depend on the differences in gravitational pulls on opposite sides of the Earth. If there were no differences in pulls, there would be no tides.

14. Why do both the sun and the moon exert a greater gravitational force on one side of the Earth than the other?
Because one side is closer to the moon and sun than the opposite side.

15. Which pulls with greater force on the Earth's oceans, the sun or the moon. Which is more effective in raising tides? Why are your answers different?
The sun pulls harder, but because of its great distance, the differences in pulls is less than for the moon. Therefore the moon is more effective in raising tides. The answers are different because one asks for force, the other for differences in force.

16. Distinguish between *spring tides* and *neap tides.*
Spring tides occur when moon, sun, and Earth are lined up. Smaller neap tides occur when from the Earth, the sun, and moon are at right angles to each other.

17. Why are all tides greatest at the time of a full moon or new moon?
At the time of a full or new moon, sun, Earth, and moon line up and tides from the sun and moon overlap each other.

18. Do tides occur in the molten interior of the Earth for the same reason that tides occur in the oceans?
Yes. In either case, one part of the Earth is closer to the moon than the opposite part and differences in pulls occur.

19. What makes the Earth round?
Gravitation pulls the parts of the Earth as close as it can and pulls in any "corners."

20. Distinguish between the *Big Bang* and the *Big Crunch.*
The Big Bang is the event that initiated the universe as we know it. The Big Crunch is the opposite, the event of universal collapse.

Solutions to Chapter 7 Exercises

1. Comment on whether or not this label on a consumer product should be cause for concern. *CAUTION: The mass of this product pulls on every other mass in the universe, with an attracting force that is proportional to the product of the masses and inversely proportional to the square of the distance between them.*
There is nothing to be concerned about on this consumer label. It simply states the universal law of gravitation, which applies to *all* products. It looks like the manufacturer knows some physics and has a sense of humor.

2. Gravitational force acts on all bodies in proportion to their masses. Why, then, doesn't a heavy body fall faster than a light body?
The reason that a heavy body doesn't fall faster than a light body is because the greater gravitational force on the heavier body (its weight), acts on a correspondingly greater mass (inertia). The ratio of gravitational force to mass is the same for every body—hence all bodies in free fall accelerate equally. And it's true not just near the Earth, but anywhere. (This was discussed in Chapter 3, Newton's 2nd law of motion.)

3. What would be the path of the moon if somehow all gravitational forces on it vanished to zero?
In accord with the law of inertia, the moon would move in a straight-line path instead of circling both the sun and Earth.

4. Is the force of gravity stronger on a piece of iron than a piece of wood if both have the same mass? Defend your answer.
The force of gravity is the same on each because the masses are the same, as Newton's equation for gravitational force verifies.

5. Is the force of gravity stronger on a crumpled piece of paper compared with the same paper uncrumpled? Defend your answer.
The force of gravity is the same on each because the masses are the same, as Newton's equation for gravitational force verifies. When dropped the crumpled paper falls faster only because it encounters less air drag than the sheet.

6. What is the magnitude and direction of the gravitational force that acts on a teacher who weighs 1000 N at the surface of the Earth?
1000 N (about 220 pounds).

7. The Earth and the moon are attracted to each other by gravitational force. Does the more massive Earth attract the less massive moon with a force that is greater, smaller, or the same as the force with which the moon attracts the Earth?
The Earth and moon equally pull on each other in a single interaction. In accord with Newton's 3rd law, the pull of the Earth on the moon is equal and opposite to the pull of the moon on the Earth.

8. What do you say to a friend who says that if gravity follows the inverse-square law, that when you are on the 20th story of a building gravity on you should be one-fourth as much as if you're on the 10th story?
You tell your friend that the force of gravity is measured from the center of the Earth, not from the ground up. Compared with the distance to the Earth's center, gravitational force is about the same on an object on the 10th and 20th floor. The difference is infinitesimal and can be neglected.

9. Most people today know that the ocean tides are caused principally by the gravitational influence of the moon. And most people therefore think that the gravitational pull of the moon on the Earth is greater than the gravitational pull of the sun on the Earth. What do you think?
The gravitational pull of the sun on the Earth is greater than the gravitational pull of the moon. The tides, however, are caused by the *differences* in gravitational forces by the moon on opposite sides of the Earth. The difference in gravitational forces by the moon on opposite sides of the Earth is greater than the corresponding difference in forces by the stronger pulling but much more distant sun.

10. If somebody tugged on your shirt sleeve, it would likely tear. But if all parts of your shirt were tugged equally, no tearing would occur. How does this relate to tidal forces?
Just as differences in tugs on your shirt will distort the shirt, differences in tugs on the oceans distort the ocean and produce tides.

11. Would ocean tides exist if the gravitational pull of the moon (and sun) were somehow equal on all parts of the world? Explain.
No. Tides are caused by differences in gravitational pulls. If there are no differences in pulls, there are no tides.

12. Why aren't high ocean tides exactly 12 h apart?
Ocean tides are not exactly 12 hours apart because while the Earth spins, the moon moves in its orbit and appears at its same position overhead every 25 hours, instead of every 24 hours. So the two-high-tide cycle occurs at about 25-hour intervals, making high tides about 12.5 hours apart.

13. With respect to spring and neap ocean tides, when are the lowest tides? That is, when is it best for digging clams?

Lowest tides occur along with highest tides—spring tides. So the spring tide cycle consists of higher-than-average high tides followed by lower-than-average low tides (best for digging clams!).

14. Whenever the ocean tide is unusually high, will the following low tide be unusually low? Defend your answer in terms of "conservation of water." (If you slosh water in a tub so it is extra deep at one end, will the other end be extra shallow?)

Whenever the ocean tide is unusually high, it will be followed by an unusually low tide. This makes sense, for when one part of the world is having an extra high tide, another part must be donating water and experiencing an extra low tide. Or as the hint in the exercise suggests, if you are in a bathtub and slosh the water so it is extra deep in front of you, that's when it is extra shallow in back of you—"conservation of water!"

15. The human body is composed of mostly water. Why does the moon overhead cause appreciably less biological tides in the fluid compartment of the body than a 1-kg melon held over your head?

Tides are produced by *differences* in forces, which relate to differences in distance from the attracting body. One's head is appreciably closer than one's feet to the overhead melon. The greater proportional difference for the melon out-tides the more massive but more distant moon. One's head is not appreciably closer to the moon than one's feet.

16. If the moon didn't exist, would the Earth still have ocean tides? If so, how often?

Yes, the Earth's tides would be due only to the sun. They'd occur twice per day (every 12 hours instead of every 12.5 hours) due to the Earth's daily rotation.

17. What would be the effect on the Earth's tides if the diameter of the Earth were very much larger than it is? If the Earth were as it presently is, but the moon very much larger and had the same mass?

Tides would be greater if the Earth's diameter were greater because the difference in pulls would be greater. Tides on Earth would be no different if the moon's diameter were larger. The gravitational influence of the moon is as if all the moon's mass were at its CG. Tidal bulges on the solid surface of the moon, however, would be greater if the moon's diameter were larger—but not on the Earth.

18. Does the strongest tidal force on our bodies come from the Earth, moon, or sun?

From the nearest body, the Earth.

19. Some people dismiss the validity of scientific theories by saying they are "only" theories. The law of universal gravitation is a theory. Does this mean that scientists still doubt its validity? Explain.

A theory, such as the theory of universal gravitation, is a synthesis of a large body of information has been tested many times. Any doubts about the theory have to do with its applications to yet untested situations, not with the theory itself. One of the features of scientific theories is that they undergo refinement with new knowledge. (Einstein's general theory of relativity has taught us that in fact there are limits to the validity of Newton's theory of universal gravitation. These limits do not invalidate it for the regions it served.)

20. Ultimately, the universe may expand without limit, or it may coast to a stop, or it may turn around and collapse to a "big crunch." What is the single most important quantity that will determine which of these fates is in store for the universe?

The total mass (or average density) of the universe. If it is less than a certain critical amount, expansion will continue. If it is greater than this critical amount, expansion will stop and give way to contraction. If it is exactly this amount, the expansion will coast to a stop. (Current theory says that in addition to dark matter, which is attractive, there may be a form of energy spread through the universe that repels matter. If this were true, a universe with less than critical mass density could still expand without limit.)

Solutions to Chapter 7 Problems

1. If you stood atop a ladder that was so tall that you were three times as far from the Earth's center, how would your weight compare with its present value?
    Solution: From $F = GmM/d^2$, three times d squared is $9\,d^2$, which means the force is one-ninth of surface weight.

2. Find the change in the force of gravity between two planets when the masses of both planets are doubled, and the distance between them stays the same.
    Solution: From $F = GmM/d^2$, $(2m)(2M) = 4\,mM$, which means the force of gravity between them is 4 times greater.

3. Find the change in the force of gravity between two planets when masses remain the same but the distance between them is increased by ten.
    Solution: From $F = GmM/d^2$, $10\,d$ squared is $100\,d^2$, with a force 100 times smaller.

4. Find the change in the force of gravity between two planets when distance between is *decreased* by ten.
    Solution: From $F = GmM/d^2$, ten times d squared is $1/100\,d^2$, which means the force is 100 times greater.

5. Find the change in the force of gravity between two planets when the masses of the planets don't change, but the distance between them is decreased by five.
    Solution: From $F = GmM/d^2$, five times d squared is $1/25\,d^2$, with a force 25 times greater.

6. By what factor would your weight change if the Earth's diameter were doubled and its mass were also doubled?
    Solution: From $F = G2m2M/(2\,d^2) = 2/4\,(GmM/d^2)$, with one-half the force of gravitation.

7. Find the change in the force of gravity between two objects when both masses are doubled and the distance between them is also doubled.
    Solution: From $F = G2m2M/(2\,d^2) = 4/4\,(GmM/d^2)$, with the same force of gravitation.

8. Consider a bright point light source located 1 m from a square opening of area one-square meter. Light passing through the opening illuminates an area of 4 m^2 on a wall 2 m from the opening. (a) Find the area illuminated if the wall is moved to a distance of 3 m, 5 m, or 10 m. (b) How can the same amount of light illuminate more area as the wall is moved farther away?
    Solution: (a) At 3 m it will cover 3^2 or 9 square meters; at 5 m it will cover 5^2 or 25 square meters; at 10 m it will cover 10^2 or 100 square meters. (b) The light is "spread out" over greater and greater area, and gets dimmer and dimmer.

9. Calculate the force of gravity between the Earth (6×10^{24} kg) and the sun (2×10^{30} kg, and 1.5×10^{11} m distant).
    Solution: $F = GmM/d^2 = [(6.67 \times 10^{-11}\,\text{N}\cdot\text{m}^2/\text{kg}^2)(6 \times 10^{24}\,\text{kg})(2 \times 10^{30}\,\text{kg})]/(1.5 \times 10^{11}\,\text{m})^2 = 3.6 \times 10^{22}$ N.

10. A 3-kg newborn baby at the Earth's surface is gravitationally attracted to Earth with a force of about 30 N. (a) Calculate the force of gravity with which the baby on Earth is attracted to the planet Mars when Mars is closest to Earth. (The mass of Mars is 6.4×10^{23} kg and its closest distance is 5.6×10^{10} m). (b) Calculate the force of gravity between the baby and the physician who delivers it. Assume the physician has a mass of 100 kg and is 0.5 m from the baby. (c) How do the forces compare?

    Solution: (a) Mars: $F = G\dfrac{mM}{d^2} = 6.67 \times 10^{-11}\dfrac{(3\text{kg})(6.4 \times 10^{23})}{(5.6 \times 10^{10})^2} = 4.1 \times 10^{-8}$ **N.**

    (b) Physician: $F = G\dfrac{mM}{d^2} = 6.67 \times 10^{-11}\dfrac{(3\text{kg})(10^2)}{(0.5)^2} = 8.0 \times 10^{-8}$ **N.**

    (c) The gravitational force due to the physician is about twice that due to Mars.

8 Projectile and Satellite Motion

Conceptual Physical Science—Explorations

Learning Objectives

After studying Chapter 8, students will be able to:

• Describe for a projectile the changes in the horizontal and vertical components of its velocity.
• Explain why a projectile moves equal horizontal distances in equal time intervals, when air drag is negligible.
• Show the connection between a fast-moving projectile and an Earth satellite.
• Explain Newton's idea that the moon falls toward the Earth like an apple does.
• Explain why the moon does not fall into the Earth and the planets do not fall into the sun.
• State Newton's law of universal gravitation.
• Explain the significance of an inverse-square law.
• Explain how the speed of a satellite in a circular orbit around the Earth is related to the distance an object falls in the first second due to gravity.
• Describe how the speed of a satellite changes for different portions of an elliptical orbit.
• Describe what is meant by an escape speed.

Possible Misconceptions to Correct

• **Not so!** A projectile needs a force to keep it going.
• **Not so!** Satellites are beyond the main pull of Earth's gravity.
• **Not so!** Satellites are pulled upward by a centrifugal force.

Demonstration Equipment

None

The spin of the Earth is helpful in launching satellites, which gives advantage to launching cites closest to the equator. The launch site closest to the equator is Kaurou, French Guiana, in South America, 5° 08', used by the European Space Agency. The U.S. launches from Cape Canaveral, 28° 22', and Vandenberg, 34° 38'. Russia used to launch at Kapustin Yar, 48° 31', Plesetsk, 62° 42', and Tyuratam (Baikonur) 45° 38'. Is Hawaii, less than 20° in our space launching future?

If you haven't shown the 15-minute oldie but goodie NASA film, "Zero g", be sure to show it now. It is of footage taken aboard Skylab in 1978, narrated by astronaut Owen Garriott. Newton's laws of motion are reviewed with excellent and entertaining examples.

Solar photon force: To a small extent, sunlight affects satellites, particularly the large disco-ball-like satellite LAGEOS, which wobbles slightly in its orbit because of unequal heating by sunlight. The side in the sun radiates infrared photons, the energy of which provides a small, but persistent, rocket effect as the photons eject from the surface. So a net force some 100 billion times weaker than gravity pushes on the satellite in a direction away from its hot end. LAGEOS has 426 prism-shaped mirrors. By reflecting laser beams off its mirrored surface, geophysicists can make precise measurements of tiny displacements in the Earth's surface.

In the **Explorations Practice Book**:
• Projectiles
• Circular Orbit
• Elliptical Orbit

In the **Next-Time Questions** Book:
• Ball Toss from Tower
• Monkey and Banana
• Cannonball Orbit
• Mechanics Quiz

In the **Lab Manual**:
• The Great Bullet Race

Overhead Transparency available for:
Figures 8.4, 8.5 and 8.6 (all one transparency)

SUGGESTED PRESENTATION

8.1 Projectile Motion
Roll a ball off the edge of your lecture table and call attention to the curve it follows. The ball is a projectile. Discuss the idea of the "downwardness" of gravity, and how there is no "horizontalness" to it, and therefore no horizontal influence on the projectile.

Pose the situation of the horizontally-held gun and the shooter who drops a bullet at the same time he pulls the trigger, and ask which bullet strikes the ground first.

DEMONSTRATION: Show the independence of horizontal and vertical motion with a spring-gun apparatus that will shoot a ball horizontally while at the same time dropping another that falls vertically. Follow this up with the popular "monkey-and hunter" demonstration.

CHECK YOUR NEIGHBOR: Point to some target at the far side of your classroom and ask your students to imagine you are going to project a rock to the target via a slingshot. Ask if you should aim at the target, above it, or below it. Easy stuff. Then ask your class to suppose it takes 1 second for the rock to reach the target. If you aim directly at the target, it will fall beneath and miss. How far beneath the target would the rock hit (supposing the floor weren't in the way)? Have your students check with their neighbors on this one. Then ask how far above should you aim to hit the target. Do a neighbor check on this one. (Here we're ignoring the fact that the horizontal component is less when aimed upward.)

8.2 Projectile Altitude and Range
Point out that the relationship of the curved path of Figure 8.11 and the vertical distance of fall of 5 meters in 1 second. Stress that the projectile is falling beneath the straight line it would otherwise follow. This idea is important for later understanding of satellite motion.

Discuss the boy's pitching speed from the 5-m high tower in the textbook. Ask for the pitching speed if the ball traveled 30 m instead of 20 m. (Note the vertical height is 5 m. If you use any height that does not correspond to an integral number of seconds, you're diverting your focus from physics to algebra.) More interesting is considering greater horizontal distances—great enough for the curvature of the Earth to make a difference in arriving at the answer. It's easy to see that the time the projectile is in the air increases when the Earth curves beneath the trajectory.

8.3 The Effect of Air Drag on Projectiles
Acknowledge the large effect that air resistance (air drag) has on fast-moving objects such as bullets and cannonballs. A batted baseball, for example, travels only about 60 percent as far in air as it would in a vacuum. Its curved path is no longer a parabola, as Figure 8.11 indicates.

Hang Time: Refer to the Practice Book exercise on hang time. Ask if hang time would be increased if on a moving skateboard. Or in a moving bus. It should be clear that the answer is no. But one can usually jump higher from a running jump. It is a mistake to assume that the horizontal motion is responsible for the higher jump and longer hang time. The action of running likely enables a greater force between the foot and floor, which gives a greater vertical lift-off component of velocity. This greater bound against the floor, and not any holiday by gravity on a horizontally moving body, is the explanation. Stress that the vertical component of velocity alone determines vertical height and hang time.

8.4 Fast-Moving Projectiles—Satellites
Sketch "Newton's Mountain" and consider the longer and longer time intervals for greater and greater horizontal speeds. Ask if there is a "pitching speed" or cannonball velocity large enough so the time in the air is forever. Not literally "in the air", which is why the cannon is atop a mountain that extends above the atmosphere. The answer of course is yes. Fired fast enough the cannonball will fall around the world rather than into it. You're into satellite motion.

> CHECK YOUR NEIGHBOR: Why is it confusing to ask why a satellite doesn't fall? [All satellites are continuously falling, in the sense that they fall below the straight line they would travel if they weren't. Why they don't crash to Earth is a different question.]

8.5 Earth Satellites
Calculating Satellite Speed: An effective skit that can have your class calculating the speed necessary for close Earth orbit is as follows: Call attention to the curvature of the Earth, Figure 8.13. Consider a horizontal laser standing about a meter above the ground with its beam shining over a level desert. The beam is straight but the desert floor curves 5 m over an 8000 m or 8 km tangent, which you sketch on your chalkboard (or overhead projector). Stress this is not to scale:

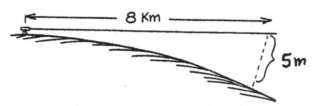

Now erase the laser and sketch in a super cannon positioned so it points along the laser line. Consider a cannonball fired at say, 2 km/s, and ask how far downrange will it be at the end of one second. A neighbor check should yield an answer of 2 km, which you indicate by drawing a cannonball 2 km from the cannon. But it doesn't really get there, you say, for it falls beneath that point because of gravity. How far? 5 m if the sand weren't in the way. Ask if 2 km/s is sufficient for orbiting the Earth. Clearly not, for the cannonball strikes the ground. If the cannonball is not to hit the ground, we'd have to dig a trench first, as you show on your sketch, which now looks like this:

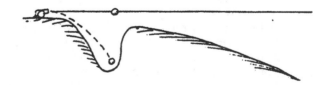

Continue by considering a greater muzzle velocity, say 4 km/s, so the cannonball travels 4 km in one second. Ask if this is fast enough to attain an Earth orbit. Student response should indicate that they realize that the cannonball will hit the ground before 1 second is up. Then repeat the previous line of reasoning, again having to dig a trench, and your sketch looks like this:

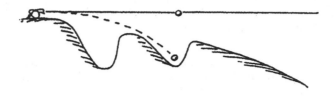

Continue by considering a greater muzzle velocity—great enough so the cannonball travels 6 km in 1 second. This is 6 km/s. Ask if this is fast enough not to hit the ground (or equivalently, if it is fast enough for Earth orbit!) Then repeat the previous line of reasoning, again having to dig a trench. Now your sketch looks like this:

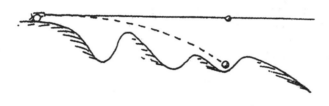

You're almost there: Continue by considering a muzzle velocity great enough so the cannonball travels 8 km in one second. (Don't state the velocity is 8 km/s here as you'll diminish your punch line.) Repeat your previous reasoning and note that this time you don't have to dig a trench! After a pause, and with a tone of importance, ask the class with what speed must the cannonball have to orbit the Earth. Done properly, you have led your class into a "derivation" of orbital speed about the Earth with no equations or algebra.

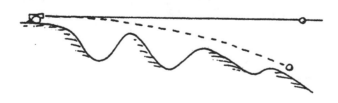

Acknowledge that the gravitational force is less on satellites in higher orbits so they do not need to go so fast. (Actually, not stated in the text, $v = \sqrt{GM/d}$, so a satellite at 4 times the Earth's radius needs to travel only half as fast, 4 km/s.)

You can wind up your brief treatment of satellite motion and catch its essence via the following skit: Ask your students to pretend they are encountered by a bright youngster, too young to have much knowledge of physics and mathematics, but who nevertheless asks why satellites seem to defy gravity and stay in orbit. You ask what answer could correctly satisfy the curiosity of the kid, then pose the following dialogue between the kid and the students in your class (you're effectively suggesting how the student might interact with the bright kid). Ask the kid to observe and then describe what you do, as you hold a rock at arm's length and then simply drop it. The kid replies, "You dropped the rock and it fell to the ground below," to which you respond, "Very good—now what happens this time?", as you move your hand horizontally and again drop the rock. The kid observes and then says, "The rock dropped again, but because your hand was moving it followed a curved path and fell farther away." You continue, "Very good—now again—"as you throw the rock still farther. The kid replies, "I note that as your hand moves faster, the path follows a wider curve." You're elated at this response, and you ask the kid, "How far away will the rock hit the ground if its curved path matches the curved surface of the Earth?" The kid at first appears very puzzled, but then beams, "Oh—I get it! The stone doesn't hit at all—it's in Earth orbit." Then you interrupt your dialogue and ask the class, "Do YOU get it?" Then back to the kid who asks, "But isn't it really more complicated than that?", to which the answer is NO. The essential idea of satellite motion IS that simple.

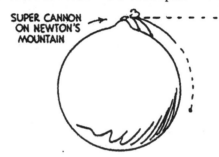

Begin by discussing the falling apple story and Newton's insight about the falling moon. Reiterate the idea that if no force were acting on the moon, it would follow a straight line in space, and that Newton saw that the force of gravity extended to the moon.

Moving Perpendicular vs Moving Non-Perpendicular to Gravity

Draw a sketch of a cannon on a mountain as shown. Simulate a cannonball fired horizontally and curving to the ground. Now suppose the cannonball leaves the cannon at a velocity of say 1 km/s. Ask the class whether the speed when it strikes the ground will be 1 km/s, more than 1 km/s, or less than 1 km/s (neglecting air resistance). The answer is that it strikes at more than 1 km/s, because gravity speeds it up. (Toss your keys horizontally from a one-story window and catching them would pose no problem. Now toss your keys horizontally from the top of a mountain. Ask if a person below would care to catch them!) Now draw "Newton's Mountain" on the entire world as shown, and sketch a trajectory that meets the Earth. Suppose the firing speed is now 4 km/s. Repeat your question: Will it be traveling faster, slower, or 4 km/s when it strikes the ground? Again, faster, because it moves in the direction of the gravitational field. Caution: Do not draw a trajectory that meets the Earth's surface at a point beyond the halfway mark (unfortunately, the Zero-g film makes this error). Why? Because the parabolic path is actually a segment of a Keplerian ellipse, Figure 10.26. Halfway around puts it all around. Now draw the circular trajectory that occurs when the firing speed is 8 km/s. Ask if the speed increases, decreases, or remains the same after leaving the cannon. This time it remains the same. Why? Neighbor checking time!

Before answering the question, pose the case of rolling a ball along a bowling alley. Does gravity pull on the ball? [Yes.] Does gravity speed up or slow down the ball? [No.] Why? The answer to this question is the answer to the satellite question. [In both cases, the ball crisscrosses gravity—with no component of the gravitational field in the direction of motion. No change in speed, no work, no change in KE, no change in PE. Aha! The cannonball and the bowling ball simply coast.

Circular Orbits: Erase the mountain from your sketch of the world and draw a huge elevated bowling alley that completely circles the world. Explain how a bowling ball on such a lane would gain no speed because of gravity. But now cut part of the lane away, so the ball rolls off the edge and crashes to the ground below. Does it gain speed after falling in the gap? [Yes, because a component of its motion is in the direction of the Earth's gravitational field.] Show how if the ball moves faster it will fall farther before crashing to the ground. Ask what speed would allow it to clear the gap (like a motorcyclist who drives off a ramp and clears a gap to meet a ramp on the other side). [8 km/s, of course.] Can the gap be bigger at this speed? Sketch a gap that nearly circles the world when you ask this question. Then ask, what happens with no lane? And your class sees at 8 km/s no supporting alley is needed. The ball orbits the Earth.

CHECK YOUR NEIGHBOR: We say that satellites are falling around the Earth. But communication satellites remain at one place overhead. Isn't this contradictory? [Communication satellites fall in a wider circle than closer satellites. Their periods are 24 hours, which coincides with the period of the spinning Earth. So from Earth they appear to be motionless.]

CHECK YOUR NEIGHBOR: Why is it advantageous to launch rockets close to the equator? [The tangential speed at the equator is 1000 miles an hour, which can be subtracted from the speed needed to put a satellite in orbit. The closer the launch site to the equator, the closer to the 1000 mph free ride.]

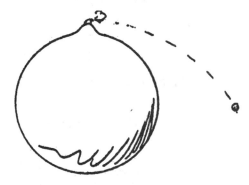

Back to Newton's Mountain. Fire the cannonball at 9 km/s. It overshoots a circular path. Your sketch looks like the one here. Ask, at the position shown, is the cannonball moving at 9 km/s, more than 9 km/s, or less than 9 km/s. And why? After a neighbor check, toss a piece of chalk upward and say you toss it upward at 9 m/s. When it's halfway to the top of its path, is it moving 9 m/s, more than 9 m/s, or less than 9 m/s? Equate the two situations. [In both cases the projectile slows because it is going against gravity.]

8.6 Elliptical Orbits

Continue your sketch and show a closed path—an ellipse. As you draw the elliptical path, show with a sweeping motion of your arm how the satellite slows in receding from the Earth, moving slowest at its farthermost point, then how it speeds in falling towards the Earth, whipping around the Earth and repeating the cycle over and over again. Move to a fresh part of the chalkboard and redraw with the mountain at the bottom, so your sketch is more like Figure 8.20. (It is more comfortable seeing your chalk moving slowest when farthest coincides with the direction "up" in the classroom. I quip that Australians have no trouble seeing it the first way.)

Sketch in larger ellipses for still greater cannon speeds, with the limit being 11.2 km/s, beyond which the path does not close—escape speed.

8.7 Escape Speed

Distinguish between ballistic speed and sustained speed, and that the value 11.2 km/s refers to ballistic speed. (One could go to the moon at 1 km/s, given a means of sustaining that speed and enough time to make the trip!) Compare the escape speeds from different bodies via Table 8.1.

Answers and Solutions to Chapter 8

Key Terms and Matching Definitions

__4__ ellipse
__5__ escape speed
__2__ parabola
__1__ projectile
__3__ satellite

Review Questions

1. What exactly is a projectile?
A projectile is any object projected by some means that continues in motion by its own inertia.

2. How much speed does a freely-falling object gain during each second of fall?
10 m/s.

3. With no gravity, a horizontally-moving projectile follows a straight-line path. With gravity, how far below the straight-line path does a projectile fall compared with the distance of free fall?
The same.

4. As an object moves horizontally through air (without air drag), how much speed does it gain moving horizontally? How much vertically?
It gains none horizontally, and gains 10 m/s each second vertically.

5. A ball is batted upward at an angle. What happens to the vertical component of its velocity as it rises? As it falls?
The vertical component changes the same way a ball tossed straight upward changes, and changes on the way down just as a stone does in free fall.

6. With no air drag, what happens to the horizontal component of velocity for the batted baseball?
It remains the same.

7. A projectile is launched upward at an angle of 75 degrees from the horizontal and strikes the ground a certain distance down range. For what other angle of launch at the same speed would this projectile land just as far away?
15 degrees (the complementary angle to 75 degrees).

8. A projectile is launched vertically at 30 m/s. If air drag can be neglected, at what speed will it return to its initial level?
30 m/s, the same as the initial speed.

9. What is meant by "hang time?'
Hang time is the time in the air for a jumper, from lift off to landing.

10. What is the effect of air drag on the height and range of a batted baseball?
Both are less due to air drag.

11. How can a projectile "fall around the Earth"?
It can fall around the Earth if its tangential velocity is sufficient to ensure its curved path matches the curve of Planet Earth.

12. Why will a projectile that moves horizontally at 8 km/s follow a curve that matches the curvature of the Earth?
Because 8 km/s tangential speed is sufficient for the 5-m vertical drop at the end of the first second to match the corresponding 5-m drop of Earth's curvature.

13. Why is it important that the projectile in the last question be above the Earth's atmosphere?
The 8 km/s will persist only in the absence of air drag. Hence the motion must be above the Earth's atmosphere.

14. Are the planets of the solar system simply projectiles falling around and around the sun?
Yes indeed!

15. Why did Isaac Newton not think humans would one day orbit the Earth?
He thought the necessary speed to do so was impossible to achieve, and he didn't consider multi-stage rockets.

16. How much time is taken for a complete revolution of a satellite in close orbit about the Earth?
90 minutes.

17. For orbits of greater altitude, is the period greater or less?
Greater. The moon, for example, takes a month to orbit the Earth.

18. Why does the speed of a satellite undergo change in an elliptical orbit?
Because half the time is going away from gravity, and the other half going with gravity. When going against gravity, speed decreases. When going with gravity, speed increases.

19. At what part of an elliptical orbit does a satellite have the greatest speed? The least speed?
Greatest speed nearest the Earth, and slowest speed farthest away.

20. What is the minimum speed for orbiting the Earth in close orbit? The maximum speed? What happens above this speed?
8 km/s; 11.2 km/s; above this speed the satellite leaves the Earth permanently.

Solutions to Chapter 8 Exercises

1. A heavy crate accidentally falls from a high-flying airplane just as it flies directly above a shiny red sports car smartly parked in a car lot. Relative to the car, where will the crate crash?
The crate will not hit the car, but will crash a distance beyond it determined by the height and speed of the plane.

2. How does the vertical component of motion for a ball kicked off a high cliff compare with the motion of vertical free fall?
When air drag is negligible, the vertical component of motion is identical to that of free fall.

3. In the absence of air drag, why does the horizontal component of the ball's motion not change, while the vertical component does?
There are no forces horizontally (neglecting air drag) so there is no horizontal acceleration, hence the horizontal component of velocity doesn't change. Gravitation acts vertically, which is why the vertical component of velocity changes.

4. At what point in its trajectory does a batted baseball have its minimum speed? If air drag can be neglected, how does this compare with the horizontal component of its velocity at other points?
Minimum speed occurs at the top, which is the same as the horizontal component of velocity anywhere along the path.

5. Two golfers each hit a ball at the same speed, but one at 60° with the horizontal and the other at 30°. Which ball goes farther? Which hits the ground first? (Ignore air resistance.)
Both balls have the same range (see Figure 8.9). The ball with the initial speed of 30°, however, is in the air for a shorter time and hits the ground first.

6. A park ranger shoots a monkey hanging from a branch of a tree with a tranquilizing dart. The ranger aims directly at the monkey, not realizing that the dart will follow a parabolic path and thus fall below the monkey. The monkey, however, sees the dart leave the gun and lets go of the branch to avoid being hit. Will the monkey be hit anyway? Defend your answer.

The monkey is hit as the dart and monkey meet in midair. For a fast-moving dart, their meeting place is closer to the monkey's starting point than for a slower-moving dart. The dart and monkey fall equal vertical distances—the monkey below the tree, and the dart below the line of sight.

7. When you jump upward, your hang time is the time your feet are off the ground. Does hang time depend on your vertical component of velocity when you jump, your horizontal component of velocity, or both? Defend your answer.
Hang time depends only on the vertical component of your lift-off velocity. If you can increase this vertical component from a running position rather than from a dead stop, perhaps by bounding harder against the ground, then hang time can be increased. In any case, hang time depends *only* on the vertical component of your lift-off velocity.

8. Since the moon is gravitationally attracted to the Earth, why doesn't it simply crash into the Earth?
The moon's tangential velocity is what keeps the moon coasting around the Earth rather than crashing into it. If its tangential velocity were reduced to zero, then it would fall straight into the Earth!

9. Which planets have a greater period than 1 Earth year, those closer to the sun than Earth or those farther from the sun than Earth?
The farther away, the longer the period. So planets farther from the sun take a longer time to complete each orbit.

10. Does the speed of a falling object depend on its mass? Does the speed of a satellite in orbit depend on its mass? Defend your answers.
Neither the speed of a falling object (without air drag) nor the speed of a satellite in orbit depends on its mass. In both cases, a greater mass (greater inertia) is balanced by a correspondingly greater gravitational force, so the acceleration remains the same ($a = F/m$, Newton's 2nd law).

11. If you have ever watched the launching of an Earth satellite, you may have noticed that the rocket starts vertically upward, then departs from a vertical course and continues its climb at an angle. Why does it start vertically? Why does it not continue vertically?
The initial vertical climb lets the rocket get through the denser, retarding part of the atmosphere most quickly, and is also the best direction at low initial speed, when a large part of the rocket's thrust is needed just to support the rocket's weight. But eventually the rocket must acquire enough tangential speed to remain in orbit without thrust, so it must tilt until finally its path is horizontal.

12. A satellite can orbit at 5 km above the moon, but not at 5 km above the Earth. Why?
The moon has no atmosphere. A satellite 5 km above the Earth's surface is still in the atmosphere, as well as in range of some mountain peaks. Atmospheric drag is the factor that most determines orbiting altitude.

13. If the space shuttle circled the Earth at a distance equal to the Earth-moon distance, how long would it take for it to make a complete orbit. In other words, what would be its period?
The period of any satellite at the same distance from Earth as the moon would be the same as the moon's, 28 days.

14. Consider a high-orbiting spaceship that travels at 7 km/s with respect to the Earth. Suppose it projects a capsule rearward at 7 km/s with respect to the ship. Describe the path of the capsule with respect to the Earth.
When a capsule is projected rearward at 7 km/s with respect to the spaceship, which is itself moving forward at 7 km/s with respect to the Earth, the speed of the capsule with respect to the Earth will be zero. It will have no tangential speed for orbit. What will happen? It will simply drop vertically to Earth and crash.

15. The orbital velocity of the Earth about the sun is 30 km/s. If the Earth were suddenly stopped in its tracks, it would simply fall directly into the sun. Devise a plan whereby a rocket loaded with radioactive wastes could be fired into the sun for permanent disposal. How fast and in what direction with respect to the Earth's orbit should the rocket be fired?

This is similar to Exercise 14. The tangential velocity of the Earth about the sun is 30 km/s. So if a rocket carrying the radioactive wastes were fired at 30 km/s from the Earth in the direction opposite to the Earth's orbital motion about the sun, the wastes would have no tangential velocity with respect to the sun. They would simply fall into the sun.

16. If you stopped an Earth satellite dead in its tracks, it would simply crash into the Earth. Why, then, don't the communications satellites that "hover motionless" above the same spot on Earth crash into the Earth?
Communication satellites only appear motionless because their orbital period coincides with the daily rotation of the Earth.

17. Escape speed from the surface of the Earth is 11.2 km/s, but a space vehicle could escape from the Earth at half this speed and less. Explain.
The escape speeds from various planets refer to "ballistic speeds"—to the speeds attained *after* the application of an applied force at low altitude. If the force is sustained, then a space vehicle could escape the Earth at any speed, so long as the force is applied for a sufficiently long time.

18. Suppose a faraway body that is initially at rest falls to the Earth under the influence of Earth's gravity only. What is the maximum possible speed of impact of the object when it hits Earth's surface?
Maximum falling speed by virtue only of the Earth's gravity is 11.2 km/s. This is the same speed it would take to go from Earth to the faraway place.

19. If Pluto were somehow stopped short in its orbit, it would fall into rather than around the sun. How fast would it be moving when it hit the sun?
This is similar to the previous exercise. In this case, Pluto's maximum speed of impact on the sun, by virtue of only the sun's gravity, would be the same as the escape speed from the surface of the sun. According to Table 8.1 in the text, the speed is 620 km/s.

20. Which requires more fuel, a rocket going from the Earth to the moon, or one going from the moon to the Earth? Defend your answer.
Going against the stronger gravity of the Earth would consume much more energy than going against the gravity of the moon. So more fuel would be needed to go from the Earth to the moon.

Solutions to Chapter 8 Problems

1. Students in a lab measure the speed of a steel ball launched horizontally from a table top to be 4.0 m/s. If it takes 0.5 seconds for a ball to fall from the table to the floor below, where should they place a small piece of paper so that the ball will hit it when it lands?
The distance wanted is horizontal velocity × time. The time to follow the parabolic path is the same 0.5 seconds it takes to drop vertically. So distance from the edge of the table should be 4.0 m/s × 0.5 s = 2.0 m.

2. Calculate the speed in m/s at which the Earth revolves about the sun. You may assume the orbit is nearly circular.
One way is: $v = distance/time$ where distance is the circumference of the Earth's orbit and time is 1 year. Then

$$v = \frac{d}{t} = \frac{2\pi r}{1 \text{ year}} = \frac{2\pi(1.5 \times 10^{11}\text{m})}{365 \text{ day} \times 24 \text{ h/day} \times 3600 \text{ s/h}} = 3 \times 10^4 \text{ m/s} = 30 \text{ km/s.}$$

3. The moon is about 3.8×10^5 km from the Earth. Find its average orbital speed about the Earth.

$$v = \frac{d}{t} = 2\pi r/t = 2\pi(3.8 \times 105\text{km})/28 \text{ days} = 1026 \text{ m/s.}$$

9 Thermal Energy

9.1 Thermal Energy—The Total Energy in a Substance
9.2 Temperature—Average Kinetic Energy per Molecule in a Substance
9.3 Absolute Zero—Nature's Lowest Possible Temperature
9.4 Heat is the Movement of Thermal Energy
9.5 Heat Units Are Energy Units
9.6 The Laws of Thermodynamics
9.7 Specific Heat Capacity—A Measure of Thermal Inertia
9.8 Thermal Expansion
        Expansion of Water

Learning Objectives
After studying Chapter 9, the students will be able to:
• Define temperature and explain how it is measured.
• Describe the relationship between temperature and kinetic energy.
• Define heat and explain why it is incorrect to think of matter as containing heat.
• Describe what determines if heat will flow into or out of a substance.
• Distinguish between thermal energy and heat.
• Describe how the quantity of heat that enters or leaves a substance is measured.
• Describe the concept of absolute zero.
• State the first law of thermodynamics and relate it to energy conservation.
• State the second law of thermodynamics.
• Compare the specific heat capacity of different substances, given the relative amounts of
   energy required to raise the temperature of a given mass by a given amount.
• Give examples of how the high specific heat capacity of water affects climate.
• Give examples of the expansion of solids as they become warmer.
• Explain the function of a bimetallic coil in a thermostat.
• Compare the thermal expansion of liquids to solids.
• Describe the unusual behavior of water as it is heated from 0°C to 15°C.
• Explain why water at certain temperatures contract as it becomes warmer.

Possible Misconceptions to Correct
• **Not so!** Heat and temperature are two words for the same thing.
• **Not so!** Hot objects contain heat.

Demonstration Equipment
• Metal ball and ring apparatus
• Bimetallic strip and a flame

The concept of heat flow between temperature differences provides some background to the concept of current flow between electric voltage differences later in Chapter 11. Here we introduce the concept of KE/molecule, *temperature*, which is analogous to the later concept of PE/charge, *voltage*. Both high temperatures and high voltages are ordinarily harmful only when large energies are transferred in a relatively short time (that is, when large power is transferred). The white-hot sparks of the 4th-of-July sparkler held by little Terrance Jones on the Part 2 opening photo have very high temperatures, but their energies are very small. So they are quite harmless. Similarly, a balloon rubbed on your hair may have thousands of volts, but the energy stored is very small. Energy per molecule or energy per charge may be high, but if the molecules or charges involved are small in number, the energy content is also small. Aside from the parallels between heat and electricity, the chapter serves as a prerequisite only for the next chapter dealing with heat transfer and thermodynamics.

In the text, temperature is treated in terms of the kinetic energy per molecule of substances. Although strictly speaking, temperature is directly proportional to the kinetic energy per molecule only in the case of ideal gases. We take the view that temperature is related to molecular translational kinetic energy in most common substances. Rotational kinetic energy, on the other hand, is only indirectly related to temperature, as is illustrated in a microwave oven. There the H_2O molecules are set oscillating with considerable rotational kinetic energy. But this doesn't cook the food. What does is the translational kinetic energy imparted to neighboring molecules that are bounced from the oscillating water-like marbles that are set flying in all directions when they encounter the spinning blades of fans. If neighboring atoms did not interact with the oscillating H_2O molecules, the temperature of the food would be no different before and after the microwave oven was activated. Temperature has to do with the translational kinetic energy of molecules. Degrees of freedom, rotational and vibrational states, and the complications of temperature in liquids and solids are not treated. Next course!

Quantity of heat is spoken of in terms of calories and joules. The definition of the calorie in the text implies that the same amount of heat will be required to change the temperature of water 1°C—whatever the temperature of the water. Although this relation holds true to a fair degree, it is not exactly correct: A calorie is precisely defined as the amount of heat required to raise a gram of water from 14° to 15° Celsius.

In the **Explorations Practice Book:**
• Temperature, Heat, and Expansion.
• Thermal Expansion.

In the **Next-Time Questions Book:**
• Holiday Sparkler
• Twice as Hot
• Metal Ring
• Metal Gap

In the **Lab Manual:**
• Dance of the Molecules (activity)
• Spiked Water (experiment)

Overhead Transparency (1) are available for:
Figures 9.19 and 9.20.

Check questions are few in the following suggested presentation. By now it is hoped that this technique is a major part of your teaching. Take pity on students who are bored by a teacher who poses questions that he or she immediately answers without involving the students. This puts the student in the role of a passive observer rather than a participant in the learning process. Pose check questions before you move onto new material.

SUGGESTED PRESENTATION

9.1 Thermal Energy—The Total Energy in a Substance
Begin by asking what the difference is between a hot cup of coffee and a cold cup of coffee. Think small for the answer: The molecules in the hot cup of coffee are moving faster—they are more energetic. Heat and temperature have to do with the kinetic energies of the molecules in substances. Heat and temperature are different: To begin with, **heat** is energy that is measured in joules, or calories. **Temperature** is measured in degrees.

Distinguish thermal energy from temperature. A neat example is the 4th-of-July type sparkler, shown by Terrence Jones in the Part 2 opening photo. The sparks that fly from the firework and strike your face have temperatures in excess of 2000°C, but they don't burn. Why? Because the thermal energy of the sparks is extremely low. It is the amount of energy you receive that burns, not the ratio of energy/molecule. Even with a high ratio (high temperature), if a relatively few molecules are involved, the energy transfer is low. (Again, this is similar to the high voltage of a balloon rubbed against your hair. It may have thousands of volts, which is to say thousands of joules per charge. But if there are a relatively small number of charges, the total energy they possess is small.)

9.2 Temperature—Average Kinetic Energy per Molecule in a Substance

Describe how the increased jostling of molecules in a substance result in expansion and show how this property underlies the common thermometer. Draw a sketch of a noncalibrated thermometer on the board, with its mercury vessel at the bottom, and describe how the energy of jostling molecules is transferred from the outer environment to the mercury within. If placed in boiling water, energy of the jostling water molecules would be transferred to the mercury, which would expand and squeeze up the tube. State that one could make a scratch on the glass at this level and label it 100. And then describe how, if placed in a container of ice water, the molecules of mercury would give energy to the cold water and slow down, contract, and fall to a lower level in the tube. One could again make a scratch and call this point zero. Then, if 100 equally spaced scratches are made between the two reference points, one would have a centigrade thermometer.

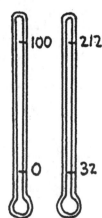

In a vein of humor draw a second noncalibrated thermometer on the board and repeat your discussion (in abbreviated fashion) of placing it in boiling water. State that the upper level needn't be called 100, that any number would do so long as all thermometers were calibrated the same. Ask the class for any random number. Someone will say 212. Then casually acknowledge the 212 response and write that on your diagram. Repeat the bit about placing the instrument in ice water and state that the position on the scale needn't be called zero, that any number would do. Ask for a random number. You'll have several students volunteer 32, which you graciously accept. The class should be in a good mood at this point, and you briefly discuss the two scales and lead into the idea of absolute zero and the Kelvin scale. (Name after "Lord Scale?")

Did Fahrenheit have a fever on the day he calibrated his temperature scale? Was a 1.4° above normal responsible for his placement of the 100° mark where he wished to be the standard for 100°? Your class may wish to speculate how he placed his zero.

CHECK YOUR NEIGHBOR: Which has the largest degrees, a Celsius thermometer or a Fahrenheit thermometer? [Celsius.]

CHECK YOUR NEIGHBOR: True or false: Cold is the absence of fast-moving molecules. [False; cold refers to very slow-moving molecules, not their absence. If you have no molecules at all, the concept of temperature is meaningless. That's why it's technically incorrect to speak of the "cold of outer space". Space has no temperature, although because it acts as a heat sink, an object in it will soon become very cold.]

9.3 Absolute Zero—Nature's Lowest Possible Temperature

Review the temperature scales and lead into the thermodynamic temperature scale. To lead into an understanding of the absolute temperature scale, begin by considering the ordering of a piece of hot apple pie in a restaurant and then being served cold pie—ice cold pie, at 0°C. Suppose you ask the waiter to heat the pie in the oven. How hot? Say twice as hot. Question: What will be the temperature of the pie? Move your class to the "check-your-neighbor" routine. Change your mind about the 0°C initial temperature of the piece of pie, and ask if the problem is easier if you begin with, say, a 10°C piece of pie. Tell your class to beware of neighbors who say the problem is simplified, and the answer is (wrongly) 20°C. This should spark interest. Now you're ready for "Celsius, the Village Tailor" story.

Celsius, the Village Tailor. Hold a measuring stick against the wall of the lecture room (so that the bottom of the vertically-oriented stick is about 1 meter above the floor) and state that you are Celsius, the village tailor, and that you measure the heights of your customers against the stick, which is firmly fastened to the wall. You state that there is no need for the stick to extend to the floor, nor to the ceiling, for your shortest and tallest customers fall within the extremities of the stick. Mention that all tailors using the same method could communicate meaningfully with each other about the relative heights of their customers providing the measuring sticks in each shop were fastened the same distance above the "absolute zero" of height. It just so happens that the distance to the floor, the "absolute zero," is 273 notches—the same size notches on the stick itself. Then one day, a very short lady enters your shop and stands against the wall, the top of her head coinciding with the zero mark on the measuring stick. As you take her zero reading, she comments that she has a brother who is twice her height. Ask the class for the height of her brother. Then ask for the temperature of the twice-as-hot apple pie. When this is understood, ask why the pie will not *really* be 273°C. Or that for the initially 10°C pie, the temperature will not really be 293°C. [Considerable heat has gone into changing the state of the water in the pie, which accounts for it being "dried out." If you wish to avoid the change of state factor, begin your discussion with the temperature of something such as a piece of metal that will not change state for the temperature range in question.]

9.4 Heat is the Movement of Thermal Energy
Distinguish between *heat* and *temperature*. Heat has to do with energy flow while temperature is a ratio of energy per molecule. They are very different. A Fourth-of-July-type sparkler emits sparks with temperatures exceeding 2000°C, but the heat one receives when one of these sparks lands on one's face is very small. High temperature means a high ratio of heat per molecule. The *ratio* and the *amount* of heat energy transferred are different things. Relatively few molecules comprise the tiny bit of white-hot matter that makes up the sparks of the sparkler. (Later you'll invoke a similar argument when you discuss the small energy associated with the high voltage of a charged party balloon rubbed on your hair.) Thermal energy is the total molecular energies, kinetic plus potential, internal to a substance. Heat is thermal energy in transit.

CHECK YOUR NEIGHBOR: How are the sparks from a sparkler that strike your skin akin to tiny droplets of boiling water striking your skin? [Both have high temperatures, but safe levels of thermal energy to transfer to your skin.]

9.5 Heat Units Are Energy Units
Define the calorie and compare it to the joule. Distinguish the calorie from the Calorie, the concern of people who watch their diet.

9.6 The Laws of Thermodynamics
First Law of Thermodynamics
Introduce the first law of thermodynamics by citing the findings of Count Rumford: When cannon barrels were being drilled and became very hot, it was the friction of the drills that produced the heating. Recall the definition of work, *force × distance*, and cite how the metal is heated by the frictional force × distance that the various parts of the drill bit move. Have your students rub their hands together and feel them warming up. Or warm part of the chair they sit on by rubbing.

Follow this up with the account of Joule with his paddle wheel apparatus and his measuring the mechanical equivalent of heat. Of interest is Joule's attempt to extend this experiment to a larger scale while on his honeymoon in Switzerland. Joule and his bride honeymooned near the Chamonix waterfall. According to Joule's conception of heat, the gravitational potential energy of the water at the top should transfer into increasing the internal energy of the water when at the bottom. Joule made a rough estimate of the increased difference in water temperature at the bottom of the waterfall. His measurements did not substantiate his predictions, however, because considerable cooling occurred due to evaporation as the water fell through the air. Without this added complication, however, his predictions would have been supported. What happens to the temperature of a penny, after all, when you slam it with a hammer? Likewise with water. Emphasize that the first law is simply the law of energy conservation for thermal systems.

Second Law of Thermodynamics
Introduce the second law by considering what occurs when you immerse a hot teacup in a large container of cold water. Thermal energy passes from the hot cup to the cool water. If the flow were in the opposite direction, the cup would become even warmer at the expense of the cold water becoming cooler. Even in this case, the first law would not be violated. You're on your way with the second law.

According to my friend Dave Wall who many years ago worked in the US patent office, the greatest shortcomings of would-be inventors was their lack of understanding the laws of thermodynamics. The patent office has long been besieged with schemes that promise to circumvent these laws. Sometimes much effort goes into debunking these schemes, and none has survived scrutiny. The patent office now directs their efforts to matters of more importance.

9.7 Specific Heat Capacity—A Measure of Thermal Inertia
Lead into a distinction between the difference between calories and degrees, and the concept of specific heat capacity by asking your class to consider the difference in touching an empty iron frying pan that has been placed on a hot stove for one minute (ouch!) and doing the same with a frying pan of water. With the water, you could place your hand in it safely even if it were on the stove for several minutes. Ask which has the higher temperature, the empty pan or the one filled with water. Clearly, it is the empty pan. Ask which absorbed the greater amount of energy. The answer is the water-filled pan, if it was on the stove for a longer time. The water has absorbed more energy for a lesser rise in temperature! Physics and chemistry types have a name for this idea—specific heat capacity, or for short, specific heat. Cite the different specific heat capacities of cooked foods, of a hot TV dinner and the aluminum foil that can be removed with bare hands while the food is still too hot to touch.

Water's High Specific Heat
Cite examples of water's high specific heat—hot water bottles on cold winter nights, cooling systems in cars, and the climate in places where there is much water. Figure 9.12 shows the sameness of latitudes for England and the Hudson Bay, and the French and Italian Riverias with Canada. State how the fact that water requires a long time to heat and to cool, enables the Gulf Stream to hold thermal energy long enough to reach the North Atlantic. There it cools off. But if the water cools, then according to the conservation of energy, something else has to warm. What is that something? The air. The cooling water warms the air, and the winds at that latitude are westerly. So warmed air moves over the continent of Europe. If this weren't the case, Europe would have the same climate as regions of northern Canada. A similar situation occurs in the United States. The Atlantic Ocean off the coast of the eastern states is considerably warmer than the Pacific Ocean off the coast of Washington, Oregon and California, yet in winter months the east coast is considerably colder. This has to do with the high specific heat of water and the westerly winds. Air that is warmed by cooling water on the west coast moves landward and gives mild winters to Washington, Oregon, and California. But on the east coast, this warmed air moves seaward, leaving the east coast frigid in winter months. In summer months, when the air is warmer than the water, the air cools and the water warms. So summer months on the west coast states are relatively cool, while the east coast is relatively hot. The high specific heat of water serves to moderate climates. The climates on islands, for example, are fairly free of temperature variations. Even San Francisco, a peninsula that is close to being an island, has the most stable climate of any city in continental America.

9.8 Thermal Expansion
State that steel lengths expand about 1 part in 100,000 for each 1°C increase in temperature. Show a steel rod and ask if anybody would be afraid to stand with their stomach between the

end of the rigidly held steel rod and a wall while the temperature of the rod is increased a few degrees. This is a safe activity, for the slight expansion of the rod would hardly be noticeable. Now ask for volunteers for a steel rod several kilometers in length. This is much different, for although the rate of change in length is the same, the total change in length could well impale you! Then discuss the expansion joints of large structures (Figures 9.14 and 9.15).

DEMONSTRATION: Place the middle of a bimetallic strip in a flame to show the unequal expansions of different metals, and the subsequent bending.

Point out that different substances expand or contract (length, area, and volume) at their own characteristic rates [coefficients of expansion]. Cite examples such as the need for the same expansion rate in teeth and teeth fillings; iron reinforcing rods and concrete; and the metal wires that are encased in glass light bulbs and the glass itself. Provision must be made when materials with different expansion rates interact; like the piston rings when aluminum pistons are enclosed in steel cylinders in a car, and the rockers on bridges (Figure 9.14), and the overflow pipe for gasoline in a steel tank.

CHECK YOUR NEIGHBOR: How would a thermometer differ if glass expanded with increasing temperature more than mercury? [Answer: The scale would be upside down, because the reservoir would enlarge (like the hole enlarged in the heated metal ring) and mercury in the column would tend to fill it up with increasing temperature.]

Expansion of Water

To lead into the idea of water's low density at 4°C you can ask if anyone in class happens to know what the temperature at the bottom of Lake Michigan was on a particular date, New Year's eve in 1905, for example. Then for the bottom of Lake Tahoe in California for any other date. And for another, until many are responding "4°C ".

CHECK YOUR NEIGHBOR: Ask the same for the bottom of a rain puddle outside the building, and be prepared for some to say 4°C.

Then ask why 4°C was the right answer for the deep lakes but the wrong answer for a puddle. Then go into the explanation as given in the book—how the microscopic slush forms as the freezing temperature is approached, yielding a net expansion below 4°C. (We haven't done this, but we have thought of showing a Galileo-type thermometer in class—a small flask with a narrow glass tube filled with colored water, so changes in temperature would be clearly evident by different levels of water in the narrow tube. Then surround the flask with perhaps dry ice to rapidly chill the water. The water level drops as the temperature of the water decreases, but its rate slows as it nears 4°C, and then the direction reverses as cooling continues. This expansion of the water is due to the formation of "microscopic slush." The level of water observed, as a function of time, yields a graph similar to that of Figure 9.21.)

Ice Formation on Lakes

Discuss the formation of ice, and why it forms at the surface and why it floats. And why deep bodies of water don't freeze over in winter because all the water in the lake has to be cooled to 4°C before colder water will remain at the surface to be cooled to the freezing temperature, 0°C. State that before one can cool a teaspoonful of water to 3°C, let alone 0°C, all the water beneath must be cooled to 4°C and that winters are neither cold or long enough for this to happen in the United States.

NEXT-TIME QUESTION: Ask your students to place an ice cube in a glass of ice water at home, and compare the water level at the side of the glass before and after the ice melts. Ask them to account for the volume of ice that extends above the water line after it melts. The answer to the original question is, of course, that the level remains unchanged. It so happens that the floating ice cube displaces its own weight of water, which is why it floats. (More on this in Appendix D.) So if the cube weighs say a newton, then when placed in the glass, one newton of water is displaced and the water level rises. If it is first melted and then poured in the glass, again the water line would be higher, but by the volume taken by one newton, the same amount. More interesting is to account for the volume all those billions and billions of open spaces in the ice crystals. Their combined volume is essentially that of the part of ice extending above the water line! When the ice melts, the part above the water line fills in the open structures as they collapse. Discuss this idea in terms of icebergs, and whether or not the coastline would change if all the floating icebergs in the world melted. The oceans would rise a bit, but only because icebergs are composed of fresh water. (They form above sea level and break off and then fall into sea [Chapter 34].) The slight rise is more easily understood by exaggerating the circumstance—think of ice cubes floating in mercury. When they melt, the depth of fluid (water on mercury) is higher than before. [Exaggeration of factors is a useful technique in "greater-than, equal-to, or less-than type" questions!]

Take note that ocean levels also rise due to thermal expansion. If you had a water-filled test tube that was 2 miles high (the average depth of the ocean), even a slight increase in temperature would raise the level of water appreciably. Similarly, a warmer ocean means a deeper ocean and quite different coastlines in many places! (Too often we attribute rising oceans only to ice-cap melting.)

NEXT-TIME QUESTION: Ask what happens to the inner diameter of a metal ring when it is heated. It's nice to have the metal ball and ring apparatus, which you demonstrate when you give the answer [that the diameter increases].

Chapter 9 Answers and Solutions

Key Terms and Matching Definitions

__3__ absolute zero
__5__ calorie
__6__ first law of thermodynamics
__4__ heat
__7__ second law of thermodynamics
__9_ specific heat capacity
__2__ temperature
__1__ thermal energy
_10__ thermal expansion
__8__ third law of thermodynamics

Review Questions

1. Why does a penny become warmer when struck by a hammer?
   Atoms are set into motion.

2. What are the temperatures for freezing water on the Celsius and Fahrenheit scales? For boiling water at sea level?
   0°C, 32°F; 100°C, 212°F.

3. Is the temperature of an object a measure of the total kinetic energy of molecules in the object, or a measure of the average kinetic energy per molecule in the object?
   Average.

4. What is meant by the statement "a thermometer measures its own temperature"?
   Both the thermometer and whatever it measures reach a common temperature—this is thermal equilibrium. In this sense, a thermometer measures its own temperature.

5. By how much does the pressure of a gas in a rigid vessel decrease when the temperature is decreased by 1 C°?
   By 1/273.

6. What pressure would you expect in a rigid container of 0°C gas if you cooled it by 273 C°?
   Zero.

7. What is the temperature of melting ice on the Kelvin scale? Of boiling water at atmospheric pressure?
   273°C; 373°C.

8. When you touch a cold surface, does "coldness" travel from the surface to your hand or does thermal energy travel from your hand to the cold surface? Explain.
   Thermal energy, not "coldness," can travel. So when your hand touches a cold surface, thermal energy travels from hand to the cold surface.

9. Distinguish between temperature and heat.
   Temperature measured in degrees. It is a measure of average translational KE per/molecule. Heat is a flow of energy measured in joules.

10. What determines the direction of heat flow?
    Temperture differences dictate direction of heat flow; from hot to cold.

11. How is the energy value of foods determined?
    By burning it and measuring energy released.

12. Distinguish between a joule and a calorie.

Both are units of energy; 4.18 J = 1 cal.

13. How does the law of the conservation of energy relate to the first law of thermodynamics?
The first law is the conservation of energy applied to thermal systems.

14. How does the second law of thermodynamics relate to the direction of heat flow?
It defines the direction—from hot to cold.

15. Does a substance that heats up quickly have a high or a low specific heat capacity?
Low.

16. Why is the West Coast of the United States warmer in winter than the East Coast?
Winds carrying energy from ocean water blow westerly over the West Coast. This is not true of the East Coast where winds blow over land.

17. How is a bimetallic strip used to regulate temperature?
One side changes length more than the other, bending the strip, which can trip a switch and activate a thermal device.

18. Which generally expands more for the same increase in temperature—solids or liquids?
Liquids.

19. When the temperature of ice-cold water is increased slightly, does it undergo a net expansion or net contraction?
Contraction (until it reaches 4°C).

20. At what temperature do the combined effects of contraction and expansion produce the smallest volume for water?
4°C

Solutions to Chapter 9 Exercises

1. In your room there are things such as tables, chairs, other people, and so forth. Which of these things has a temperature (1) lower than, (2) greater than, and (3) equal to the temperature of the air?
Inanimate things such as tables, chairs, furniture, and so on, have the same temperature as the surrounding air (assuming they are in thermal equilibrium with the air—i.e., no sudden gush of different-temperature air or such). People and other mammals, however, generate their own heat and have body temperatures that are normally higher than air temperature.

2. Which is greater, an increase in temperature of 1 C° or one of 1 F°?
Since Celsius degrees are larger than Fahrenheit degrees, an increase of 1 C° is larger. It's 9/5 as large.

3. A friend says the temperature inside a certain oven is 500 and the temperature inside a certain star is 50,000. You're unsure about whether your friend means Celsius degrees or kelvins. How much difference does it make in each case?
In the case of the 500-degree oven it makes a lot of difference. 500 kelvins is 227°C, quite a bit different than 500°C. But in the case of the 50,000-degree star, the 273 increments either way makes practically no difference. Give or take 273, the star is still 50,000 K or 50,000°C when rounded off.

4. The temperature of the sun's interior is about 10^7 degrees. Does it matter whether this is degrees Celsius or kelvins? Explain.
No, for as in the previous exercise, a difference of 273 in 10,000,000 is insignificant.

5. Which has the greater amount of thermal energy, an iceberg or a cup of hot coffee? Explain.
The hot coffee has a higher temperature, but not a greater thermal energy. Although the iceberg has less thermal energy per mass, its enormously greater mass gives it a greater

total energy than that in the small cup of coffee. (For a smaller volume of ice, the fewer number of more energetic molecules in the hot cup of coffee may constitute a greater total amount of thermal energy—but not compared to an iceberg.)

6. On which temperature scale does the average kinetic energy of molecules double when the temperature doubles?
The Kelvin temperature scale.

7. Adding the same amount of heat to two different objects does not necessarily produce the same increase in temperature. Why not?
Different substances have different thermal properties due to differences in the way energy is stored internally in the substances. When the same amount of heat produces different changes in temperatures in two substances of the same mass, we say they have different specific heat capacities. Each substance has its own characteristic specific heat capacity. Temperature measures the average kinetic energy of random motion, but not other kinds of energy.

8. Why will a watermelon stay cool for a longer time than sandwiches when both are removed from a cooler on a hot day?
Water has a high specific heat capacity, which is to say, it normally takes a long time to heat up, or cool down. The water in the watermelon resists changes in temperature, so once cooled it will stay cool longer than sandwiches or other non-watery substances under the same conditions. Be glad water has a high specific heat capacity the next time you're enjoying cool watermelon on a hot day!

9. Iceland, so named to discourage conquest by expanding empires, is not at all ice-covered like Greenland and parts of Siberia, even though it is nearly on the Arctic Circle. The average winter temperature of Iceland is considerably higher than regions at the same latitude in eastern Greenland and central Siberia. Why is this so?
The climate of Iceland, like that of Bermuda mentioned in the chapter, is moderated by the surrounding water.

10. Why does the presence of large bodies of water tend to moderate the climate of nearby land—make it warmer in cold weather, and cooler in hot weather?
In winter months when the water is warmer than the air, the air is warmed by the water to produce a seacoast climate warmer than inland. In summer months when the air is warmer than the water, the air is cooled by the water to produce a seacoast climate cooler than inland. This is why seacoast communities and especially islands do not experience the high and low temperature extremes that characterize inland locations.

11. If the winds at the latitude of San Francisco and Washington, D.C., were from the east rather than from the west, why might San Francisco be able to grow only cherry trees and Washington, D.C., only palm trees?
As the ocean off the coast of San Francisco cools in the winter, the heat it loses warms the atmosphere it comes in contact with. This warmed air blows over the California coastline to produce a relatively warm climate. If the winds were easterly instead of westerly, the climate of San Francisco would be chilled by winter winds from dry and cold Nevada. The climate would be reversed also in Washington D.C., because air warmed by the cooling of the Atlantic Ocean would blow over Washington D.C. and produce a warmer climate in winter there.

12. Desert sand is very hot in the day and very cool at night. What does this tell you about its specific heat?
Sand has a low specific heat, as evidenced by its relatively large temperature changes for small changes in internal energy. A substance with a high specific heat, on the other hand, must absorb or give off large amounts of internal energy for comparable temperature changes.

13. Cite an exception to the claim that all substances expand when heated.
Water is an exception.

14. Creaking noises are often heard in the attic of old houses on cold nights. Give an explanation in terms of thermal expansion.

   Temperature differences cause differences in expansion and contraction, which produce the creaking sounds.

15. An old remedy for a pair of nested drinking glasses that stick together is to run water at different temperatures into the inner glass and over the surface of the outer glass. Which water should be hot, and which cold?

   Cool the inner glass and heat the outer glass. If it's done the other way around, the glasses will stick even tighter (if not break).

16. A metal ball is just able to pass through a metal ring. When the ball is heated, however, it will not pass through the ring. What would happen if the ring, rather than the ball, were heated? Does the size of the hole increase, stay the same, or decrease?

   Every part of a metal ring expands when it is heated—not only the thickness, but the outer and inner circumference as well. Hence the ball that normally passes through the hole when the temperatures are equal will more easily pass through the expanded hole when the ring is heated. (Interestingly enough, the hole will expand as much as a disk of the same metal undergoing the same increase in temperature. Blacksmiths mounted metal rims in wooden wagon wheels by first heating the rims. Upon cooling, the contraction resulted in a snug fit.)

17. Suppose you cut a small gap in a metal ring. If you heat the ring, will the gap become wider or narrower?

   The gap in the ring will become wider when the ring is heated. Try this: Draw a couple of lines on a ring where you pretend a gap to be. When you heat the ring, the lines will be farther apart—the same amount as if a real gap were there. Every part of the ring expands proportionally when heated uniformly—thickness, length, gap and all.

18. State whether water at the following temperatures will expand or contract when warmed a little: 0°C; 4°C; 6°C.

   At 0°C it will contract when warmed a little; at 4°C it will expand, and at 6°C it will expand.

19. Why is it important to protect water pipes so they don't freeze?

   It is important to keep water in pipes from freezing because when the temperature drops below freezing, the water expands as it freezes. The pipes (if metal) will fracture if water in them freezes.

20. If a metal object of 0°C is heated until it has twice as much thermal energy, what will its temperature be?

   To double its thermal energy you double its absolute temperature, 273 K. Double this and you have 546 K. To convert to Celsius, subtract 173 and you have 273°C.

Solutions to Chapter 9 Problems

Quantity of heat, Q, is equal to the specific heat capacity of the substance c multiplied by its mass m and the temperature change ΔT; that is, $Q = cm\Delta T$.

1. The thermal energy of helium gas is directly proportional to its absolute temperature. Consider a flask of helium with a temperature of 10°C. If it is heated until it has twice the thermal energy, what will its temperature be?

   Its absolute temperature is 273 +10 = 283 K. Double this and you have 566 K. Expressed in Celsius; 566 - 273 = 293 °C.

2. What would be the final temperature of a mixture of 50 g of 20°C water and 50 g of 40°C water?

   Heat gained by the cooler water = heat lost by the warmer water. Since the masses of water are the same, the final temperature is midway, 30°C. So you'll end up with 100 g of 30°C water.

3. If you wish to warm 100 kg of water by 20°C for your bath, how much heat is required? (Give your answer in calories and joules.)

   Each kilogram requires 1 kilocalorie for each degree change, so 100 kg needs 100 kilocalories for each degree change. Twenty degrees means twenty times this, which is 2,000 kcal.

   By formula, $Q = mc\Delta T$ = (100,000 g)(1 cal/g°C)(20°C) = 2000 kcal. We can convert this to joules knowing that 4.184 J = 1 cal. In joules this quantity of heat is 8370 kJ.

4. What would be the final temperature when 100 g of 25°C water is mixed with 75 g of 40°C water? (Hint: Equate the heat gained by the cool water to the heat lost by the warm water.)

   Heat gained by cool water = heat lost by warm water

   $$cm_1 \, \Delta T_1 = cm_2 \, \Delta T_2$$

   $$c(100)(T - 25) = c(75)(40 - T)$$

   (Note that common sense dictates that ΔT_1 is final temperature T minus 25°, since T will be greater than 25°, and ΔT_2 is 40° minus T, because T will be less than 40°. ΔT_1 does not equal ΔT_2 as in Problem 1 because of the different masses of cool and warm water.)

   From 100 T - 2500 = 3000 −75 T, T = 31.4°C.

5. (Challenge!) Consider a 40,000-km steel pipe that forms a ring to fit snugly all around the circumference of the world. Suppose people along its length breathe on it so as to raise its temperature 1 Celsius degree. The pipe gets longer. It also is no longer snug. How high does it stand above ground level? (To simplify, consider only the expansion of its radial distance from the center of the Earth, and apply the geometry formula that relates circumference C and radius r, $C = 2\pi r$. The result is surprising!)

   If a snugly fitting steel pipe that girdled the world were heated by 1 Celsius degree, it would stand about 70 meters off the ground! The most straight-forward way to see this is to consider the radius of the 40,000 long kilometer pipe, which is the radius of the Earth, 6370 kilometers. Steel will expand 11 parts in a million for each C° increase in temperature; the radius as well as the circumference will expand by this fraction. So 11 millionths of 6370 kilometers = 70 meters. Is this not astounding?

   Or if you know the formula for thermal expansion,

   $$\Delta L = L_0\alpha\Delta T = (6370 \times 10^3 \text{m})(11 \times 10^{-6}/°C)(1°C) = 70 \text{ m}.$$

10 Heat Transfer and Change of Phase

> Link to Entomology—Life at the Extremes

Learning Objectives

After studying Chapter 10, students will be able to:
• Explain why two materials at the same temperature may not feel like they are the same temperature when touched.
• Explain why porous materials with air spaces are better insulators than nonporous materials.
• Distinguish between conduction and convection from an atomic point of view.
• Explain how heat is transmitted through empty space.
• Compare the ability of an object to emit radiant energy with its ability to absorb it.

Possible Misconceptions to Correct

• Not so! Surfaces that feel cooler than others have a lower temperature.
• Not so! A blanket is a source of heat energy.
• Not so! Walking barefoot without harm on red-hot wooden coals involves nonscience considerations.
• Not so! Only hot things radiate energy.
• Not so! Constant temperature of something indicates that all the molecules have the same energy.
• Not so! Boiling is a warming process.
• Not so! Ice melts only when heat is added.

Demonstration Equipment

• Aluminum soda pop cans, hot plate, and pan of water
• Metal bar, sheet of paper, and a flame
• Paper cup filled with water and a flame

This chapter begins with conduction, convection, and radiation of heat with emphasis again on bodies of water and the atmosphere, which will be treated again in Chapter 34 and Chapter 37. The section on radiation serves as some background to later chapters on light.

If you wish to introduce the idea of distribution curves in your course, this is a good place to do it. Treat the cooling produced by evaporation with plots of relative numbers of molecules in a liquid versus their speeds, and show how the distribution shifts as the faster-moving molecules evaporate. You may wish to point to the bell-shaped distribution curves that represent the distributions of so many things, from molecular speeds to examination scores to people's IQ scores. Regrettably, many people tend to regard such distributions not as bell-shaped, but as spikes. This makes a difference in attitudes. For example, suppose you compare the grade distributions for two sections of your course, Group 1 and Group 2, and that the average score for Group 1 is somewhat greater than that for Group 2. For whatever reason, Group 1 outperforms Group 2. With this information can we make any judgment about individuals from either group? One who looks at these distributions as spiked shaped behaves as if he can—he'll say (or not say but think) that individuals from Group 1 are "better" than particular individuals from Group 2. On the other hand, one who thinks in terms of the broad shape of the bell-shaped distribution will not make any assumptions about such individuals. He is well aware of the region of overlap in the two distribution curves. His attitude toward individuals from either group is unbiased by unwarranted prejudice. Hence the difference between narrow-mindedness and broad-mindedness!

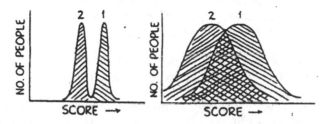

This chapter introduces the concepts of evaporation, condensation, melting, and freezing, which will be treated in more detail in Part 6—Chemistry.

In the **Practicing Physics** book:
• Evaporation
• Change of Phase

In the **Next-Time Questions** book:
• Firewalk
• Space Shuttle Convection
• Coffee Cream Right Away
• Energy to Melt Ice
• Earth-Sun Body Glow

In the **Lab Manual**:
• Canned Heat I
• Canned Heat II
• I'm Melting, I'm Melting

Overhead Transparency (1) available for:
Figures 10.7, 10.14 and 10 28.

SUGGESTED PRESENTATION

10.1 Conduction—Heat Transfer via Particle Collision
Begin by asking why pots and pans have wooden or plastic handles, why one can safely touch wood at a high temperature—then discuss conduction from an atomic point of view, citing the role of the electrons in both heat and electrical conductors. You might demonstrate the oldie of melting wax on different metal rods equidistant from a hot flame, and illustrate relative conductivities. Other materials can be compared in their ability to conduct heat, like newspaper when having to sleep outdoors. Discuss the poor conductivity of water, which ties to the previous chapter where you discussed the 4°C temperature of the bottom of deep lakes all year round.

DEMONSTRATION: Wedge some pieces of ice at the bottom of a test tube with some steel wool. Then heat the top part of the tube in a flame. It is impressive to see that the water at the top is brought to a boil by the flame of a burner while the ice below barely melts!

DEMONSTRATION: Wrap a piece of paper around a thick metal bar and attempt to burn it in the flame. The paper does not reach its ignition temperature because heat is conducted into the metal.

DEMONSTRATION: Extend the previous demo and place a paper cup filled with water in the flame. Again, the paper will not reach its ignition temperature and burn because heat from the flame is conducted into the conductor—this time water. Water is not *that* poor a conductor—its high specific heat comes into play here as well.

Discuss the poor conductivity of air, and its role in insulating materials—like snow. Discuss thermal underwear, and how the fish-net open spaces actually trap air between the skin and the undergarment. Discuss double-window thermopane.

10.2 Convection—Heat Transfer via Movements of Fluid
Illustrate convection by considering the case of rising warm air.

CHECK YOUR NEIGHBOR: Why does smoke from a candle rise and then settle off? [It's interesting to note that helium, unlike smoke particles, continues rising even when cool. That's because the small mass of the helium finds it faster than more massive molecules at the same KE. Interestingly, helium is not found in the air but must be mined from beneath the ground like natural gas. (The helium nucleus is the alpha particle that emanates from radioactive ores.) This idea of faster-moving helium underscores the relationship of kinetic energy to temperature].

Expanding Air Cools
Depart from the order of topics in the text and first treat the warming of compressed air. The familiar bicycle pump offers a good example. Why does the air become warm when the handle is depressed. It's easy to see that the air molecules speed up when the piston slams against them. A Ping-Pong ball similarly speeds up when a paddle hits it. Now, consider what happens to the speed of a Ping-Pong ball when it encounters a receding paddle! Can your students see that its rebound speed will be less than its incident speed? Now you're ready to discuss the cooling of expanding air and compare it to the case of the slowing Ping-Pong balls with molecules that are on the average receding from one another.

Here's a great one: Have everyone in class blow against their hands with open mouths. Their breaths feel warm. Then repeat with very small mouth openings. Their breaths are remarkably cooler. They **experience** first hand that expanding air *really does* cool!

Discuss the role of convection in climates. Begin by calling attention to the shift in winds as shown in Figure 10.6. This leads you into radiation, the heat from the sun.

Warm at the Equator; Cold at the Poles
You may want to discuss why the Earth is warmer at the equator than at the poles, and get into the idea of solar energy per unit area. This is treated in Chapter 38, so if you're not going to teach that chapter, do it here. Draw a large circle on the board that represents the Earth (like the one on page 103, only without the sun's rays at this point). Ask for a neighbor check and speculate why it is warm near the equator and cold at the poles. To dispel the idea that the farther distance to the poles is the reason, do the following:

SKIT: Ask the class to pretend there is a vertical rainfall, into which you reach out your window with two sheets of paper—one held horizontally and the other held at an angle as shown. You bring the papers inside as a friend strolls by and inquires what you're doing. You remark that you have been holding the sheets of paper out in the rain. Your friend sees that the horizontally held paper is much wetter and asks why. You repeat with both papers held outward as before, and your friend says, "Oh, I see why. You're holding the tilted sheet further away from the clouds!" Ask your class if you are holding it farther away from the overhead clouds. The answer is yes. Ask if this is the reason the paper is not as wet. The answer is no!

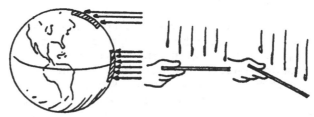

10.3 Radiation—Heat Transfer via Radiant Energy

Discuss the radiation one feels from red hot coals in a fireplace. And how the radiation decreases with distance. Consider the radiation one feels when stepping from the shade to the sunshine. Amazing! The heat is not so much because of the sun's temperature, because like temperatures are to be found in the torches of some welders. One feels hot not because the sun is hot, but because it is *big*. Comfortably big!

Acknowledge that everything emits radiation—everything that has any temperature. But everything does not become progressively cooler because everything absorbs radiation. We live in a sea of radiation, everything emitting and everything absorbing. When emission rate equals absorption rate, temperature remains constant. Some materials, because of their molecular design, emit better than others. They also absorb better than others. They're easy to spot, because they absorb visible radiation as well and appear black.

DEMONSTRATION: Make up and show the black hole in the white box, as shown by Helen Yan in Figure 10.13. (Helen is a physicist. Those of you familiar with *Conceptual Physics*, editions 5, 6, and 7, may recall the earlier black and white photo of Helen showing the same box when she was Paul Hewitt's 21-year-old student teaching assistant at CCSF in 1983.)

DEMONSTRATION: Pour hot water into a pair of vessels, one black and the other shiny silver. Ask for a neighbor check as to which will cool faster. Have thermometers in each that you ask a student to read aloud at the beginning and a few minutes later. (You can repeat this demo with initially cold water in each vessel.)

10.4 Heat Transfer Occurs Whenever Matter Changes Phase

Ask if it is possible to heat a substance without raising its temperature, and why a steam burn is more damaging than a burn from boiling water at the same temperature. In answering these, discuss the change of phase diagram of Figure 10.28. After citing examples of changes of phase where energy is absorbed, cite examples where energy is released—like raining and snowing. People sometimes say that it is too cold to snow. Explain that this statement arises from the fact that the process of snowing warms the air!

Ask about cooling a room by leaving the refrigerator door open, and compare it to putting an air conditioner in the middle of a room instead of mounting it in a window. Ask what the result would be of mounting an air conditioner backwards in a window.

10.5 Evaporation—a Change of Phase from Liquid to Gas

Begin by citing the familiar case of leaving the water when bathing and feeling chilly in the air, especially when it is windy. Explain the cooling of a liquid from an atomic point of view, and reinforce the idea of temperature being a measure of the average molecular kinetic energy, and acknowledge molecules that move faster and slower than the average.

CHECK YOUR NEIGHBOR: Why does cooling occur in the water of a leaky canvas water bag? [Water seeps through the canvas. More faster-moving molecules leak and vaporize, leaving less energy per molecule behind.]

CHECK YOUR NEIGHBOR: Cite at least two ways to cool a hot cup of coffee. [You can increase evaporation by blowing on it or pouring it into the saucer to increase the evaporating area. You can cool it by conduction by putting silverware in it, which absorbs heat and provides a radiating antenna.]

Sketch a bell-shaped distribution curve on the board to represent the wide array of molecular speeds in a container of water. The peak of the curve represents the speeds that correspond to the temperature of the water. (It is not important to distinguish here between the mean speed, the rms speed, and the most probable speeds.) Stress the many lower and higher speeds to the left and right of the peak of your curve at any moment in the water. Which molecules evaporate? The fast ones, which you clip from the right hand tail of your curve. What is the result? A shift toward the left of the peak of the curve—a lowering of temperature. [Actually, this approach is highly exaggerated, for the molecules that do penetrate the surface and escape into the air have energies that correspond to 3400K! See Paul Hewitt's article on page 492 of *The Physics Teacher*, October, 1981.]

The relatively strong bond between water molecules (hydrogen bonding) prevents more evaporation than presently occurs. It also enhances condensation. [This idea is explained in detail in Chapter 23.]

10.6 Condensation—a Change of Phase from Gas to Liquid
If evaporation is a cooling process, what kind of process would the opposite of evaporation be? This is condensation, which is a warming process.

CHECK YOUR NEIGHBOR: Why is it that many people after taking a shower will begin drying in the shower stall before getting outside. [While still in the shower region, appreciable condensation offsets the cooling by evaporation.]

Make the point that a change of state from liquid to gas or vice versa is not merely one or the other. Condensation occurs while evaporation occurs and vice versa. The net effect is usually what is spoken about. If you haven't shown the collapsing can demo in your atmospheric pressure lecture, now is a good time:

DEMONSTRATION: Heat some aluminum soda pop cans on a burner, empty except for a small amount of water that is brought to a boil to make steam. With a potholder or tongs, pick up a can and quickly invert it into a basin of water. Crunch! The atmospheric pressure immediately crushes the can with a resounding WHOP! Very impressive. Do this first by inverting cans into a cold basin of water. It is evident that condensation of the steam and vapor on the interior takes place, pressure is correspondingly reduced, and the atmospheric pressure on the exterior crunches the can. Then repeat but this time invert cans into a basin of very hot water, just short of the boiling temperature. Crunch again, but less forceful than before. Steam molecules stick to the water surface, hot or cool, like flies sticking to fly paper. [If you do this with hot water just short of boiling, you'll still get a crunch, though less violent. If you do this in boiling water, then there is no crunch. Lead your class into the explanation wherein the *net* effect is no change, as condensation of steam is met with just as much vaporization from the boiling water.]

And make clear just what is cooling when evaporation occurs. To say that one thing cools is to say that another warms. When a hot cup of coffee cools by evaporation, the surrounding air is warmed. Conservation of energy reigns!

10.7 Boiling is Evaporation Within a Liquid
Discuss boiling and the roles of adding heat and pressure in the boiling process. A tactic we use throughout our teaching is to ask the class members to pretend they are having a one-to-one conversation with a friend about the ideas of physics. Suppose a friend is skeptical about the idea of boiling being a cooling process. We tell our class just what to say to convince the friend of what is going on. We tell them to first point out the distinction between heating and boiling. If the friend knows that the temperature of boiling water remains at 100°C regardless of the

amount of heat applied, point out that this is so because the water is cooling by boiling as fast as it is being warmed by heating. Then if this still is not convincing, ask the friend to hold his or her hands above a pot of boiling water—in the steam. Your friend knows the hands will be burned. But burned by what? By the steam. And where did the steam get its energy? From the boiling water; so energy is leaving the water—that's what we mean by cooling! Bring in the role of pressure on boiling, and illustrate this with the pressure cooker.

CHECK YOUR NEIGHBOR: In bringing water to a boil in the high mountains, is the time required to bring the water to a boil longer or shorter than at sea level? Is the time required for cooking longer or shorter? (Preface this second question with the statement that you are posing a different question, for any confusion about this is most likely due to failing to distinguish between the two questions.)

DEMONSTRATION: Evacuate air from a flask of water that is at room temperature, enough so that the water in the flask will boil from the heat of the students' hands as it is passed around the classroom. [Take care that the flask is strong enough so that it doesn't implode!]

Explain how a geyser is like a pressure cooker. Discuss the operation of a coffee percolator.

Boiling and Freezing at the Same Time. This must be seen to be appreciated!

DEMONSTRATION: The triple-point demonstration, Figure 10.26. [A film loop or short video should be made of this impressive demo for those who don't have the equipment!]

10.8 Melting and Freezing—Opposite Directions in Phase Change

Add energy to ice and it melts. Add energy to water and it boils.

10.9 Energy is Needed for Changes of Phase

Clearly energy changes phase in these cases. Call attention to the change in energy in the other direction—from gas to solid.

Air Conditioning. In view of the ozone-destroying chemicals used as refrigerants, cite present efforts you are acquainted with in developing alternative systems. One approach introduced in mid 1992 by ICC Technologies in Philadelphia uses ordinary water in place of chlorofluorocarbons, with reports of providing cooling for a small fraction of the energy of conventional systems. The device utilizes the evaporation condensation cycle with a new type of desiccant, or drying agent, that chills air without increasing its humidity. Alternative air conditioning systems will likely be in the forefront of news on new technologies. It's needed.

Chapter 10 Answers and Solutions

Key Terms and Matching Definitions

__7__ boiling
__6__ condensation
__1__ conduction
__2__ convection
__4__ evaporation
__9__ freezing
_10_ heat of fusion
_11_ heat of vaporization
__8__ melting
__3__ radiation
__5__ sublimation

Review Questions

1. What is the role of "loose" electrons in heat conductors?
   They carry energy from one part of the conductor to another.

2. Distinguish between a heat conductor and an insulator.
   A heat conductor readily conducts thermal energy; an insulator inhibits flow of thermal energy.

3. In what sense do we say there is no such thing as cold?
   Cold isn't a thing in itself, but is an absence of thermal energy.

4. How is thermal energy transferred from one place to another by convection?
   By motion of the heated fluid itself.

5. What happens to the pressure of air as the air rises? What happens to its volume? Its temperature?
   Decreases. Increases. Decreases.

6. How does the frequency of radiant energy vary with the temperature of the radiating source?
   Both vary the same—they're proportional to each other.

7. Which body glows, the sun, the Earth, or both? Explain.
   Both. They glow at different frequencies because of their different surface temperatures.

8. Which normally cools faster, a black pot of hot water or a silver pot of hot water? Explain.
   A hot black pot cools faster. Its blackness is evidence that it is a good absorber of visible light, indicating it is also a good absorber of heat, which in turn indicates that it is a good emitter of heat.

9. Is a good absorber of radiation a good emitter or a poor emitter?
   Good absorber is also a good emitter.

10. What are the four phases of matter?
    Solid, liquid, gas, and plasma.

11. Do the molecules in a liquid all have about the same speed or is there a wide variety of speeds?
    Wide variety of speeds.

12. Why is perspiration a cooling process?
    Because faster-moving molecules of perspiration evaporate.

13. What happens to the temperature of a body of water when water molecules condense upon it?

The temperature is increased.

14. Why is a steam burn more damaging than a burn from boiling water at the same temperature?

Because of relatively great amount of energy given up by condensing steam.

15. Distinguish between evaporation and boiling.

Evaporation is change of phase at a liquid surface; boiling is change of phase throughout the liquid.

16. What condition permits water to boil at a temperature below $100°C$?

Reduced atmospheric pressure.

17. Why does increasing the temperature of a solid make it melt?

KE of molecules increases to the point of shaking them apart.

18. Why does decreasing the temperature of a liquid make it freeze?

KE of molecules reduces to where molecules bond.

19. Does a liquid release or absorb energy when it evaporates? When it solidifies?

Releases. Absorbs.

20. Why does the temperature of boiling water not rise when thermal energy is added?

Energy goes into changing phase instead of increasing molecular speed.

Solutions to Chapter 10 Exercises

1. If you hold one end of a metal nail against a piece of ice, the end in your hand soon becomes cold. Does cold flow from the ice to your hand? Explain.
   Energy "flows" from higher to lower temperature, from your hand to the ice. It is the thermal energy flowing from your hand that produces the sensation of coolness. There is no flow from cold to hot; only from hot to cold.

2. What is the purpose of a layer or copper or aluminum on the bottom of stainless steel cookware?
   Copper and aluminum are better conductors than stainless steel, and therefore more quickly transfer heat to the cookware's interior.

3. Many tongues have been injured by licking a piece of metal on a very cold day. Why would no harm result if a piece of wood were licked on the same day even when both have the same temperature?
   In touching the tongue to very cold metal, enough thermal energy can be quickly conducted away from the tongue to bring the saliva to sub-zero temperature where it freezes, locking the tongue to the metal. In the case of relatively nonconducting wood, much less energy is conducted from the tongue and freezing does not take place fast enough for sudden sticking to occur.

4. All objects continuously emit radiant energy. Why then doesn't the temperature of all objects continuously decrease?
   Because all objects also continuously absorb radiant energy.

5. All objects continuously absorb energy from their surroundings. Why then doesn't the temperature of all objects continuously increase?
   Because all objects also continuously emit radiant energy.

6. What determines whether an object is a net emitter or a net absorber of radiant energy?
   Whether its temperature is above or below ambient temperature.

7. Wood is a better insulator than glass. Yet fiberglass is commonly used as an insulator in wooden buildings. Explain.
   Air is an excellent insulator. The reason that fiberglass is a good insulator is principally because of the vast amount of air spaces trapped in it.

8. You can comfortably hold your fingers close beside a candle flame, but not very close above the flame. Why?
   You can hold your fingers quite close to the side of a candle flame without harm because the air between is a good insulator. But you will burn your fingers if you hold them above the flame because of the convection of hot gases in the flame. (Interestingly enough, candle flames will quickly snuff out in orbiting space facilities or any gravity free region. This is because convection depends on gravity, and without convection new oxygen cannot get to the flame.)

9. When a hot object is placed in contact with a cooler object, the hot object warms the cooler one. Can you say it loses as much temperature as the cooler one gains? Defend your answer.
   No, it's energy, not temperature, that is exchanged and energy, not temperature, that is conserved. So the quantity of heat lost by one object is equal to the quantity of heat gained by the other. The point of this question is to distinguish between temperature and heat.

10. Consider two equal size rooms connected by an open door. One room is maintained at a higher temperature than the other one. Which room contains more air molecules?
    More molecules are in the cooler room. The greater number of slower-moving molecules there produce air pressure at the door equal to the fewer number of faster-moving molecules in the warmer room.

11. In a still room, smoke from a candle will sometimes rise only so far, not reaching the ceiling. Explain why.

The smoke, like hot air, is less dense than the surroundings and is buoyed upward. It cools with contact with the surrounding air and becomes more dense. When its density matches that of the surrounding air, its buoyancy and weight balance and rising ceases.

12. In a mixture of hydrogen and oxygen gases at the same temperature, which molecules move faster? Why?

Hydrogen molecules will be the faster moving when mixed with oxygen molecules. They will have the same temperature, which means they will have the same average kinetic energy. Recall that KE = 1/2 mv^2. Since the mass of hydrogen is considerably less than oxygen, the velocity must correspondingly be greater.

13. Turn an incandescent lamp on and off quickly while you are standing near it. You feel its thermal energy but find when you touch the bulb that it is not hot. Explain why you felt thermal energy from it.

The heat you received was from radiation.

14. The thermal energy of volcanoes and natural hot springs comes from trace amounts of radioactive minerals in common rock in the Earth's interior. Why isn't the same kind of rock at the Earth's surface warm to the touch?

The energy given off by rock at the Earth's surface transfers to the surroundings practically as fast as it is generated. Hence there isn't the buildup of energy that occurs in the Earth's interior.

15. Why does blowing over the surface of hot soup cool the soup?

When you blow over the top of a bowl of hot soup, you increase net evaporation and its cooling effect by removing the warm vapor that tends to condense and reduce net evaporation.

16. Why does the temperature of boiling water remain the same as long as the heating and boiling continue?

When water is boiling, it is being cooled by the boiling process as fast as it is being heated by the stove. Hence its temperature remains the same—100°C.

17. Why does the water in a car radiator sometimes boil explosively when the radiator cap is removed?

Water in the pressurized radiator doesn't boil, even when its temperature exceeds 100°C (like water in a pressure cooker). But when the radiator cap is suddenly removed, pressure drops and the high-temperature water immediately boils. Do not have your head above a hot radiator when removing the cap!

18. Why does dew form on a cold soft drink can?

Water vapor in the warm air condenses on the relatively low-temperature surface of the can.

19. Air-conditioning units contain no water whatever, yet it is common to see water dripping from them when they're running on a hot day. Explain.

Water vapor in the warm air condenses on the low-temperature metal surface of the unit.

20. Why does a hot dog pant?

To cool by evaporation of fluid in the mouth and the respiratory system.

Solutions to Chapter 10 Problems

1. Use the quantity of heat relationships to determine the number of calories to change (a) 1 kg of 0°C ice to 0°C ice water; (b) 1 kg of 0°C ice water to 1 kg of 100°C boiling water; (c) 1 kg of 100°C boiling water to 1 kg of 100°C steam; and (d) 1 kg of 0°C ice to 1 kg of 100°C steam.
    a. 1 kg 0°C ice to 0°C water requires 80 kilocalories.
    b. 1 kg 0°C water to 100°C water requires 100 kilocalories.
    c. 1 kg 100°C water to 100°C steam requires 540 kilocalories.
    d. 1 kg 0°C ice to 100°C steam requires (80 + 100 + 540) = 720 kilocalories,
    or 720,000 calories.

2. The specific heat capacity of ice is about 0.5 cal/g°C. Supposing that it remains at that value all the way to absolute zero, calculate the number of calories it would take to change a 1-gram ice cube at absolute zero (-273°C) to 1 gram of boiling water. How does this number of calories compare to the number of calories required to change the same gram of 100°C boiling water to 100°C steam?
    From -273°C "ice" to 0°C ice requires (273)(0.5) = 140 calories.
    From 0°C ice to 0°C water requires 80 calories.
    From 0°C water to 100°C water requires 100 calories. That's a total of 320 calories.
    Boiling this water at 100°C takes 540 calories, considerably more energy than it took to bring the water all the way from absolute zero to the boiling point! (In fact, at very low temperature, the specific heat capacity of ice is less than 0.5 cal/g°C, so the true difference is even greater than calculated here.)

3. Find the mass of 0°C ice that 10 g of 100°C steam will completely melt.
    First, find the number of calories that 10 g of 100°C steam will give in changing to 10 g of 0°C water.   10 g of steam changing to 10 g of boiling water at 100°C releases 5400 calories. 10 g of 100°C water cooling to 0°C releases 1000 calories.
    So 6400 calories are available for melting ice.
    $$\frac{6400 \text{ cal}}{80 \text{ cal/g}} = 80 \text{ grams of ice.}$$

4. If 50 grams of hot water at 80°C is poured into a cavity in a very large block of ice at 0°C, what will be the final temperature of the water in the cavity? How much ice must melt in order to cool the hot water down to this temperature?
    The final temperature of the water will be the same as that of the ice, 0°C. The quantity of heat given to the ice by the water is $Q = cm\Delta T$ = (1 cal/g°C)(50 g)(80°C) = 4000 cal. This heat melts ice. How much? From $Q = mL$, $m = Q/L$ = (4000 cal)/(80 cal/g) = 50 grams. So water at 80°C will melt an equal mass of ice at 0°C.

5. A 50-gram chunk of 80°C iron is dropped into a cavity in a very large block of ice at 0°C. How many grams of ice will melt? (The specific heat capacity of iron is 0.11 cal/g°C.)
    The quantity of heat lost by the iron is $Q = cm\Delta T$ = (0.11 cal/g°C)(50 g)(80°C) = 440 cal. The iron will lose a quantity of heat to the ice $Q = mL$. The mass of ice melted will therefore be $m = Q/L$ = (440 cal)/(80 cal/g) = 5.5 grams. (The lower specific heat capacity of iron shows itself compared with the result of the previous problem.)

6. A 0.6 gram peanut is burned beneath 50 grams of water. The water increases in temperature from 22°C to 50°C. (a) Assuming 40% efficiency, what is the food value in calories of the peanut? (b) What is the food value in calories per gram?
    (a) The amount of heat absorbed by the water is $Q = cm\Delta T$ = (1.0 cal/g C°)(50.0 g)(50°C – 22°C) = 1400 cal. At 40% efficiency only 0.4 the energy from the peanut raises the water temperature, so the calorie content of the peanut is 1400/0.4 = 3500 cal. (b) The food value of a peanut is 3500 cal/0.6 g = 5.8 kilocalories per gram.

7. Radioactive decay of granite and other rocks in the Earth's interior provides enough energy to keep the interior molten, heat lava, and provide warmth to natural hot springs. This is due to the average release of about 0.03 joules per kilogram each year. How many years are needed for a chunk of thermally insulated granite to increase 500°C in temperature. Assume the specific heat capacity of granite is 800 J/kg-°C.
    From $Q = cm\Delta T$, $Q/m = c\Delta T$ = (800 J/kg.C°)(500°C) = 400,000 J/kg. The time required is (400,000J/kg)/(0.03 J/kg.yr) = 13.3 million years. Small wonder it remains hot down there!

II Electricity

Conceptual Physical Science—Explorations

Learning Objectives
After studying Chapter 11, the students will be able to:
• Describe electrical forces between objects.
• Explain, from the point of view of electron transfer, how an object becomes positively charged or negatively charged and relate this to the object's net charge.
• Describe the relationship of the electrical force between two charged objects, the charge of each object, and the distance between the charges.
• Distinguish between a conductor and an insulator.
• Distinguish between electric potential energy and voltage.
• Describe the conditions necessary for electric charge to flow.
• Relate the current in a circuit to the resistance of the circuit and the voltage across it.
• Explain why wet skin increases the likelihood of receiving a damaging electric shock when a faulty electrical device is touched.
• Distinguish between direct current and alternating current.
• Relate the power used by an electrical device to its current and voltage.
• Distinguish between series circuits and parallel circuits.
• Predict what will happen in a series circuit if there is a break in the wire.
• Relate the current at any point in a series circuit to the current at any other point in the circuit.
• Predict what will happen to the current at any point in a series circuit if an additional device is connected to the circuit.
• Predict what will happen in a parallel circuit if there is a break in any branch of the circuit.
• Relate the current in the lead to a parallel circuit to the current in each branch of the circuit.
• Predict what will happen to the current at any point in a parallel circuit if an additional device is connected to the circuit.

Possible Misconceptions to Correct
• **Not so!** Electric charges occur in some materials but not in others.
• **Not so!** A current-carrying wire is electrically charged.
• **Not so!** Electric current is a fluid of some kind.

- **Not so!** Electric current flows out of a battery, rather than flowing through a battery.
- **Not so!** Voltage flows through a circuit, instead of being impressed across a circuit.
- **Not so!** Power companies deliver electrons, rather than energy, from a power plant to consumers.
- **Not so!** Electrons travel at about the speed of light in a dc circuit.
- **Not so!** In a series circuit, the amount of current can vary in devices of different electrical resistances.
- **Not so!** Unlike water that flows continuously in a water pipe, electrons can bunch up as they flow though a circuit.
- **Not so!** In a parallel circuit, the equivalent resistance of the circuit increases with the addition of more resistors.

Demonstration Equipment
- Fur, silk, rubber rod, glass or plastic rod, and suspended pith balls
- Electrophorus
- Electrostatic generator
- Batteries, bulbs, and connecting wires
- A 12-volt automobile battery with metal rods extended from the terminals with alligator clips used to fasten lamps between them (see the sketch below)

Here we begin with electrostatics, continue on to electric current, to series and parallel electric circuits, and end with electric power. There's easily enough material here for two or three more chapters. This is heavy stuff, so unless you're going to spend more than a week or so on this chapter, you may want to set your plow setting near the surface. The material in this chapter should be supported with lecture demonstrations.

For electrostatics, you'll want charging apparatus such as rubber and glass rods, silk and cat's fur or the equivalent, the electrophorus (a metal plate charged by induction that rests on a sheet of Plexiglas which has been charged with cat's fur, or equivalently, a pizza pan that rests on a charged phonograph record), and the Whimshurst machine (electrostatic generator). If you're equipment lucky, toss in demonstrations with a Van de Graaff generator.

For electric currents you simply must use an automobile storage battery with extended terminals as shown here. The extended terminals are simply a pair of rigid rods, welding rods or simply pieces of thick wire. They are easily inserted and removed if female connectors are permanently fastened into the battery terminals. Also fasten alligator clips to the ends of three short lengths of wire fastened to lamps of equal resistance. This is a MUST! It puts the **conceptual** in *Conceptual Physical Science*!

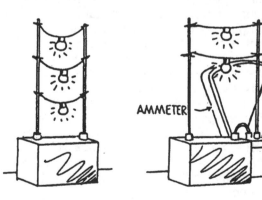

AMMETER

If you're into puns in your lectures on rainy days, Marshall Ellenstein has a few pictorial puns on the symbol for resistance that he and coworkers Connie Bownell and Nancy McClure came up with ("Ohmwork" or $\Omega F \times D$, *The Physics Teacher*, Sept 1991, page 347). A few are:

Answers in order are: Mobile Ohm; Ohm Run; Ohm Stretch; Ohm Sick; Ohmwork; Ohmless; Ohm on the Range; Broken Ohm.

In the **Practice Book**:
• Coulomb's Law
• Electric Pressure—Voltage
• Ohm's Law
• Electric Power
• Series Circuits
• Parallel Circuits

In the **Next-Time Questions** book:
• High-voltage Terminals
• Van de Graaff Generator
• Series Circuit
• Parallel Circuit

In the **Lab Manual**:
• Charge It (activity)
• Batteries and Bulbs (activity)
• Open and Short Case (activity)
• Be the Battery (activity)
• Logic Gates (activity)
• Three-Way Switch (activity)

Overhead Transparencies (2) available for:
Figures 11.7, 11.9, 11.12, 11.20, 11.21

The order of topics in the lecture sequence below departs somewhat from the order of topics in the chapter. The ideas of each demo flow nicely to the next. Have your lecture table set up with rods, pith balls, and charging demos at one end of the table, then an electrophorus, then a Whimshurst or whatever electrostatic machine, and possibly, the Van de Graaff generator. Then your lecture begins at one end of the table and proceeds in order to the opposite end. Begin with electrostatics in one lecture, and follow with electric currents and their circuits.

SUGGESTED PRESENTATION

Begin by comparing the strength of the electric force to gravitational force—billions of billions of times stronger. Acknowledge the fundamental rule of electricity: That *like charges repel and unlike charges attract*. Why? Nobody knows. Hence we say it is fundamental.

11.1 Electric Charge is a Basic Characteristic of Matter
Electrical effects have to do with electric charges, minus for the electron and plus for the proton. Discuss the near balance that exists in common materials, and the slight imbalance

when electrons transfer from one material to another. Different materials have different affinities for electrons, which explains why charge transfers from fur to rubber when rubbed. It also explains why it's painful for people with silver fillings in their teeth to chew aluminum spitballs. Silver has more affinity for acquiring electrons than aluminum. The mildly acidic saliva in your mouth facilitates a flow of electrons, which when transmitted to the nerves of your teeth produce that familiar unpleasant sensation. Discuss **charging**.

DEMONSTRATION: Bring out the cat's fur, rubber and glass rods, and suspended pith balls (or their alternatives). Explain the transfer of electrons when you rub fur against rubber rod (and silk against glass). Explain what it means to say an object is electrically charged, and discuss the **conservation of charge**.

11.2 Coulomb's Law—The Force Between Charged Particles
Call attention to the similarity and difference between Newton's law of gravitation and Coulomb's law.

11.3 Charge Polarization

DEMONSTRATION: Rub a balloon on your hair and show how it sticks to the wall. Draw a sketch on the board (Figure 11.6) and show in induction how the attracting charges are slightly closer than the repelling charges. Closeness wins and it sticks! (Induction will be treated in great detail in Chapter 23, *Chemical Bonding*.)

DEMONSTRATION: Show the effects of electrical force and polarization by holding a charged rod near the ends of a more-than-a-meter-long wooden 2 by 4, that balances and easily rotates sideways at its midpoint on a protrusion such as the bottom of a metal spoon. You can easily set the massive piece of wood in motion. This is quite impressive!

DEMONSTRATION: Charge the electrophorus, place the insulated metal disk on top of it, and show that the disk is not charged when removed and brought near a charged pith ball. Why should it be, for the insulating surface of the electrophorus has more grab on the electrons than the metal plate. But rest the plate on the electrophorus again and touch the top of the plate. You're grounding it (producing a conducting path to ground for the repelling electrons). Bring the plate near the pith ball and show that it is charged. Then show this by the flash of light produced when the charged metal plate is touched to the end of a gas discharge tube—or a fluorescent lamp. Engage neighbor discussion of the process demonstrated. Only after this is generally understood, proceed to the next demo.

DEMONSTRATION: Move up the lecture table to the Whimshurst machine, explaining its similarity to the electrophorus (actually a rotating electrophorus!). Show sparks jumping between the spheres of the machine and so forth, and discuss the sizes (radii of curvature) of the spheres in terms of their capacity for storing charge. [The amount of charge that can be stored before discharge into the air is directly proportional to the radius of the sphere.]

Fasten a metal point, which has a tiny radius of curvature and hence a tiny charge storing capacity, to one of the Whimshurst spheres and demonstrate the leakage of charge.

Under mutual repulsion, charges gather to the region of greatest curvature, the point. Although all parts of the needle are charged to the same electric voltage, the charge density is greatest at the point. The **electric field** intensity about the needle, on the other hand, is greatest about the point, usually great enough to ionize the surrounding air and provide a conducting path from the charge concentration. Hence charge readily gathers at points and readily leaks from points. DEMONSTRATE this leakage and the reaction force (ion propulsion) with a set of metal points arranged to rotate when charged. This is the "ion propulsion" that science fiction buffs talk about in space travel. Interestingly enough, this leaking of charge from points causes static with radio antennas; hence the small metal ball atop automobile antennas.

Discuss **lightning rods** and show how the bottoms of negatively charged clouds and the resulting induced positive charge on the surface of the Earth below arc similar to the electrophorus held upside down; where the charged Plexiglas plate is analogous to the clouds and the metal plate is analogous to the Earth. After sketching the charged clouds and Earth on the chalkboard, be sure to hold the inverted electrophorus pieces against your drawing on the board in their respective places. Discuss the lightning rod as a preventer of lightning while showing the similar function of the metal point attached to the Whimshurst machine. [Notice that one idea is related to the next in this sequence—very important, as the ideas of electricity are usually difficult to grasp the first time through. So be sure to take care in moving through this sequence of demonstrations and their explanations.]

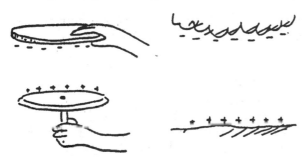

Benjamin Franklin's kite, by the way, was not struck by lightning. If it had, he would likely have not been around to report his experience. Franklin showed that the kite collected charges from the air during a thunderstorm. Hairs on the kite string stood apart, implying that lightning was a huge electric spark.

After establishing the idea that charge capacity depends on the size and curvature of the conductor being charged, advance to what your students have been waiting for: **The Van de Graaff generator** (for humor, invented by Robert Generator).

DEMONSTRATION: When showing the long sparks that jump from the dome of the generator to the smaller grounded sphere, do as Bruce Bernard suggests and hold a lightning rod (any sharp pointed conductor) in the vicinity of the dome and the sparking will stop. Bring the lightning rod farther away and the frequency of sparking will resume.

DEMONSTRATION: Set a cup of puffed rice or puffed wheat on top of the Van de Graaff generator. Your students will like the fountain that follows when you charge it. Or do as

Marshall Ellenstein does and place a stack of aluminum pie plates on the dome and watch them one by one levitate and fly away. Then snuff out a match by holding it near the charged dome. Introduce (or reintroduce) the idea of the **electric field** at this time, the aura of energy that surrounds all charged things. Compare electric and gravitational fields.

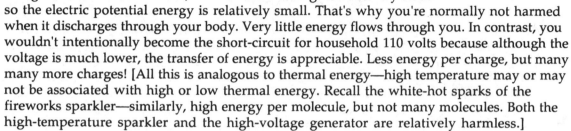

DEMONSTRATION: Hold a fluorescent lamp tube in the field to show that it lights up when one end of the tube is closer to the dome than the other end. Relate this to potential difference, and show that when both ends of the fluorescent tube are equidistant from the charged dome, light emission ceases. (This can be effected when your hand is a bit closer to the dome than the far end of the tube, so current does not flow through the tube when the dome discharges through you to the ground. There is no potential difference across the tube and therefore no illuminating current, which sets the groundwork for your next lecture on electric current.)

The Van de Graaff generator nicely illustrates the difference between **electric potential energy** and **electric voltage**: Although it is normally charged to thousands of volts, the amount of charge is relatively small so the electric potential energy is relatively small. That's why you're normally not harmed when it discharges through your body. Very little energy flows through you. In contrast, you wouldn't intentionally become the short-circuit for household 110 volts because although the voltage is much lower, the transfer of energy is appreciable. Less energy per charge, but many many more charges! [All this is analogous to thermal energy—high temperature may or may not be associated with high or low thermal energy. Recall the white-hot sparks of the fireworks sparkler—similarly, high energy per molecule, but not many molecules. Both the high-temperature sparkler and the high-voltage generator are relatively harmless.]

Your electrostatics lecture should end with the Van de Graaff demo and discussion of electric fields, potential energy, and potential. The following question is a bridge to your next lecture on electric currents.

NEXT-TIME QUESTION: Why does current flow when one end of the fluorescent tube is held closer to the charged Van de Graaff generator, but not when both ends are equidistant? [The simplified answer you're looking for at this point is that the close end is in a stronger part of the field than the far end. More energy per charge means more voltage at the near end. With a voltage difference across the tube, you get a current. When both ends are equidistant, there is no voltage difference across the tube, and no current. This leads into electric current. Strictly speaking, the current path is more

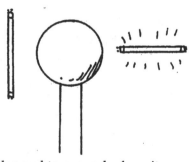

than simply between the ends of the tube; it goes through you also and to ground where it returns to the generator.]

11.4 Electric Current—The Flow of Electric Charge
Define electric current and relate it to the lighting of the lamp via the Van de Graaff generator from your previous lecture. Explain this in terms of current being directly proportional to a difference in voltage. That is, one end of the lamp was in a stronger part of the energy field than the other—more energy per charge on one end than the other—more voltage at one end than the other. Write on the board *Current ~ voltage difference*. (You're on your way to Ohm's law.)

11.5 An Electric Current is Produced by Electrical Pressure—Voltage

Relate voltage to the idea of electrical pressure. Emphasize that a *difference* in electric voltage must exist. Cite how a battery provides this difference in a sustained way compared to suddenly discharging a Van de Graaff generator. Generators at power plants also provide a voltage difference across wires that carry this difference to consumers. Cite examples of voltage differences in cases of birds sitting on bare high-voltage wires, walking unharmed on the third rail of electric-powered train tracks, and the inadvisability of using electric appliances in the bathtub.

11.6 Electrical Resistance

Introduce the idea of electrical resistance, and complete Ohm's law. Compare the resistances of various materials, and the resistances of various thickness of wires of the same metal. Call attention to the glass supports on the wires that make up high-voltage power lines; the rubber insulation that separates the pair of wires in a common lamp cord.

11.7 Ohm's Law—the Relationship between Current, Voltage, and Resistance

Complete your chalkboard equation by introducing resistance and you have Ohm's law.

> DEMONSTRATION: Connect two or three lamps to a battery and relate the current, as viewed by the emitted light, to the voltage of the battery and the resistance of the lamps. (Be sure the lamps are not bright enough to make viewing uncomfortable.) Interchange lamps of low and high resistance, relating this to the brightness of the lamps.

11.8 Electric Shock

Discuss electric shock and why electricians place one hand behind their back when probing questionable circuits [to prevent a difference in potential across the heart of the body]. Discuss how being electrified produces muscle contractions that account for such instances as "not being able to let go" of hot wires, and "being thrown" by electric shock.

Discuss the function of the **third prong on electric plugs** (that it provides a ground wire between the appliance and the ground). The ground prong is longer than the pair of flat prongs. Why? (So it will be first to be connected when plugging it into a socket, establishing a ground connection slightly before the appliance is electrically connected. This path to ground prevents harm to the user if there is a short circuit in the appliance that would otherwise include the user as a path to ground.)

11.9 Direct Current and Alternating Current

Discuss the differences between DC and AC. Compare the DC current that flows in a circuit powered with a battery to the AC current that flows in a household circuit (powered by a generator). A hydrodynamic analogy for AC is useful: Imagine powering a washing-machine agitator with water power. Verbally describe with gestures a pair of clear plastic pipes connected to a paddle wheel at the bottom of the agitator, fashioned so water that sloshes to-and-fro in the pipes causes the agitator to rotate to-and-fro. Suppose the free ends of the plastic pipe are connected to a special socket in the wall. The socket is powered by the power utility. It supplies no water, but consists of a couple of pistons that exert a pumping action, one out and the other in, then vice versa, in rapid alternation. When the ends of the pipe containing water are connected to the pistons, the water in the pipes is made to slosh back and forth: Power is delivered to the washing machine. There is an important point to note here: The **source** of flowing substance, water or electrons, is supplied by you. The power company supplies no water, just as the power utilities supply no electrons! The greater the load on the agitator, the more energy the power company must deliver to the action of the alternating pistons, affording a visual model for household current—especially with the transparent plastic pipes where your students can "see" the sloshing water!

Speed of Electrons in a Circuit

To impart the idea of how DC current travels in a circuit, use the following analogy. Ask the class to suppose that there is a long column of marchers at the front of the room, all standing at rest close together. Walk to the end of this imaginary column and give a shove to the "last person." Ask the class to imagine the resulting impulse traveling along the line until the first marcher is jostled against the wall. (Or use the analogy of loosely coupled railroad cars.) Then ask if this is a good analogy for how electricity travels in a wire. The answer is no. Such is a good analogy for how sound travels, but not electricity. Cite how slowly the disturbance traveled, and how slowly sound travels compared to light or electricity. Again call attention to the column of marchers and walk to the far end and call out, "Forward march!" As soon as the command reaches each individual, each steps forward. The marcher at the beginning of the column, except for the slight time required for the sound to reach her, steps immediately. State that this is an analogy for electricity. Except for the brief time it takes for the electric *field* set up at the power source to travel through the wire, nearly the speed of light, electrons at the far end of the circuit respond immediately. State that the speed at which the command "forward march" traveled is altogether different from how fast each marcher moved upon receiving that command—and that the velocity of the electric signal (nearly the speed of light) is quite a bit different than the drift velocity of electrons (typically 0.01 cm/s) in a circuit.

> CHECK YOUR NEIGHBOR: When turning the key to start a car, electrons migrate from the negative battery terminal through the electric network to the starter motor and back to the positive battery terminal. Estimate the time required for electrons to leave the negative terminal, go through the circuit, and return to the battery? Less than a millisecond? Less than a second? About a second or two? Or about a day? (Class interest should be high when you announce the latter answer!)

Ask for an estimate of the number of electrons pumped by the local power plant into the homes and industries locally in the past year. [Zero.] Stress the idea that power plants sell not electrons, but energy. Discuss the origin of electrons in electric circuits.

11.10 Electric Power—the Rate at of Doing Work

Distinguish between energy and power. Electric power is usually expressed in kilowatts, and electric energy in kilowatt-hours. It is effective if you use an actual electric bill to make your point. Note that a kilowatt-hour is 1000 joules per second times 3600 seconds, or 3600 kJ.

11.11 Electric Circuits—Series and Parallel

We recommend introducing series and parallel circuits using only equal resistances. Use small lamps of equal resistance connected to short wires with alligator clips at their ends for easy connection to the extended terminals of the auto battery described earlier. Three lamps are sufficient. Sketches are repeated for emphasis.

DEMONSTRATION: Connect the ends of one of the lamps directly to the battery terminals. It glows, evidence of current flow. Then insert the rods and repeat. It glows as before. Slide the lamp farther up the rods and its glow is the same. It is easily accepted that the 12-volt potential difference between the terminals is also established along and across the full length of the rods. State how the rods could extend across campus and someone far away could similarly light up a lamp. State how the resistance of the rods is very small compared to the resistance of the lamp filament. Compare the rods to a long lamp cord. Then to power lines from power plants to consumers. Take your time with these ideas, for they are central!

Series Circuits

DEMONSTRATION CONTINUED: Attach two lamps in series via alligator clips. Before connecting the double lamp circuit to the rods, ask for a neighbor check about the relative brightness of light. [Since the resistance is doubled, the current is halved and the brightness diminished—brightness is "less than half" because most of the energy is going to heat and not light. The effects of heat can be discerned for low currents when no light is seen.] Point out that the voltage across each lamp is 6 volts when connected in series. Repeat the process for three lamps in series, where three lamps share the 12 volts, and describe the reduced current in terms of Ohm's law. This is even more effective if you connect a lecture-size ammeter to your circuit.

Parallel Circuits

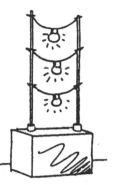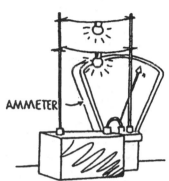

AMMETER

DEMONSTRATION CONTINUED: Now connect a pair of lamps in parallel. Before making the second connection, ask for a neighbor check about the relative brightnesses. It's easy to see that the voltage across each lamp is not reduced as with the series connection, but each is impressed with a full 12 volts. [Nearly a full 12 volts; line voltage diminishes with increased current through the battery—perhaps information overload at this stage of learning.] Repeat with three lamps after a neighbor check. Ask about the "equivalent resistance" of the circuit as more lamps are attached in parallel (or the equivalent resistance to people flow if more doors are introduced to the classroom). The lesser resistance is consistent with Ohm's law. An ammeter between one of the rods and the terminal shows line current, which is seen to increase as lamps are added. This is the simplest and most visually comprehensible demo of parallel circuits I have discovered. Neat?

CHECK YOUR NEIGHBOR: Consider two resistors to be connected in a circuit. Which will have more resistance, if they are connected in series or in parallel? [A series connection will have more resistance, regardless of the values of resistance; the equivalent resistance of a parallel connection will always be less than that of the smaller resistor.]

Home Circuits and Fuses. Discuss home lighting circuits. Draw a simple parallel circuit of lamps and appliances on the board. Estimate the current flowing through each device, and point out that it makes no difference how many of the other devices are turned on. Show on your diagram the currents in the branches and in the lead wires. Show where the fuse goes and describe its function. Then short your circuit and blow the fuse.

Overloading. Discuss the consequences of too many appliances operating on the same line, and why different sets of lines are directed to various parts of the home. Most home wiring is rated at 30 amperes maximum. A common air conditioner uses about 2400 watts, so if operating on 120 volts the current would be 20 amps. To start, the current is more. (Why the starting current is larger would be premature to explain here—if it comes up you can explain that every motor is also a generator, and the input electricity is met with a generated output that reduces the net current flow.) If other devices are drawing current on the same line, the fuse will blow when the air conditioner is turned on, so a 220-volt line is usually used for such heavy appliances. Point out that most of the world operates normally at 220 - 240 volts.

Chapter 11 Answers and Solutions

Key Terms and Matching Definitions

_10__ alternating current (ac)
__5__ ampere
__2__ coulomb
__1__ Coulomb's law
__9__ direct current (dc)
__4__ electric current
_11__ electric power
__7__ electrical resistance
__3__ electrically polarized
__8__ Ohm's law
_13__ parallel circuit
_12__ series circuit
__6__ voltage

Review Questions

1. Which part of an atom is *positively* charged and which part is *negatively* charged?
    Nucleus (with protons) is positive; electrons are negative.

2. How does the charge of one electron compare with that of another electron?
    Same.

3. How does the number of protons in the atomic nucleus normally compare with the number of electrons that orbit the nucleus?
    Same. (When the numbers don't match, we have an *ion*.)

4. What is meant by saying charge is *conserved*?
    That charge is rearranged and always there. It is not created or destroyed, similar to the way energy is conserved.

5. How is Coulomb's law similar to Newton's law of gravitation? How is it different?
    Similar in form, both an inverse-square law. Different in that there are attractive and repelling forces in Coulomb's law, but only attractive in Newton's law of gravitation.

6. How does an electrically *polarized* object differ from an electrically *charged* object?
    An electrically charged object has a net charge. An electrically polarized object is one with opposite charges concentrated at opposite ends, with no net charge. Charges are rearranged in a polarized object.

7. Why do electrons rather than protons make up the flow of charge in a metal wire?
    Protons are anchored in the nucleus. Electrons, at least the outermost ones in metals, are not strongly tied to atoms and can easily flow.

8. How much energy is given to each coulomb of charge passing through a 6-V battery?
    6 joules.

9. Does electric charge flow *across* a circuit or *through* a circuit? Does voltage *flow* across a circuit or is it *impressed* across a circuit? Explain.
    Charge flows through a circuit. Voltage is impressed across a circuit. Just as water flows through a pipe when a difference in pressure exists across its ends, charge flows in a circuit when a voltage difference exists across it.

10. Which has the greater resistance, a thick wire or a thin wire of the same length?
Thin wire has more resistance, like a thin pipe is to water flow.

11. When the voltage across the ends of a piece of wire is doubled, what effect does this have on the current in the wire?
Doubles.

12. When the resistance of a circuit is doubled, and no other changes occur, what effect does this have on the current in the circuit?
Halves.

13. What is the function of the third prong on the plug of an electric appliance?
To ground the appliance by conducting away unwanted current.

14. Distinguish between *dc* and *ac*.
AC is alternating current, where charges surge to-and-fro. DC is direct current, where charges flow in only one direction.

15. Does a battery produce *dc* or *ac*? Does the generator at a power station produce *dc* or *ac*?
Battery, dc. Generators, ac.

16. Which draws more current, a 40-W bulb or a 100-W bulb?
More current flows in the higher wattage bulb.

17. In a circuit consisting of two lamps connected in series, if the current through one lamp is 1 A, what is the current through the other lamp?
Same, 1 A.

18. In a circuit consisting of two lamps connected in parallel, if there is 6 V across one lamp, what is the voltage across the other lamp?
Same, 6 V.

19. How does the total current through the branches of a parallel circuit compare with the current through the voltage source?
Adds up to equal the current in the source.

20. Are household circuits normally wired in series or in parallel?
Parallel (if in series and one burns out, all go out!).

Solutions to Chapter 11 Exercises

1. When combing your hair, you transfer electrons from your hair onto the comb. Is your hair then positively or negatively charged? How about the comb?
Excess electrons rubbed from your hair leave it with a positive.

2. If electrons were positive and protons were negative, would Coulomb's law be written the same or differently?
The law would be written no differently.

3. The five thousand billion billion freely moving electrons in a penny repel one another. Why don't they fly out of the penny?
The electrons don't fly out of the penny because they are attracted to the five thousand billion billion positively charged protons in the atomic nuclei of atoms in the penny.

4. How does the magnitude of electrical force between a pair of charged objects change when the objects are moved twice as far apart? Three times as far apart?
By the inverse-square law, the force reduces to one-quarter when the particles are twice as far apart, and to one-ninth when three times as far apart.

5. How does the magnitude of electric force compare between a pair of charged particles when they are brought to half their original distance of separation? To one-quarter their original distance? To four times their original distance? (What law guides your answers?)

The inverse-square law plays a role here. At half the distance the electric force field is four times as strong; at 1/4 the distance, 16 times stronger. At four times the distance, one-sixteenth as strong.

6. Two equal charges exert equal forces on each other. What if one charge has twice the magnitude of the other. How do the forces they exert on each other compare?
    The forces they exert on each other are still the same! Newton's third law applies to electrical forces as well as all forces.

7. Why is a good conductor of electricity also a good conductor of heat?
    For both electricity and heat, the conduction is via electrons, which in a metal are loosely bound, easy flowing, and easy to get moving. (Many fewer electrons in metals take part in heat conduction than in electric conduction, however.)

8. What happens to the brightness of light emitted by a lamp when the current that flows in it increases?
    As the current in the filament of a light lamp increases, the lamp glows brighter.

9. Your tutor tells you that an *ampere* and a *volt* really measure the same thing, and the different terms only serve to make a simple concept seem confusing. Why should you consider getting a different tutor?
    Your tutor is incorrect. An ampere measures current, and a volt measures electric potential (electric pressure). They are entirely different concepts; voltage produces amperes in a conductor.

10. In which of the circuits below does a current exist to light the bulb?
    Only circuit number 5 is complete and will light the bulb. (Circuits 1 and 2 are "short circuits" and will quickly drain the cell of its energy. In circuit 3 both ends of the lamp filament are connected to the same terminal and are therefore at the same potential. Only one end of the lamp filament is connected to the cell in circuit 4.)

11. Does more current flow out of a battery than into it? Does more current flow into a light bulb than out of it? Explain.
    Current flows *through* electrical devices, just as water flows through a network of pipes. If a water pump produces water pressure, water flows through both the pump and the circuit. Likewise with electric current in an electric circuit. For example, in a simple circuit consisting of a battery and a lamp, the electric current that flows in the lamp is the same electric current that flows through the wires that connect the lamp and the same electric current that flows through the battery. Current flows through these devices. (As a side point, it is common to speak of electric current flowing in a circuit, but strictly speaking, it is electric *charge* that flows in an electric circuit; the flow of charge *is* current. So if you want to be grammatically correct, say that current *is* in a circuit and charge *flows* in a circuit.)

12. Only a small percentage of the electric energy going into a common light bulb is transformed into light. What happens to the rest?
    Most of the energy, typically 95%, of the electrical energy in an incandescent lamp goes directly to heat. Thermal energy is the graveyard of electrical energy.

13. Why are thick wires rather than thin wires usually used to carry large currents?
    Thick wires have less resistance and will more effectively carry currents without excessive heating.

14. What is the effect on current in a wire if both the voltage across it and its resistance are doubled? If both are halved?
    If both voltage and resistance are doubled, current remains unchanged. Likewise if both voltage and resistance are halved.

15. Will the current in a light bulb connected to a 220-V source be greater or less than when the same bulb is connected to a 110-V source?
    Current will be greater in the bulb connected to the 220-volt source. Twice the voltage would produce twice the current if the resistance of the filament remained the same. (In

practice, the greater current produces a higher temperature and greater resistance in the lamp filament, so the current is greater than that produced by 110 volts, but appreciably less than twice as much for 220 volts. A bulb rated for 110 volts has a very short life when operated at 220 volts.)

16. Which will do less damage—plugging a 110-V appliance into a 220-V circuit or plugging a 220-V appliance into a 110-V circuit? Explain.

Damage generally occurs by excess heating when too much current is driven through an appliance. For an appliance that converts electrical energy directly to thermal energy this happens when excess voltage is applied. So don't connect a 110-volt iron, toaster, or electric stove to a 220-volt circuit. Interestingly, if the appliance is an electric motor, then applying too *little* voltage can result in overheating and burn up the motor windings. (This is because the motor will spin at a low speed and the reverse "generator effect" will be small and allow too great a current to flow in the motor.) So don't hook up a 220-volt power saw or any 220-volt motor-driven appliance to 110 volts. To be safe use the recommended voltages with appliances of any kind.

17. The damaging effects of electric shock result from the amount of current that flows in the body. Why, then, do we see signs that read "Danger—High Voltage" rather than "Danger—High Current"?

The amount of current any device puts through any conductor depends upon the voltage of the device and the resistance of the conductor. Also important is the amount of charge the device can deliver; a relatively large amount of charge at high voltage represents high energy (like that from a power line) while a small amount of charge at high voltage represents low energy (like discharging a balloon rubbed on your hair). The device being warned about is likely highly energized to a high voltage, and should be respected. It possesses no current to be warned about, but because of its high energy and high voltage, may produce a lethal current in anyone offering a conducting path from it to the ground.

18. If several bulbs are connected in series to a battery, they may feel warm to the touch but not visibly glow. What is your explanation?

Most of the electric energy in a lamp filament is transformed to heat. For low currents in the bulb, the heat that is produced may be enough to feel but not enough to make the filament glow red or white hot.

19. In the circuit shown, how does the brightness of each identical light bulb compare? Which light bulb draws the most current? What will happen if bulb A is unscrewed? If C is unscrewed?

Bulb C is the brightest because the voltage across it equals that of the battery. Bulbs A and B share the voltage of the parallel branch of the circuit and have half the current of bulb C (assuming resistances are independent of voltages). If bulb A is unscrewed, the top branch is no longer part of the circuit and current ceases in both A and B. They no longer give light, while bulb C glows as before. If bulb C is instead unscrewed, then it goes out and bulbs A and B glow as before.

20. As more and more bulbs are connected in series to a flashlight battery, what happens to the brightness of each bulb? Assuming heating inside the battery is negligible, what happens to the brightness of each bulb when more and more bulbs are connected in parallel?

As more bulbs are connected in series, more resistance is added to the single circuit path and the resulting current produced by the battery is diminished. This is evident in the dimmer light from the bulbs. On the other hand, when more bulbs are connected to the battery in parallel, the brightness of the bulbs is practically unchanged. This is because each bulb in effect is connected directly to the battery with no other bulbs in its electrical path to add to its resistance. Each bulb has its own current path.

Solutions to Chapter 11 Problems

1. Two point charges are separated by 6 cm. The attractive force between them is 20 N. Find the force between them when they are separated by 12 cm. (Why can you solve this problem without knowing the magnitudes of the charges?)
    By the inverse-square law, $F \sim 1/2^2$, twice as far is 1/4 the force; 5 N.
    The solution involves relative distance only, so the magnitude of charges is irrelevant.

2. Make use of Coulomb's law here. Suppose you have a pair of electrically charged metal spheres suspended from insulating threads, a certain distance from each other. There is a specific amount of electrical force between them.

    a. If the charge on one sphere were doubled, what would happen to the force between them?
    $1 \cdot 2/1^2 = 2$, so the force would be double.

    b. If the charge on *both* spheres were doubled, what would happen to the force between them?
    $2 \cdot 2/1^2 = 4$ so the force would be quadrupled.

    c. If the distance between the spheres were tripled, what would happen to the force between them?
    $1 \cdot 1/3^2 = 1/9$ so the force would be 1/9 the original value.

    d. If the distance between them were reduced to one-fourth the original distance, what would happen to the force between them?
    $1 \cdot 1/(1/4)^2 = 16$ so the force would be 16 times the original value.

    e. If the charge on each sphere was doubled and the distance between them were doubled, what would happen to the force between them?
    $2 \cdot 2/2^2 = 1$ so there would be no change in force.

3. The unit of charge is the coulomb (C). The charge on an electron is 1.6×10^{-19} C. How many electrons make a charge of 1 C?
    $1 C/1.6 \times 10^{-19}$ C per electron $= 6.25 \times 10^{18}$ electrons.

4. A flow of charge of 1.0 C/s is called one *ampere* (1.0 A). How many electrons per second must pass a given point in order to have a current of 2.0 A?
    Twice the number of the previous problem per second; $2(1.6 \times 10^{-19} C) = 3.2 \times 10^{-19}$ C per second.

5. How much current flows through a radio speaker that has a resistance of 8 Ω when 12 V is impressed across the speaker?
    1.5 A.

6. If 6 V is impressed across the above circuit and the voltage across the first lamp is 2 V, what is the voltage across the second lamp?
    4 V. (Sum of voltage in series = total voltage.)

7. Rearrange the equation Current = voltage/resistance to express *resistance* in terms of current and voltage. Then solve the following: A certain device in a 120-V circuit has a current rating of 20 A. What is the resistance of the device (how many ohms)?
    From current $= \dfrac{\text{voltage}}{\text{resistance}}$, resistance $= \dfrac{\text{voltage}}{\text{current}} = \dfrac{120V}{20A} = 6 \, \Omega$

8. What is the effect on current through a circuit of steady resistance when the voltage is doubled? What if both voltage and resistance are doubled?
    Doubled also. If voltage and resistance are doubled, then no change.

9. Using the definition of power (current × voltage), how much current flows in a 6-watt clock radio that operates in a common household?
    From Power = current × voltage, current = Power/voltage = 6 W/120 V = 0.05 A. Note that this problem re-expresses the Concept Check in Section 11.10.

12 Magnetism

Conceptual Physical Science—Explorations

Magnetic Therapy

Learning Objectives
After studying Chapter 12, students will be able to:
- Describe the differences and similarities between magnetic poles and electric charges.
- Interpret the strength of a magnetic field at different points near a magnet by using the pattern formed by iron filings.
- Describe what happens to the magnetic domains of iron in the presence of a strong magnet.
- Explain why magnets lose their magnetism when dropped or heated.
- Describe the magnetic field produced by a current-carrying wire and give examples of how the field can be made stronger.
- Describe the conditions necessary for a magnetic field to exert a force on a charged particle in the field.
- Cite some practical applications of a magnetic field exerting a force on a current-carrying wire.
- Suggest possible causes for the Earth's magnetic field.
- Describe how voltage is induced in a coil of wire.
- Relate the induced voltage in a coil to the number of loops in the coil and the rate of change of external magnetic field intensity through the loops.
- Describe a generator and explain how it works.
- Compare and contrast the motor effect and generator effect.
- Relate the magnitude and direction of an induced electric field to the inducing magnetic field.
- Relate the magnitude and direction of an induced magnetic field to the inducing electric field.
- Explain how the electric and magnetic fields of an electromagnetic wave regenerate each other so that the wave pattern moves outward.

Possible Misconceptions to Correct
- **Not so!** Magnetic poles move in iron in the same way as electrons move in electrical conductors.
- **Not so!** The direction of a magnetic field is in straight lines about magnetic poles.
- **Not so!** The magnetic force on charged particles is in a direction along the magnetic field (rather than perpendicular to the field).
- **Not so!** A magnetic field can increase the speed of a charged particle (rather than only deflect it).
- **Not so!** Voltage is produced by a magnet, rather than by the work done when a magnet and closed loops of wire are moved relative to each other.
- **Not so!** A generator and a motor are fundamentally different devices.

Demonstration Equipment
- Iron filings, magnet and transparent plastic
- Compass and wire that carries DC current
- DC current-carrying wire and a horseshoe magnet
- Galvanometer, loop of wire and horseshoe magnet
- Demonstration motor-generator device
- Hand-cranked generators and lamps to light them with

Like the previous chapter, this is a meaty chapter and could easily be two chapters. It focuses on the important features of simple magnets and electromagnetic induction, and avoids such complications as the distinctions between ferro and paramagnetism, reactances, back emf, Lenz's law, and the left and right hand rules that normally serve to overwhelm your students. An important function of the chapter is to implant the idea of transferring energy from one place to another without means of physical contact. The chapter should be supported with various lecture demonstrations of electromagnetic induction, such as those in the figures of the chapter.

Make iron-filing permanent displays by spraying water on iron filings on a paper atop a magnet. The rust stains will leave a permanent impression of the magnetic field. (This idea is from Matt Keller.)

See the interesting article in *The Physics Teacher*, March 2002, by Howie Brand, *"Forces Acting at a Distance—A Demonstration of Newton's Third Law."* When a magnet is dropped in a vertical copper pipe, the magnetic force preventing it from accelerating is registered on a scale that supports the pipe.

American Journal of Physics former editor Robert Romer of Amherst College reports his fascination with a compass on subways (*The Physics Teacher*, February1993). Rather than simply pointing north, the compass dances erratically in response to the strong DC that varies as the cars maneuver. Magnetic fields some 20 times larger than the Earth's are produced by DC in the wires, and the 600-V third rail that carries current—often in excess of 5000 A. Changes in field direction are noted when the cars brake by using motors as generators, feeding energy back into the third rail. If your students ride subway or other electric cars, urge them to note the effects of the currents on small hand-held compasses!

This chapter serves as a background for the study of light.

In the **Practice Book:**
- Magnetism
- Faraday's Law

In the **Next-Time Questions** book:
- Tack and Magnet
- Trick Magnet
- Wire in Magnetic Field
- Induction

In the **Lab Manual:**
- Magnetic Personalities (activity)

Overhead Transparencies (2) available for:
Figures 12.15, 12.17, and 12.21, 12.26

SUGGESTED PRESENTATION

Begin by holding a magnet above some nails or paper clips on your lecture table. State that the nails or clips are flat on the table because every particle of matter in the entire world is gravitationally pulling them against the table. Then show that your magnet out pulls the whole world and lifts the nails or clips off the table.

Show that iron is not the only ferromagnetic substance. Certain Canadian nickels and quarters (1968 to 1981 which are pure nickel) are easily attracted to a magnet. The United States 5 cent piece is no longer pure nickel, is 75% copper, and won't respond to a magnet.

12.1 Magnetic Poles—Attraction and Repulsion
Show how a bar magnet affects a large lecture compass and discuss magnetic poles. Similar to the fundamental rule of electricity, *like poles repel and opposite poles attract.*

12.2 Magnetic Fields—Regions of Magnetic Influence
Show field configurations about bar magnets, as per Figure 12.3. For a large class, use an overhead projector and iron filings. Simply lay a magnet on the glass surface of the projector and cover it with a sheet of plastic, and sprinkle iron filings over the plastic.

12.3 Magnetic Domains—Clusters of Aligned Atoms
Acknowledge the alignment of magnetic domains in the magnet material.

Magnetic Induction
Explain magnetic induction, and show how bringing a nonmagnetized nail near a magnet induces it to become a magnet and be attracted. Then contrast this with an aluminum rod—discuss unpaired electron spins and magnetic domains. Stress the similarities of electrically inducing charge polarization and magnetically inducing the alignment of magnetic domains.

12.4 The Interaction Between Electric Currents and Magnetic Fields
Discuss the source of magnetism—the motion of charges (Figure 12.6 in the text). All magnetism begins with a moving electric charge: In the spin of the electron about its own axis (like a top), in the revolution about the nuclear axis, and as it drifts as part of an electric current.

DEMONSTRATION: Place a lecture compass near a wire and show the deflection when current is passed through the wire.

The magnetic field is actually a relativistic "side effect" or "distortion" in the electric field of a moving charge. (Einstein's paper on special relativity, after all, was entitled, *On the Dynamics of Moving Charges*.)

Side point: When the magnetic field about a current-carrying wire is undesirable, double wires are used, with the return wire adjacent to the wire. Then the net current for the double wire is zero, and no magnetic field surrounds it. Wires are often braided to combat slight fields where the cancellation is not perfect.

Electromagnets
Call attention to the circular shape of the magnetic field about a current-carrying wire (Figures 12.10, 12.11 and the photos of field lines of Figure 12.12). It's easy to see how the magnetic field is bunched up in a loop of current-carrying wire, and then in a coil of many loops. Then place a piece of iron in the coil and the added effect of aligned domains in the iron produces an electromagnet.

DEMONSTRATION: Make a simple electromagnet in front of your class. Simply wind wire around a spike and pick up paper clips when you place a current through the wire. Mimic the operation of a junk yard magnet, where the clips are dropped when the current is turned off.

DEMONSTRATION: Show your department's electromagnets, and your superconducting electromagnets!

If you have an electromagnetic levitator, discuss the train application when you are fascinating your students with its demonstration. The idea of a **magnetically-levitated train** was described in 1909 by Robert Goddard, an American better known for inventing the liquid-fueled rocket. Although Europe and Japan now have the lead in this field, the first modern design for a maglev train comes from Americans, nuclear-engineer James R. Powell, and particle-acceleration physicist Gordon T. Danby. They were awarded a patent in 1968 for their design.

Whatever the present variations in design, once the train is levitated there is no mechanical friction to contend with, so only modest force is needed to accelerate it. Fixed electromagnets along the guideway alternately pull and push by switching polarity whenever one of the train's propulsion magnets passes it. The phased switching is timed by computers under the control of the driver to accelerate or decelerate the train, or simply keep it moving. Various designs have the overall result of propelling the train like a surfboard riding a wave. Speculation by co-inventor Danby is that future travel in partially evacuated tubes will permit cross-country passage in about an hour. Maglev trains may play a large role in transportation in this new century.

12.5 Magnetic Forces are Exerted on Moving Charges

DEMONSTRATION: Show how a magnet distorts the electron beam of an oscilloscope or TV picture. Stress the role of motion.

Discuss the motion of a charged particle injected into a magnetic field perpendicularly, and explain how it will follow a circle. The perpendicular push is a centripetal force that acts along the radius of its path. (This is what underlies cyclotrons and bevatrons with radii ranging from less than a meter to more than a kilometer.)

Magnetic Force on Current-Carrying Wires
Simple logic tells you that if forces act on electrons that move through a magnetic field, then forces act on electrons traveling through a wire in a magnetic field.

DEMONSTRATION: Show how a wire jumps out of (or into) a magnet when current is passed through the wire (Figure 12.17). Reverse current (or turn wire around) to show both cases.

If you have a large lecture galvanometer, show your class the coil of wire that is suspended in the magnetic field of the permanent magnet (Figure 12.19). The same is found in ammeters and voltmeters. Now you are ready to extend this idea to the electric motor.

DEMONSTRATION: Show the operation of a DC demonstration motor.

Earth's Magnetic Field
Discuss the field configuration about the Earth and how cosmic rays are deflected by the magnetic field lines. In discussing pole reversals, add that the magnetic field of the sun undergoes reversals about every eleven years.

Biomagnetism
Acquaint yourself with the latest findings regarding magnetic field sensing by living things. Bacteria, bees, and pigeons are mentioned briefly in the text. The list grows with new findings.

Magnetic Resonance Imaging (MRI)
As a side topic not treated in the text you might discuss what used to be called NMR—nuclear magnetic resonance—the now widely used application in medicine; particularly as a method of cancer detection. An external alternating magnetic field is applied to the part of the body of a patient to be examined. Slight differences in the natural frequencies of magnetic quadrapole moments of atomic nuclei, commonly protons, due to the environment of neighboring atoms are detected by a "magnetic echo." The resonant signals from the nuclei of atoms in living cells

differ slightly for cancerous tissue and is picked up by a sensitive magnetometer. Why the name change from NMR to MRI? The word *nuclear*, honey! It's simply out with the public, who are phobic about anything with the dreaded word nuclear. Another reason for conceptual physical science for the common student!

12.6 Electromagnetic Induction—How Voltage is Created

Up to this point you have discussed how one can begin with electricity and produce magnetism. The question was raised in the first half of the 1800s; can it be the other way around—can one begin with magnetism and produce electricity? Indeed it can, enough to light entire cities with electric lighting! Now you produce your galvanometer, magnet, and wire loop—conspicuously well away from your previous electric power source.

> DEMONSTRATION: Plunge a magnet in and out of a single coil, as in Figure 12.22, and show with a galvanometer the current produced. This is nice with a large lecture demonstration galvanometer.

This need not be mysterious, for it follows from the deviations of electrons in a magnetic field. Invoke the argument shown previously in Figure 12.15. [Electrons are moved across the magnetic field lines when you push the wire downward, and they experience a sideways force. This time there *is* a path for them and they move along the wire.] Then repeat with the wire bent into two coils—twice the effect. Many coils (Figure 12.24), many times more current.

> DEMONSTRATION: Drop a small bar magnet through a vertically held copper or aluminum pipe. It will take appreciably longer to drop through than an unmagnetized piece of iron (which you show first). The explanation is that the falling magnet constitutes a changing magnetic field in the metal pipe. It induces a voltage and hence a current flow in the conducting pipe. The magnetic field set up by the current loops repel the falling magnet and account for its slow fall. Electromagnetic induction! [The magnetic field so induced opposes the change in the original field—Lenz's law. If the induced field enhanced the change in the original field, the falling magnet would be attracted rather than repelled and increase in its acceleration and gain more KE than its decrease in PE. A conservation of energy no-no!] (This demo is a kit available from Pasco Scientific Co.)

Faraday's Law

We have seen that charges moving in a magnetic field experience forces. In the last chapter, the force deviated the direction of electrons, both in a free beam and traveling along a wire, in which case the wire was deviated. Now we see that if we push electrons that are in a wire into a magnetic field, the deviating force will be along the direction of the wire and current is induced. Another way to look at this is to say that *voltage* is being induced in the wire. The current then, is an outcome of that voltage. Faraday states that the voltage induced in a closed loop equals the time rate of change of the magnetic field in that loop. Another way of looking at induction. So rather than saying current is induced, Faraday says voltage is induced, which produces current.

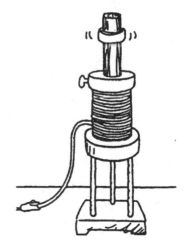

> DEMONSTRATION: Show the various demonstrations with the classical Elihu Thompson Electromagnetic Demonstration Apparatus—With the power on, levitate an aluminum ring over the extended pole of the Elihu Thompson device.

CHECK YOUR NEIGHBOR: Do you know enough physics to state how much electromagnetic force supports this 1-newton aluminum ring (assuming the ring weighs 1 N)? [Answer: 1 N, not particularly from a knowledge of electromagnetic forces, but from a knowledge about forces in general that go back to Newton's laws. Since the ring is at rest and not accelerating, the upward electromagnetic force (in newtons!) must be equal to the downward force of gravity.]

DEMONSTRATION: With the power off, place the ring at the base of the extended pole. When you switch on the power the current induced in the ring via electromagnetic induction converts the ring into an AC electromagnet. (By Lenz's law, not developed in the text, the polarity of the induced magnet is always such to oppose the magnetic field imposed.)

CHECK YOUR NEIGHBOR: Do you know enough physics to state whether or not the electromagnetic force that popped the ring was more, equal to, or less than the magnetic force that produced levitation earlier? [Answer: More, because it accelerated upward, evidence the upward force was more than the weight. This is also understandable because the ring was lower and intercepting more changing magnetic field lines.]

Emphasize the importance of this discovery by Faraday and Henry, and how its application transformed the world. Isn't it difficult to imagine having no electric lights—to live in a time when illumination after the sun goes down is by candles and whale-oil lamps? Not so long ago, really. In our older cities many buildings still have pre-electric light fixtures: gas and oil lamps.

State that underlying all the things discussed and observed is something more basic than voltages and currents—the induction of *fields*, both electric and magnetic. And because this is true we can send signals without wires—radio and TV—and furthermore, energy reaches us from the sun, sunlight.

12.7 Generators and Alternating Current
Point out that strictly speaking generators do not generate electricity—nor do batteries. What they do is pump a fluid composed of electrons. As stressed in the previous chapter, they don't make the electrons they pump. The electron fluid is in the conducting wires.

DEMONSTRATION: Return to the motor demo and show that when you reverse the roles of input and output, and apply mechanical energy, it becomes a generator. Light a bulb with the hand-cranked generator and show how the turning is easier when the bulb is loosened and the load removed. Allow students to try this themselves during or at the end of class.

Compare motor and generator—in principle the same. When electric energy is put in it converts it to mechanical energy—motor. When mechanical energy is put in it converts it to electrical energy—generator. In fact, a motor acts also as a generator and creates a "back voltage" [back emf] and an opposing current. The net current in a motor is the input current minus the generated back current. The net current in a power saw will not cause its overheating and damage to its motor windings—so long as it is running and generating a back current that keeps the net current low. But if you should jam the saw so that it can't spin, without the back current generated by the spinning armature, the net current is dangerously high and can burn out the motor.

It is interesting that electric motors are used in diesel-powered railroad engines. The combustion engine cannot bring a heavy load from rest, but an electric motor can. Why? Because when the armature is not turning, the current in the windings is huge, with a corresponding huge force. As both the train and the motor gain speed, the back current generated by the motor brings the net current in the motor down to nonoverheating levels.

Stress the fact that we don't get something for nothing with electromagnetic induction, and acknowledge Figure 12.25. This can be readily felt when lamps powered with a hand-cranked or a bicycle generator are switched on. Each student should experience this. The conservation of energy reigns!

12.8 Power Production—a Technological Extension of Electromagnetic Induction
Continue with a historical theme: With the advent of the generator the task was to design methods of moving coils of wire past magnetic fields, or moving magnetic fields past coils of wire. Placing turbines beneath waterfalls, and boiling water to make steam to squirt against turbine blades and keep them turning—enter the industrial revolution.

12.9 The Induction of Fields—Both Electric and Magnetic

Point to the similarity of the field induction laws of Faraday and Maxwell—how a change in either field induces the other. This concept led Einstein to the development of his special theory of relativity. Einstein showed that a magnetic field appears when a purely electric field is seen by a moving observer, and an electric field appears when a purely magnetic field is seen from a moving vantage point.

Because of the electric and magnetic induction of fields in free space we can "telegraph" signals without wires—hence radio and TV—and furthermore, we shall see that because of field induction, there is light.

Chapter 12 Answers and Solutions

Key Terms and Matching Definitions

__4__ electromagnet
__7__ electromagnetic induction
__6__ Faraday's law
__8__ generator
__3__ magnetic domains
__2__ magnetic field
__1__ magnetic force
__9__ Maxwell's counterpart to Faraday's law
__5__ motor

Review Questions

1. In what way is the rule for the interaction between magnetic poles similar to the rule for the interaction between electric charges?
   Just as like charges repel and unlikes attract, like poles repel and unlikes attract.

2. In what way are *magnetic poles very* different from *electric charges*?
   Magnetic poles come in pairs (like heads and tails of a coin), whereas electric charges can occur by themselves in isolation.

3. An electric field surrounds an electric charge. What additional field surrounds a moving electric charge?
   Magnetic field.

4. What two kinds of motion are exhibited by electrons in an atom?
   Spinning (like a top) and revolving (like an orbiting planet).

5. Why are some pieces of iron magnets and others not?
   Magnets are the pieces of iron with aligned domains. Unmagnetized pieces of iron have domains that are not aligned.

6. Why will dropping an iron magnet on a hard floor make it a weaker magnet?
   Sudden changes in motion can jostle atoms out of alignment.

7. What is the shape of magnetic field lines about a current-carrying wire?
   Magnetic lines take the shape of concentric circles about the wire.

8. What happens to the direction of the magnetic field about an electric current when the direction of the current is reversed?
   Direction reverses also.

9. In what direction relative to a magnetic field does a charged particle move in order to experience maximum deflecting force? Minimum deflecting force?
   Maximum force occurs when motion is perpendicular to the field. No force occurs when charged particles move parallel to field lines.

10. Both gravitational and electrical forces act along the direction of the force fields. How is the direction of the magnetic force on a moving charge different?
    Magnetic force acts perpendicular to field lines. Gravitational forces act along field lines.

11. Since a magnetic force acts on a moving charged particle, does it make sense that a magnetic force also acts on a current-carrying wire? Defend your answer.
    Yes, of course. If it acts on single charges, it acts on many moving charges.

12. What happens to the direction of the force on a wire when the current in it is reversed?

Direction of force reverses also.

13. What is a galvanometer called when calibrated to read current? Voltage?
Ammeter; voltmeter.

14. What must change in order for electromagnetic induction to occur?
Changes in magnetic-field strength.

15. What are the three ways that voltage can be induced in a wire?
By moving a loop of wire near a magnet; by moving a magnet near a loop of wire, or by changing the current in the wire.

16. What is the basic difference between a generator and an electric motor?
Generator converts mechanical energy to electrical energy; a motor converts electrical energy to mechanical energy.

17. What is the basic similarity between a generator and an electric motor?
Both are geometrically the same. Only the roles of input and output make them different.

18. What commonly supplies the energy input to a turbine?
A moving fluid, often steam or flowing water.

19. What is induced by the rapid alternation of a magnetic field?
An electric field.

20. What is induced by the rapid alternation of an electric field?
A magnetic field.

Solutions to Chapter 12 Exercises

1. Since every iron atom is a tiny magnet, why aren't all iron materials themselves magnets?
All iron materials are not magnetized because the tiny magnetic domains are most often oriented in random directions and cancel one another's effects.

2. What is different about the magnetic poles of common refrigerator magnets compared with common bar magnets?
Refrigerator magnets have narrow strips of alternating north and south poles. These magnets are strong enough to hold sheets of paper against a refrigerator door, but have a very short range because the north and south poles cancel a short distance from the magnetic surface.

3. What surrounds a stationary electric charge? A moving electric charge?
An electric field surrounds a stationary electric charge. An electric field and a magnetic field surround a moving electric charge. (And a gravitational field also surrounds both.)

4. An electron always experiences a force in an electric field, but not always in a magnetic field." Defend this statement.
An electron always experiences a force in an electric field because that force depends on nothing more than the field strength and the charge. But the force an electron experiences in a magnetic field depends on an added factor: velocity. If there is no motion of the electron through the magnetic field in which it is located, no magnetic force acts. Furthermore, if motion is along the magnetic field direction, and not at some angle to it, then no magnetic force acts also. Magnetic force, unlike electric force, depends on the velocity of the charge relative to the magnetic field.

5. Why will a magnet attract an ordinary nail or paper clip, but not a wooden pencil?
A magnet will induce the magnetic domains of a nail or paper clip into alignment. Opposite poles in the magnet and the iron object are then closest to each other and

attraction results. (This is similar to a charged comb attracting bits of electrically neutral paper.) A wooden pencil, on the other hand, does not have magnetic domains that will interact with a magnet.

6. A friend tells you that a refrigerator door, beneath its layer of white painted plastic, is made of aluminum. How could you check to see if this is true (without any scraping)?
Apply a small magnet to the door. If it sticks, your friend is wrong because aluminum is not magnetic. If it doesn't stick, your friend might be right (but not necessarily—there are lots of nonmagnetic materials).

7. Why will a magnet placed in front of a television picture tube distort the picture? (*Note:* Do NOT try this with a set that you value. You may magnetize the metal mask in back of the glass screen and have picture distortion even when the magnet is removed!)
Moving electrons are deflected from their paths by a magnetic field. A magnet held in front of a TV picture deflects the electron beam from its intended path and distorts the picture.

8. Magnet A has twice the magnetic field strength of magnet B (at equal distance) and at a certain distance pulls on magnet B with a force of 50 N. With how much force, then, does magnet B pull on magnet A?
Back to Newton's 3rd law! Both A and B are equally pulling on each other. If A pulls on B with 50 newtons, then B also pulls on A with 50 newtons. Period!

9. A strong magnet attracts a paper clip to itself with a certain force. Does the paper clip exert a force on the strong magnet? If not, why not? If so, does it exert as much force on the magnet as the magnet exerts on it? Defend your answers.
Newton's 3rd law again: Yes, the paper clip, as part of the interaction, certainly does exert a force on the magnet—just as much as the magnet pulls on it. The magnet and paper clip pull equally on each other to comprise the single interaction between them.

10. A common pickup for an electric guitar consists of a coil of wire around a small permanent magnet. The magnetic field of the magnet induces magnetic poles in the nearby guitar string. When the string is plucked, the rhythmic oscillations of the string produce the same rhythmic changes in the magnetic field through the coil, which in turn induce the same rhythmic voltages in the coil, which when amplified and sent to a speaker produce music! Why will this type pickup not work with nylon strings?
Magnetic induction will not occur in nylon, since it has no magnetic domains. That's why electric guitars use steel strings.

11. Why is a generator armature harder to rotate when it is connected to a circuit and supplying electric current?
Work must be done to move a current-carrying conductor in a magnetic field. This is true whether or not the current is externally produced or produced as a result of the induction that accompanies the motion of the wire in the field. It's also a matter of energy conservation. There has to be more energy input if there is more energy output.

12. If your metal car moves over a wide, closed loop of wire embedded in a road surface, will the magnetic field of the Earth within the loop be altered? Will this produce a current pulse? Can you think of a practical application for this at a traffic intersection?
Part of the Earth's magnetic field is enclosed in the wide loop of wire imbedded in the road. If this enclosed field is somehow changed, then in accord with the law of electromagnetic induction, a pulse of current will be produced in the loop. Such a change is produced when the iron parts of a car pass over it, momentarily increasing the strength of the field. A practical application is triggering automobile traffic lights. (When small ac voltages are used in such loops, small "eddy currents" are induced in metal of any kind that passes over the loop. The magnetic fields so induced are then detected by the circuit.)

13. At the security area of an airport, you walk through a weak ac magnetic field inside a coil of wire. What is the result of a small piece of metal on your person that slightly alters the magnetic field in the coil?

As in the previous answer, eddy currents induced in the metal change the magnetic field, which in turn changes the ac current in the coils and sets off an alarm.

14. A piece of plastic tape coated with iron oxide is magnetized more in some parts than in others. When the tape is moved past a small coil of wire, what happens in the coil? What is a practical application of this?
The changing magnetic field of the moving tape induces a voltage in the coil. A practical application is a tape recorder.

15. Joseph Henry's wife tearfully sacrificed part of her wedding gown for silk to cover the wires of Joseph's electromagnets. What was the purpose of the silk covering?
Copper wires were not insulated in Henry's time. A coil of noninsulated wires touching one another would comprise a short circuit. Silk was used to insulate the wires so current would flow along the wires in the coil rather than across the loops touching one another.

16. What is the primary difference between an electric *motor* and an electric *generator*?
There is no fundamental difference between an electric motor and electric generator. When mechanical energy is put into the device and electricity is produced, we call it a generator. When electrical energy is put in and it spins and does mechanical work, we call it a motor. (While there are usually some practical differences in the designs of motors and generators, some devices are designed to operate either as motors or generators, depending only on whether the input is mechanical or electrical.)

17. Your friend says that if you crank the shaft of a dc motor manually, the motor becomes a dc generator. Do you agree or disagree?
Agree with your friend. Any coil of wire spinning in a magnetic field that cuts through magnetic field lines is a generator.

18. A length of wire is bent into a closed loop and a magnet is plunged into it, inducing a voltage and, consequently, a current in the wire. A second length of wire, twice as long, is bent into two loops of wire and a magnet is similarly plunged into it. Twice the voltage is induced, but the current is the same as that produced in the single loop. Why?
Since all the electric resistance in this case is merely that of the wire itself (no other external load), twice the wire length means twice the resistance. So although twice the number of loops means twice the voltage, twice-as-much resistance results in the same current.

19. Two separate but similar coils of wire are mounted close to each other, as shown below. The first coil is connected to a battery. The second coil is connected to a galvanometer. How does the galvanometer respond when the switch in the first circuit is closed? After being closed when the current is steady? When the switch is opened?
Induction occurs only for a *change* in the intercepted magnetic field. The galvanometer will display a pulse when the switch in the first circuit is closed and current in the coil increases from zero. When the current in the first coil is steady, no current is induced in the secondary and the galvanometer reads zero. The galvanometer needle will swing in the opposite direction when the switch is opened and current falls to zero.

20. A friend says that changing electric and magnetic fields generate one another, and this gives rise to visible light when the frequency of change matches the frequencies of light. Do you agree? Explain.
Agree with your friend, for light is electromagnetic radiation having a frequency that matches the frequency to which our eyes are sensitive.

13 Waves and Sound

Learning Objectives
After studying Chapter 13, students will be able to:
• Relate the pitch of a sound to its frequency.
• Describe what happens to air when sound moves through it.
• Compare the transmission of sound through air with its transmission through solids, liquids, and a vacuum.
• Describe factors that affect the speed of sound.
• Give examples of forced vibrations.
• Describe the conditions for resonance.
• Describe the conditions for beats.

Possible Misconceptions to Correct
• **Not so!** The speed of sound is the same in all media.
• **Not so!** Combinations of waves can be added but not cancelled.
• **Not so!** Changes in wave speed, rather than changes in wave frequency, produce the Doppler effect.
• **Not so!** Resonance is another word for forced vibrations.
• **Not so!** Wave speed and wave frequency are the same thing.
• **Not so!** When a wave moves in a medium, the medium moves with it.
• **Not so!** A sonic boom is a momentary burst of high pressure produced when something exceeds the speed of sound, rather than being a continuous front of high pressure generated by faster-than-sound sources.

Demonstration Equipment
• Simple pendulum and meterstick
• Slinky or loose coil of wire
• Large tuning fork and container of water
• Large bare loudspeaker and power source
• Pair of matched tuning forks to show resonance
• Stereo tape player with mono mode, matching speakers, and switch or jacks to reverse the polarity of one of the speakers

Some instructors begin the study of the physics part of physical science with waves, vibrations, and sound—topics that have greater appeal to many students than mechanics. Your course could begin here, and you could pick up mechanics later. A useful feature of the text is that for a large part, chapters can stand alone.

This chapter lends itself to interesting whatever lecture demonstrations you can muster from the list above.

Forced vibrations, resonance, and interference provide a very useful background for the same concepts applied to light in the following two chapters.

In the **Practice Book**:
• Vibrations and Waves
• Sound
• Shock Waves

In the **Next-Time Questions** book:
• Standing Wave
• Radio Waves
• Concert and the Speed of Sound
• Shock Waves

In the **Lab Manual**:
• Slow-Motion Wobbler
• Sound Off

Overhead Transparencies (2) available for:
Figures 13.1, 13.6, 13.8, and Figures 13.13, 13.20.

Recommended reading: *The Physics of Musical Instruments*, reviewed in *Physics Today*, December 1991, p 75, and an article, *The Acoustics of Drums*, in *Physics Today*, March 1992, pp 40-47, reviewed in *Science*, June 21, 1991, pp 1728-9, both by Neville H. Fletcher and Thomas D. Rossing. It is well known that Richard Feynman loved drums.

SUGGESTED PRESENTATION

13.1 Special Wiggles—Vibrations and Waves
Demonstrate the periods of pendula of different lengths, and compare the strides of short and tall people, and animals with short and long legs. Giraffes certainly run at a different stride than dachshunds!

Wave Description
Move a piece of chalk up and down, tracing and retracing a vertical straight line on the board. Call attention to how "frequently" you oscillate the chalk, and tie this to the definition of frequency. Also discuss the idea of amplitude. With appropriate motions, show different frequencies and different amplitudes. Then do the same while walking across the front of the board tracing out a sine wave. Show waves of different wavelengths.

DEMONSTRATION: Show waves on a Bell Telephone torsion type wave machine (if you're fortunate enough to have one).

DEMONSTRATION: In jest, do as Tom Gordon at Bronx High School does and suspend a harmonica from a spring, bob it up and down, and ask, "What do we have here?" Answer: Simple "harmonica" motion!

Swing a pendulum to-and-fro and discuss the reciprocal relationship between frequency and period: $f = 1/T$, and $T = 1/f$. Or $fT = Tf = 1$.

Distinguish between wiggles in time—vibrations, and wiggles in space and time—waves. Stress the sameness of the frequency of a wave and the frequency of its vibrating source.

13.2 Wave Motion—Transporting Energy

Explain or derive the *wave speed = frequency × wavelength* formula. Support this with the freight car question in the text. Calculate the wavelength of one of your local popular radio stations. If you discuss electromagnetic waves, be sure to contrast them with longitudinal sound waves and distinguish between them. You may refer ahead to the family of electromagnetic waves in Figure 14.3 in the next chapter.

13.3 Two Types of Waves—Transverse and Longitudinal

Distinguish between transverse and longitudinal waves. This is best done with a Slinky.

DEMONSTRATION: You and a student hold the ends of a stretched spring or a Slinky and send transverse pulses along it, stressing the idea that only the disturbance rather than the medium moves along the spring. Shake it and produce a sine wave. Then send a stretch or compression down the spring, showing a longitudinal pulse, and wave. After some discussion, produce standing waves.

13.4 Sound Travels in Longitudinal Waves

Begin by stating that the source of sound or all wave motion, is a vibrating object. Ask your class to imagine a room filled with Ping-Pong balls and that you hold a giant Ping-Pong paddle. When you shake the paddle to-and-fro you set up vibrations of the balls. Ask how the frequency of the vibrating balls will compare with the frequency of the vibrating paddle. Sound is understood if we "think small."

DEMONSTRATION: Tap a large tuning fork and show that it is vibrating by dipping the vibrating prongs in a cup of water. The splashing water is clear evidence that the prongs are moving! (Small forks do not work as well.)

DEMONSTRATION: Hold an aluminum rod (a meter long or so) horizontally at the midpoint and strike one end with a hammer. You will create vibrations that travel and reflect back and forth along the length of the rod. The sustained sound heard is due to energy "leaking" from the ends, about 1% with each reflection. So at any time the sound inside is about 100 times as intense as that heard at the ends. (This is similar to the behavior of light waves in a laser.) Shake the rod to-and-fro as Paul Doherty does and illustrate the Doppler effect.

DEMONSTRATION: Rub some pine pitch or rosin on your fingers and stroke the aluminum rod. If you do it properly, it will "sing" very loudly. Do this while holding the rod at its midpoint and then at different places to demonstrate harmonics. (Of course you practiced this first!)

Media That Transmit Sound

Discuss the speed of sound through different media—four times as fast in water than in air—about eleven times as fast in steel. The elasticity of these materials rather than their densities accounts for the different speeds. Cite how the American Indians used to place their ears to the ground to hear distant hoofbeats. And how one can put the ear to a track to listen for distant trains.

Speed of Sound. Discuss the speed of sound and how one can estimate the distance from a lightning storm.

Compute or state that a radio signal takes about 1/8 second to go completely around the world, while in the same time sound travels about 42.5 m. Pose the following: Suppose a person attends a concert that is being broadcast over the radio, and that he sits about 45 m from the stage and listens to the radio broadcast with a transistor radio over one ear and the nonbroadcast sound signal with the other ear. Which signal will reach his ear first? The answer is that the radio signal would reach his ear first, even if the radio signal traveled completely around the world before reaching his radio!

13.5 Sound Can Be Reflected
Bats and echoes, charting of the ocean bottom, reverberations in the shower, and acoustics in music halls—go to it.

13.6 Sound Can Be Refracted
Explain refraction with a chalkboard drawing similar to Figure 13.13. As an example different than the sound of the bugle waking the dog, consider the temperature inversion over a lake at night, and how one can hear whispers of people on the opposite side of the lake. You may want to follow this up with the similar case of refraction by wind, where wind speed is greater higher up than near the ground.

A useful medical application of sound refraction is ultrasound technology (Figure 13.14), especially in examining the unborn children in pregnant women. Fortunately, the method appears to be relatively free of dangerous side effects.

The most fascinating example of reflection and refraction of sound is the dolphin. Dolphins have been doing all along what humans have just learned to do. Add to the boxed material about dolphins, that unlike humans, dolphins breathe voluntarily. They cannot be put to sleep for medical operations because they will cease breathing and die. They are subject to drowning, as any mammal is. When in trouble other dolphins hold the troubled dolphin at the surface so breathing can take place. When sick, they will beach themselves so they won't drown. Many shipwrecked sailors owe their lives to dolphins who have beached them. Fascinating creatures!

13.7 Forced Vibrations and Natural Frequency
Tap various objects around you and explain what is happening at the atomic level—that crystalline or molecular structures are made to vibrate, and that due to the elasticity and bonding of the material constituents, natural modes of vibration are produced. Objects have their own characteristic frequencies. The organs of humans have a natural frequency of about 7 hertz.

13.8 Resonance and Sympathetic Vibrations

DEMONSTRATION: Show resonance with a pair of tuning forks, explaining how each set of compressions from the first fork push the prongs of the second fork in rhythm with its natural motion. Compare this to pushing somebody on a playground swing. Illuminate the forks with a strobe light for best effect!

When you are adjusting the frequency of one of your tuning fork boxes, by moving the weights up or down the prongs, call attention to the similarity of this with tuning a radio receiver. When one turns the knob to select a different station, one is adjusting the frequency of the radio set to resonate with incoming stations.

Cite other examples of resonance—the chattering vibration of a glass shelf when a radio placed on it plays a certain note—the loose front end of a car that vibrates at only certain speeds—crystal wine glass shattering by a singer's voice,—troops breaking step in bridge crossing.

Conclude your treatment of resonance with the exciting film loop "The Tacoma Narrows Bridge Collapse". This short film is by far the most impressive of the physics films. (It is included in *Sound and Vibrations II*, in the *Conceptual Physics Alive!* videotape or DVD.)

13.9 Interference—The Addition and Subtraction of Waves

Introduce interference by sketching a sine wave on the board—actually a water wave. Then superpose another identical wave on it and ask what happens. Nothing spectacular, simply a wave of twice the amplitude. Now repeat and superpose the second wave a half wavelength out of step. State that physicers don't say "out of step," but "out of phase." Same thing.

DEMONSTRATION: Play a stereo radio, tape or CD player, on a monosetting and demonstrate the different quality of sound when the speakers, set apart from each other, are out of phase. I have mine connected to a DPDT switch to flip the phase. Face the stereo speakers toward each other, at arm's length apart. Flip one speaker out of phase and gradually bring them closer. The volume of sound fades dramatically as they are brought face to face. Interference. This may likely be one of the more memorable of your demos.

The question may arise as what happens to the sound energy when sound cancels. Interestingly enough, each radio loudspeaker is also a microphone. When the speakers face each other they "drive" each other, inducing back voltages in each other that reduce the currents down in each. Thus energy is diminished, but not canceled.

DEMONSTRATION: Show the reason for speakers mounted in boxed enclosures by producing a bare speaker connected to a music source. The sound is "tinny". State why that as compressions are produced by one side of the speaker cone, rarefactions are produced by the other. Superposition of these waves results in destructive interference. Then produce a square piece of board (plywood or cardboard) close to a meter on a side with a hole the size of the speaker in its center. Place the speaker at the hole and let your class hear the difference in the fullness of the sound that results. You have diminished the superposition of waves that previously canceled. The effect is dramatic.

I kid around about my keen ability to completely cancel sound by striking one tuning fork and then the other at precisely the time to produce cancellation. When I do this I quickly grab and release the prongs of the sounding fork while not really making contact with the second. It is especially effective for students who weren't watching carefully. I exclaim that when I'm lucky enough to achieve complete cancellation on the first try, I never repeat it. Is this real science? No, but it's a mood elevator so that my students are receptive to the real science I discuss the remainder of the time.

Beats. Acknowledge you were kidding around before about producing interference with the pair of tuning forks, but now you're for real with them. Strike the slightly different frequency forks and hear the beats. This is even nicer when your students see an oscilloscope trace what they hear.

13.10 The Doppler Effect—Changes in Frequency Due to Motion

Introduce the Doppler Effect by throwing a ball, perhaps sponge rubber or Styrofoam, around the room. In the ball you first place an electronic whistle that emits a sound of about 3000 Hz.

Relate this to the sound of a siren on a fire engine (Figure 13.28) and radar of the highway patrol. [Note that sound requires a medium; radar is an E&M wave and doesn't.]

13.11 Wave Barriers and Bow Waves

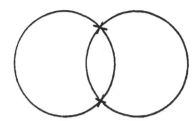

Describe the Doppler effect via the bug in water sequence as treated in the text. From this lead into bow and shock waves. After sketching Figures 13.26, 13.27, and 13.29, ask the class to consider the waves formed by two stones thrown in the water. Sketch the overlapping waves as shown. Ask where the water is highest above the water level, then indicate the two places where the waves overlap with X's. Then show that this is what happens with a bow wave, that a series of such overlaps make up the envelope of many circular waves forming a V-shape. Then discuss the shock waves produced by supersonic aircraft.

13.12 Shock Waves and the Sonic Boom

The analogy between bow waves in water and shock waves in air is very useful. Questions raised by students about shock waves and the sonic boom can be effectively answered by translating the question from one of an aircraft in the air to one of a speedboat knifing through the water, a much easier-to-visualize situation.

If you wish to go further with shock waves than is treated in the text, consider explaining how the speed of an aircraft can be estimated by the angle of its shock wave [shock waves are visible (Figure 13.33), for light is refracted in passing through the denser air].

Shock Wave Construction. Construct a shock wave on the board by the following sequence: First place your chalk on the board anywhere to signify time zero. Draw a meter-long horizontal line, say to the right, to represent how far an aircraft has traveled in a certain time. Suppose it travels twice the speed of sound (Mach 2). Then during the time it travels your one meter, the sound it made initially has traveled half this distance, which

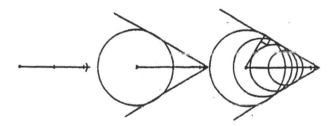

you mark on the midpoint of your line. State that the initial sound has expanded spherically, which you represent two-dimensionally by drawing a circle as shown. Explain that this circle represents only one of the nearly infinite circles that make up the shock wave, which you draw. The shock wave should be a 60 degree wedge (30 degrees above your horizontal line, and 30 degrees below). The next line you draw is important: Draw the radius of the circle, from its center to a point tangent to the shock wave. Explain how the speed of the craft is simply the ratio of the horizontal line to this radial distance. (If your students are science students, at this point and not before, introduce the sine function). Now your test of all this: Construct a shock wave of a different angle on the board and ask your class to estimate the generated speed of the craft. In making constructions, working backwards now, the most common student error is constructing the right angle from the horizontal line rather than from the shock wave line that is tangent to the circle.

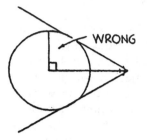

Such geometrical constructions are the subject of this chapter's activity in the **Practice Book.**

Chapter 13 Answers and Solutions

Key Terms and Matching Definitions

__2__ amplitude
_21__ beats
_16__ bow wave
_15__ doppler effect
_12__ forced vibration
__4__ frequency
__5__ hertz
_13__ interference
__9__ longitudinal wave
_19__ natural frequency
__6__ period
_11__ refraction
_20__ resonance
_17__ shock wave
_18__ sonic boom
_10__ sound wave
_14__ standing wave
__8__ transverse wave
__1__ wave
__7__ wave speed
__3__ wavelength

Review Questions

1. What is the source of all waves?
   Something vibrating.

2. How do frequency and period relate to each other?
   Inversely; frequency = 1/period; period = 1/frequency.

3. What is it that moves from source to receiver in wave motion?
   Energy (not the medium itself).

4. What is the relationship among frequency, wavelength, and wave speed?
   Wave speed = frequency × wavelength.

5. In a transverse wave, in what direction are the vibrations relative to the direction of wave travel?
   Perpendicular.

6. In a longitudinal wave, in what direction are the vibrations relative to the direction of wave travel?
   Parallel.

7. Why will sound not travel in a vacuum?
   There is no medium to vibrate.

8. How does the speed of sound in water compare with the speed of sound in air? How does the speed in steel compare with the speed in air?
   Faster in water, and even faster in steel.

9. How does the angle of incidence compare with the angle of reflection for sound?
   Like that of light; angle of incidence equals angle of reflection.

10. What is a *reverberation?*
Multiple reflections of sound.

11. What causes refraction?
Slowing or speeding of one part of a sound wave relative to other parts.

12. Does sound tend to bend upward or downward when its speed near the ground is greater than its speed at a higher level?
Upward.

13. Why does a struck tuning fork sound louder when it is held against a table?
It sets the surface of the table vibrating, which has greater surface area.

14. Give three examples of forced vibration.
A vibrating tuning fork held against a table, vibration of a factory floor with vibrating machines, and the sounding boards of musical instruments.

15. Distinguish between *forced vibrations* and *resonance.*
Forced vibration occurs at any frequency, whereas resonance occurs when vibration is at a frequency matching an object's natural frequency.

16. When you listen to a radio, why are you able to hear only one station at a time rather than all stations at once?
The radio resonates to the frequency of one station.

17. What kind of waves exhibit interference?
All waves. Interference is characteristic of all wave motion.

18. Distinguish between *constructive interference* and *destructive interference.*
Constructive adds to intensity, destructive subtracts and diminishes.

19. In the Doppler effect, does frequency change? Does wavelength change? Does wave speed change?
Yes. Yes. No.

20. Can the Doppler effect be observed with longitudinal waves, transverse waves, or both?
Both.

21. How does the V shape of a bow wave depend on the speed of the wave source?
Greater source speed means narrower V-shape bow wave.

22. How does the V shape of a shock wave depend on the speed of the wave source?
Greater source speed means narrower V-shape shock wave.

23. True or false: A sonic boom occurs only when an aircraft is breaking through the sound barrier.
False (aircraft may have broke through long before one encounters a sonic boom).

24. True or false: In order for an object to produce a sonic boom, it must be a sound source.
False (a bullet, for example, doesn't generate sound like a droning aircraft engine, but nevertheless produces a crack when it passes a listener. The crack is a sonic boom.)

Solutions to Chapter 13 Exercises

1. If we double the frequency of a vibrating object, what happens to its period?

   Frequency and period are reciprocals of one another; $f = \frac{1}{T}$, and $T = \frac{1}{f}$. Double one and the other is half as much. So doubling the frequency of a vibrating object halves the period.

2. If the frequency of a sound wave is doubled, what change occurs in its speed? In its wavelength?

   If the frequency of sound is doubled, its speed will not change at all, but its wavelength will be crowded to half its original size. The speed of sound depends only on the medium through which it travels, rather than on the properties of sound itself.

3. Red light has a longer wavelength than blue light. Which has the greater frequency?

   Blue light, with the shorter wavelength, has the higher frequency.

4. You dip your finger repeatedly into a puddle of water and make waves. What happens to the wavelength if you dip your finger more frequently?

   As you dip your fingers more frequently into still water, the waves you produce will be of a higher frequency (we see the relationship between "how frequently" and "frequency"). The higher-frequency waves will be closer together—their wavelengths will be shorter.

5. How does the frequency of vibration of a small object floating in water compare with the number of waves passing the object each second?

   The frequency of vibration and the number of waves passing by each second are the same.

6. Why will marchers at the end of a long parade following a band be out of step with marchers near the front?

   Marchers at the end of a long parade will be out of step with marchers nearer the band because time is required for the sound of the band to reach the marchers at the end of a parade. They will step to the delayed beat they hear.

7. What two physics mistakes occur in a science fiction movie that shows a distant explosion in outer space, where you see and hear the explosion at the same time?

   First, sound cannot travel in the vacuum of outer space. Second, light would certainly travel faster than sound, if there were any, so you wouldn't see and hear the explosion at the same time.

8. A cat can hear sound frequencies up to 70,000 Hz. Bats send and receive ultrahigh-frequency squeaks up to 120,000 Hz. Which hears shorter wavelengths, cats or bats?

   The shorter wavelengths are heard by bats (higher frequencies have shorter wavelengths).

9. At the stands of a racetrack, you notice smoke from the starter's gun before you hear it fire. Explain.

   Light travels about a million times faster than sound, so you see a distant event a million times sooner than you hear it.

10. Why is it so quiet after a snowfall?

    Because snow absorbs well, it reflects little sound, which is responsible for the quietness.

11. Why is the moon described as a "silent planet"?

    The moon is described as a silent planet because it has no atmosphere to transmit sound.

12. If the speed of sound depended on frequency, how would distant music sound?

    If the speed of sound was different for different frequencies, say, faster for higher frequencies, then distant music would be distorted, for the higher frequency notes would reach the ear of the listener first. (Be glad this is so, particularly if you like outdoor concerts.)

13. Why is an echo weaker than the original sound?

    An echo is weaker than the original sound because sound spreads and is therefore less intense with distance. If you are at the source, the echo will sound as if it originated on

the other side of the wall from which it reflects (just as your image in a mirror appears to come from behind the glass). It is weaker still because the wall is likely not perfectly reflecting.

14. Would there be a Doppler effect if the source of sound were stationary and the listener in motion? Why or why not? In which direction should the listener move to hear a higher frequency? A lower frequency?

    So if you moved toward a stationary sound source, yes, you would encounter waves more frequently and the frequency of the received sound would be higher. Or if you moved away from the source, the waves would encounter you less frequently, and you would hear sound of a lower frequency.

15. When you blow your horn while driving toward a stationary listener, the listener hears an increase in the horn frequency. Would the listener hear an increase in the horn frequency if he were in another car traveling at the same speed in the same direction as you? Explain.

    No, for there would be no relative motion between sender and receiver. Saying this another way, the increased frequency the listener would receive if at rest is canceled by the decreased frequency of recession.

16. Astronomers find that light coming from one edge of the sun has a slightly higher frequency than light from the opposite edge. What do these measurements tell us about the sun's motion?

    The higher-frequency side is moving toward us, and the lower frequency side away from us. So we can tell the direction of the sun's spin.

17. What can you say about the speed of a boat that makes a bow wave? How about the speed of an aircraft that produces a shock wave?

    The boat is traveling faster than the water waves. Likewise for an aircraft that produces a shock wave.

18. What physical principle is used by Manuel when he pumps in rhythm with the natural frequency of the swing?

    Resonance. If he pumps in rhythm with the natural frequency, amplitude is significantly increased.

19. A special device can transmit out-of-phase sound from a noisy jackhammer to earphones worn by its operator. Over the noise of the jackhammer, the operator can easily hear your voice while you are unable to hear his. Explain.

    These devices use interference to cancel the sound of the jackhammer in the operator's ears. Because of the resulting low jackhammer noise in the operator's ears, he can hear your voice clearly. But you, however, without the earphones experience no such cancellation of sound, so the voice of the operator is drowned out by the loud jackhammer noise.

20. If a single disturbance some unknown distance away sends out both transverse and longitudinal waves that travel with distinctly different speeds in the medium, such as in the ground during earthquakes, how could the origin of the disturbance be located?

    If a single disturbance at some unknown distance away sends longitudinal waves at one known speed, and transverse waves at a lesser known speed, and you measure the difference in time of the waves as they arrive, you can calculate the distance. The wider the gap in time, the greater the distance—which could be in any direction. If you use this distance as the radius of a circle on a map, you know the disturbance occurred somewhere on that circle. If you telephone two friends who have made similar measurements of the same event from different locations, you can transfer their circles to your map, and the point where the three circles intersect is the location of the disturbance.

Solutions to Chapter 13 Problems

1. A weight suspended from a spring bobs up and down over a distance of 20 centimeters twice each second. What is its frequency? Its period? Its amplitude?
Frequency is twice per second, or 2 hertz. Period is reciprocal frequency, or 1/2 second. Amplitude is 10 centimeters.

2. A rule of thumb for estimating the distance in kilometers between an observer and a lightning stroke is to divide the number of seconds in the interval between the flash and the sound by 3. Is this rule correct?
The rule is correct: This is because the speed of sound in air (340 m/s) can be rounded off to 1/3 km/s. Then, from distance = speed × time = (1/3)km/s × (number of seconds). Note that the time in seconds divided by 3 yields the same value.

3. In terms of wavelength, how far does a wave travel during one period?
Think of a period as one cycle in time, and a wavelength as one cycle in space, and a little thought will show that in a time of one period, a wave travels a full wavelength.
Formally, we can see this as follows:
distance = speed × time
where speed = frequency × wavelength, which when substituted for speed,
distance = frequency × wavelength × time

$$\text{distance} = \frac{1}{\text{period}} \times \text{wavelength} \times \text{period} = \text{wavelength}$$

4. From far away you watch a woman driving nails into her front porch at a regular rate of 1 stroke per second. You hear the sound of the blows exactly synchronized with the blows you see. And then you hear one more blow after you see her cease hammering. How far away is she?
The woman is about 340 meters away. The clue is the single blow you hear after you see her stop hammering. That blow originated with the next-to-last blow you saw. The very first blow would have appeared as silent, and succeeding blows synchronous with successive strikes. In one second sound travels 340 meters.

5. A skipper on a boat notices wave crests passing his anchor chain every 5 s. He estimates the distance between wave crests to be 15 m. He also correctly estimates the speed of the waves. What is this speed?
The skipper notes that 15 meters of wave pass each 5 seconds, or equivalently, that 3 meters pass each 1 second, so the speed of the wave must be

$$\text{Speed} = \frac{\text{distance}}{\text{time}} = \frac{15\,\text{m}}{5\,\text{s}} = 3\,\text{m/s}.$$

Or in wave terminology:
Speed = frequency × wavelength = (1/5 Hz)(15 m) = 3 m/s.

6. An oceanic depth-sounding vessel surveys the ocean bottom with ultrasonic sound that travels 1530 m/s in seawater. How deep is the water if the time delay of the echo from the ocean floor is 6 s?
The ocean floor is 4590 meters deep. The 6-second time delay means that the sound reached the bottom in 3 seconds. Distance = speed × time = 1530 m/s × 3 s = 4590 m.

7. A bat flying in a cave emits a sound and receives its echo 0.1 s later. How far away is the cave wall?
Assuming the speed of sound to be 340 m/s, the cave is 17 meters away. This is because the sound took 0.05 second to reach the wall (and 0.05 second to return).
Distance = speed × time = 340 m/s × 0.05 s = 17 m.

8. What frequency of sound produces a wavelength of 1 meter in room-temperature air?
$$\text{From } v = f\lambda,\ f = v/\lambda = \frac{340\,\text{m/s}}{1\,\text{m}} = 340\,\text{Hz}.$$

14 Light and Color

Learning Objectives
After studying Chapter 14, students will be able to:
• Describe the dual nature of light.
• Describe the relation between light, radio waves, microwaves, and X-rays.
• Explain what happens to light when it enters a substance and how the light frequency affects what happens.
• Give evidence to show that light waves are transverse.
• Explain why polarized sunglasses are helpful in decreasing the glare of the sun from horizontal surfaces such as water and roads.
• Explain why black and white are not colors in the same sense that red and green are colors.
• Describe why the interaction of light with the atoms or molecules of a material varies for different frequencies.
• Describe the factors that determine whether a material will reflect, transmit, or absorb light of a particular color.
• Explain how color television screens are able to display pictures in full color, even though the television tube produces only spots of red, green, or blue light.
• Define complementary colors and give examples of pairs of them.
• Distinguish between color mixing by subtraction and color mixing by addition.
• Explain why the sky is blue and why it changes color when the sun is low in the sky.
• Explain why water is greenish blue.

Possible Misconceptions to Correct
• **Not so!** Light and sound have the same wave nature but different frequencies.
• **Not so!** Light is fundamentally different than radio waves, microwaves, and X-rays.
• **Not so!** Light passes though transparent materials in a way similar to bullets passing though materials.
• **Not so!** Black and white are colors.
• **Not so!** Red, yellow, and blue light make white light.
• **Not so!** Red and green light make brown light.
• **Not so!** The sky is blue because it reflects the blue ocean.

Demonstration Equipment
• Three lamps, red, green, and blue, that can be clamped to a lecture table (or the equivalent)
• Two trays of tuning forks
• Transparent container of water and powdered milk, and a source of white light that gives a strong beam

Note that the "depth of the plow" in the treatment of light is respectably deep. The aim is not to separate and name categories such as transmission, reflection, and absorption, but to get into the physics. Your students will get into some good physics in this chapter—and understand it. Understanding more than you may expect, and discovering more than you thought there was, is a real joy of learning. So this should be an enjoyable chapter—why some instructors opt to begin their physical science course here.

In this chapter we introduce a model of the atom in which electrons behave as tiny oscillators that resonate or are forced into vibration by external influences. If you haven't preceded light with a study of sound, and if you haven't demonstrated resonance with a pair of tuning forks, do it now, for the tuning fork model is used in the text to account for selective reflection and transmission of light.

We continue to refer to color primarily by frequency rather than wavelength, in effort to reduce the number of terms students must learn to understand concepts. There is a trend toward using wavelength in nanometers (Angstroms are "out") for the color spectrum, probably because there seems to be evidence that the color sensitive elements of the retina-optic-nerve-brain system are more reasonably a function of wavelength than frequency due to velocity variation. There is a trend to terahertz (THz) in place of exponential notation for visible light frequencies.

If you haven't shown your class the black hole that appears in a box with the white interior, back in the heat chapters (Figure 10.13) do it now. It nicely illustrates the "color" black.

Be sure to mount three floodlights on your lecture table, red, green, and blue, of shades such that all three overlapping produce white on a white screen. Then stand in front of the lamps, illuminated one at a time and show the interesting colors of the shadows, as is shown by the shadows of the golf ball in Figure 14.17. Impressive!

In the **Practice Book:**
• Light
• Color

In the **Next-Time Questions** book:
• Radiating Lamps
• Red, Green, and Blue Lamps

Overhead Transparency available for:
Figure 14.3.

SUGGESTED PRESENTATION

14.1 The Electromagnetic Spectrum—a Tiny Bit of Which is Light
If you have already delved into E&M from Chapter 12 with your class, then begin your teaching with **Begin 1** that follows. If you're jumping into light without having covered E&M, then jump ahead to **Begin 2**.

Begin 1: Electromagnetic Waves
Usually I begin my lecture by asking the class to recall my recent demonstration of charging a rubber rod with cat's fur and how when I brought it near a charged pith ball, I produced action at a distance. When I moved the charged rod, the charged ball moved also. If I gently oscillate the rod, the ball in turn oscillates. State that one can think of this behavior as either action-at-a-distance or the interaction of the ball with the space immediately around

it—the electric field of the charged rod. For low frequencies, the ball will swing in rhythm with the shaking rod. But the inertia of the ball and its pendulum configuration makes response poor for any vigorous shaking of the rod (that's why it's best not to actually show this, but to only describe it and go through the motions as if the equipment were present—you avoid the "that's the way it would behave" situation). You can easily establish in your students' minds the reasonableness of the ball shaking back and forth in response to the shaking electric field about the shaking rod. Carry this further by considering the ball to be simply a point charge with negligible mass. Now it will respond in synchronous rhythm with the shaking rod. Increase the frequency of the shaking rod and state that not only is there a shaking electric field about the rod, but because of its changing, there is a also different kind of field.

CHECK YOUR NEIGHBOR: What kind of field is induced by the shaking rod? What kind of field in turn, does this induced field induce? And further in turn, what kind of field does this further induced field induce? And so on.

Begin 2: Electromagnetic waves

Begin by stating that everybody knows that if you placed the end of a stick in a pond and shook the stick back and forth, you'd generate waves across the water surface. But what everybody doesn't know is that if you shook a charged rod back and forth in free space, you'd generate waves also. Not waves of water, or even waves of the medium in which the stick exists, but waves of electric and magnetic fields. You'd generate *electromagnetic waves*. Shaking the rod at low frequencies generates radio waves. Shaking at a million billion times per second generates waves one could see in the dark. For those waves would be seen as light.

Electromagnetic Spectrum

Continue by stating that, strictly speaking, light is the only thing we see. And to understand what light is, we will first try to understand how it behaves. Call attention to the rainbow of colors that are dispersed by a prism or by raindrops in the sunlight. We know white light can be spread into a spectrum of colors. Ask your students to consider the world view of little creatures who could only see a tiny portion of the spectrum, creatures who would be color-blind to all the other parts. Their world view would be very limited. Then state that we are like those little creatures, in that the spectrum of colors we can see are a tiny portion of the *electromagnetic spectrum* (Figure 14.3)—less than a tenth of one percent! We are color-blind to the other parts.

Buckminster Fuller put it well when he stated that ninety-nine percent of all that is going to affect our tomorrows is being developed by humans using instruments that work in ranges of reality that are nonhumanly sensible. The instruments of science have extended our view of the other parts. These instruments are not microscopes and telescopes, for they enable closer viewing of the part of the spectrum we are familiar with. It is the infrared detecting devices, microwave and radio receivers, that allow us to explore the lower-frequency end of the spectrum, and ultraviolet, X-ray, and gamma-ray detectors that let us "see" the higher-frequency end. What we see with unaided eyes is a tiny part of what's out there in the world around us.

CHECK YOUR NEIGHBOR: Where does sound fit in the electromagnetic spectrum? [It doesn't of course!]

CHECK YOUR NEIGHBOR: A photographer wishes to photograph a lightning bolt, and comes up with the idea of having the camera triggered by the sound of thunder. A good idea or a poor idea? [Very poor, for light travels about a million times faster than sound. By the time the sound of thunder arrives, the lightning bolt is long gone!]

CHECK YOUR NEIGHBOR: So the speed of light is finite; does this mean your image in the mirror is always a bit younger or a bit older than you? [Older, but of course not by very much!]

14.2 Why Materials are Either Transparent or Opaque

Recall your earlier demonstration of sound resonance [or if you haven't done this, demonstrate now the resonance of a pair of tuning forks mounted on sounding boxes (Figure 14.4)]. The tuning fork demo provides important experience for your students in understanding the interaction of light and matter. In some cases light strikes a material and rebounds—reflection (next chapter). In cases where light continues through the material, we say the material is *transparent*.

DEMONSTRATION: Show the swinging balls apparatus that is usually used to illustrate momentum and energy conservation. Here you are showing that the energy that cascades through the system of balls is analogous to light energy cascading through transparent matter. Just as the incident ball is not the same ball that emerges, the incident "photon" of light upon glass is not the same photon that emerges through the other side. Although too difficult to see, slight interaction times between balls produces a slight time delay between incidence and emergence of balls. Likewise for light.

(Note that the text does not mention photons in the light-through-glass explanation. Photons aren't introduced until Chapter 16.)

Point out the value of **scientific models**, in understanding physical phenomena. Hence the discussion of cascading balls, tuning forks, and imaginary springs that hold electrons to the nuclei of atoms. A model is not correct or incorrect, but useful or nonuseful. Models must be refined or abandoned whenever they fail to account for various aspects of a phenomenon.

CHECK YOUR NEIGHBOR: Compared to the speed of light in a vacuum, why is the speed of light less in transparent materials such as water or glass? [Answer: According to the model treated in the text, there is a time delay between the absorption of light and its re-emission. This time delay serves to decrease the average speed of light in a transparent material.]

Another analogy for light traveling through glass is the average speed of a basketball moving down a court. It may fly through the air from player to player at one constant speed, but its average speed down the court depends on the holding time of the players. Carrying the analogy further, different materials have different players, and although the instantaneous speed of light is always the same, the average speed depends on both the number of players encountered, and the holding time of each player.

On the subject of glass, it's interesting to note that we see through it for the same reasons we see through water. Despite the appearance of glass, it is really a highly viscous liquid rather than a solid. Its internal structure is not the regular crystalline latticework of most solids, but is essentially random-like that of liquids. Whereas conventional liquids have a freezing point at which they become solid, liquid glass gets stiffer as it cools. At room temperature its rate of flow is so slow that it takes centuries for it to appreciably ooze out of shape. Because of the downward flow due to gravity, window panes only several decades old show a lens effect at their bottoms due to the increased thickness there.

Opaque Materials. State that light generally has three possible fates when incident upon a material: (1) reflects, (2) is transmitted through the material, or (3) is absorbed by the material. Usually a combination of all three fates occurs. When absorption occurs, the vibrations given to electrons by incident light are often great enough to last for a relatively long time, during which the vibratory energy is shared by collisions with neighboring atoms. The absorbed energy warms the material.

CHECK YOUR NEIGHBOR: Why in the sunlight is a black tar road hotter to the touch than a pane of window glass? [Sunlight is absorbed and turned into internal energy in the road surface, but transmitted through the glass to somewhere else.]

For the record, we say that ultraviolet light cannot penetrate glass. Hence you cannot get a sunburn through glass. But *some* ultraviolet light does pass through glass—long wavelength ultraviolet light, which has insufficient energy to cause a sunburn. Most sunlamps *aren't* made of ordinary glass—they're made of quartz or special UV-transparent glass.

14.3 Color Science
What first made Isaac Newton a famous physicist was not his contributions to mechanics, but to light. He was the first to explain the colors produced by a prism held in the sunlight. White light, after all, is all the colors "smudged" together.

Selected Reflection. Discuss the oscillator model of the atom, and the ideas of forced vibration and resonance as they relate to color, as you display different colored objects. A red object, for example, reflects red. It absorbs the other colors. Resonance is *not* occurring for red, by the way, for light of the resonant frequencies is being *absorbed*. (I was confused about this point for years!)

Selective Transmission. Similarly for colored glass—the resonant frequencies are absorbed and becomes the internal energy of the transparent material. The frequencies to pass through the glass are those away from the resonant frequencies. Frequencies close to resonance undergo more interactions with the molecules and take longer to travel than frequencies far from resonance. Hence different colors have different speeds in transparent materials. (If not, no rainbows, as we shall see in the following chapter!)

14.4 Mixing Colored Lights
How many colors are there in the spectrum? Although we commonly group the colors into seven categories: red, orange, yellow, etc., there are an infinite number of colors. The "in-between" colors are not mixtures of their neighboring colors. The red-orange between red and orange, for example, is not a mixture of red and orange but is a distinct frequency present in sunlight.

DEMONSTRATION: Show the overlapping of the primary colors with the Singerman Color Apparatus (or its equivalent). Show complementary colors, and discuss the rule of color mixing.

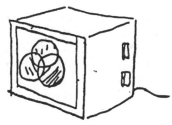

DEMONSTRATION: (This is a must!!) Show the overlapping of light from three lamps on your lecture table aimed at a white screen behind you. The variety of colors in the shadows of you are very impressive. And their explanation by showing only the black shadow from one lamp, then two lamps where the black shadow is now the color of the second lamp, and then three lamps with explanation, is quite satisfying. (If you would like a detailed

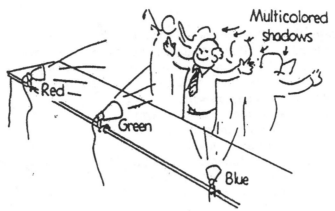

lecture on the three lamps demo, 3 pages long, send a note to Paul Hewitt who will be glad to send it to you.)

14.5 Mixing Colored Pigments
It is enough to let your students know the basic difference in mixing light and mixing pigments. Light adds when mixed, and light is absorbed when it encounters dyes and pigments.

Why Water is Greenish Blue
Water absorbs infrared. It also absorbs visible light up into the red end of the color spectrum. Take away red from white light and you are left with the complementary color—cyan. You can demonstrate this with all three lamps illuminating the white screen. When you turn down the red lamp, the screen turns cyan—the color of the sea! A piece of white paper deep in the water looks cyan. There is no red left in the sunlight to make it white. A red crab and a black crab have the same appearance on the ocean floor.

14.6 Why the Sky Is Blue
Compare the molecules in the atmosphere to tiny bells, that when struck, ring with high frequencies. They ring mostly at violet, and next at blue. We're better at hearing blue, so we "hear" a blue sky. On the other hand, bumble bees and other creatures that are good at seeing violet see a violet sky.

LECTURE SKIT — PART 1; Blue sky: Place a variety of six tuning forks at one end of your lecture table—calling their "colors"—a "red" one, "orange" one, "yellow" one, etc., to a "violet" one. Ask what "color" sound they would hear if you struck all the tuning forks in unison. Your class should answer, "White." Then suppose you have a mirror device around the forks so that when you "strike" them again, a beam of sound travels down the length of your lecture table. Ask what color they will hear. Several might say "White" again, but state that if there is no medium to scatter the beam that they will hear nothing (unless, of course, the beam is directed toward them). Now place a tray of tuning forks at the opposite

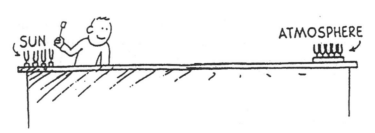

end of your lecture table (the tray I use is simply a 2 x 4 piece of wood, about a third meter long, with about a dozen holes drilled in it to hold a dozen tuning forks of various sizes).

Ask your class to pretend that the ends of your lecture table are 150 million km apart, the distance between the Earth and the sun. State that your tray of assorted tuning forks represents the Earth's atmosphere—point to the tuning forks, calling out their colors; a blue one, a violet one, a blue one, a blue one, a red one, a blue one, a violet one, a blue one, a green one, a blue one, a violet one, and so forth emphasizing the preponderance of blue and violet forks. Your tray of forks is perpendicular to the imaginary beam from the sun (to simulate a noonish thin atmosphere). Walk to the sun end of the table and again pretend to strike the forks and show how the beam travels down the table and intercepts and scatters from the atmospheric tuning forks in all directions. Ask what color the class hears. Since blue is predominantly scattered, you have a blue sky, especially if they're a bit deficient in hearing violet.

14.7 Why Sunsets Are Red

PART 2; Red sunset: Sketch a rendition of Figure 14.24 on the board and show that at sunset the sunlight must travel through many kilometers of air to reach an observer—that blue light is scattered all along these kilometers. What frequencies survive, you ponder. Then back to your sun and Earth forks on the lecture table. Select a student (a cooperative one, of course) from the class to sit beside the tray of Earth forks. State to the class that your volunteer represents an Earth observer. Place the observer's ear next to the tray of tuning forks (still perpendicular to the length of the lecture table and "sun rays"). Repeat your procedure from Part I and ask what color the class hears as the sunlight strikes the forks. Again, they say blue. Ask your volunteer what color he or she heard (while whispering "white" to avoid embarrassment). "White," your volunteer states, to which you acknowledge explaining that most of the sun's white light penetrated the forks, as sunlight does when you stare at it when the sun is high in the sky. Now conspicuously rotate the tray of forks 90° to represent the Earth's thicker atmosphere at sunset. Go back to the sun forks which you pretend to strike. Down the table comes the beam, which you follow. Whap, into the Earth's atmosphere where most of it scatters throughout the classroom. Again, ask the class what color they "hear." "Blue" is the answer. Correct. Now you ask your volunteer what color he or she heard. "Orange," is the answer! Your demonstration has been a success. For humor, by "experiment" you have proved your point. Your student volunteer has simply heard a composite of the lower-frequency leftover colors after the class received most all the higher-frequency blues. So those nice colors at sunset are what? Leftover colors.

Put another way, you can say the orange of the sunset is the complementary color of the blue-violet sky.

DEMONSTRATION: Back to the three-lamps demo. With the three lamps fully illuminated to produce white on the screen, gradually turn down the blue and the screen turns a yellow, and then turning the green lamp down a bit, you produce an orange—the colors of the sunset. Most impressive! (Don't turn the green all the way down—save this for the red color of the eclipsed moon.)

Why the Moon is Red During a Solar Eclipse
This is discussed in Chapter 39, and a view of the red moon shown in the Part 8 opening photo at the end of the book. It is also featured as a Chapter 39 Next-Time Question, in the Next-Time Questions Book. Show it as an OHT, and then return to your three-lamps demo. Begin with all lamps fully illuminated to produce white. Then turn down the blue and green lamps,

gradually, until all that remains on the screen is red. This is what happens when all the higher frequencies (green as well as blue) are scattered, leaving only the red to refract through the "lens" of the Earth's atmosphere to shine on the eclipsed moon. Again, most impressive!

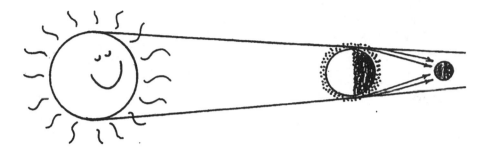

DEMONSTRATION: (An alternative to the above sequence.) Shine a beam of white light through a colloidal suspension of a very small quantity of instant nonfat dry milk in water, to show the scattering of blue and transmission of orange.

14.8 Why Clouds Are White
Small particles scatter high frequencies. Larger molecules and particles also scatter lower frequencies (like larger bells ring at lower frequencies). Very large ones ring in the reds. In a cloud there are a wide assortment of particles—all sizes. They ring with all colors. Ask your class if they have any idea why clouds are white! (Cumulus clouds, composed of droplets, are white because of the multitude of particle sizes, but higher-altitude cirrus clouds are composed of ice crystals, which like snow, reflect all frequencies.) When drops become too big, they absorb rather than scatter light, and we have a dark rain cloud. (And the rain cleans the sky of particles that make for a whitish sky, and the cleaner sky is a more vivid blue.)

CHECK YOUR NEIGHBOR: Sometimes the sky is not blue, but whitish. Why is it sometimes whitish, and what does your answer have to do with the variety of particle sizes in the atmosphere at these times? [Of course your double question leads directly to the answer of a wide variety of particle sizes—Question for you: Isn't the question technique preferable than simple statements of fact?]

Chapter 14 Answers and Solutions

Key Terms and Matching Definitions

__5__ additive primary colors
__6__ complementary colors
__1__ electromagnetic wave
__2__ electromagnetic spectrum
__4__ opaque
__7__ subtractive primary colors
__3__ transparent

Review Questions

1. Does visible light make up a relatively large part or a relatively small part of the electromagnetic spectrum?
    Very small part!

2. What is the principal difference between a radio wave and light?
    Different frequencies.

3. How do the speeds of various electromagnetic waves compare?
    All the same speed.

4. What color do we perceive for the lowest visible frequencies? The highest?
    Red. Violet.

5   How does the frequency of a radio wave compare with the frequency of the vibrating electrons that produces it?
    Same frequency.

6. In what region of the electromagnetic spectrum is the resonant frequency of electrons in glass?
    Ultraviolet.

7. What is the fate of the energy in ultraviolet light incident on glass?
    Absorption (passed on to neighboring atoms as heat).

8. How does the average speed of light in glass compare with its speed in a vacuum?
    Slower in glass, fastest in vacuum.

9. Which has the higher frequency, red light or blue light?
    Blue light.

10. Distinguish between the white of this page and the black of this ink in terms of what happens to the white light that falls on both.
    Light is reflected by blank part of page, absorbed by ink.

11. What is the evidence for the statement that white light is a composite of all the colors of the visible part of the electromagnetic spectrum?
    A prism shows this to be true. Also, a rainbow.

12. What is the color of the peak frequency of solar radiation?
    Yellow-green.

13. What color light are our eyes most sensitive to?
    Yellow-green.

14. What frequency ranges of the radiation curve do red, green, and blue light occupy?
    Red, low; green, medium; blue, high.

15. Why are red, green, and blue called the *additive primary colors?*

Because in equal amounts they add to produce white light.

16. What are the subtractive primary colors? Why are they so called?
    Magenta, cyan, yellow. When mixed, the color seen is the color that survives subtraction.

17. Why are red and cyan called *complementary colors?*
    Because they are opposites; when added they produce white (because cyan is the addition of blue and green—and red + blue + green = white).

18. Why does the sky sometimes appear whitish?
    Because of the mixture of many size particles, and many scattered colors.

19. Why does the sun look reddish at sunrise and sunset but not at noon?
    The sun is low in the sky at sunrise and sunset, resulting in a longer light path through the air, which scatters away blue leaving primarily lower-frequency light to reach an observer.

20. What is the evidence for a variety of particle sizes in a cloud?
    The whiteness, produced by a variety of scattered colors.

Solutions to Chapter 14 Exercises

1. Which waves have the longest wavelengths: light waves, X-rays, or radio waves? Which have the highest frequencies?
   Radio waves are longer than light waves, which are longer than the waves of X-rays.

2. What evidence can you cite to support the idea that light can travel in a vacuum?
   Between the sun, stars, and Earth is the vacuum of interstellar and intersolar space. The fact that we can see the sun and stars from Earth is convincing evidence that light travels through a vacuum.

3. Is glass transparent or opaque to frequencies of light that match its own natural frequencies? Explain.
   Glass is opaque to frequencies of light that match its own natural frequencies. This is because the electrons in the absorbing medium are driven to vibrations of much larger amplitudes than occurs for nonresonant frequencies. These large amplitudes result in energy transfer to neighboring atoms and an increase in internal energy rather than a re-emission of light.

4. What determines whether a material is transparent or opaque?
   Transparency or opaqueness is determined by the match between incident light frequencies and the resonant frequency of the material. A substance that is transparent to a range of light frequencies will be opaque to those frequencies that match its own resonant frequency.

5. You can get a sunburn on a cloudy day, but you can't get a sunburn even on a sunny day if you are behind glass. Explain.
   Clouds are transparent to ultraviolet light, which is why clouds offer no protection from sunburn. Glass, however, is opaque to ultraviolet light, and will therefore shield you from sunburn.

6. Suppose that sunlight falls on both a pair of reading glasses and a pair of dark sunglasses. Which pair of glasses would you expect to be warmer in sunlight? Defend your answer.
   The sunglasses will be warmer in sunlight than regular reading glasses. This is because the reading glasses transmit most of the light energy that is incident upon them, whereas the sunglasses absorb more light energy, which increases their internal energy.

7. In a clothing shop lit only by fluorescent lighting, a customer during daytime insists on taking garments by the doorway to check their color. Is the customer being reasonable? Explain.

The customer is being reasonable in requesting to see the colors in the daylight. Under fluorescent lighting, with its predominant higher frequencies, the bluer colors rather than the redder colors will be accented. Colors will appear quite different in sunlight.

8. What is the common color of tennis balls, and why?
Yellow-green, because that color is more noticed by our eyes.

9. What color does red cloth appear when illuminated by sunlight? By red light from a neon sign? By cyan light?
Red cloth appears red in sunlight, and red by the illumination of the red light from a neon tube. But because the red cloth absorbs cyan light, it appears black when illuminated by cyan light.

10. Why does a white piece of paper appear white in white light, red in red light, blue in blue light, and so on for every color?
A piece of white paper reflects all the colors in sunlight so it will reflect whatever color shines on it.

11. A spotlight that has a white-hot filament is coated so that it won't transmit yellow light. What color is the emerging beam of light?
The color that will emerge from a spotlight coated to absorb yellow is blue, the complementary color. (White - yellow = blue.)

12. Below is a photo of science editor Suzanne with son Tristan wearing red and daughter Simone wearing green. Below that is the negative photo, which shows these colors differently. What is your explanation?
The red shirt in the photo is seen as cyan in the negative, and the green shirt appears magenta—the complementary colors of these two. When white light shines through the negative, red is transmitted where cyan is absorbed. Likewise, green is transmitted where magenta is absorbed. Negatives show the complementary colors of those in the photo.

13. Complete the following equations:
Yellow light + blue light = _____ light.
Green light + _____ light = white light.
Magenta light + yellow light + cyan light = _____ light.
Yellow light + blue light = *white* light.
Green light + *magenta* light = white light.
Magenta light + yellow light + cyan light = *white* light.

14. Check to see if the following three statements are accurate. Then fill in the last statement. (All colors are combined by addition of light.)
Red + green + blue = white.
Red + green = yellow = white – blue.
Red + blue = magenta = white – green.
Green + blue = cyan = white – _____.
Green + blue = cyan = white - *red*.

15. If the sky were composed of atoms that predominantly scattered orange light rather than blue, what color would sunsets be?
If the sky normally scattered orange light, then sunsets would be the complementary color of orange, a "sky blue." (White - sunset orange = sky blue.)

16. Does light travel faster through the lower atmosphere or the upper atmosphere? Defend your answer.
Light travels faster through the upper atmosphere where the density is less and there are fewer interactions with molecules in the air.

17. Comment on the statement, "Oh, that beautiful red sunset is just the leftover colors that weren't scattered on their way through the atmosphere."
The statement is true. A more positive tone would omit the word "just," for the sunset is not *just* the leftover colors, but *is* those colors that weren't scattered in other directions.

18. Volcanic emissions spew fine ashes in the air that scatter red light. What color does a full moon appear through these ashes?

Through the volcanic emissions, the moon appears cyan, the complementary color of red.

19. If the atmosphere of the Earth were several times thicker, would ordinary snowfall still seem white or would it be some other color? What color?
If the atmosphere were several times thicker, the sunlight reaching the Earth would be of predominantly low frequencies because most of the blue light would be scattered away. Snow would likely appear orange at noon, and a deep red when the sun is not directly overhead.

20. Tiny particles, like tiny bells, scatter high-frequency waves more than low-frequency waves. Large particles, like large bells, mostly scatter low frequencies. Intermediate-size particles and bells mostly scatter intermediate frequencies. What does this have to do with the whiteness of clouds?
Clouds are composed of atoms, molecules, and particles of a variety of sizes. So not only are high-frequency colors scattered from clouds, but middle and low frequencies as well. A combination of all the scattered colors produces white.

Solutions for Chapter 14 Problems

1. The sun is 1.50×10^{11} meters from the Earth. How long does it take for the sun's light to reach the Earth?

From $v = \dfrac{d}{t}$, $\quad t = \dfrac{d}{v} = \dfrac{d}{c} = \dfrac{1.5 \times 10^{11} m}{3 \times 10^{8} m/s} = 500$ s (which equals 8.3 min).

2. In about 1675 the Danish astronomer Olaus Roemer found that light from eclipses of Jupiter's moon took an extra 1000 s to travel 300,000,000 km across the diameter of the Earth's orbit around the sun. Show how this finding provided the first reasonably accurate measurement for the speed of light.

Speed $= \dfrac{\text{distance}}{\text{time}} = \dfrac{300\,000\,000 \text{ km}}{1000 \text{ s}} = 300{,}000$ km/s.

3. In 1969 people had the opportunity to sense the speed of light when on TV they heard on a NASA controller in Houston speak to an astronaut on the moon. A longer than normal delay occurred in the back and forth conversation. How long did it take the signals to get to the moon and back?

$t = \dfrac{d}{v} = 3.84 \times 10^{8}$ m/3×10^{8} m/s = 1.3 s. Round trip is twice this, 2.6 s.

4. The nearest star beyond the sun is Alpha Centauri, 4.2×10^{16} meters away from the Earth. If we receive a radio message from this star today, how long ago was it sent?

$t = \dfrac{d}{v} = \dfrac{4.2 \times 10^{16} \text{ m}}{3 \times 10^{8} \text{ m/s}} = 1.4 \times 10^{8}$ s. (That's a bit more than 4.4 years ago!)

15 Reflection and Refraction

15.1 Reflection of Light
15.2 Refraction—the Bending of Light Due to Changing Speed
15.3 Illusions and Mirages are Caused by Atmospheric Refraction
15.4 Light Dispersion and Rainbows
15.5 Lenses Are a Practical Application of Refraction
 | Link to Physiology—Your Eye |
15.6 Image Formation by a Lens
 | Link to Optometry |

Learning Objectives

After studying Chapter 15, students will be able to:

• Distinguish between what happens to light when it strikes a metal surface and when it strikes glass or water.
• Given the direction of light striking a reflective surface, predict the path of the reflected light.
• Explain why the image formed by a mirror is a virtual image.
• Describe the conditions for diffuse reflection.
• Give examples of ways to control reflected sound.
• Explain the change in direction of a water wave when it crosses a boundary between deep and shallow water.
• Give examples of refraction of sound waves and its effects.
• Give examples of refraction of light and its effects.
• Explain how a prism separates white light into colors.
• Describe the conditions for a rainbow.
• Distinguish between a converging and diverging lens.
• Distinguish between a real image and a virtual image formed by a lens.
• Give examples of aberration in lenses.

Possible Misconceptions to Correct

• **Not so!** The average speed of light is constant in all transparent materials.
• **Not so!** The average speed of light and the instantaneous speed of light are the same.
• **Not so!** The law of reflection applies only to plane surfaces.
• **Not so!** Both sound and light travel only in straight lines.
• **Not so!** A prism changes (rather than separates) white light into colors.
• **Not so!** A rainbow is a physical thing that can be approached and grasped if you're lucky.

Demonstration Equipment

• Glass tank of water with dye added, prism, mirror, and light source (laser)
• Rainbow sticks (shown below)

Reflection is highlighted by the half-size mirror problem, Exercises 2 through 5, which nicely illustrate one of the valuable things about your course—that the richness in life is not only seeing the world with wide open eyes, but in knowing what to look for. Concepts in this chapter provide a lot of guidance in this respect.

Paul Doherty makes rainbows that his students can study first hand at the Exploratorium. You can too. Your giant water drop is a glass sphere filled with water. Cut a hole that's slightly larger than your sphere in a piece of white cardboard. Shine a bright beam of light from a slide projector or the sun through the hole so that the beam illuminates the entire water drop. The drop will project a colored circle of light onto the cardboard screen around the hole you have cut. If at first you don't see a circle of light, move the screen closer to the drop, as Paul shows to the left! (See his article on rainbows in the Exploratorium quarterly, *Exploring* (Summer 1992). Thanx Paul!

Courtesy Exploratorium

I owe the conical treatment of the rainbow to one of Cecil Adams' syndicated newspaper columns, *The Straight Dope*.

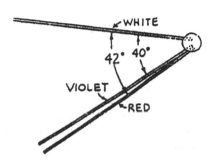

An explanation of why a rainbow is bow-shaped is aided with this simple apparatus that is easily constructed: Stick three colored dowels into a sphere of clay, Styrofoam, wood, or whatever that represents a raindrop. One dowel is white, one violet, and the other red, to represent incident white light and refracted red and violet. The angles between dowels are shown in the sketch. A student volunteer crouching in front of your chalkboard shows the class how the only drops that cast light to him or her originate in drops along a bow-shaped region. (More on this in the lecture below.)

In the **Practice Book**:
• Reflection
• Refraction
• Measuring the Diameter of the Sun with a Ruler
• Lenses

In the **Next-Time Questions** book:
• Girl with Mirror
• Full-Length Mirror
• Pocket Mirror
• Bridge Reflection
• Coin Refraction
• Laser Spearfishing
• Atmospheric Laser Shoot
• Underwater Viewing

In the **Lab Manual**:
• Pinhole Image
• Pinhole Camera
• Mirror, Mirror, on the Wall

Overhead Transparencies (4) available for:
Figures 15.1, 15.2, 15.5; Figures 15.8, 15.10, 15.11, 15.15 and Figures 15.18, 15.19, 15.20.

SUGGESTED PRESENTATION

Begin by pointing out that light from a point source follows the inverse-square law (first treated in Chapter 7, and again for Coloumb's law in Chapter 11). A camera flash is a point source, obeys the inverse-square law, something that is not understood by people who attempt to take pictures of far-away nighttime scenes with flash cameras—like snapping long-distance shots at a nighttime concert, or a night view of a distant city. I cite the airline passenger I saw some years ago taking flash shots of a distant dark city below through the aircraft window! Cite how light from the flash spreads out on both the outgoing and return trip to the camera, consequently delivering very little light to the camera. And if through a window, how the light reflected from the window overwhelms what little light would survive the roundtrip anyway.

On the subject of flash photography, cite the futility of using a flash to take pictures of slides or a movie projected on a screen in a dark room. Of course, the flash overwhelms the image projected and the picture ends up showing a blank white screen.

15.1 Reflection of Light
Anybody who has played pool is familiar with the law of reflection—angle of incidence equals angle of rebound. Likewise for light. Sketch Figure 15.2 on the board and carefully show how image and object distance are the same. Call attention to the curved mirrors of Figure 15.3 and stress that the law reigns in whatever small region a light ray strikes. Likewise with **diffuse reflection**. Discuss Exercise 8, about the diffuse dry road becoming a "plane mirror" when wet, and hence the difficulty of seeing the road in a car on a rainy night.

15.2 Refraction—the Bending of Light Due to Changing Speed
Do not fail to emphasize the cause of refraction: A change in the speed of light in going from one medium to another. The slowing of light in transparent mediums was established in Chapter 14. The analogy of the wheels rolling onto the grass lawn (Figure 15.8) shows that bending of path is the result of this change of speed. This is reinforced in *Practicing Physical Science—Explorations*.

Cite common examples of refraction: shallower looking pools, distorted viewing in fish tanks, and the operation of lenses, as we shall soon see.

15.3 Illusions and Mirages are Caused by Atmospheric Refraction
The most interesting, perhaps, are mirages. With chalkboard diagrams, show how gradual refraction, caused by a gradually changing air density, produces such phenomena as the displaced sun at sunset (and consequently a longer day, Figure 15.13), and the mirages of Figures 15.15 and 15.16.

15.4 Light Dispersion and Rainbows
Now that you've established refraction as a result of changes in light speed, it follows that different speeds of different frequencies of light in transparent materials refract at different angles. This is dispersion, nicely illustrated with a prism.

Rainbows
Amplify the section on rainbows, and liken them to viewing a cone held with its apex to the eye. The deeper the misty region, the more intense the rainbow appears. The cone bit explains why the rainbow is round. Another is via the ball-and-sticks demo.

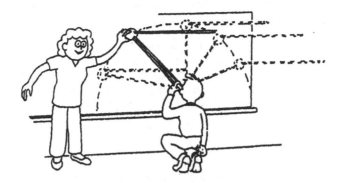

DEMONSTRATION: Show the rainbow-sticks apparatus described earlier and compare it to the rainbow schematic drawing of Figures 15.18 and 15.19. The white stick represents incoming white light, and the red and violet sticks the refracted rays. Have a student volunteer crouch in front of the board as shown in the sketch. Place the ball near the chalkboard so the white dowel is perpendicular to the board (from the sun at the horizon for simplicity). Position the free end of the violet dowel so that it nearly meets the volunteer's eye. State that a drop at this location refracts violet light to the eye. The question follows: Are there other locations that will also refract violet light to the eye? Move the "drop" to other locations along the board while keeping the white dowel perpendicular to the board. It is easy to see that refracted violet from drops farther away miss the eye altogether. The only locations that send violet light to the eye are along a bow—which you trace with violet or blue chalk. This is easy to do if the students hold the end of the violet dowel near the eye while you scribe the arc in compass fashion.

CHECK YOUR NEIGHBOR: With the ball and dowels positioned at the top of the bow, ask where the volunteer must look to see red—above the violet, or below? [Above (2° to be exact).] Show this by moving the "drop" up, whereupon the red dowel lines up with the eye. Complete your demo by sweeping this wider bow with red chalk.

Enlist a second volunteer to crouch in front of the board at a different position. Show how this volunteer must look to different drops in the sky to see a rainbow. Ask the class if the two volunteers see the same rainbow. [No, each sees his or her own personal rainbow!] Do as Marshall Ellenstein does and quip that when one person says to another, "Look at the beautiful rainbow," an appropriate response is, "Move over and let me see!"

Rainbows cannot be seen when the sun is more than 42 degrees in the sky because the bow is below the horizon where no water drops are to be seen. Hence rainbows are normally seen early and late in the day. So we don't see rainbows in midday in summer in most parts of the world (except from an airplane, where they are seen in full circles).

Point out a significant yet commonly unnoticed feature about the rainbow—that the disk segment bounded by the bow is appreciably brighter than the rest of the sky. This is clearly shown in Figure 15.22 (a photo out my bedroom window). The rainbow is similar to the chromatic aberration around a bright spot of projected white light.

Show Paul Doherty's rainbow from a sphere of water (described before this suggested presentation).

Extend rainbows to the similar phenomenon of the halo around the moon. Explain how the halo is produced by refraction of moonlight through ice crystals in the atmosphere. Note the important difference: Whereas both refraction and internal reflection produce rainbows, only refraction produces halos. And whereas the observer is between the sun and the drops for seeing a rainbow, the ice crystals that produce halos are between the observer and the moon.

Moonlight is refracted through ice crystals high in the atmosphere—evidence of the coldness up there even on a hot summer night.

15.5 Lenses Are a Practical Application of Refraction
The explanation of lenses follows from your demo of light deviating through a prism. Whereas a study of lenses is properly a laboratory activity, all the ray diagrams in the world are of little value unless paired with a hands-on experience with lenses. So if a laboratory experience is not part of your course, I would recommend lenses be treated very briefly if at all in lecture.

15.6 Image Formation by a Lens

DEMONSTRATION: Show examples of converging and diverging lenses. A white light source will do, but a neat source of light is a laser beam that is widened by lenses and then directed through a mask of parallel slits. Then parallel rays of light are incident upon your lenses.

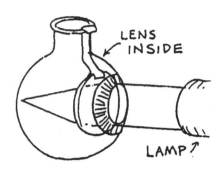

DEMONSTRATION: Simulate the human eye with a spherical flask filled with water and a bit of fluorescein dye. Paint an "iris" on the flask and position appropriate lenses in back of the iris for normal, farsighted and nearsighted vision. Then show how corrective lenses placed in front of the eye put the light in focus on the retina.

Exercise 16 about the sheet of lenses that supposedly direct more solar energy into a swimming pool makes a good lecture topic. It underscores the conservation of energy—that no lens system or other device can get more energy out of sunlight than the energy it carries. A small lens can concentrate energy, but it's only taking what there is and directing it to a smaller area. The lenses on a swimming pool cover do that locally, but overall, the energy hitting the pool is the energy that meets the water.

Seeing Light: The Eye
An interesting tidbit not in the chapter is the explanation for the seemingly luminous eyes of nocturnal animals such as cats and owls at night. It turns out there are reflective membranes located in back of the rods in the animals' eyes, which provide a "second chance" for the animal to perceive light that initially misses the rods. This arrangement, common in night predators, gives excellent night vision. Hence also the reflection from their eyes when light is shone on them.

Discuss the function of the rods and three types of cones in the retina of the eye, and how color cannot be perceived in dim light, and how the colored stars appear white to us whereas they show up clearly colored with camera time exposures. (I show a colored slide that I took of the stars, and discuss the curved lines encircling the north star, and get into a discussion of how long the camera shutter was held open.)

In discussing color vision, point out that in a bullfight, the bull is angry not at the redness of the cape that is flaunted before him, but because of the darts that have been stuck into him! Whereas a frog is "wired" to see only motion, so it is also on the periphery of human vision. Discuss the fact that we see only motion and no color at the periphery of our vision.

DEMONSTRATION: Stand at a corner of the room and shake brightly colored cards, first turned backward so the color is hidden and students can adjust their head positions (somewhat facing the opposite corner of the room). When they barely see the moving cards, turn them over so the color shows. They'll see the cards, but not their colors. Try with different colors. This goes over well, and is quite surprising!

NEXT-TIME QUESTIONS: Be sure to ask for the minimum size mirror bit, Exercises 2 - 5, and a Next-Time-Question. [I regret to report, that seldom do I find half of my class answering Exercises 2 and 3 correctly—particularly when I first emphasize that the results will be surprising, and that if they are careful they will learn something about their image in a mirror that has likely escaped them all their lives (that the size of the mirror is independent of their distance from it). Most correctly get the first part, the half-size answer, but miss the second. That's where I ask them to mark the mirror where they see the top of their head and bottom of their chin, and then to step back and look carefully for the effect of distance.

Perhaps like the visual illusion of Exploration 1 at the end of Chapter 7 (judging hand sizes), their belief in their uninvestigated answer is so strong, that they will not see what is there unless it is explicitly pointed out to them. Are your students more perceptive than ours?] In any event, when you discuss the answer, bring into class a full-length mirror or pass a few small mirrors among your students. It's worth the extra effort.

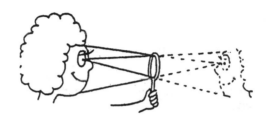

Chapter 15 Answers and Solutions

Key Terms and Matching Definitions

__5__ converging lens
__4__ diffuse reflection
__6__ diverging lens
__3__ law of reflection
__1__ reflection
__8__ real image
__2__ refraction
__7__ virtual image

Review Questions

1. What does incident light that falls on this page do to the electrons in the atoms of the page?
   Sets them into vibration.

2. What do the electrons in this illuminated page do when they are energized?
   They re-emit the light.

3. What is the law of reflection?
   The angle of reflection equals the angle of incidence.

4. Relative to the distance of an object in front of a plane mirror, how far behind the mirror is the image?
   Same.

5. How does a change in speed of a ray of light affect its direction when it passes from one medium to another?
   A change in speed causes the ray to bend from its original path.

6. When a wheel rolls from a smooth sidewalk onto grass, the interaction of the wheel with the blades of grass slows the wheel. What slows light when it passes from air into glass or water?
   Interaction of light with atoms in the medium.

7. What is the angle between a ray and its wave front?
   90°.

8. Why does a setting sun often appear elliptical instead of round?
   Light from its upper surface travels faster through slightly less dense air and bends downward, shrinking the vertical diameter.

9. Why do stars twinkle?
   Because of varying densities of air with resulting variable atmospheric refraction.

10. What happens to light of a certain frequency when it resonates with electrons of atoms in a material?
    That light is absorbed.

11. Which travels more slowly in glass, red light or violet light?
    Violet light.

12. If light of different frequencies has different speeds in a material, does it also refract at different angles in the same material? Explain.
    Yes. Light rays change direction because of differences in speed; the greater the differences, the greater the angles of refraction.

13. What prevents rainbows from being seen as complete circles?

13. What prevents rainbows from being seen as complete circles?
The ground gets in the way.

14. Where must the sun be to view a rainbow?
In back of you.

15. Does a viewer see a single color or a spectrum of colors coming from a single faraway raindrop?
A single color because the pupil is small. To see different colors, look to drops in different locations.

16. Why is a secondary rainbow dimmer than a primary bow?
Dimmer because of an extra reflection and refraction.

17. Distinguish between a *converging lens* and a *diverging lens*.
Converging lens converges parallel light; diverging lens diverges same.

18. What is the *focal length* of a lens?
Distance where parallel light rays converge after passing through the lens.

19. Distinguish between a *virtual image* and a *real image*.
A virtual image is one formed by light rays that converge at the location of the image. A real image is formed by light rays that converge at the location of the image.

20. What kind of lens can be used to produce a real image? A virtual image?
Converging. Diverging.

Solutions to Chapter 15 Exercises

1. An eye at point P looks into the mirror. Which of the numbered cards is seen reflected in the mirror?

Only light from card number 2 reaches her eye.

2. What must be the minimum length of a plane mirror in order for you to see a full view of yourself?
The minimum length of a vertical mirror must be half your height in order for you to see a full-length view of yourself. This is because the light from your feet that reaches your eyes via the mirror meets the mirror halfway up. Then its angle of incidence (from your feet) equals the angle of reflection (to your eyes). Likewise, light from the top of your head meets the mirror halfway down to reflect at the same angle to reach your eyes. Halfway up and halfway down means you can see all of yourself with a mirror that is half your height (and half your width).

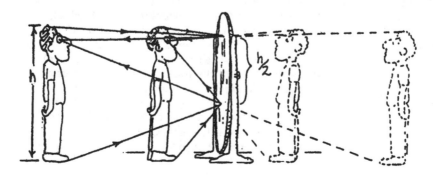

3. What effect does your distance from the plane mirror have in the above answer? (Try it and see!)
    **The half-height mirror works at any distance, as shown in the sketch above. This is be-
    cause if you move closer, your image moves closer as well. If you move farther away,
    your image does the same. Many people must actually try this before they believe it. The
    confusion arises because people know that they can see whole distant buildings or even
    mountain ranges in a hand-held pocket mirror. Even then, the distance the object is from
    the mirror is the same as the distance of the virtual image on the other side of the mirror.
    You can see all of a distant person in your mirror, but the distant person cannot see all of
    herself in your mirror.**

4. On a steamy mirror wipe away just enough to see your full face. How tall will the wiped area be
    compared with the vertical dimension of your face?
    It will be half as tall.

5. Hold a pocket mirror at almost arm's length from your face and note the amount of your face you can
    see. To see more of your face, should you hold the mirror closer or farther, or would you have to have
    a larger mirror? (Try it and see!)
    **Note in your pocket mirror that the amount of your face you can see is twice the size of
    the mirror—whether you hold it close or at arm's length. Interesting information!**

6. The diagram shows a person and her twin at equal distances on opposite sides of a thin wall.
    Suppose a window is to be cut in the wall so that each twin can see a complete view of the other.
    Show the size and location of the smallest window that can be cut in the wall to do the job. (*Hint:*
    Draw rays from the top of each twin's head to the other twin's eyes. Do the same from the feet of each
    to the eyes of the other.)
    **The smallest window will be half the height of the person or her twin. Note that this
    does not depend on distance, providing both subjects are the same distance from the
    wall. This illustrates Exercises 3 , 4, and 5 above.**

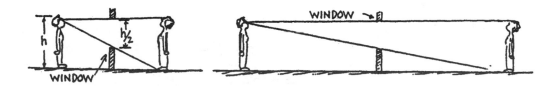

7. Why is the lettering on the front of some vehicles "backwards"?
    Such lettering is seen in proper form in the rearview mirrors of cars ahead.

8. Which kind of road surface is easier to see when driving at night, a pebbled uneven surface or a
    mirror-smooth surface? Explain.
    **A pebbled uneven surface produces more diffuse reflection when your headlights shine
    on it. This is good, for the part directed backward is what you see. A mirrored surface
    won't do this, and furthermore, a mirrored surface would direct glare from oncoming
    cars to you. Go for a rough surface.**

9. A person in a dark room looking through a window can clearly see a person outside in the daylight,
    whereas the person outside cannot see the person inside. Explain.
    **A window is both transparent to light and a reflector of light. Whether it serves
    principally as a reflector or a transmitter depends on the relative intensities of light
    being reflected and transmitted. The person outside in the daylight who looks at the
    window of a room that is dark inside sees only outside light reflected from the window
    and almost no light transmitted from the room. The glass serves as a mirror. From the
    point of view of a person inside the dark room, only outside light is seen when looking
    at the window glass. The situation is reversed at nighttime when it is dark outside and
    the room is lit up. People in the room cannot see outside, and see only reflections of the
    room interior when they look at the window glass. The room or the outside does not
    have to be perfectly dark for this effect. A typical window may only reflect about 8% of**

the light that is incident upon it, and transmit most of the other 92%. In the daytime 8% of the outside bright daylight reflected from the glass will likely be brighter than 92% of the relatively dim inside light that is transmitted from the room to the outside.

10. A pair of toy cart wheels are rolled obliquely from a smooth surface onto two plots of grass, a rectangular plot and a triangular plot as shown below. The ground is on a slight incline so that after slowing down in the grass, the wheels speed up again when they emerge on the smooth surface. Finish each sketch by showing some positions of the wheels inside the plots and on the other sides, thereby indicating the direction of travel.

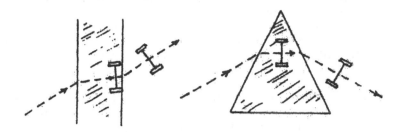

11. If light of all frequencies traveled at the same speed in glass, how would white light appear after passing through a prism?
If light of all frequencies traveled at the same speed in glass there would be no refraction, no dispersion, and no spectrum of colors. The white light incident upon a prism would emerge as white light.

12. If you were in a boat and spearing a fish you see in the water, would you aim above, below, or directly at the fish to make a direct hit? (Assume the fish is stationary in the water.) If you instead used light from a laser as your "spear," would you aim above, below, or directly at the observed fish? Defend your answers.
In spearing a fish with a laser, make no corrections and simply aim directly at the fish. This is because the light from the fish you see has been refracted in getting to you, and the laser light will refract along the same path in getting to the fish. A slight correction may be necessary, depending on the colors of the laser beam and the fish—see the next exercise.

13. If you were to send a beam of laser light to a space station above the atmosphere and just above the horizon, would you aim the laser above, below, or at the visible space station? Defend your answer.
In sending a laser beam to a space station, make no corrections and simply aim at the station you see. This is like spearing the fish in Exercise 12. The path of refraction is the same in either direction.

14. Two observers standing apart from one another do not see the "same" rainbow. Explain.
The fact that two observers standing apart from one another do not see the same rainbow can be understood by exaggerating the circumstance: Suppose the two observers are several kilometers apart. Obviously they are looking at different drops in the sky. Although they may both see a rainbow, they are looking at different rainbows. Likewise if they are closer together. Only if their eyes are at the very same location will they see exactly the same rainbow.

15. A rainbow viewed from an airplane may form a complete circle. Where will the shadow of the airplane appear? Explain.
Seen from high enough, as from an airplane, the rainbow makes a complete circle. The shadow of the airplane will appear in the center of the circular bow. This is because the airplane is directly between the sun and the drops or rain cloud producing the bow.

16. Transparent plastic swimming-pool covers called *solar heat sheets* have thousands of small lenses made up of air-filled bubbles. The lenses in these sheets are advertised as being able to focus heat from the sun into the water and raise its temperature. Do you think the lenses of such sheets direct a greater amount of solar energy into the water? Defend your answer.

A magnifying lens used as a "burning glass" does nothing more than gather a certain amount of energy and concentrate it at some focal point. The important point is that the lens is considerably larger than the area over which the light is concentrated. But the solar heat sheet is not larger than the surface area of the swimming pool, and doesn't collect any more solar energy than the pool receives anyway. The sheet may help warm the pool by preventing evaporation, as would be the case with any cover, but in no way do the lenses direct additional solar energy to the water beneath. This fraudulent advertising plays on the ignorance of the public.

17. Would the average intensity of sunlight measured by a light meter at the bottom of the pool in Figure 15.27 be different if the water were still?
The average intensity of sunlight at the bottom is the same whether the water is moving or is still. Light that misses one part of the bottom of the pool reaches another part. Every dark region is balanced by a bright region—"conservation of light."

18. In taking a photograph, what would happen to the image if you cover up the bottom half of the lens?
By covering half the lens you cut the light intensity on the film in half, but you do not cut out half the image. Light from all parts of the lens contribute to all parts of the image, so the light through the top half of the lens carries a full image to the film. Similarly, when your pupils contract, the amount of light entering your eye is reduced, but not the amount of image. (Experiment and see!)

19. Why do you have to put slides into a slide projector upside down?
You put slides upside down because the lens inverts the image.

20. Maps of the moon are upside down. Why?
Maps of the moon are upside down because images of the moon through the lenses of telescopes show an inverted image of the moon. The maps then match what the astronomy type sees.

Solutions for Chapter 15 Problems

1. If you take a photo of your image in a plane mirror, how many meters away should you set your focus for if you are 3 meters in front of the mirror?
6 meters, the distance between your camera and your image.

2. If you walk toward a mirror at 2 m/s, how fast do you and your image approach each other?
Velocity is relative. You and your image approach each other at 4 m/s.

3. No glass is perfectly transparent. Consider a pane of glass that transmits 92% of the light incident upon it. How much light is transmitted through two of these sheets together?
The amount of light transmitted through two sheets of glass is 84.6%. To see this, consider an incident intensity of 100 units. Then 92 units are transmitted through the first pane. 92% of this amount are transmitted through the second pane (0.92 of 92 = 84.6).

16 Properties of Light

Learning Objectives
After studying Chapter 16, the students will be able to:
• Explain why water waves have curved wave fronts after passing through a narrow opening.
• Describe the conditions necessary for visible diffraction of waves.
• Describe the conditions necessary for visible bright and dark fringes of light caused by interference.
• Explain what causes the bright and dark bands reflected from a thin material.
• Explain what causes the colors that shine from soap bubbles or gasoline slicks on a wet surface.
• Distinguish between light from a laser and light from a lamp.
• Distinguish between a hologram and a photograph.

Possible Misconceptions to Correct
• **Not so!** Light travels only in straight lines.
• **Not so!** Light cannot cancel light.
• **Not so!** A laser is an energy source that can put out more energy than it consumes.
• **Not so!** Light cannot be both a particle and a wave.

Demonstration Equipment
• Pieces of cards with a slit cut in them, and a vertical fluorescent lamp
• Laser
• Polarized sheets
• Soap bubble production gear

Quantum physics is introduced at the end of this chapter. Much of the confusion about quantum physics has to do with the questions one asks. The answers one gets often depends on the way the question is asked. This is illustrated by the two monks who wished to smoke in the prayer room of a monastery. The first monk wrote a letter to his superior asking if it was permissible to smoke while praying. The answer was a resounding no. The second monk wrote a letter to his superior asking if it was permissible to pray while smoking. The answer was a resounding yes—one can pray always. In a sort of similar way, many of the perplexities of quantum physics have to do with the way questions are asked, and more particularly with what kind of questions are asked. For example, asking for the energy of a hydrogen atom in its first excited state has a definite answer, accurate to one part in 10^{12}. The answer to asking exactly when the electron makes its transition to the ground state, on the other hand, is probabilistic. The probabilistic answers to such questions foster the false notion that there are no exact answers at the quantum realm. Questions appropriate to the quantum realm, however, are crisply and precisely answered by quantum mechanics.

In the **Practice Book**:
• Interference
• Polarization
• Wave-Particle Duality

In the **Next-Time Questions** book:
• Polarized Glasses
• Sandwiched Polaroids

Overhead Transparencies (3) available for:
Figures 16.5, 16.9, Figure 16.11, and Figure 16.17.

SUGGESTED PRESENTATION

This chapter is best begun with a ripple tank to show wave patterns as they pass though narrow openings. A model is shown in Figure 16. 1. This is a place to play with soap bubbles. Call attention to how colors best show against a dark background. Against a bright background, they are overwhelmed by brighter light.

16.1 Diffraction—the Spreading of Light
Introduce diffraction with the following demonstration.

> DEMONSTRATION: Pass some index cards with razor slits in them throughout the class. Show a vertical show-case lamp or fluorescent lamp separated into three segments by colored plastic: red, clear, and blue. Have your students view the diffraction of these three segments through the slit, or through a slit provided by their own fingers. Note the different fringe spacings of different colors.

16.2 Interference—Constructive and Destructive
Diffraction fringes are produced by interference, introduced in the previous chapter with sound. Review this by sketching the overlapping of water waves on the board, like that shown in Figure 16.5. Point out that interference is a property of light waves, sound waves, and ALL kinds of waves.

Prepare your class for your laser demonstration by holding a piece of glass with an irregular surface (shower door glass, sugar bowl cover, crystal glassware) against a laser and show the interference pattern on a screen. Be sure to hold the glass steady so the pattern is fixed. Then make a sketch similar to Figure 16.9 on the board to explain the fringes (a dark area is the result of waves meeting out of phase; a bright area where waves meet in phase).

> DEMONSTRATION: This is a great one! With the lights out, shine laser light through the same irregular piece of glass and display beautiful interference patterns on the wall, but this time while you make slight movements of the glass. I do this in rhythm with music (Bach's Suite Three in D.) Your students will not forget this demonstration!

> DEMONSTRATION: Set up a sodium lamp and show interference fringes due to reflection from a pair of glass plates with a toothpick or bit of paper in between to separate them slightly. Press lightly on the top plate and show the changed interference pattern.

The practice sheet that treats Figure 16.9 should be helpful at this point. Pass around diffraction gratings if available.

16.3 Interference Colors by Reflection from Thin Films
Bubble time! Your class will be delighted if you show a display of giant bubbles (made with a wide hoop in a wide tray of bubble solution—a mixture of equal amounts of Joy or Dawn dishwashing liquid, glycerin, and water). Point out that the film of the soap bubble is the thinnest thing seen by the unaided eye—5000 times thinner than a human hair or cigarette

paper. The smallness of light waves is sensed here also. Emphasize the need for two surfaces for interference colors, and why the film should be thin.

Go through the text explanation of interference colors seen from splotches of gasoline on a wet street. Treat a single wave of blue light, first from only a single surface where one would see a blue reflection. This would be the case with no gasoline film on a water surface. Then draw a second surface, that of the thin film of gasoline and show that the proper thickness (1/4 wave) will produce cancellation of the blue light. Ask how many students have ever seen gasoline films illuminated with blue light. None. But sunlight, yes. And when sunlight is incident the blue part is canceled. The complementary color of blue, yellow, is what is seen.

> CHECK YOUR NEIGHBOR: Why are interference colors not seen from gasoline spilled on a dry surface? [Only one plane reflecting surface is present. The lower surface of the gasoline film is also not plane, but as irregular as the road surface it rests upon.]

16.4 Polarization—Evidence for the Transverse Wave Nature of Light
Distinguish between polarized and nonpolarized light.

> DEMONSTRATION: Tie a rubber tube to a distant firm support and pass it through a grating (as from a refrigerator or oven shelf). Have a student hold the grating while you shake the free end and produce transverse waves. Show that when the grating "axis" and the plane of "polarization" are aligned, the wave passes. And when they are at right angles, the wave is blocked.

Crossed Polaroids with another sandwiched between, as shown by Ludmila in Figure 16.20 is a dandy. Second only to the sailboat sailing into the wind, it is my favorite illustration of vectors. The explanation for the passage of light through the system of three Polaroids is not given in the chapter, but is indicated in Figure C.12, Appendix C (repeated here more quantitatively).

[For an ideal polarizer, 50% of nonpolarized incident light is transmitted. That is why a Polaroid passes so little light compared to a sheet of window pane. The transmitted light is polarized. So in the above diagram, only the electric vector aligned with the polarization axis is transmitted; this is 50% of the incident light transmitted by the first sheet. The magnitude of this vector through the second sheet is 50% cos ø, where ø is the angle between the polarization axes of both sheets, and (50% cos ø) cos α of the original vector gets through the third sheet,

where α is the angle between the polarization axes of the second and third sheet. The intensity of light is proportional to the square of the emerging vector (not treated in the textbook). In any event, the polarizers are less than ideal, so less than this actually gets through the three-sheet system.]

After explaining how the light that reflects from nonmetallic surfaces is polarized in a plane parallel to the surface (by drawing an analogy of skipping flat rocks off a water surface only when the plane of the rock is parallel to the water surface), draw a couple of pair of sunglasses on the board with the polarization axes as shown in the text and ask which are the best for reducing road glare. (If you want to discuss the viewing of three-dimensional slides and movies, you'll have a transition to such by the third choice of sunglasses with Polaroids at right angles to each other.)

Colors by Transmission Through Polarizing Materials

DEMONSTRATION: The vivid colors that emerge from cellophane between crossed Polaroids makes a spectacular demonstration. Have students make up some 2 x 2 inch slides of cut and crinkled cellophane mounted on Polaroid material (which can be obtained inexpensively from Edmund Scientific Co.). Place in a slide projector and rotate a sheet of Polaroid in front of the projecting lens so that a changing montage of colors is displayed on the screen. Also include a showing of color slides of the interference colors seen in the everyday environment, as well as of microscopic crystals. This is more effective with two projectors with hand dissolving from image to image on the screen. Do this in rhythm to some music, and while you're at it, shine a laser on a vibrating mirror stuck to a bare speaker cone, and you'll have an unforgettable lecture demonstration!

16.5 Wave-Particle Duality—Light Travels as a Wave, and Strikes Like a Particle
Cite the flavor of physics at the turn of the century, wherein many in the physics community felt that the bulk of physics was in the can and only applications and engineering were left. And then along came Einstein and Max Planck, who fell through cracks that turned out to be Grand Canyons! Quantum mechanics was born.

Discuss how light travels in bunches of light—*photons*, whose energies are directly proportional to their frequencies—$E \sim f$. Conventional thinking about light is that it is wave-like in traveling from place to place, but particle-like when incident upon matter, as evident in various **double slit experiments**. It travels like waves and lands like particles. Note the photon-by-photon buildup of the photograph of Figure 16.23.

Discussion of the wave-particle duality sets the stage for the brief treatments of quantum physics in following chapters.

Chapter 16 Answers and Solutions

Key Terms and Matching Definitions

__1__ diffraction
__2__ interference
__5__ photon
__4__ photoelectric effect
__3__ polarization

Review Questions

1. Is diffraction more pronounced through a small opening or through a large opening?
   Small opening.

2. For an opening of a given size, is diffraction more pronounced for a longer wavelength or a shorter wavelength?
   Longer wavelength.

3. What are some of the benefits and problems created by diffraction?
   Benefit in radio broadcast, where diffraction fills in shadow regions, particularly for longer wavelength AM radio. Benefit for dolphins who use diffraction to sense detail in their environment. Problem in microscopy, where fuzziness of an image occurs.

4. Is interference restricted to only some types of waves or does it occur for all types of waves?
   Interference is characteristic of ALL waves.

5. What is monochromatic light?
   Light of a single frequency (and wavelength).

6. What produces iridescence?
   Interference of light in double reflections.

7. What causes the variety of colors seen in gasoline splotches on a wet street?
   Interference by double reflection of light from top surface of gasoline and from top surface of water beneath.

8. What accounts for the variety of colors in a soap bubble?
   The variety of path lengths between inner and outer reflecting surfaces.

9. If you look at a soap bubble from different angles so that you're viewing different apparent thicknesses of soap film, do you see different colors? Explain.
   Yes, because different colors are canceled by interference via different apparent path lengths.

10. What phenomenon distinguishes between longitudinal and transverse waves?
    Polarization.

11. How does the direction of polarization of light compare with the direction of vibration of the electrons that produced it?
    Same.

12. Why does light pass through a pair of Polaroid filters when the axes are aligned but not when the axes are at right angles to each other?
    When axes are aligned, transverse waves have a path through each filter. When crossed, the path is blocked (see Figure 16.17).

13. How much unpolarized light does an ideal Polaroid filter transmit?
    50%.

14. When unpolarized light is incident at a grazing angle upon water, what can you say about the reflected light?
It is largely polarized in the plane of the water surface.

15. What evidence can you cite for the wave nature of light? For the particle nature of light?
Interference. Photoelectric effect.

16. Which are more successful in dislodging electrons from a metal surface, photons of violet light or photons of red light? Why?
Violet because each photon has more energy.

17. Why won't a very bright beam of red light impart more energy to an electron than a feeble beam of violet light?
The brightness of a beam has to do with the number of photons in it, but only one photon in the beam normally hits a single electron at one time. If a red one hits, low energy is given to it than if a higher-energy violet photon hits it. Energy per photon, not overall energy, is the gist of the photoelectric effect.

18. Does light behave primarily as a wave or as a particle when it interacts with the crystals of matter in photographic film?
Particle.

19. Does light travel from one place to another in a wave-like way or a particle-like way?
Wave-like.

20. When does light behave as a wave? When does it behave as a particle?
Travels as a wave, strikes as a particle.

Solutions to Chapter 16 Exercises

1. Why do radio waves diffract around buildings but light waves do not?
Radio waves are much longer and therefore diffract more than the shorter waves of light.

2. A pattern of fringes is produced when monochromatic light passes through a pair of thin slits. Is such a pattern produced by three parallel thin slits? By thousands of such slits? Give an example to support your answer.
Multiple slits of identical spacings produce a wider and brighter interference pattern. Such an arrangement makes up a diffraction grating (Figure 16.10), which is a popular alternative to a prism for dispersing light into its component parts.

3. The colors of peacocks and hummingbirds are the result not of pigments but of ridges in the surface layers of their feathers. By what physical principle do these ridges produce colors?
Diffraction is the principle by which peacocks and hummingbirds display their colors. The ridges in the surface layers of the feathers act as diffraction gratings.

4. The colored wings of many butterflies are due to pigmentation, but in some species, such as the Morpho butterfly, the colors do not result from any pigmentation. When the wing is viewed from different angles, the colors change. How are these colors produced?
Interference colors result from double reflections from the upper and lower surfaces of the thin transparent coating on the butterfly wings. Some other butterfly wings produce colors by diffraction, where ridges in the surface act as diffraction gratings.

5. Why do the iridescent colors seen in some seashells, especially abalone shells, change as the shells are viewed from different positions?
The optical paths of light from upper and lower reflecting surfaces change with different viewing positions. Thus, different colors can be seen by holding the shell at different angles.

6. When dishes are not properly rinsed after washing, different colors are reflected from their surfaces. Explain.

Interference of light from the upper and lower surfaces of the soap film is taking place.

7. If you notice the interference patterns of a thin film of oil or gasoline on water, you'll note that the colors form complete rings. How are these rings similar to the lines of equal elevation on a contour map?
The different colors reveal different thickness of the film. A contour map does the same with its different elevations connected by line that make complete "rings."

8. Why aren't interference colors seen on films of gasoline on a dry street?
On a dry street there are *not* two reflecting mirrored surfaces to produce interference.

9. Because of wave interference a film of oil on water is seen to be yellow to observers directly above in an airplane. What color does it appear to a scuba diver directly below?
What is seen below is the complementary color to yellow, blue.

10. Polarized light is a part of nature, but polarized sound is not. Why?
Polarization occurs only for transverse waves. Sound is longitudinal.

11. Why do Polaroid sunglasses reduce glare, whereas unpolarized sunglasses simply cut down on the total amount of light reaching the eyes?
Glare is composed largely of polarized light in the plane of the reflecting surface. Most glaring surfaces are horizontal (roadways, water, etc.), so sunglasses with vertical polarization axes filter the glare of horizontally polarized light. Conventional non-polarizing sunglasses simply cut down on overall light transmission either by reflecting or absorbing incident light.

12. The digital displays of watches and other devices are normally polarized. What problem occurs when wearing polarized sunglasses?
Depending on the axis of the Polaroid and that of the polarized display, cancellation may occur and one would see nothing.

13. How can you determine the polarization axis for a single sheet of Polaroid?
You can determine the polarization axis for a single sheet of Polaroid by viewing the glare from a flat surface. Glare is most intense when the polarization axis is parallel to the flat surface.

14. To reduce the glare of light from a polished floor, should the axis of a Polaroid filter be horizontal or vertical?
The axis should be vertical, to block the glare that is horizontal.

15. How can a single sheet of Polaroid film be used to show that the sky is partially polarized? (Interestingly enough, unlike humans, bees and many insects can discern polarized light and use this ability for navigation.)
You can determine that the sky is partially polarized by rotating a single sheet of Polaroid in front of your eye while viewing the sky. You'll notice the sky darken where polarization is greatest.

16. What percentage of light is transmitted by two ideal Polaroid filters atop each other with their polarization axes aligned? With their axes at right angles to each other?
With polarization axes aligned, a pair of Polaroids will transmit all components of light along the axes. That's 50%, as explained in the preceding answer. With axes at right angles, no light will be transmitted.

17. A beam of red light and a beam of blue light have exactly the same energy. Which beam contains the greater number of photons?
Since red light carries less energy per photon, and both beams have the same energy, there must be more photons in the beam of red light.

18. Silver bromide (AgBr) is a light-sensitive substance used in some types of photographic film. In order to be exposed, the film must be illuminated with light having sufficient energy to break apart the AgBr molecules. Why do you suppose this film may be handled without exposure in a darkroom

illuminated with red light? How about blue light? How about very bright red light as compared with very dim blue light?

The energy of red light is too low per photon to trigger the chemical reaction in the photographic crystals. Very bright light simply means more photons that are unable to trigger a reaction. Blue light, on the other hand, has sufficient energy per photon to trigger a reaction. Very dim blue light triggers fewer reactions only because there are fewer photons involved.

19. Suntanning produces cell damage in the skin. Why is ultraviolet radiation capable of producing this damage, but visible radiation is not?
More energy is associated with each photon of ultraviolet light than with photons that make up visible light. This extra energy per photon alters skin composition and produces sunburn.

20. Does the photoelectric effect *prove* that light is made of particles? Do interference experiments *prove* that light is composed of waves? (Is there a distinction between what something *is* and how it *behaves*?)
The photoelectric effect doesn't prove that light is corpuscular, but rather supports the corpuscular model of light, which is compatible with the particle-like behavior observed. Likewise with interference experiments that support the wave model of light and are compatible with the wave-like behavior of light. We have models to help us conceptualize what something *is*; knowledge of the details of how something behaves helps us to refine the model. It is important that we keep in mind that our models for understanding nature are just that: models.

Conceptual Physical Science—Explorations **Teaching Guide**

17 Atoms and the Periodic Table

Conceptual Physical Science—Explorations

17.1 Elements Contain a Single Kind of Atom
17.2 Atoms Are Mostly Empty Space
17.3 The Atomic Nucleus Is Made of Protons and Neutrons
17.4 Protons and Neutrons Determine Mass Number and Atomic Mass
17.5 Elements Are Organized in the Periodic Table by Their Properties
17.6 A Period Is a Horizontal Row, a Group a Vertical Column

Learning Objectives

After studying Chapter 17, students will be able to:
• Describe the relationship between atoms and elements.
• Compare the ages of atoms to the ages of the materials they compose.
• Give examples to illustrate the small size of atoms.
• Identify the parts of the atomic nucleus.
• Explain the significance of the horizontal rows and the vertical columns in the periodic table.

Possible Misconceptions to Correct

• **Not so!** Material things are made of thousands of different kinds of atoms.
• **Not so!** The atoms that make up a newborn baby were made in the mother's womb.
• **Not so!** The age of the atoms in a baby is less than the age of atoms in an old person.

No Demonstrations for this Chapter

In the **Practice Book:**
• Subatomic Particles
• Melting Points of the Elements
• Densities of the Elements

In the **Next-Time Questions** Book:
• Germanium Capsules
• Number of Carbon Atoms
• Neon
• Atomic Size

In the **Lab Manual:**
• Thickness of a BB Pancake (activity that nicely leads into the following experiment)
• Oleic Acid Pancake

Overhead Transparencies (3) available for:
Figures 17.5, 17.7, Figure 17.8, 17.11, and Figure 17.12.

Although only one neighbor check question is identified in the suggested presentation here, please make your own as your lecture unfolds.

SUGGESTED PRESENTATION

Begin by posing the situation of breaking a boulder into rocks, rocks into stones, stones into pebbles, pebbles into gravel, gravel into sand, sand into powder, and so forth until you get to the fundamental building block—the atom. Relate how from the earliest days of science the fundamental building block—the atom. Relate how from the earliest days of science people wondered how far the idea of breaking boulders into stones, pebbles, sand, powder, and so on, would go. Does it ever end? Hundreds of years ago, people had no way of finding out, and they instead carried on with philosophical speculation. Not until "modern" chemistry in the late 1700's did people begin to get indirect evidence of some basic order in the combinations of things. The first real "proof" that there were atoms was given by Einstein in 1905, the same year he published his paper on relativity. He calculated what kind of motion there ought to be in Brownian motion, based on ideas we've considered already, like energy and momentum conservation, and the idea of heat as atomic motion. Many of the "heavies" in physics at that time didn't believe in atoms until Einstein's work.

17.1 Elements Contain a Single Kind of Atom

This section contains the first mention of the periodic table. You might consider taking the opportunity to alleviate the fears some, if not many, of your students will have about having to memorize this chart. Of course, it is a good way to test memory skills, but memorizing the periodic table has very little to do with learning physical science. Instead, emphasize to students that through this course they will instead learn how to "read" the periodic table, which is a roadmap to the fundamental ingredients of all that surrounds us.

This section presents the modern definition of an *element*: A substance that contains only one kind of atom. Note how it is that the terms "element" and "atom" are sometimes used interchangeably. Generally, however, "element" is used to indicate a macroscopic sample, while "atom" is used to indicate the fundamental submicroscopic particle of the element.

Smallness of Atoms

Give examples to convey the idea of the smallness of the atom, i.e., an atom is as many orders of magnitude smaller than a person as an average star is larger than a person—so we stand between the atoms and the stars. The size of an atom is to the size of an apple as the size of an apple is to the size of the Earth. So if you want to imagine an apple full of atoms, think of the Earth, solid-packed with apples.

> CHECK QUESTION: Ask what an atom would "look like" if viewed through a vertical bank of about 40 high-powered optical microscopes stacked one atop the other. [It turns out they wouldn't have an appearance, at least not in the range of frequencies we call light. The atom is smaller than the wavelength of light.]

Recycling of Atoms

Complement the interesting information in the box, "A Breath of Air," with this info. State that if you put a drop of ink in a bathtub full of water, that you (the students) know that in a short time you can sample any part of the water and find ink in it. The atoms of ink spread out. We can get an idea of how small atoms are from this fact: There are more atoms in a thimbleful of ink than there are thimblefuls of water in the Atlantic Ocean. That means if you throw a thimbleful of ink into the Atlantic Ocean and give it enough years to mix uniformly, and then dip anywhere in the ocean with a thimble, you'll have some atoms of ink in your sample. Relate this to the statement made by Maitreya Suchocki in the part opening photo of Part 5.

17.2 Atoms Are Mostly Empty Space

Discuss the Bohr model of the atom and the electrical role of the nucleus and surrounding electrons. Stress the emptiness of the atom and lead into the idea of solid matter being mostly empty space. State how our bodies are 99.999% empty spaces, and how a particle, if tiny enough and not affected by electrical forces, could be shot straight through us without even making a hole! Making a direct hit with an atomic nucleus or an electron is as improbable as making a direct hit with a planet or the sun if you throw a gravity-free dart from outer space at the solar system. Both the solar system and an atom are mostly empty space. Walk through a beam of neutrons and very few if any will interact with your body. Still smaller neutral particles called neutrinos, the most elusive yet most numerous and fastest of all particles, pass though us every moment. But they do so without consequence, for only very rarely, perhaps once or so per year, do any make a bull's-eye collision with any of our atomic nuclei. They freely pass through the entire Earth with rare interactions.

LECTURE SKIT: Start with a drawing similar to Figure 17.5 on the chalkboard only indicate electrons as tiny fast-moving specks. State that your drawing is all out of scale. That to be more accurate you need to draw the nucleus much smaller. Erase the nucleus you first drew and replace it with a speck tinier than the electrons. Note that the electrons are actually thousands of times less massive than the atomic nucleus, so it would do far better to just erase them. Erase everything except the tiny speck of a nucleus and, perhaps, leaving the perimeter. "Thus, it is, we understand that atoms are made mostly of empty space." Finish up by noting that although the atom is mostly empty space, the tiny, tiny subatomic particles it contains have these force fields. It is the electric force of attraction between the electrons and the protons that holds the electrons to the atomic nucleus. Likewise, it is the electric force of repulsion between the electrons of one atom and the electrons of another atom that causes the two atoms to repel. The exception, of course, is when a chemical bond forms between those two atoms, which is a completely different story to be discussed at a later time.

Electrical Forces
Discuss the role of electrical forces in preventing us from oozing into our chairs and so forth. Ask the class to imagine that the lecture table is a large magnet, and that you wear magnetic shoes that are repelled by the table you "stand" on. Ask them to imagine whether or not a sheet of paper could be passed between your shoes and the table. For there is a space there. Then state that on the submicroscopic scale that this is indeed what happens when you walk on any solid surface. Only the repelling force isn't magnetic, its electric! Discuss the submicroscopic notion of things touching. Acknowledge that under very special circumstances the nucleus of one atom can physically touch the nucleus of another atom—that this is what happens in a thermonuclear reaction.

17.3 The Atomic Nucleus Is Made of Protons and Neutrons
Draw a proton about 2 inches in diameter on the chalkboard or overhead projector. Move the chalk or pen wildly about this proton to indicate an electron whizzing about this proton. End by making a speck some distance from the proton and let the class know that this represents a crude model of the hydrogen atom. Add a proton, electron, and two neutrons to transform the atom into a helium atom. Continue in this manner building a lithium, then boron atom, and so forth. Point out to students that this is how atoms differ from one another—by the number subatomic particles they contain. Point out the relationship between the atomic number and the periodic table and how an atom is defined by its atomic number.

Note that when you consider the electrical forces in the atom you're discussing the implications of Coulomb's law at short distances. Relative distances between charges is important, as later chapters will show.

In discussing isotopes, point out that isotopes are associated with all atoms, not just radioactive ones. Start with the isotopes of hydrogen and then discuss the isotopes of uranium, which will be important in Chapter 19.

17.4 Protons and Neutrons Determine Mass Number and Atomic Mass

Which contributes most to an atom's mass, protons or electons? [Protons, by far.] Which contributes to an atom's size? [Electrons, by far.] Distinguish between mass number and atomic mass. Help students write the chemical symbol for specific elements with atomic numbers and atomic mass numbers.

Point out that the atomic configurations depicted in Figures 17.4 and 17.5 and those you sketch on the board are simply models, not to be taken as visually correct. For example, if the nuclei were drawn to scale they would be scarcely visible specks. And the electrons don't really "orbit", as your drawings suggest—such terms don't seem to have much meaning at the atomic level. It would be more precise to say they "swarm", or are "smeared", around the central nuclei. Atomic models are discussed in Chapter 18, but it is good to set the stage at this point, especially if you plan on skipping Chapter 18.

Start with the isotopes of hydrogen (Figure 17.7) and then discuss the isotopes of uranium (which will be important in the next chapter).

17.5 Elements Are Organized in the Periodic Table by Their Properties
(To help students keep track of all the terms presented, use the Practice Pages for these sections.) Elements are the fundamental ingredients of all that surrounds us. Draw an analogy to how it is that food ingredients, such as spices, properly organized in a kitchen allows a cook to cook more efficiently. Scientists have looked for a similar way to organize the elements of nature. The end result is the periodic table.

Mock Quiz: Go back to a wall-sized periodic table and let students know that atoms of elements to the upper right tend to be the smallest while the atoms of elements to the lower left tend to be the largest. Now ask the students which is a larger atom: Sulfur, S, or Arsenic, As? Ideally the class responds that the sulfur atom is larger. Mockingly inquire of the students how they knew the answer, and in the same breath: "Gee, you must have memorized all the properties of all the elements of the periodic table to be able to answer a question like that." Pick two more elements that are on a lower left to upper right diagonal and ask again. Comment on how you are able to pick elements by random and they're *still* able to answer! Your grand finale, of course, is to point out that the periodic table is like a book. We don't memorize books—we learn to read them. Likewise with the periodic table. "As a student of chemistry, you are here to learn how to read the periodic table. Let's begin..."

One of the more apparent organizations of the periodic table is by metals, nonmetals and metalloids. Your discussion here will likely be brief. The main intent should be to identify metals, nonmetals, and metalloids by their physical properties. The theme of the periodic table's organization is carried well by pointing out the greater electrical conducting properties of germanium versus silicon.

The text's discussion of the periodic table does not go into sufficient detail to account for the traditional method of numbering the atomic groups, e.g. 1A, 2A, 3B, etc. For this reason we follow the numbering system recommended by IUPAC, e.g. 1 through 18.

17.6 A Period Is a Horizontal Row, a Group a Vertical Column
This section presents the opportunity for much descriptive chemistry. A good way to enhance your lectures is to bring to class many samples of different elements. Or better yet, make it an assignment for your students to bring to class as many elements as they could find within their households. Examples would include aluminum (aluminum foil), carbon (graphite from pencil), helium (from helium balloon), nitrogen and oxygen (from the air we breathe), iron (nails), nickel (the 5 cent piece, though this is actually an alloy containing little nickel),

Conceptual Physical Science—Explorations **Teaching Guide**

copper (copper penny), silver (silverware), iodine (disinfectant swab), gold (jewelry), mercury (old fashion thermometer—careful!), lead (fishing line sinker).

Atomic Group Discussions and Demonstrations

Group 1: Drop a small amount (less than a pea-size) into a beaker of water containing phenolphthalein pH indicator to demonstrate its reactivity. Contrast the reactivity of sodium with two other group 1 elements, lithium, and potassium (Exercise extra caution when adding these metals, especially potassium, to water. Hydrogen gas is produced, which is often ignited by the heat of reaction. Sodium hydroxide, which turns the solution alkaline, is also produced. These metals must be stored under kerosine or mineral oil. Wear protective clothing, latex gloves, and safety glasses).

If your students will not be performing flame tests of group 1 and 2 elements in the laboratory, you might consider demonstrating these flame tests. Chloride or nitrate salts of lithium (scarlet), sodium (yellow), potassium (purple), strontium (red), and barium (green) are most impressive. These materials give the color to fireworks. Interestingly, fireworks had little or no color prior to the discovery of these compounds in the late 1800's. The world really was black and white back then!

Group 2: In a plastic weigh boat (5" × 5") mix 10 grams of sand with 3.33 grams of lime (calcium oxide). Stir in 5 mL of water to create a thick paste of brick mortar. Use universal pH paper to note its alkalinity. Measure its weight and ask the class to predict whether the mortar will weigh more or less after it hardens. [Hardening cement mortar gains mass as it absorbs carbon dioxide from the air. Chemically, the calcium oxide reacts with water to form calcium hydroxide (slaked lime). This material, in turn, absorbs carbon dioxide to form calcium carbonate, limestone, which is reinforced by sand particles. As CO_2 is absorbed, water is lost. Since carbon dioxide is more massive than water, the mortar gains weight. Protective clothing and safety glasses should be worn as calcium oxide is a powerful dehydrating agent and is irritating to skin. Avoid breathing any calcium oxide dust. Calcium hydroxide is very caustic and should be handled with care. Interestingly, calcium hydroxide is the active ingredient of many hair removal products.]

It is always interesting to burn a small ribbon of magnesium. The brightness of the flame is impressive. If you can find some "Magicube" flash bulbs, this reaction can be used to demonstrate the conservation of mass principle. First demonstrate how the magnesium strip is "consumed" as it burns. Ask students if matter was destroyed. Point out the magnesium strips inside one of the flash bulbs and ask whether the bulb should weigh more or less after being ignited. Weigh the bulb before and after igniting it with a 9-V battery and wire leads. Despite the intense heat, the bulbs are thick enough to contain all the reactants and products.

Groups 3-10: Transition Elements: Compare various transition elements in their metallic state to the some of the highly colored compounds they form. Search your stockroom for examples such as: iron III nitrate, $Fe(NO_3)_3$ (orange); cobalt II nitrate, $Co(NO_3)_2$ (purple); nickel II nitrate, $Ni(NO_3)_2$ (green). Many pigments consist of transition element compounds.

Group 13 & 14: Students should recognize that elements in the same group don't always share similar properties. With group 13 and 14, for example, upper elements are nonmetallic while lower elements are metallic. The statement that elements in the same group often share many properties is a broad generalization with numerous exceptions.

Aluminum is commonly thought of as an inert metal. In fact, aluminum is quite reactive, especially in a powdered form. The reaction between powdered aluminum and ammonium perchlorate, NH_4ClO_4, for example, is used to lift the space shuttle into orbit. Aluminum also reacts rapidly with atmospheric oxygen to form relatively inert aluminum oxide, Al_2O_3. Interestingly, you do not touch aluminum. Instead, you touch a very thin, transparent, and protective coat of aluminum oxide. Tear a piece of aluminum foil and the freshly exposed aluminum immediately transforms into aluminum oxide. A piece of aluminum foil ground up in a sealed container lacking oxygen—in a vacuum, for example— will burn spontaneously as it is exposed to atmospheric oxygen. Sodium chloride is able to "eat through" aluminum's thin protecting coat. This can be demonstrated by submerging a small sheet of aluminum foil in a shallow dilute solution of copper (II) sulfate. Sprinkle some salt onto the aluminum. Where the salt contacts, it exposes the aluminum, which is then able to react with the copper ions to form copper metal. The reaction can release enough heat to cause the water within the vicinity of the salt to boil. Look for small bubble formations.

Place a sample of the group 13 element gallium, Ga, in a sealed vial and pass it around the class. The warmth from students' hands will cause this intriguing metal to melt (m.p. 30 °C). Interestingly enough, gallium, like water, is one of those rare materials that expands upon freezing. Also, the compound gallium arsenide, GaAs, is a remarkable semiconductor used to make integrated circuits that operate up to five times faster than silicon circuits. Gallium arsenide, however, is relatively expensive to produce.

Display molecular models of graphite, diamond, and buckminsterfullerene. Mention how carbon is unique from all other elements in that it is able to bond with itself repeatedly. An astounding variety of materials can be produced when carbon also forms bonds to elements such as hydrogen, oxygen, and nitrogen. These are the organic compounds discussed in Chapter 27.

Group 15: Comment to your students that you need not bring nitrogen to class for it's already there—air is almost 80% nitrogen. As an exciting alternative (if you haven't done so already), bring in a Dewar of liquid nitrogen. The last element in group 15 is bismuth, Bi, which is the heaviest of the nonradioactive elements. Crystals of bismuth are iridescent and quite beautiful. Bismuth salts make the active ingredient of Pepto-Bismol. The great atomic mass of these salts assists in their ability to "soothe and coat" the digestive tract.

Group 16: Along with showing the properties of liquid nitrogen you might demonstrate the properties of liquid oxygen. The boiling point of oxygen (-183 °C) is higher than that of nitrogen (-196 °C). So, liquid oxygen can be generated by flowing gaseous oxygen into a container immersed in liquid nitrogen. Clamp a large test tube and immerse it into about a liter of liquid nitrogen in a Dewar flask. Connect one end of rubber tubing to the valve of an oxygen tank and the other end to about 30 cm of glass tubing. Place the free end of the glass tubing into the test tube and open the valve to allow a gentle flow of oxygen. In a few minutes about 20 - 30 mL of liquid oxygen can be collected. Transfer the liquid oxygen to an unsilvered Dewar flask to show its pale blue color (water quickly condenses on the outside of the test tube obscuring the oxygen from view). To show the effects of high concentrations of oxygen, pour several milliliters of the liquid into a 250 mL beaker and then quickly toss in a smoldering wood splint. The splint will rapidly catch fire. Substances that do not combust under ordinary conditions, such as clothing, can be quite flammable in such high concentrations of oxygen. Open flames, therefore, are particularly dangerous and caution should be exercised.

Conceptual Physical Science—Explorations **Teaching Guide**

Sulfur has the elemental formula S8. The chemical structure of the most stable allotrope of sulfur is that of an eight-membered ring, which has the shape of a crown. Heat several grams of sulfur in a crucible over a Bunsen burner flame. At 119°C the sulfur will melt. Then, as the temperatures rises above 150°C the ring structure breaks apart and the melt becomes viscous due to tangling of the sulfur chains. The chains recombine upon cooling. Pour the viscous melt into water and the sulfur will appear back in its original form. (If you've saved this demo for Chapter 21, you should ask your students whether it is a physical or chemical change.) Note how elemental sulfur is not the same as hydrogen sulfide, which is a compound that gives the smell of rotten eggs. As was discussed earlier, compounds are uniquely different from the elements from which they are composed.

Group 17: The halogens iodine and bromine may be shown for their different phases. Keep them in sealed containers. The sublimation and deposition of iodine may be presented as a demonstration (but only under a fume hood!).

Group 18: Blow soap bubbles using various noble gases. The rate at which noble gases heavier than helium fall is directly proportional to their masses. If you don't have any argon available, it is interesting to note that carbon dioxide is only 4 amu more massive than is argon. You may also choose to demonstrate several noble gas containing discharge tubes.

Antimatter
Discuss antimatter, and the speculations that other galaxies may be composed of antimatter. There are even antiquarks. Or knowledge of quarks is relatively new, newer than the first edition of this text. Until recent times it was a fact that the fundamental building block of matter was the protons, neutrons, and electrons discussed in this chapter. Now it is a fact that the proton and neutron are not the fundamental particles, but are composed of quarks. This change of view or advancement in our knowledge, like others, is often cited as a weakness by people who do not understand what science is about. Science is not a bag of answers to all the questions of the world, but is a process for finding answers to many questions about the world. We continue to refine our models and add new layers to our understanding—sometimes building onto layers and other times replacing layers. It is unfortunate that some people see this as a weakness. This is remindful of Bertrand Russell, who publicly changed his mind about certain ideas in the course of his life—changes that were part of his growth, but were looked upon by some as a sign of weakness (as discussed in Chapter 1). Likewise with physical science. Our knowledge grows. And that's nice!

Dark Matter
Lest anyone feel that physics is near its end insofar as what there is still to be known in this realm, consider dark matter—today's major science mystery. Whatever it is, there is very little chance it will occupy any place on the periodic table of the elements. How intriguing—most of the stuff of the universe isn't on the periodic table. And it is "out there?" Bear in mind, that we are "out there." Dark matter is likely infused in matter as we know it. Interesting point: There is likely dark matter in the platinum cylinder that defines the kilogram, locked in a glass case in France. (What does this say about our knowledge of the number of platinum atoms in the standard mass?) And there's perhaps traces of dark matter in you and me, not to mention in the core of the Earth which is thought to be all iron. Interesting speculations!

Chapter 17 Answers and Solutions

Key Terms and Matching Definitions

_12_ atomic mass
_4_ atomic nucleus
_7_ atomic number
_3_ atomic symbol
_5_ electron
_1_ element
_17_ group
_10_ isotope
_11_ mass number
_13_ metal
_15_ metalloid
_8_ neutron
_14_ nonmetal
_9_ nucleon
_16_ period
_2_ periodic table
_18_ periodic trend
_6_ proton

Review Questions

1. How many types of atoms can you expect to find in a sample of any element?
   An element consists of only one type of atom.

2. Distinguish between an atom and an element.
   Atom is used to refer to submicroscopic particles in a sample and element is used for microscopic and macroscopic samples.

3. If atoms are mostly empty space, why can't we walk through walls?
   Because of the electric force of repulsions that occur between atoms as they meet.

4. What kind of force prevents atoms from squishing into one another?
   Electrical repulsion prevents atoms from meeting, unless they join in a chemical bond.

5. How much more massive is a proton compared to an electron?
   A proton is nearly 2000 times more massive than an electron.

6. Compare the electric charge on the proton with the electric charge on the electron.
   A proton has a charge equal to, but opposite, that of an electron.

7. What is the definition of atomic number?
   Atomic number is the number of protons in the nucleus of an atom.

8. What role does atomic number play in the periodic table?
   Elements are listed in the periodic table in order of increasing atomic number.

9. What effect do isotopes of a given element have on the atomic mass calculated for that element?

Atomic mass is the weighted average of the masses of all the isotopes based on their relative abundance, percentage-wise.

10. Name two nucleons.
    Protons and neutrons are two nucleons.

11. Distinguish between atomic number and mass number.
    Atomic number is the number of protons in the nucleus. Mass number is the total number of protons and neutrons in the nucleus.

12. Distinguish between mass number and atomic mass.
    Mass number is the count of the number of nucleons in an isotope. Atomic mass is a measure of the average mass of an atom taking into account the relative abundances of the various isotopes of the element.

13. How is the periodic table more than just a listing of the known elements?
    The period table organizes elements based on physical and chemical properties.

14. Are most elements metallic or nonmetallic?
    Most of the known elements are metals.

15. Why is hydrogen, H, most often considered a nonmetallic element?
    Hydrogen only behaves like a liquid metal at very high pressures. Under normal conditions, hydrogen atoms combine to form H_2 which behaves as a nonmetallic gas.

16. Where are metalloids located in the periodic table?
    The metalloids are situated between the metals and the nonmetals.

17. How many periods are there in the periodic table? How many groups?
    The periodic table has 7 periods and 18 groups.

18. Why are group 17 elements called halogens?
    The halogens tend to form salts. Halogens means salt forming in Greek.

19. Which group of elements are all gases at room temperature?
    Group 18 or the noble gases are all gases at room temperature.

20. Why are the inner transition metals not listed in the main body of the periodic table?
    The inner transition metals are below the main body of the periodic table so it will all fit on one page.

Solutions to Chapter 17 Exercises

1. A cat strolls across your backyard. An hour later a dog with its nose to the ground follows the trail of the cat. Explain this occurrence from a molecular point of view.
   The cat leaves a trail of molecules on the grass. These in turn leave the grass and mix with the air, where they enter the dog's nose, activating its sense of smell.

2. If all the molecules of a body remained part of that body, would the body have any odor?
   A body would have no odor if all its molecules remained intact. A body has odor only if some of its molecules enter a nose.

3. Which are older, the atoms in the body of an elderly person or those in the body of a baby?
   The age of the atoms in either a newborn baby or in an elderly person are the same; appreciably older than the solar system.

4. In what sense can you truthfully say that you are a part of every person around you?

You really are a part of every person around you in the sense that you are composed of atoms not only from every person around you, but from every person who ever lived on Earth!

5. Considering how small atoms are, what are the chances that at least one of the atoms exhaled in your first breath will be in your last breath?
With every breath of air you take, it is highly likely that you inhale one of the atoms exhaled during your very first breath. This is because the number of atoms of air in your lungs is about the same as the number of breaths of air in the atmosphere of the world.

6. Germanium, Ge, (number 32) computer chips operate faster than silicon computer chips. So how might a gallium chip, Ga, compare with a germanium chip?
Based upon its location in the periodic table we find that gallium, Ga, is more metallic in character than germanium, Ge. This means that gallium should be a better conductor of electricity. Computer chips manufactured from gallium, therefore, operate faster than chips manufactured from germanium. (Gallium has a low melting point of 30°C, which makes it impractical for use in the manufacture of computer chips. Mixtures of gallium and arsenic, however, have found great use in the manufacture of ultra fast, though relatively expensive, computer chips.)

7. Helium, He, is a nonmetallic gas and the second element after hydrogen, H, in the periodic table. Rather than being placed adjacent to hydrogen, however, helium is place over to the far right-hand side. Why?
Helium is placed over to the far right-hand side of the periodic table in group 18 because it has physical and chemical properties most similar to those of the other elements of group 18.

8. Name ten elements that you have access to as a consumer here on planet Earth.
Here is a list of eighteen: Aluminum (as in aluminum foil); tin (as in tin foil and tin cans); carbon (as in graphite and diamond); helium (as in a helium balloon); nitrogen (which comprises about 78% of the air we breathe); oxygen (which comprises about 21% of the air we breathe); argon (which comprises about 1% of the air we breathe); silicon (as in integrated circuits for computers and calculators); sulfur (a mineral used for many industrial processes); iron (as in most metal structures); chromium (as in chromium bumpers on cars); zinc (as in the coating of any galvanized nail or as the insides of any post 1982 copper penny); copper (as in copper pennies); nickel (as in nickel nickels); silver (as in jewelry and old silver coins); gold (as in jewelry); platinum (as in jewelry); mercury (as in mercury thermometers).

9. Srontium, Sr (number 38) is especially dangerous to humans because it tends to accumulate in calcium-dependent bone marrow tissues (calcium, Ca, number 20). How does this fact relate to what you know about the organization of the periodic table?
Calcium is readily absorbed by the body for the building of bones. Since calcium and strontium are in the same atomic group they have similar physical and chemical properties. The body, therefore, has a hard time distinguishing between the two and strontium is absorbed just as though it were calcium.

10. With periodic table as your guide, describe the element selenium, Se (number 34) using as many of this chapter's key terms as you possibly can.
Selenium is a nonmetallic element found just adjacent to the metalloids in the periodic table. Its atomic symbol is Se and it has properties similar to those of other elements in its group. This element is found in the fourth period and its atoms are likely smaller than those of the elements to its left, which is an example of a periodic trend. Each selenium atom has 34 protons and 34 electrons. The number of neutrons it has in its atomic nucleus can vary. Atoms of selenium that have different numbers of neutrons are known as isotopes. Each selenium isotope can be identified by its mass number, which is a count of its nucleons. The average mass of all of selenium's isotopes is its atomic mass. Check out that vocabulary!

Conceptual Physical Science—Explorations Teaching Guide

11. Which of the following diagrams best represents the size of the atomic nucleus relative to the atom?
The one on the far right where the nucleus is not visible.

12. If two protons and two neutrons are removed from the nucleus of an oxygen atom, what nucleus remains?
The remaining nucleus is that of Carbon-12.

13. You could swallow a capsule of germanium without ill effects. But if a proton were added to each of the germanium nuclei, you would not want to swallow the capsule. Why? (Consult the periodic table of the elements.)
The resulting nucleus would be that of arsenic, which is poisonous—darn!

14. What happens to the properties of elements across any period of the periodic table?
The properties of elements across any periodic of the periodic table change gradually. For example, the size of the atoms of elements gradually decreases in moving from left to right.

15. If an atom has 43 electrons, 56 neutrons, and 43 protons, what is its approximate atomic mass? What is the name of this element?
Atomic mass would be 99 amu, and the element would be technetium, Tc, atomic number 43.

16. The nucleus of an electrically neutral iron atom contains 26 protons. How many electrons does this iron atom have?
The iron atom is electrically neutral when it has 26 electrons to balance its 26 protons.

17. Evidence for the existence of neutrons did not come until many years after the discoveries of the electron and the proton. Give a possible explanation.
The neutron was elusive because of its lack of electric charge.

18. Which has more atoms: A one gram sample of carbon-12, or a one gram sample of carbon-13? Briefly explain.
Carbon-13 atoms are heavier than carbon-12 atoms. Because of this, any sample of carbon-13 will have a fewer number of atoms than any sample of carbon-12 of the same mass. Look at it this way—golf balls are more mass than Ping-Pong balls. So, which contains more balls: a kilogram of golf balls or a kilogram of Ping-Pong balls? Because Ping-Pong balls are so much lighter, you need many more of them to get to that kilogram amount.

19. Why are the atomic masses listed in the periodic table not whole numbers?
The atomic masses listed in the periodic table are average numbers that reflect the variety of isotopes that exist for an element.

20. From where did the carbon atoms in Leslie's hair originate? (Shown below is a photo of author Leslie at the age 16.)
The carbon atoms that make up Leslie's hair or anything else in this world originated in the explosions of ancient stars. So we're all made of stardust!

18 Atomic Models

Conceptual Physical Science—Explorations

18.1   Models Help Us Visualize the Invisible World of Atoms
18.2   Atoms Can Be Identified by the Light They Emit
18.3   Niels Bohr Used the Quantum Hypothesis to Explain Atomic Spectra
18.4   A Shell Is a Region of Space Where an Electron Can Be Found

Learning Objectives
After studying Chapter 18, students will be able to:
• Distinguish between a physical and a conceptual model.
• Explain why scientists know the identity of the chemical composition of stars.
• Explain how the quantum hypothesis explains atomic spectra.
• Explain the usefulness of the shell model of the atom.

Possible Misconceptions to Correct
• **Not so!** If one could see an atom, it would look like the models used to represent it.
• **Not so!** No two atoms can emit exactly the same frequency of light.
• **Not so!** The quantum hypothesis illustrates the uncertain nature of science.

Demonstration Materials
• Gas discharge tubes and a spectrometer (or diffraction gratings passed out to students)

One of the main goals of this chapter is to show students how conceptual models help us to understand atomic behavior. A simplified conceptual model depicting the atom as a series of concentric shells is presented. This model is used to explain periodic trends and it also sets the stage for a deeper understanding of concepts presented in subsequent chapters, such as chemical bonding.

This chapter is the most esoteric chapter of the textbook. If you are on a fast-track to the topical chapters you may decide to skip it, or use it for introducing only selected concepts, such as electromagnetic radiation.

Nonetheless, this is an important chapter in that it digs to the heart of how chemists make sense of the invisible world of atoms. Interestingly, when I poll students at the end of the semester for what was their favorite chapter of the book, this chapter on atomic models invariably shows up at the top or close to the top of the list. The shell model, in its simplified form, is easy for the students to grasp, yet the model is very powerful in its predictive properties. The greatest joy is seeing students impress themselves as they apply the model to come up with chemical insight "all on their own". An example that arises later in the course is understanding why elements to the upper right of the periodic table tend to behave as oxidizing agents, while those the lower left tend to behave as reducing agents. They then realize that chemistry is more about applying conceptual models than it is about memorizing facts.

In the **Practice Book:**
• Losing Valence Electrons

In the **Next-Time Questions** book;
• Spectroscope

Overhead Transparencies (4) available for:
Figures 18.1, 18.6; Figure 18.5; Figure 18.23; Figure 18.14

SUGGESTED PRESENTATION

18.1 Models Help Us Visualize the Invisible World of Atoms
Consider beginning this chapter with the following lecture skit.

LECTURE SKIT: Hold up a stick of chalk to the class and ask them what you are holding. They'll reply that you are holding chalk. Ask them how they know this. Bring them to the notion that they recognize the chalk by its properties. Help them in describing these properties by including the following: It is white; it writes on the chalkboard; it's good for alleviating acid indigestion (to illustrate this last property, add a sample of chalk to a test tube containing white distilled vinegar). Split the chalk in two and hold up one of the halves and ask the students what you have. Ask them how they know this and point out that the material has all the same properties as before. Split the half in half and go through the routine again. Take a quarter of chalk and smash it to the floor. Pick of a fragment and ask the students what you are holding. Show them the evidence of its same color, how it can still be used to write on the board and how it might cure the acid indigestion of a mouse. Take your small fragment of chalk and smash it with a heavy object so that all you have is powder. Wipe up some of the powder with your finger. Hold your finger up to your students and ask them what it is that you have on your finger. How do they know? Show them the color, how it might be used to cure the acid indigestion of an ant and that you can still write on the board with it—wipe your finger across the board to show how this is so. The class will be in a good mood by this point. Ask them how far one might be able to go with this process and still have chalk? Might it go on without end, or is there a fundamental unit of chalk...for example, a "chalk atom"? In jest, consider pointing to the symbol for calcium in the periodic table and asking students whether this might be the symbol for a "chalk atom". Alternatively, point out that the fundamental unit for chalk is the compound calcium carbonate, $CaCO_3$. It is only after you break the fundamental unit of a material in half that you no longer have what you had. Comment that an atom is sometimes defined as "the smallest unit of an element that retains all the properties of that element." Or that a molecule is sometimes defined as "the smallest unit of a compound (technically a covalent compound) that retains all the properties of that compound."

From this, lead into a discussion of how the fundamental units of matter are so small that hundreds of years ago people had no way of finding out if they existed. Any discussion of the existence of these fundamental units was no more than philosophical speculation. As mentioned in our discussion of Chapter 17, not until "modern" chemistry in the late 1700s did people begin to get indirect evidence of some basic order in the combinations of things. The first real "proof" that there were atoms was given by Einstein in 1905, the same year he published his paper on relativity. He calculated what kind of motion there ought to be in Brownian motion, based on the idea of heat as atomic motion. Many of the "heavies" in science at that time didn't believe in atoms until Einstein's work.

CALCULATION ASSIGNMENT: The diameter of an atom is about 10^{-10} m. (a) How many atoms make a line a millionth of a meter (10^{-6}) long? (b) How many atoms cover a square a millionth of a meter on a side? (c) How many atoms fill a cube a millionth of a meter on a side? (d) If a dollar were attached to each atom, what could you buy with your line of atoms? With your square of atoms? With your cube of atoms? [Solutions: (a) 10^4 atoms (length 10^{-6} m divided by size 10^{-10} m). (b) 10^8 atoms ($10^4 \times 10^4$). (c) 10^{12} atoms ($10^4 \times 10^4 \times 10^4$). (d) $10,000 buys a small car, for instance. $100 million buys a few jet aircrafts and an airport on which to keep them, for instance. $1 trillion buys a medium-sized country, for instance. (Answers limited only by the imagination of the student.)]

Models are not to be judged as being "true" or "mistaken"; models are useful or nonuseful. The particle model of light is useful in making sense of the details of the photoelectric effect, whereas the wave model of light is not useful in understanding these details. Likewise, the wave model of light is useful for understanding the details of interference, whereas the particle model is not useful. The effectiveness of one model over another means simply that: One model is more effective than another. This effectiveness doesn't mean that one model is correct and the other invalid. As we gather more data and gain new insights, we refine our models.

Buckminster Fuller as mentioned back on page 150, he stated that ninety-nine percent of all that is going to affect our tomorrows is being developed by humans using instruments that work in ranges of reality that are nonhumanly sensible. The instruments of science are not microscopes and telescopes, for they enable closer viewing of the part of the spectrum we are familiar with. Infrared detecting devices, microwave and radio receivers, allow us to explore the lower-frequency end of the spectrum, and ultraviolet, X-ray, and gamma-ray detectors that let us "see" the higher-frequency end. What we see with unaided eyes is a tiny part of the world around us.

18.2 Atoms Can Be Identified by the Light They Emit
Cite that a century ago, the chemical composition of the stars were thought to be forever beyond the knowledge of humankind—and now today we know as much about their composition as we do the Earth's.

Cite examples of the uses of spectrometers—how very minute quantities of materials are needed for chemical analysis—how tiny samples of ores are sparked in carbon arcs and the light directed through prisms or diffraction gratings to yield precise chemical composition—note their use in fields as diverse as chemistry and criminology.

Emphasize the discreteness of the lines from atoms in the gaseous state. Consider going beyond the book treatment and lead into the idea of excitation in an incandescent lamp, where the atoms are in the solid state. Why do we get a continuous spectrum from a solid lamp filament, but spectral lines from the same atoms in the gaseous state? The answer is that in the crowded condition the energy levels interact with one another and produce a smudged distribution of frequencies rather than discrete frequencies characteristic of the gaseous state. It's like the difference between the tone of bells that are struck while packed together in a box, and their tone when suspended apart from one another. The distribution of frequencies of atoms in the solid state make up the standard radiation curve, which you can approximate by sketching a bell-shaped curve on the board. Where the curve peaks indicates the temperature of the source of light. Hence the difference between red hot, white hot, and blue hot sources—stars, for example. The peak of the curve is the peak frequency (referred to as average frequency back in Chapter 10), which is proportional to the absolute temperature of the source—$f \sim T$ (we'll discuss this again when we explain the greenhouse effect in Chapter 37. The equation tells us that the frequency of light emitted by the hot sun is proportionally higher than the frequency of radiation emitted by the Earth's relatively cool surface).

> CHECK YOUR NEIGHBOR: Hold up an obviously broken light bulb and ask if it is presently emitting electromagnetic energy. [Sure is, as is everything—its temperature is simply too low for the corresponding frequency to trigger our retinas.]

Get into the idea of the infrared part of the spectrum. Show in a sequence of radiation curves on the board how an increase in temperature brings the curve "sloshing over" into the lower frequency portion of the visible spectrum—hence the red hotness of a hot poker. Show how an increase in temperature brings the curve into the visible spectrum producing white light. Show why a hot poker does not become green hot, and how sharp the curve would have to be to produce green without sloshing into the other frequencies to produce white light.

18.3 Niels Bohr Used the Quantum Hypothesis to Explain Atomic Spectra
This chapter introduces quantum mechanics by way of the classic wave-particle duality in which light behaves as a wave when it travels in empty space, and lands like a particle when it hits something. It is mistaken to insist it must be both a particle and a wave at the same time. This is not the case. What something *is* and *what it does* are not the same.

Using the Bohr model, explain energy levels with the following analogy: Hold a book above the lecture table and drop it. Then hold it higher and drop it again. State that the potential energy you supplied to the book was converted to kinetic energy and then to sound energy. State that the higher you boost the book before dropping it, the louder the sound. State that a similar thing happens in the case of atoms. Parallel your book example and consider the case of an electron being boosted to a higher orbit in an atom. Just as a screen door that is pushed open against a spring snaps back and produces sound, the displaced electron snaps back to its ground state and produces light. It emits a throbbing spark of light we call a *photon*. Show that when it is boosted to higher levels, it emits a higher-frequency photon upon de-excitation. Introduce the relationship $E \sim f$ for the resulting photons. Discuss the variety of energy-level jumps for a simple atom.

CHECK YOUR NEIGHBOR: Two photons are emitted as a result of the transitions shown on the board. If one photon is red and the other blue, which is which? [Be sure to draw the shorter wavelength for the greater transition, from the second level to ground state, and the longer wavelength for the smaller transition from level one to ground.]

DEMONSTRATION: Show the spectra of gas discharge tubes. Either use a large diffraction grating that you hold in front of the tube (I use one the size of a sheet of typing paper, Edmund Scientific Co.), or pass small gratings among the class, so the spectral lines can be observed.

18.4 A Shell Is a Region of Space Where an Electron Can Be Found
Recall in Chapter 16 that electrons have wave properties as well as particle properties. Like light, they travel as waves and hit as particles. Waves are invoked in the atomic shell model presented here, which provides a working, albeit simplified, model that explains not only the organization of the periodic table but the nature of chemical bonding.

Begin with the analogy of musical notes as is described in the text. Add to this that electrons behave as though they are arranged about the atomic nucleus in a series of 7 concentric shells. Also, be sure to qualify this model as a simplification of a more accurate, but more complex model (atomic orbitals), which may be explored in a follow-up chemistry course.

You might wish to show students how to draw a shell model using the following steps. Not all students, however, will catch on. Thus, you should also announce that a series of concentric circles works just as well, as shown in Figure 18.14.

1. Draw a diagonal guideline in pencil. Then, draw a series of 7 semicircles. Note how the ends of the semicircles are not perpendicular to the guideline. Instead, they are parallel to the length of the page (Figure A).

2. Connect the ends of each semicircle with another semicircle such that a series of concentric hearts is drawn. The ends of these new semicircles should be drawn perpendicular to the ends of the previously drawn semicircles (Figure B).

Guideline →

Figure A

Figure B

3. Now the hard part. Draw a portion of a circle that connects the apex of the largest vertical and horizontal semicircles as in Figure C.

4. Now the fun part. Erase the pencil guideline drawn in step 1, then add the internal lines, as shown in Figure D, that create a series of concentric shells.

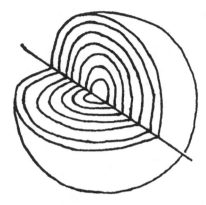 

Figure C   Figure D

Point out the various electron capacities of each shell and how this corresponds to the organization of the periodic table. Define valence electrons.

The big challenge is to convince students that these shells are not meant to represent the Bohr planetary orbits, though they are analogous. Rather, as is explored in the higher level text, *Conceptual Chemistry*, each shell consists of a collection of atomic orbitals of similar energy levels. These shells differ from Bohr's planetary model, therefore, in that they are drawn with an understanding of the wave nature of electrons and the quantum mechanics that they follow.

You should recognize this shell model as a glorified version of the electon-dot structures as presented in Chapter 23. Both these models were developed by G. N. Lewis, who is described in Section 23.1.

There are many rewards for bringing students to understand the shell model. An in-depth understanding of periodic trends—and thus the glory of the periodic table—is one of these rewards.

To get to the periodic trends you'll need to use the shell model to explain the concepts of inner-shell shielding and effective nuclear charge. *Inner Shell Shielding* is the process of inner shell electrons weakening the attraction between outer shell electrons and the nucleus. The diminished nuclear charge is referred to as the *effective nuclear charge*.

From left to right across any row of the periodic table, the atomic diameters get *smaller*. Let's look at this trend from the point of view of effective nuclear charge. Consider lithium's outermost electron, which experiences an effective nuclear charge of +1. Then look across period 2 to neon, where each outermost electron experiences an effective nuclear charge of +8. Because the outer-shell neon electrons experience a greater attraction to the nucleus, they are pulled in closer to it than is the outer-shell electron in lithium. So neon, although nearly three times as massive as lithium, has a considerably smaller diameter. In general, across any period from left to right, atomic diameters become smaller because of an increase in effective nuclear charge. Look carefully to Figure 18.14 and you will see this illustrated for the first three periods.

Moving down a group, atomic diameters get larger because of an increasing number of occupied shells. Whereas lithium has a small diameter because it has only two occupied shells, francium has a much larger diameter because it has seven occupied shells.

Chapter 18 Answers and Solutions

Key Terms and Matching Definitions

_4_ atomic spectrum
_2_ conceptual model
_1_ physical model
_7_ principal quantum number
_6_ quantum
_5_ quantum hypothesis
_8_ shell
_3_ spectroscope
_9_ valence electrons

Review Questions

1. If a baseball were the size of the Earth, about how large would its atoms be?
   The atoms in the baseball would be the size of Ping-Pong balls if the baseball were the size of Earth.

2. When we use a scanning tunneling microscope, do we see atoms directly or do we see them only indirectly?
   A scanning tunneling microscope allows us to see atoms indirectly.

3. Why are atoms invisible to visible light?
   Atoms are smaller than the wavelength of visible light. Therefore, they cannot be seen.

4. What is the difference between a physical model and a conceptual model?
   A physical model attempts to replicate an object at a different scale. A conceptual model describes a system.

5. What is the function of an atomic model?
   An atomic model predicts the behavior of a system that we cannot see.

6. What causes an atom to emit light?
   Atoms give off light as they are subjected to energy.

7. Why do we say atomic spectra are like fingerprints of the elements?
   The atoms of each element emit only select frequencies of light.

8. What did Rydberg note about the atomic spectrum of hydrogen?
   Rydberg noted that the sum of the frequencies of two lines in the spectrum of hydrogen sometimes equals the frequency of a third line.

9. What was Planck's quantum hypothesis?
   Planck's quantum hypothesis states that light energy is emitted in small discrete packets called quanta.

10. Which has more potential energy—an electron close to an atomic nucleus or one far from an atomic nucleus?

   An electron has more potential energy when it is farther away from the nucleus than when it is closer to the nucleus.

11. What happens to an electron as it absorbs a photon of light?

   The electron is boosted from a position of low potential energy to one of high potential energy.

12. What is the relationship between the light emitted by an atom and the energies of the electrons in the atom?

   The greater the frequency of a photon of light, the greater the energy packed into that photon.

13. Did Bohr think of his planetary model as an accurate representation of what an atom looks like?

   No, Bohr's model demonstrated the different energy levels of an electron in an atom.

14. How is the number of shells an atom of a given element contains related to the row of the periodic table in which that element is found?

   The seven shells correspond to the seven periods in the periodic table.

15 What is the relationship between the maximum number of electrons each shell can hold and the number of elements in each period of the periodic table?

   The number of electrons that each shell can hold corresponds to the number of elements in the period.

Solutions to Chapter 18 Exercises

1. With scanning tunneling microscopy (STM) technology, we do not see actual atoms. Rather, we see images of them. Explain.

   Atoms are smaller than the wavelengths of visible light and hence they are not visible in the true sense of the word. We can, however, measure the topography a collection of atoms by scanning an electric current back and forth across the topography. The data from such scanning can be assembled by a computer into an image that reveals how individual atoms are organized on the surface. It would be more appropriate to say that with the scanning tunneling microscope that we "feel" atoms, rather than "see" them.

2. Why is it not possible for the STM to make images of the inside of an atom?

   The STM only shows us the relative sizes and positions of atoms. It does this by detecting the electrical forces that occur between the tip of the STM needle and the outer electrons of the atom. Recall from Section 17.2 that the atom itself is made of mostly empty space. So the best "image" of the inside of an atom would be a picture of nothing. So, it doesn't make sense to talk about taking an "image" of the inside of an atom. Instead, we develop models that provide a visual handle as to how it is that the components of atoms behave.

3. Would you use a physical model or a conceptual model to describe the following: the brain; the mind; the solar system; birth of the universe; a stranger; best friend; gold coin; dollar bill; a car engine; virus; the spread of a cold virus?

   Many objects or systems may be described just as well by a physical model as by a conceptual model. In general, the physical model is used to replicate an object or system of objects on a different scale. The conceptual model, by contrast, is used to represent abstract ideas or to demonstrate the behavior of a system. Of the examples given in the

exercise the following might be adequately described using a physical model: the brain, the solar system, a stranger, a gold coin, a car engine, and a virus. The following might be adequately described using a conceptual model: the mind, the birth of the universe, your best friend (whose complex behavior you have some understanding of), and a dollar bill (which represents wealth but is really only a piece of paper, and the spread of a contagious disease, such as a cold.

4. How might you distinguish a sodium vapor street lamp from a mercury vapor street lamp?
    Observe the atomic spectra of each using a spectroscope.

5. How can a hydrogen atom, which has only one electron, have so many spectral lines?
    The one electron can be boosted to many energy levels, and therefore make many combinations of transitions to lower levels. Each transition is of a specific energy and accompanied by the emission of a photon of a specific frequency. Thus the variety of spectal lines.

6. Suppose that a certain atom possesses four distinct energy levels. Assuming that all transitions between levels are possible, how many spectral lines will this atom exhibit? Which transitions correspond to the highest-energy light emitted? To the lowest-energy light?
    Six transitions are possible. The transition from the 4th to the 1st level corresponds to the greatest ΔE and therefore highest frequency of light. The transition from the 4th to the 3rd level corresponds to the lowest ΔE and therefore lowest frequency of light.

7. An electron drops from the fourth energy level in an atom to the third level and then to the first level. Two frequencies of light are emitted. How does their combined energy compare with the energy of the single frequency that would be emitted if the electron dropped from the fourth level directly to the first level?
    In accord with the conservation of energy, the combined energies equal the energy of the single transition. (Thus the sum of the frequencies of light emitted by the two steps will equal the frequency of light emitted with the one long step.)

8. Figure 18.12 shows three energy-level transitions that produce three spectral lines in a spectroscope. Note that the distance between the $n = 1$ and $n = 2$ levels is greater than the distance between the $n = 2$ and $n = 3$ levels. Would the number of spectral lines produced change if the distance between the $n = 1$ and $n = 2$ levels were exactly the same as the distance between the $n = 2$ and $n = 3$ level?
    The drop from $n = 3$ to $n = 2$ would be the same energy difference as the drop from $n = 2$ to $n = 1$. The frequencies emitted from these transitions, therefore, would be the same and would overlap each other in the atomic spectrum. The effect would be that two otherwise separate lines would converge into a single more intense line.

9. Which color of light comes from the higher energy transition, red or blue?
    The blue light is a higher frequency and therefore corresponds to a higher energy level transition.

10. Place the proper number of electrons in each shell for sodium, Na (atomic number 11), rubidium, Rb (atomic number 37), krypton, Kr (atomic number 36), and chlorine, Cl (atomic number 17).

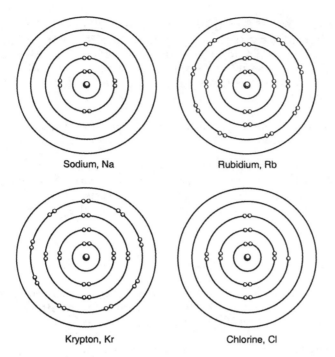

Sodium, Na

Rubidium, Rb

Krypton, Kr

Chlorine, Cl

11. Which element is represented by the model shown in Figure 18.13 if all seven shells are filled to capacity?
This would make the element 118.

12. Does a shell have to contain electrons in order to exist?
A shell is just a region of space in which an electron may reside. This region of space exists with or without the electron.

19 Radioactivity

Learning Objectives

After studying Chapter 19, students will be able to:
• Distinguish among the three types of rays given off by radioactive nuclei and compare their penetrating powers.
• Given the half-life of a radioactive isotope and the original amount of the isotope, predict how much of the isotope will remain at the end of some multiple of the half-life.
• Given the symbol for a radioactive isotope and the particle it gives off, predict the product of its decay.
• Explain why additional exposure to radiation is harmful.

Possible Misconceptions to Correct

• **Not so!** Radioactive is sinister, as is everything else we can't see and can't understand.
• **Not so!** Radioactivity is something that has been introduced since 20th century technology.
• **Not so!** Most of the radiation that people receive stems from technology.
• **Not so!** Atoms cannot be changed from one element to another.
• **Not so!** Atoms are the smallest particles of matter that exist.
• **Not so!** Atoms exposed to radiation differ from those that are not exposed to radiation.

Demonstrations for this Chapter

None

The point of this chapter is to dispel the notion that radioactivity is something new—a product of technology gone wrong. Or that it is all bad.

Common smoke detectors in the home make use of the very low dose radioactive americium-241, used to make the air in the detector's ionization chamber electrically conductive. When smoke enters the chamber it inhibits the flow of electricity, which activates the alarm. The lives saved each year by these devices number in the thousands (which dwarfs the numbers seriously harmed by radiation).

Being ignorant of radioactive decay, Lord Kelvin (1824-1907) made the extravagant claim that the age of the Earth was between 20 to 400 million years. Penetration of the Earth's crust by bore-holes and mines showed that temperature increases with depth. This means there is a flow of heat from the interior to the surface. Kelvin argued that this loss of heat meant the Earth had been progressively hotter in the past. His premise was that the molten interior of the Earth was the remnant of its hot birth. With this assumption and the rate at which the Earth loses heat, Kelvin calculated the age of the Earth. He allowed wide limits, due to uncertainties, and pronounced the Earth's age as between 20 and 400 million years.

This initiated a great controversy with geologists of Victorian times. Despite their protests, Kelvin felt justified by 1897 in narrowing his limits to 20 and 40 million years. It is interesting to note that with the superior data of the present day, the solution to Kelvin's problem, as he posed it, is between 25 and 30 million years. Although radioactivity had just been discovered (1896), Kelvin didn't acknowledge its role in heating the Earth's interior. Sadly, when this was pointed out to him, he held to his previous hard-earned but incorrect views. Was it Bernard Shaw who said that human progress depends on finite lifetimes of people?

We don't say an electric fire is cooling because it is losing heat. From the moment when it is first switched on it is losing energy, as evidenced by the heated surroundings. The fire gets hotter until a balance is achieved between the heat electrically generated and the heat lost by radiation, conduction, and convection. Only when the current is reduced or switched off does cooling begin. Kelvin's treatment of his problem was concerned with the case of the current being turned off; when there was no internal source of heat at all.

With the discovery of radioactivity and knowledge that the Earth's interior has a source of energy, estimates of the Earth's age based on the outward heat flow become valueless. Volcanic activity shows the Earth has ample heat-generating resources.

In much of the country radon is relatively abundant in the air. Art Schmidt (Northwestern University) did the following at a recent meeting of physics teachers in Chicago. He inflated a balloon (about 25 cm in diameter), rubbed it and gave it a static charge, and hung it in the room before the meeting. A charged balloon attracts dust particles in the air and traps a daughter product of radon in the dust on the balloon surface. Art deflated the balloon by cutting the neck. When placed before a Geiger counter the balloon was more noticeably radioactive than many commercial sources. If you have a radiation counter, consider this as a demo.

Food Irradiation is a current controversy. Many people vigorously and actively oppose it, based on their perception of its dangers. Ironically, hundreds die of food poisoning in the US each week—deaths that would have been averted if the food eaten had been irradiated. How many published photographs of the people who die daily would it take to re-channel the misplaced zeal of those who actively oppose food irradiation?

In the **Practice Book**:
• The Atomic Nucleus and Radioactivity
• Natural Transmutation
• Radioactive Half-Life

In the **Next-Time Questions** book:
• Child's Balloon
• Half Life

In the **Lab Manual**:
• Get a Half-Life

Overhead Transparencies (2) available for:
Figures 19.1 and 19.11.

SUGGESTED PRESENTATION

When electricity was first harnessed, people were fearful of it and its effects on life forms. Now it is commonplace, for its dangers are well understood. We are at a similar stage with regard to anything called nuclear. Even the very beneficial medical science *nuclear magnetic resonance* (NMR) has undergone a name change to *magnetic resonant imaging* (MRI). Why? "I don't want *my* Aunt Minnie near any *nuclear* machine!"

Hundreds of thousands of Americans live in houses that have a yearly radiation dose from radon in the ground equal to the dose residents living in the vicinity of Chernobyl received in 1986 when one of its reactors exploded and released radioactive materials into the environment (*Scientific American*, May 1988). This is not to say it is unharmful to live in the vicinity of radon emission, but to say that radioactivity is not a modern problem and not a byproduct of science per se. It's been with us since day 1.

19.1 Alpha, Beta, and Gamma Radiation Result From Radioactivity
Distinguish between alpha, beta, and gamma rays. If you've covered electricity and magnetism, ask if the rays could be separated by an electric field, rather than the magnetic field depicted in Figure 19.1.

19.2 Radioactivity Is a Natural Phenomenon
Cite the story of Lord Kelvin in the late 1800s who miscalculated the age of the Earth because he didn't know about radioactivity and its heat generating qualities. Every hot spring, geyser, and volcano owes its energy to that of radioactive decay—from day one. Figure 19.4 is instructive.

Radiation is not good for anybody, but we can't escape it. It is everywhere. However, we can take steps to avoid unnecessary radiation. Radiation, like everything else that is both damaging and little understood, is usually seen to be worse than it is. You can alleviate a sense of hopelessness about the dangers of radiation by pointing out that radiation is nothing new. It not only goes back before science and technology but before the Earth came to be. It goes back to day 1. It is a part of nature that must be lived with. Good sense simply dictates that we avoid unnecessary concentrations of radiation.

19.3 Radioactivity Results from an Imbalance of Forces in the Nucleus
Discuss the continual tug-of-war in atomic nuclei between electrical repulsion and the strong nuclear force. Make the point that although neutrons provide a sort of nuclear cement, too many of them separate the protons and lead to instability. The nuclear fragments of fission (Chapter 20) are radioactive because of their preponderance of neutrons.

19.4 A Radioactive Element Can Transmute to a Different Element
Discuss the symbolic way of writing atomic equations. Write some transmutation formulas on the board while your students follow along with their books opened to the periodic table of the elements. A repetition and explanation of the reactions cited in the chapter is in order, if you follow up with one or two new ones as check questions. Be sure that your class can comfortably write equations for alpha decay before having them write equations for beta decay, which are more complex because of the negative charge. Your treatment is the same for both natural and artificial transmutations.

> CHECK YOUR NEIGHBOR: If all the neutrons in a chunk of carbon-14 were converted to protons, and all protons converted to neutrons, would the substance still be carbon-14? How about uranium? [C-14 has the same number of neutrons and proton, so the substance would still be C-14. But uranium, say U-238, would be an element of atomic number 146! Different!]

19.5 The Shorter the Half-Life, the Greater the Radioactivity
Talk of jumping halfway to the wall, then halfway again, then halfway again and so on, and ask how many jumps will get you to the wall. Similarly with radioactivity. Of course, with a sample of radioactivity, there is a time when all the atoms undergo decay. But measuring decay rate in terms of this occurrence is a poor idea if only because of the small sample of atoms one deals with as the process nears the end of its course. Insurance companies can make accurate predictions of car accidents and the like with large numbers,

but not so for small numbers. Dealing with radioactive half-life at least insures half the large number of atoms you start with.

CHECK YOUR NEIGHBOR: If the half-life of a certain isotope is one day, how much of the original isotope in a sample will still exist at the end of two days? [1/4] Three days? [1/8] Four days? [1/16]

Radiation Detectors
Discuss and compare the various radiation detectors. The conceptually nice bubble chamber is fading fast and arrays of fine wires in concert with fast computers have replaced them.

DEMONSTRATION: Show any radiation detector you can bring to class.

19.6 Isotopic Dating Measures the Age of a Material
Pose the Concept Check about the archaeologist finding an ancient axe handle in a cave. It makes a good lecture skit, after explaining the nitrogen-carbon-nitrogen cycle.

NEXT-TIME QUESTION: With the aid of the periodic table, consider a decay-scheme diagram similar to the one shown in Figure 19.11 but beginning with U-235 and ending up with an isotope of lead. Use the following steps and identify each element in the series with its chemical symbol. What isotope does this produce? [Pb-207]

1. Alpha	5. Beta	9. Beta
2. Beta	6. Alpha	10. Alpha
3. Alpha	7. Alpha	11. Beta
4. Alpha	8. Alpha	12. Stable

Chapter 19 Answers and Solutions

Key Terms and Matching Definitions

__2__ alpha particle
__3__ beta particle
__8__ carbon-14 dating
__4__ gamma radiation
__7__ half-life
__1__ radioactive
__5__ strong nuclear force
__6__ transmutation

Review Questions

1. How do the electric charges of alpha, beta, and gamma rays differ from one another?

    Alpha rays consist of particles that each have 2 protons and 2 neutrons for a net charge of +2; beta rays consist of particles (electrons) that each have a charge of -1; gamma rays are a form of electromagnetic radiation and have no charge.

2. Which of the three rays has the greatest penetrating power?

    Gamma rays have the greatest penetrating power of the three rays.

3. What is the origin of most of the radiation you encounter?

    Most of the radiation we encounter is natural background radiation that originated in Earth and in space.

4. Is radioactivity on the Earth something relatively new? Defend your answer.

    No. It has been around longer than the human race and has been a part of the environment as long as the sun, rain and soil have been.

5. How are the strong nuclear force and the electric force different from each other?

    Strong nuclear force is strong over short distances whereas electrical force is relatively long-ranged.

6. What role do neutrons play in the atomic nucleus?

    Neutrons act as "nuclear cement" to hold the nucleus together.

7. When thorium, atomic number 90, decays by emitting an alpha particle, what is the atomic number of the resulting nucleus?

    The atomic number of the resulting nucleus, after alpha emission, is 88, which is 90 minus 2.

8. When thorium decays by emitting a beta particle, what is the atomic number of the resulting nucleus?

    The atomic number of the resulting nucleus, after beta emission, is 91, which is 90 plus 1.

9   What change in atomic number occurs when a nucleus emits an alpha particle? A beta particle?

    Emission of an alpha particle decreases the atomic number of the nucleus by 2. Emission of a beta particle increases the atomic number of the nucleus by 1.

10. What is the long-range fate of all the uranium that exists in the world today?

    All uranium will eventually decay to lead.

11. What is meant by *radioactive half-life*?

Radioactive half-life is the amount of time it takes for one-half of the original quantity of a radioactive element to decay.

12. What is the half-life of radium-226?

The half-life of radium-226 is 1,620 years.

13. How does the decay rate of an isotope relate to its half-life?

The rate of decay of a radioactive isotope is measured by its half-life.

14. What do cosmic rays have to do with transmutation?

Cosmic rays bombard the Earth's atmosphere and cause atoms to transmutate, resulting in protons and neutrons being "sprayed out" into the environment.

15. How is carbon-14 produced in the atmosphere?

Nitrogen captures a neutron to produce C-14 and a proton.

16. Which is radioactive, carbon-12 or carbon-14?

Carbon-14 is radioactive.

17. Why is there more carbon-14 in living bones than in once-living ancient bones of the same mass?

Carbon-14 lost to decay is replenished with carbon-14 from the atmosphere. When a living thing dies, replenishment stops and the percentage of carbon-14 decreases at a constant rate.

18. Why is carbon-14 dating useless for dating old coins but not old pieces of cloth?

Carbon dating is a technique used only on carbon-containing artifacts (things that were once alive) and not on coins, metals, etc.

19. Why is lead found in all deposits of uranium ores?

All uranium isotopes eventually decay to lead. So, any deposit of uranium ore will contain some lead which has been converted from uranium.

20. What does the proportion of lead and uranium in rock tell us about the age of the rock?

As rocks age, the uranium they contain will decay into lead. Therefore, the higher the proportion of lead to uranium, the older the rock; likewise, a lower proportion of lead to uranium indicates a younger rock.

Solutions to Chapter 19 Exercises

1. Why is a sample of radium always a little warmer than its surroundings?
A radioactive sample is always a little warmer than its surroundings because the radiating alpha or beta particles impart internal energy to the atoms of the sample. (Interestingly enough, the heat energy of the Earth originates with radioactive decay of the Earth's core and surrounding material.)

2. Is it possible for a hydrogen nucleus to emit an alpha particle? Defend your answer.
It is impossible for a hydrogen atom to eject an alpha particle, for an alpha particle is composed of a pair of hydrogen isotopes (deuterium). It is equally impossible for a one-kilogram melon to spontaneously break into four one-kilogram melons.

3. Why are alpha and beta rays deflected in opposite directions in a magnetic field? Why are gamma rays undeflected?
Alpha and beta rays are deflected in opposite directions in a magnetic field because they are oppositely charged—alpha are positive and beta negative. Gamma rays have no electric charge and are therefore undeflected.

4. The alpha particle has twice the electric charge of the beta particle but deflects less in a magnetic field. Why?
The alpha particle has twice the charge, but almost 8000 times the inertia (since each of the four nucleons has nearly 2000 times the mass of an electron). Hence it bends very little compared to the much less massive electrons.

5. Which type of radiation—alpha, beta, or gamma—results in the greatest change in mass number? The greatest change in atomic number?
Alpha radiation decreases the atomic number of the emitting element by 2 and the atomic mass number by 4. Beta radiation increases the atomic number of an element by 1 and does not affect the atomic mass number. Gamma radiation does not affect the atomic number or the atomic mass number. So alpha radiation results in the greatest change in atomic number, and hence charge, and mass number as well.

6. Which type of radiation—alpha, beta, or gamma—results in the least change in atomic mass number? The least change in the atomic number?
Gamma radiation produces not only the least change in mass and atomic numbers, but produces no change in mass number, atomic number, or electric charge. Both alpha and beta radiation do produce these changes, as discussed in the previous answer.

7. Which type of radiation—alpha, beta, or gamma—predominates on the inside of a high flying commercial airplane? Why?
Only gamma rays are able to penetrate the metal hull of an airplane. Flight crew are required to limit their flying time so as to minimize the potential harm caused by the significant radiation at high altitudes. Recall from the text that a single flight from New York to Los Angeles exposes each human in the plane to about as much radiation as a chest X-ray.

8. Why would you expect alpha particles to be less able to penetrate materials than beta particles?
Alpha particles are first of all, much bigger in size than beta particles, which makes them less able to pass through the "pores" of materials. Second, alpha particles are enormously more massive than beta particles. So if beta particles have the same kinetic energy, they must be moving considerably faster. The faster moving and smaller beta particles are therefore more effective in penetrating materials.

9. When the isotope bismuth-213 emits an alpha particle, what new element results? What new element results if it instead emits a beta particle?

Bismuth-213 becomes thallium-209 when it emits an alpha particle.

10. Elements above uranium in the periodic table do not exist in any appreciable amounts in nature because they have short half-lives. Yet there are several elements below uranium in the table that have equally short half-lives but do exist in appreciable amounts in nature. How can you account for this?
The elements below uranium in atomic number with short half-lives exist as the product of the radioactive decay of uranium. As long as uranium is decaying, their existence is assured.

11. You and a friend journey to the mountain foothills to get closer to nature and escape such things as radioactivity. While bathing in the warmth of a natural hot spring, she wonders aloud how the spring gets its heat. What do you tell her?
The Earth's natural energy that heats the water in the hot spring is the energy of radioactive decay, which keeps the Earth's interior molten. Radioactivity heats the water, but doesn't make the water itself radioactive. The warmth of hot springs is one of the "nicer effects" of radioactive decay. You and your friend will most likely encounter more radioactivity from the granite out croppings of the foothills than would be encountered near a nuclear power plant. Furthermore, at high altitude you'll both be exposed to increased cosmic radiation. But these radiations are not appreciably different than the radiation one encounters in the "safest" of situations. The probability of dying from something or other is 100%, so in the meantime you and your friend should enjoy life anyway!

12. A friend checks the local background radiation with a Geiger counter, which ticks audibly. Another friend, who normally fears most that which is understood least, makes an effort to keep away from the region of the Geiger counter and looks to you for advice. What do you say?
You can tell your friend who is fearful of the radiation measured by the Geiger counter that his attempt to avoid the radiation by avoiding the instrument that measures it, is useless. He might as well avoid thermometers on a hot day in effort to escape the heat. If it will console your fearful friend, tell him that he and his ancestors from time zero have endured about the same level of radiation he receives whether or not he stands near the Geiger counter. They had, and he has, no better options. Make the best of the years available anyway!

13. Why is carbon-14 dating not accurate for estimating the age of materials more than 50,000 years old?
Radioactive decay rates are statistical averages of large numbers of decaying atoms. Because of the relatively short half-life of carbon-14, only trace amounts would be left after 50,000 years—too little to be statistically accurate.

14. The age of the Dead Sea Scrolls was determined by carbon-14 dating. Could this technique have worked if they had been carved on stone tablets? Explain.
Stone tablets cannot be dated by the carbon dating technique. Nonliving stone does not ingest carbon and transform that carbon by radioactive decay. Carbon dating pertains to organic material.

15. A certain radioactive element has a half-life of 1 hour. If you start with a 1-gram sample of the element at noon, how much is left at 3:00 P.M.? At 6:00 P.M.? At 10:00 P.M.?
At 3:00 PM there will be 1/8 g left-over. At 6:00 PM there will be 1/64 g left-over. At 10:00 PM there will be 1/1024 g left-over.

20 Nuclear Fission and Fusion

20.1 Nuclear Fission Is the Splitting of the Atomic Nucleus
20.2 Nuclear Reactors Convert Nuclear Energy to Electrical Energy
   The Breeder Reactor Breeds Its Own Fuel
20.3 Nuclear Energy Comes from Nuclear Mass and Vice Versa
20.4 Nuclear Fusion Is the Combining of Atomic Nuclei
20.5 An Important Goal of Nuclear Research Is Controlled Fusion

Learning Objectives
After studying Chapter 20, students will be able to:
• Describe the role of neutrons in causing and sustaining nuclear fission.
• Explain how nuclear fission can be controlled in a reactor.
• Distinguish between a breeder reactor and a uranium-based fission reactor.
• Describe current problems associated with the use of fission as a source of power.
• Predict, from a graph of mass per nucleon vs atomic number, whether energy would be
   released if a given nucleus split via fission into fragments.
• Distinguish between nuclear fission and nuclear fusion.
• Describe the advantages of fusion over fission as a source of power.
• Describe the current problems associated with using fusion as a source of power.

Possible Misconceptions to Correct
Not so! Nuclear power is sinister, as were electricity, steam power, and other technological
   advances when they were introduced.
Not so! Nuclear fission and fusion are something new in the universe.
Not so! Nuclear fusion can only occur at high temperatures.
Not so! Nuclear power is ecologically more devastating than fossil-fuel power is.

Demonstrations for this Chapter
None

The material in this chapter is of great technological and sociological importance. Nuclear
bombs are not avoided in the applications of nuclear energy, but the emphasis of the few
applications discussed in the chapter is on the positive aspects of nuclear power and its
potential for improving the world. Much of the public sentiment against nuclear power has to
do with a distrust of what is generally not understood, and with the sentiments against
centralized power, rather than with the technological pros and cons. In this climate, we have a
responsibility to provide our students with an understanding of the basics physics of nuclear
power. In your physics class, an appropriate slogan is "KNOW NUKES."

Note that in this text, the energy release from the opposite processes of fission and fusion is
approached from the viewpoint of decreased mass rather than the customary treatment of
increased binding energy. Hence the usual binding energy curve is "tipped upside-down" in
Figure 20.9, and shows the relationship of the mass per nucleon versus atomic number. We
consider this way conceptually more appealing, for it shows that any reaction involving a
decrease in mass releases energy in accordance with mass-energy equivalence.

Mass-energy can be measured in either joules or kilograms (or in ergs or grams). For example,
the kinetic energy of a 2-gram beetle walking 1 cm/s = 1 erg, and the energy of the Hiroshima
bomb = 1 gram. So we can express the same quantity in essentially different units.

In a uranium mine in Western Africa in the Republic of Gabon, at Oklo, a mining geologist in 1972 discovered evidence of an ancient natural nuclear fission reactor that produced sustained low-level power for several hundred thousand years. The sustained fission reactions occurred about two billion years ago, when concentrations of U-235 were higher than they are now. The byproduct isotopes of this ancient reactor have been found to be almost exactly those found in present day reactors—even with the production of plutonium. So it's interesting to note that the achievement of Fermi and his team of some of the brightest minds in modern physics and engineering duplicated what nature did some two billion year ago.

Nuclear waste need not plague future generations indefinitely, as is commonly thought. Teams of scientists are presently designing devices in which long-lived radioactive atoms of spent reactor fuel can be turned into short-lived, or nonradioactive, atoms. See "Will New Technology Solve the Nuclear Waste Problem?" in *The Physics Teacher*, Vol. 35, February 1997.

In the **Practice Book**:
• Nuclear Fission and Fusion
• Nuclear Reactions

In the **Next-Time Questions** book:
• Fission
• Fusion Reactions

In the **Lab Manual**:
• Chain Reaction

Overhead Transparencies (3)available for:
Figures 20.1, 20.2, Figure 20.6, and Figures 20.9, 20.10, 20.11.

SUGGESTED PRESENTATION

20.1 Nuclear Fission Is the Splitting of the Atomic Nucleus
Briefly discuss the world atmosphere back in the late 30s when fission was discovered in Germany, and how this information was communicated to American physicists who urged Einstein to write his famous letter urging President Roosevelt to consider its potential in warfare. The importance of the fission reaction was not only the release of enormous energy, but the ejected neutrons that could stimulate other fissions in a chain reaction. In the practice of writing equations from the previous chapter, write on the board the reaction shown that accompanies the art at the beginning of the chapter (also an OHT) and discuss its meaning. To give some idea as to the magnitude of the 200,000,000 eV of energy associated with one fission reaction, state that New York City is powered by water falling over Niagara Falls, and that the energy of one drop over the falls is 4 eV; the energy of a TNT molecule is 30 eV, the energy of a molecule of gasoline oxidizing is 30 eV. So 200,000,000 eV is impressive. (Spelling it out like this rather than saying 200 Mev underscores the comparison of fission and conventional energy sources.) Discuss the average 3 neutrons that are kicked out by the reaction and what a chain reaction is (Figure 34.2). Discuss critical mass, and a nuclear device, simplified in Figure 34.4.

20.2 Nuclear Reactors Convert Nuclear Energy to Electrical Energy
A piece of uranium or any radioactive material is slightly warmer than ambient temperature because of the thermal activity prodded by radioactive decay. Major concentrations of energy occur with fission reactions and material becomes quite hot—hot enough to boil water and then some. Make clear that a nuclear reactor of any kind is no more than a means to heat water to steam and generate electricity as a fossil fuel plant does. The principle difference is the fuel used to heat the water. You could quip that nuclear fuel is closer to the nature of the Earth than fossil fuels, whose energies come from the sun.
Discuss the mechanics of a reactor via Figure 20.6.

The Breeder Reactor Breeds Its Own Fuel
Reactors designed to maximize the production of plutonium are the breeder reactors. Make clear that they don't make something from nothing, but merely convert a nonfissionable isotope of uranium (U-238) to a fissionable isotope of plutonium (Pu-239).

Plutonium
Show the production of plutonium from uranium-238. Make this two steps, from U-238 + n —> Np-239. Then by beta decay Np-239 to Pu-239. Neptunium's half-life of 2.3 days quickly produces plutonium, with a half life of 24,000 years. Acknowledge that to some degree all reactors produce plutonium. Although plutonium in its elemental form is poisonous like arsenic, in its common form as Pu-2, it is harmless chemically. As a radioactive substance, however, it is harmful. Much of the scare of plutonium as a chemical poison fails to acknowledge that any elemental plutonium very quickly assumes the Pu-2 molecule.

20.3 Nuclear Energy Comes from Nuclear Mass and Vice Versa
It's helpful if students are knowledgeable about relativity at this point, but a brief discussion of what $E= mc^2$ says and what it doesn't say should suffice. This is the most important part of your lecture—the *why* of nuclear power.

Begin by supposing that one could journey into fantasy and compare the masses of different atoms by grabbing their nuclei with bare hands and shaking the nuclei back and forth. Show with hand motion, holding an imaginary giant nucleus, how the difference might appear in shaking a hydrogen atom and a lead atom. State that if you were to plot the results of this investigation for all the elements, that the relationship between mass and atomic number would look like Figure 20.9, (which you draw on the board). Ask if this plot is a "big deal?" The answer is "no," it simply shows that mass increases with the number of nucleons in the nucleus. No surprise.

Distinguish between the mass of a nucleus and the mass of the nucleons that make up a nucleus. Ask what a curve of mass/nucleon versus atomic number would look like—that is, if you divided the mass of each nucleus by the number of nucleons composing it, and compared the value for different atoms. If all nucleons had the same mass in every atomic configuration, then of course the graph would be a horizontal line. But the masses of nucleons differ. The interrelationship between mass and energy is apparent here, for the nucleons have "mass-energy", which is manifest partly in the "congealed" part which is the material matter of the nucleons, and the other part which we call binding energy. The most energetically bound nucleus has the least mass/nucleon (iron). Go into the nucleon shaking routine again and demonstrate how the nucleons become easier to shake as you progress from hydrogen to iron. Do this by progressing from the student's left to right the full-length of your lecture table. Indicate how they become harder to shake as you progress beyond iron to uranium. Then draw the curve that represents your findings, and you have Figure 20.9 on the board. Announce that this is the most important graph in the book!

From the curve you can show that any nuclear reaction that produces products with less mass than before reaction, will give off energy, and any reaction in which the mass of the products is increased will require energy. Further discussion will show how the opposite processes of fission and fusion release energy.

CHECK YOUR NEIGHBOR: Will the process of fission or fusion release energy from atoms of lead? Gold? Carbon? Neon? (Be careful in selecting atoms too near atomic number 26 in this exercise—for example, elements slightly beyond 26 when fissioned will have more massive products, that extend "up the hydrogen hill"; elements near 26 when fused will combine to elements "up the uranium hill". Acknowledging this point, however, may only serve to complicate the picture—unless, of course, a student brings it up in class.)

State how the graph can be viewed as an pair of "energy hills" on both sides of a valley, and that to progress "down" the hill is a reaction with less mass per nucleon and therefore a gain in energy.

20.4 Nuclear Fusion Is the Combining of Atomic Nuclei

By way of the energy-hill-valley idea, there are two sides to go down. Going from hydrogen down to iron is even steeper—more mass "defect" in combining light nuclei than splitting heavy ones. This combining atomic nuclei is nuclear fusion—the energy releasing process of the sun and the stars.

CHECK YOUR NEIGHBOR: Will the process of fission or fusion release energy from the nucleus of iron? [Neither! Iron is the nuclear sink; either process results in "going up the hill," gaining rather than losing mass.]

20.5 An Important Goal of Nuclear Research Is Controlled Fusion

Discuss the methods being pursued in controlling fusion. Also discuss one future application, the speculative fusion torch and its role in recycling.

Fusion Torch and Recycling

A discussion of the prospects of fusion power is most fascinating. With all the inputs students get from the prophets of doom, it is well to balance some of this negativity with some of our positive prospects. Abundant energy from controlled fusion is one such positive prospect, which should concern not only physicists, but economists, political scientists, sociologists, ecologists, psychologists, and the everyday person on the street. Particularly exciting is the prospect of the fusion torch, which may provide a means of recycling material and alleviate the scarcity of raw material—not to mention the sink it could provide for wastes and pollutants. Ideally, all unwanted wastes could be dumped in the fusion torch and vaporized. Atoms could be separated into respective bins by being beamed through giant mass spectrographs. Point out that the fusion torch may never come to be—but not because technology won't progress to such a point, but because it most likely will progress further. If the past is any guide, something even better will make this 1970's idea obsolete. Whether or not the fusion torch is around the corner, the more important questions to consider are how this or comparable achievements will affect the life of people.

Conceptual Physical Science—Explorations **Teaching Guide**

Chapter 20 Answers and Solutions

Key Terms and Matching Definitions

__2__ chain reaction
__3__ critical mass
__1__ nuclear fission
__4__ nuclear fusion
__5__ thermonuclear fusion

Review Questions

1. Why does a chain reaction not occur in uranium mines?

    A chain reaction does not occur in uranium mines because not all uranium atoms fission very easily. Uranium-238 accounts for 99.3% of uranium found in pure uranium metal, but this isotope does not undergo fission. Therefore, any chain reaction that might start with uranium-235 will end once the prevalent uranium-238 absorbs neutrons from fission.

2. Is a chain reaction more likely to occur in two separate pieces of uranium-235 or in the same pieces stuck together?

    A chain reaction is more likely to occur in two pieces of uranium-238 stuck together.

3. How is a nuclear reactor similar to a conventional fossil-fuel power plant? How is it different?

    A nuclear reactor and a fossil fuel power plant both boil water to produce steam for turbines. The main difference between them is the amount of fuel involved. Nuclear reactors are much more efficient—one kilogram of uranium fuel yields more than 30 freight car loads of coal.

4. What is the function of control rods in a nuclear reactor?

    Control rods are appropriately named because they are rods that control the reaction rate of a nuclear reactor. They do this by absorbing freed neutrons that would otherwise instigate further nuclear fission.

5. Is work required to pull a nucleon out of an atomic nucleus? Does the nucleon, once outside the nucleus, have more mass than it had inside the nucleus?

    Yes, work is required to remove a nucleon by force to the outside of the nucleus. This energy to pull it outside manifests itself as a change in the nucleon's mass.

6. How does the mass per nucleon in uranium compare with the mass per nucleon in the fission fragments of uranium?

    Mass per nucleon is greater in uranium than the mass per nucleon of fission fragments of uranium.

7. If an iron nucleus split in two, would its fission fragments have more mass per nucleon or less mass per nucleon?

    Fission fragments of iron have more mass per nucleon than the original nucleus.

8. If a pair of iron nuclei were fused, would the product nucleus have more mass per nucleon or less mass per nucleon?

    If a pair of iron nuclei were fused, the product nuclei have more mass per nucleon than the original nucleus. Remember, nucleons have their smallest mass when located within an iron nucleus.

9. When a pair of hydrogen isotopes are fused, is the mass of the product nucleus more or less than the total mass of the hydrogen nuclei?

When a pair of hydrogen isotopes are fused, the mass of product is less than the total mass of the nuclei before fusion.

10. From where does the sun gets its energy?

    The sun gets its energy from thermonuclear fusion.

11. How do the product particles of fusion reactions differ from the product particles of fission reactions?

    Fusion produces a single product whose nucleus mass is less than the mass of the two nuclei before fusion. Fission produces two fragments that are roughly equal in size.

12. What kind of containers are used to contain multimillion-degree plasmas?

    Magnetic fields confine multi-million-degree plasmas to a circular path.

Solutions to Chapter 20 Exercises

1. Why will nuclear fission probably never be used directly for powering automobiles? How could it be used indirectly?
   Nuclear fission is a poor prospect for powering automobiles primarily because of the massive shielding that would be required to protect the occupants and others from the radioactivity, and the problem of radioactive waste disposal.

2. Why does a neutron make a better nuclear bullet than a proton or an electron?
   A neutron makes a better "bullet" for penetrating atomic nuclei because it has no electric charge and is therefore not deflected from its path by electrical interactions, nor is it electrically repelled by an atomic nucleus.

3. Does the average distance a neutron travels through fissionable material before escaping increase or decrease when two pieces of fissionable material are assembled into one piece? Does this assembly increase or decrease the probability of an explosion?
   This exercises refers to another application of the ratio of surface area to volume. Surface area for a given volume decreases when small pieces of material are assembled. (It's easier to see the opposite process where surface area for a given volume is increased when big pieces are broken up into little pieces; for example, you break a sugar cube into little pieces to increase the surface area exposed to tea for quick dissolving.) In the case of uranium fuel, the process of assembling small pieces into a single big piece decreases the surface area, reduces neutron leakage, and increases the probability of a chain reaction and an explosion.

4. Why does plutonium not occur in appreciable amounts in natural ore deposits?
   Plutonium has a short half life (24,360 years), so any plutonium initially in the Earth's crust has long since decayed. The same is true for any heavier elements with even shorter half-lives from which plutonium might originate. Trace amounts of plutonium can occur naturally in U-238 concentrations, however, as a result of neutron capture, where U-238 becomes U-239 and after beta emission becomes Np-239, and further beta emission to Pu-239. (There are elements in the Earth's crust with half-lives even shorter than plutonium's, but these are the products of uranium decay; between uranium and lead in the periodic table of elements.)]

5. Uranium-235 releases an average of 2.5 neutrons per fission, while plutonium-239 releases an average of 2.7 neutrons per fission. Which of these elements might you therefore expect to have the smaller critical mass?
   Because plutonium triggers more reactions per atom, a smaller mass will produce the same neutron flux as a somewhat larger mass of uranium. So plutonium has a smaller critical mass than a similar shape of uranium.

6. After a uranium fuel rod reaches the end of its fuel cycle (typically three years), why does most of its energy come from plutonium fission?

Conceptual Physical Science—Explorations Teaching Guide

Because fissionable Pu-239 is formed as the U-238 absorbs neutrons from the fissioning U-235.

7. To predict the approximate energy release of either a fission or a fusion reaction, explain how a physicist uses a table of nuclear masses and the equation $E = mc^2$.

   To predict the energy release of a nuclear reaction, simply find the difference in the mass of the beginning nucleus and the mass of its configuration after the reaction (either fission or fusion). This mass difference (called the "mass defect") can be found from the curve of Figure 20.9 or from a table of nuclear masses. Multiply this mass difference by the speed of light squared: $E = mc^2$. That's the energy released!

8. Which process would release energy from gold, fission or fusion? From carbon? From iron?

   Energy would be released by the fissioning of gold and from the fusion of carbon, but by neither fission nor fusion for iron. Neither fission nor fusion will result in a decrease of mass for iron nucleons.

9. Does the mass of a nucleon after it has been pulled from an atomic nucleus depend on which nucleus it was extracted from?

   Yes. Figure 20.9 shows the mass per nucleon as a function of atomic number. Since the mass per nucleon increases when pulled out of a nucleus, then a nucleon's mass would depend on the element from which it was pulled.

10. If a uranium nucleus were to fission into three segments of approximately equal size instead of two, would more energy or less energy be released? Defend your answer using Figure 20.10.

    If uranium were split into three parts, the segments would be nuclei of smaller atomic numbers, more toward iron on the graph of Figure 20.10. The resulting mass per nucleon would be less, and there would be more mass converted to energy in such a fissioning.

11. Explain how radioactive decay has always warmed the Earth from the inside and how nuclear fusion has always warmed the Earth from the outside.

    The radioactive decay of radioactive elements found under the Earth's surface warms the interiors of the Earth and responsible for the molten lava that spews from volcanoes. The thermonuclear fusion of our sun is responsible for warming everything on our planet's surface exposed to the sun.

12. What percentage of nuclear power plants in operation today are based upon nuclear fusion?

    There are no fusion -based nuclear power plants in operation today. They are all of the fission type.

13. Speculate about some worldwide changes likely to follow the advent of successful fusion reactors.

    Such speculation could fill volumes. The energy and material abundance that is the expected outcome of a fusion age will likely prompt several fundamental changes. Obvious changes would occur in the fields of economics and commerce which would be geared to relative abundance rather than scarcity. Already our present price system, which is geared to and in many ways dependent upon scarcity, often malfunctions in an environment of abundance. Hence we see instances where scarcity is created to keep the economic system functioning. Changes at the international level will likely be worldwide economic reform, and at the personal level in a re-evaluation of the idea that scarcity ought to be the basis of value. A fusion age will likely see changes that will touch every facet of our way of life.

21 Elements of Chemistry

21.1 Chemistry Is a Central Science Useful to Our Lives
21.2 The Submicroscopic World Is Made of Atoms and Molecules
21.3 Matter Has Physical and Chemical Properties
> Hands-On Exploration: Fire Water
21.4 An Element Is Made of a Collection of Atoms
21.5 Elements Can Combine to Form Compounds
> Hands-On Exploration: Oxygen Bubble Bursts
21.6 Chemical Reactions Are Represented by Chemical Equations

Learning Objectives
After studying Chapter 21, students will be able to:
• Understand the nature of chemistry.
• Distinguish between atoms and molecules.
• Describe and explain properties of elements.
• Analyze and explain atomic and molecular changes in a chemical reaction.
• Compare and contrast physical and chemical properties.

Possible Misconceptions to Correct
• **Not so!** Chemistry is more complex than biology.
• **Not so!** Ice and liquid water to two different materials.
• **Not so!** Chemical and physical changes are easy to distinguish.
• **Not so!** Compounds retain properties of the elements from which they are made.
• **Not so!** Balancing chemical equations is an important skill.

This chapter serves as an introduction to the language of chemistry and its submicroscopic perspectives. It is designed to set the foundation for all subsequent chemistry chapters.

In the **Explorations Practice Book**:
• The Submicroscopic.
• Physical and Chemical Changes
• Balancing Chemical Equations

In the **Next-Time Questions Book**:
• Open Structure in Ice
• Rusting
• Chemical or physical change?
• Chemical or physical change?

In the **Lab Manual**:
• Tubular Rust (allows students to measure the % oxygen in air).
• Foamy Bubble Round-Up (introduces the collection of a gas by displacement of water).

Overhead Transparencies available for:
Figures 21.2, 21.6, 21.8, 21.12

SUGGESTED PRESENTATION

21.1 Chemistry is a Central Science Useful to Our Lives

Ask students if they would prefer to live without medicines, an abundant and safe food supply, or anything made of plastic or metal. Yes, there are numerous problems we encounter living in this modern age, but the many benefits we enjoy should not be ignored. Emphasize that we solve our current problems not by retreating to our past—to those "simpler" times. Rather, why not embrace all that we have learned and apply this knowledge with as much wisdom and foresight that we can muster.

This section does not delve into the risks of technology verses the benefits of technology. This is a good time, however, for you to bring this subject up for general class discussion.

You might also discuss where chemistry stands relative to other sciences. Ask your students: "Which is the most complex science: physics, chemistry, or biology?" The answer, of course, is biology for it involves the application of chemistry to living organisms. Chemistry, in turn, involves the application of physics. In this sense, chemistry is the "Central Science" situated between physics and biology. Go to any biology lab and you'll see chemistry on the chalkboard. Go to any chemistry lab and you'll see physics on the chalkboard. (What might you see on the chalkboard of a physics laboratory?)

21.2 The Submicroscopic World Is Made of Atoms and Molecules

This section is a good opportunity to introduce (or re-introduce) the idea that the materials around us are made of these incredibly small particles called atoms and molecules. How they comprise the different phases of matter should be emphasized. Consider using your hands as an analogy: Particles of a solid are fixed and can only vibrate relative to one another (hold your two fists together while giving them a vibrating motion). Particles in a liquid, on the other hand, are able to tumble over one another much like a bunch of marbles in a plastic bag (tumble your fists over each other). Particles in the gaseous phase are moving so rapidly that they separate from one another altogether (Rapidly bring your two fists together and bounce them off each other).

> DEMONSTRATION: To show how gases occupy much more volume than do solids or liquids, crush some dry ice and use a powder funnel to add about a tablespoon to a 9-inch balloon. Place the expanding balloon in a tub of warm water for a more rapid effect. In talking about phase changes you may find that the water directly beneath the dry-ice containing balloon has frozen. Be sure to identify the dry-ice as solidified carbon dioxide having nothing in common with water ice except for its solid phase. Note how the dry ice "sublimes" directly from the solid to gaseous phase. Snow does the same thing, especially high on mountain tops where it is sunny and dry.

Fill a punching balloon with little plastic beads. Blow the punching balloon to full size and then holding the balloon firmly with the palms of your hands shake vigorously. This is certainly a "hands-on" activity as only the person performing the activity can feel the many pulses of beads hitting against your hands. This is nicely analogous to what happens inside the hot-water balloon of demonstration as described below. Pass the bead-containing balloon around for some student testimonials. Ask for volunteers to explain how the balloon shaking with plastic beads inside is analogous to the hot-water balloon demonstration. Confirm their understandings with an explanation of your own.

> DEMONSTRATION: Pour 2 teaspoons of water into a 9-inch rubber balloon. Squeeze out as much air as you can and knot the balloon. Put the balloon in the microwave oven and cook at full power for however many seconds it takes for boiling to begin, which is indicated by a rapid growth in the size of the balloon. It may take only about 10 seconds for the balloon to

reach full size once it starts expanding. (The balloon will pop if you add too much water or if you cook it for too long.) Remove the heated balloon with the oven mitt, shake the balloon around, and listen for the return of the liquid phase. You should be able to hear it raining inside the balloon. A marble hitting your hand pushes against your hand. In a similar fashion, a gaseous water molecule hitting the inside of the balloon pushes against the balloon. The force of a single water molecule is not that great, but the combined forces of the billions and billions of them in this activity is sufficient to inflate the balloon as the liquid water evaporates to the gaseous phase. Thus, you saw how the gaseous phase occupies much more volume than the liquid phase. If you observed the balloon carefully, you noticed it continues to inflate (although not so rapidly) after all the water has been converted to water vapor. This occurs because the microwaves continue to heat the gaseous water molecules, making them move faster and faster, pushing harder and harder against the balloon's inner surface.

After you take the balloon out of the microwave, the balloon is in contact with air molecules, which, being cooler, move more slowly than the water molecules. Gaseous water molecules colliding with the inner surface of the balloon pass their kinetic energy to the slower air molecules, and the air molecules get warmer because their kinetic energy increases. (This is similar to how the kinetic energy of a hammer pounding a nail into a flimsy wall can be transferred to a picture frame hanging on the opposite side of the wall.) You can feel this warming by holding your hand close to the balloon. As the gaseous water molecules lose kinetic energy, they begin to condense into the liquid phase, a noisy process amplified by the balloon (listen carefully).

21.3 Matter Has Physical and Chemical Properties
The main difference between a physical and chemical change is that only a chemical change involves the production of a new material. Distinguishing between the two in the laboratory, however, is not easy because in both cases there are changes in physical attributes.

Because physical and chemical properties are such broad concepts, almost any chemistry demonstration can be performed within their context. Here are some favorites.

DEMONSTRATIONS: Demonstrate the physical properties of liquid nitrogen by quick freezing flowers, balloons, etc. Here's an interesting aside: solidify liquid nitrogen by placing about 100 mL inside a bell jar and reducing the pressure with a good vacuum pump. Demonstrate the physical properties of metallic sodium (can be cut with a knife) then drop a small amount (less than a pea-size) into some phenolphthalein containing water to demonstrate chemical change. (Metallic sodium is very hazardous as it reacts violently with water to form sodium hydroxide and combustible hydrogen gas. It should be stored under mineral oil or kerosene). Flash paper from your local magicians shop also works well for demonstrating chemical change. A crowd favorite is to blow soap bubbles using methane gas. Since methane is less dense than air (a physical property), the bubbles rise. Dim the lights and ignite one of the bubbles (a chemical property) with a butane lighter. CAUTION: Only ignite bubbles that are still relatively far from the ceiling. If your natural gas soap bubbles persistently fall rather than rise, they contain not methane but propane, which I've not so ignited before and so cannot recommend, except to say that, perhaps, such a demo would be more dangerous.

DEMONSTRATION: React baking soda and vinegar in a tall drinking glass. Let settle. Because the carbon dioxide is heavier than the air it remains within the glass. Dip a lighted match within the carbon dioxide containing glass to demonstrate that chemical property of carbon dioxide.

DEMONSTRATION: React a 3% hydrogen peroxide solution with bakers yeast in a bowl. Poke the resulting bubbles with a red-hot wood splint to demonstrate the formation of oxygen. This is a repeat of the Hands-On Explorations: Oxygen Bubble Bursts.

DEMONSTRATION: For distinguishing between a physical and chemical change, a favorite demonstration is the comparison of what happens upon the heating of potassium chromate verses the heating of ammonium dichromate. Unfortunately, the potassium chromate is a known carcinogen while the ammonium dichromate is classified as an explosive, which means extra precautions on the handling of these compounds. The potassium chromate can be recycled. The ammonium dichromate, however, transforms into chromium oxide (a common component of green paint) along with ammonia and water vapor.

21.4 An Element Is Made of a Collection of Atoms

This Section is similar to Section 17.1, except that it goes into the concept of elemental formula. The concept check question on page 361 is valuable enough for you to should consider using it during class as an Ask Your Neighbor question:

ASK YOUR NEIGHBOR: The oxygen we breathe, O_2, is converted to ozone, O_3, in the presence of an electric spark. Is this a physical or chemical change? [Oxygen, O_2, and ozone, O_3, are both elemental forms of oxygen, much in the same way that diamond and graphite are elemental forms of carbon. Oxygen, O_2, and ozone, O_3, however, are fundamentally different materials because they differ in the way the atoms are bonded together. The change, therefore, is a chemical change.]

21.5 Elements Can Combine to Form Compounds

A *compound* results when different types of atoms bond to one another. It should be emphasized that a compound is uniquely different from the elements from which it is made. Sodium and chlorine, for example, are toxic, but sodium chloride is essential for good health. The reason that a compound is uniquely different from the elements from which it is made is because of a different arrangement of atoms. You might stress to your class that it is the arrangement of atoms within a material that defines its identity as judged by its physical and chemical properties. That a new material is formed when atoms connect differently is exactly what gives rise to the great diversity of materials around us. Many different compounds can be produced out of a smaller variety of elements.

A most effective way of illustrating the point of how a compound is uniquely different from the elements from which it is made is as follows:

DEMONSTRATION: Hold up a samples of copper, sulfur, and oxygen. Rather, than pulling out a genuine tank of oxygen, merely scoop up some air into a transparent plastic canister and then capping it before your students. Ask them what the properties of a compound formed from copper, sulfur, and oxygen might be. Perhaps, a combination of all the various properties of copper, sulfur and oxygen? Surprise them by showing some large blue crystals of copper sulfate pentahydrate, though you need not mention the pentahydrate part. In short, there is really no way to predict what the properties of the compound might be. A compound really is uniquely different from the elements from which it is made.

21.6 Chemical Reactions Are Represented by Chemical Equations

The chemical equation is used to depict the chemical reaction. Significant features of the chemical equation are presented in this section. The importance of having a balanced chemical equation should be related back to the conservation of mass principle.

A good way to keep the art of balancing chemical equations low key in your quizzes and exams is to present an equation and simply ask whether or not it is balanced. Learning how to balance chemical equations is good mental exercise, but it is not a prerequisite for subsequent chapters.

A methodology explored in one of the Practice Pages is as follows:

1. Focus on balancing only one element at a time. Start with the left-most element and modify the coefficients such that this element appears on both sides of the arrow the same number of times.

2. Move to the next element and modify the coefficients so as to balance this element. Do not worry if you incidentally unbalance the previous element. You will come back to it in subsequent steps.

3. Continue from left to right balancing each element individually.

4. Repeat steps 1 - 3 until all elements are balanced.

Six reasonable equations you might try balancing with your class—reviewing techniques as you go along—are given below.

$$3\,O_2 \rightarrow 2\,O_3$$
$$4\,Cr + 3\,O_2 \rightarrow 2\,Cr_2O_3$$
$$2\,SO_2 + O_2 \rightarrow 2\,SO_3$$
$$2\,N_2O \rightarrow 2\,N_2 + O_2$$
$$2\,NO + O_2 \rightarrow 2\,NO_2$$
$$3\,HNO_2 \rightarrow HNO_3 + 2\,NO + H_2O$$
$$2\,N_2H_4O_3 \rightarrow 2\,N_2 + O_2 + 4\,H_2O$$

When dealing with odd and even subscripts, as in $O_2 \rightarrow O_3$, it's useful to "barrow the opposite subscript as the coefficient". In this manner, the subscript of O_3 is used as the coefficient of O_2, and vice versa. Alternatively, an extra oxygen atom might simply be added to the left side: $O + O_2 \rightarrow O_3$. This is illegal, however, because it alters the identity of the reactants (O is not O_2). A way around this is to use a fraction of a coefficient, such as $1/2$, which gives $1/2\,O_2 + O_2 \rightarrow O_3$, which can also be written as $3/2\,O_2 \rightarrow O_3$. The fraction of oxygen can be corrected by multiplying every term by 2, which gives: $2(3/2)\,O_2 \rightarrow 2(O_3)$, which equals: $3\,O_2 \rightarrow 2\,O_3$.

Chapter 21 Answers and Solutions

Key Terms and Matching Definitions

__4__ applied research
__3__ basic research
_10_ chemical change
_15_ chemical equation
_14_ chemical formula
__9__ chemical properties
_11_ chemical reaction
__1__ chemistry
_13_ compound
_12_ elemental formula
_18_ law of mass conservation
__2__ matter
__5__ molecules
__8__ physical change
__7__ physical properties
_17_ products
_16_ reactants
__6__ submicroscopic

Review Questions

1. What is the difference between basic research and applied research?
   Basic research leads to useful applications of science. Applied research develops the applications of science discovered by basic research.

2. Why is chemistry often called the central science?
   Chemistry is often called a central science because it touches all of the sciences.

3. What do members of the Chemical Manufacturers Association pledge in the Responsible Care program?
   The members of the Chemical Manufacturers Association pledge to manufacture without causing environmental damage through a program called Responsible Care.

4. Are atoms made of molecules, or are molecules made of atoms?
   Molecules are made of atoms. Atoms link together to form larger but still small basic units of matter called molecules.

5. Which is smaller: the microscopic or the submicroscopic?
   The microscopic refers to that which is observable through a microscope, such as the hair on a mosquito's leg. The submicroscopic, which is smaller than the microscopic, refers to that which is so small it is invisible to even to the most powerful optical microscopes. Atoms and molecules are submicroscopic.

6. What is a physical property?
   A physical property is the description of the physical attributes of a substance such as color, hardness, density, texture, and phase.

7. What is a chemical property?

Chemical properties characterize the tendency of a substance to react with or transform into other substances.

8. What doesn't change during a physical change?

During a physical change the chemical composition of a substance does not change.

9. Why is it sometimes difficult to decide whether an observed change is physical or chemical?

Determining whether a change is physical or chemical can be difficult because both involve changes in appearance.

10. What are some of the clues that help us determine whether an observed change is physical or chemical?

If by returning to the original set of conditions you return to the original physical appearance, then the change was physical. If the substance that has undergone the change has new physical properties then the change was a chemical change.

11. Is it possible for an element to have more than one atomic formula?

Yes, it is possible for an element to have more than one atomic formula. Oxygen, for example, exists as both O_2, which we need to breathe, and O_3, which is ozone.

12. How many atoms are in a sulfur molecule that has the elemental formula S_8?

There are 8 sulfur atoms in a molecule with the formula S_8.

13. What is the difference between an element and a compound?

An element has only one type of atom. A compound has combinations of different types of atoms.

14. How many atoms are there in one molecule of H_3PO_4? How many atoms of each element are there in one molecule of H_3PO_4?

The total number of atoms in H_3PO_4 is 8. There are three H atoms, one P atom, and four O atoms in H_3PO_4.

15. Are the physical and chemical properties of a compound necessarily similar to those of the elements from which it is composed?

Compounds have physical and chemical properties that are different from the properties of their elemental components.

16. What is the purpose of coefficients in a chemical equation?

Coefficients are used to show the ratio in which reactants combine and products for in a chemical reaction.

17. How many chromium atoms and how many oxygen atoms are indicated on the right side of this balanced chemical equation:
$$4\,Cr(s) + 3\,O_2(g) \rightarrow 2\,Cr_2O_3(g)$$

There are four chromium atoms and six oxygen atoms on the right hand side of the equation.

18. What do the letters (s), (l), (g), and (aq) stand for in a chemical equation?

Solid is represented by (s), (l) stands for liquid, (g) stands for gas, and (aq) for aqueous.

19. Why is it important that a chemical equation be balanced?

A chemical equation must be balanced because the law of conservation of mass says that mass can neither be created nor destroyed. There must be the same number of each atom on both sides of the equation.

20. Why is it important never to change a subscript in a chemical formula when balancing a chemical equation?

The subscript describes how the molecule is put together and cannot be changed or it will describe a different molecule.

21. Which equations are balanced?
    a. $Mg(s) + 2\,HCl(aq) \rightarrow MgCl_2(aq) + H_2(g)$
    b. $3\,Al(s) + 3\,Br_2(l) \rightarrow Al_2Br_3(s)$
    c. $2\,HgO(s) \rightarrow 2\,Hg(l) + O_2(g)$

A and C are balanced.

Solutions to Chapter 21 Exercises

1. Why is it important to work through the Review Questions before attempting the Exercises?
The exercises are designed to allow you to work with the concepts you have already learned through reading the chapter and performing the review questions. If you have not already worked with the chapter and the review questions, you will have a most difficult time with these exercises, which are the types of questions found on exams. To benefit most from these exercises you should try writing out your answers or, better yet, explain your answers verbally to a friend.

2. In what sense is a color computer monitor or television screen similar to our view of matter? Place a drop (and only a drop) of water on your computer monitor or television screen for a closer look.
When looked at macroscopically, matter appears continuous. On the submicroscopic level, however, we find that matter is made of extremely small particles, such as atoms or molecules. Similarly, a TV screen looked at from a distance appears as a smooth continuous flow of images. Up close, however, we see this is an illusion. What really exists are a series of tiny dots (pixels) that change color in a coordinated way to produce the series of images.

3. Of the three sciences physics, chemistry, and biology, which is the most complex? Explain.
Biology is based upon the principles of chemistry as applied to living organisms, while chemistry is based upon the principles of physics as applied to atoms and molecules. Physics is the study of the fundamental rules of nature, which more often than not are rather simple in their design and readily described by mathematical formula. Because biology sits at the top of these three sciences, it can be considered to be the most complex of them all.

4. Is chemistry the study of the submicroscopic, the microscopic, the macroscopic, or all three? Defend your answer.
Chemistry is the careful study of matter and can take place at a number of different levels including the submicroscopic, microscopic, or macroscopic levels.

5. Each night you measure your height just before going to bed. When you arise each morning, you measure your height again and consistently find that you are 1 inch taller than you were the night before but only as tall as you were 24 hours ago! Is what happens to your body in this instance best described as a physical change or a chemical change? Be sure to try this activity if you haven't already.

That this process is so reversible suggests a physical change. As you sleep in a reclined position, pressure is taken off of the discs within your spinal column, which allows them to expand so that you are significantly taller in the morning. Astronauts returning from extended space visits may be up to two inches taller upon their return.

6. Classify the following changes as physical or chemical. Even if you are incorrect in your assessment, you should be able to defend why you chose as you did.
   a. grape juice turns to wine ————
   b. wood burns to ashes ————
   c. water begins to boil ————
   d. a broken leg mends itself ————
   e. grass grows ————
   f. an infant gains 10 pounds ————
   g. a rock is crushed to powder————

   a) chemical. b) chemical. c) physical. d) chemical. e) chemical. f) chemical. g) physical.

7. Is the following transformation representative of a physical change or a chemical change?

   The atoms are connected differently in B than they are in A, which means that this represents a chemical change.

8. Each sphere in the diagrams below represents an atom. Joined spheres represent molecules. Which box contains a liquid phase? Why can you not assume that box B represents a lower temperature?

   Box B appears to contain a liquid as evidenced by the randomly oriented molecules condensed at the bottom of the box. These molecules in the liquid phase of Box B represent a compound because they consist of different types of atoms joined together. The physical properties of the compound in Box B will be markedly different from the elements in Box A. For example, if the two boxes are of the same temperature, we would see that the compound of Box B has a higher boiling point. It could be, however, that the boiling point of the substance in Box B is lower than either of the elements in Box A. In such a case, the temperature of Box B must be lower than that of Box A. In short, there's no way to assume the relative temperatures of the boxes based upon the phases of the materials they contain because these materials are uniquely different from each other.

9. Based on the information given in the following diagrams, which substance has the higher boiling point?

   The change from A to B represents a physical change because no new types of molecules are formed. The collection of blue/yellow molecules on the bottom of B represents these molecules in the liquid or solid phase after having been in the gaseous phase in A. This must occur with a decrease in temperature. At this lower temperature the purely yellow molecules are still in the gaseous phase which means that they have a lower boiling point, while the blue/yellow molecules have a higher boiling point.

10. What physical and chemical changes occur when a wax candle burns?

    The melting of the wax near the flame is an example of a physical change. This liquid wax is drawn up the wick where it is burned, which is an example of a chemical change.

11. Which elements are some of the oldest known? What is your evidence?

    The ones that have atomic symbols that don't match their modern atomic names. Examples include iron, Fe; gold, Au; and copper, Cu.

12. Oxygen atoms are used to make water molecules. Does this mean that oxygen, O_2, and water, H_2O, have similar properties? Why do we drown when we breathe in water despite all the oxygen atoms present in this material?

All the oxygen present in this material is bound to hydrogen atoms making water molecules. This water is uniquely different from the elements oxygen, O_2, and hydrogen, H_2, from which it is made. The oxygen our bodies are designed to breathe is gaseous molecular oxygen, O_2. We drown when we breathe in water because it contains so little O_2.

13. Is this chemical equation balanced:
    $$2\ C_4H_{10}(g) + 13\ O_2(g) \rightarrow 8\ CO_2(g) + 10\ H_2O(l)$$
    This equation is balanced.

14. Balance these equations:
    a. ____ $Fe(s)$ + ____ $O_2(g) \rightarrow$ ____ $Fe_2O_3(s)$
    b. ____ $H_2(g)$ + ____ $N_2(g) \rightarrow$ ____ $NH_3(g)$
    c. ____ $Cl_2(g)$ + ____ $KBr(aq) \rightarrow$ ____ $Br_2(l)$ + ____ $KCl(aq)$
    d. ____ $CH_4(g)$ + ____ $O_2(g) \rightarrow$ ____ $CO_2(g)$ + ____ $H_2O(l)$
    a) 4, 3, 2 b) 3, 1, 2 c) 1, 2, 1, 2 d) 1, 2, 1, 2 (Remember that, by convention, 1's are not shown in the balanced equation.)

15. Balance these equations:
    a. ____ $Fe(s)$ + ____ $S(s) \rightarrow$ ____ $Fe_2S_3(s)$
    b. ____ $P_4(s)$ + ____ $H_2(g) \rightarrow$ ____ $PH_3(g)$
    c. ____ $NO(g)$ + ____ $Cl_2(g) \rightarrow$ ____ $NOCl(g)$
    d. ____ $SiCl_4(l)$ + ____ $Mg(s) \rightarrow$ ____ $Si(s)$ + ____ $MgCl_2(s)$
    a) 2,3,1 b) 1,6,4 c) 2,1,2 d) 1,2,1,2

22 Mixtures

22.1 Most Materials Are Mixtures
22.2 Mixtures Can Be Separated by Physical Means
22.3 Chemists Classify Matter as Pure or Impure
22.4 A Solution Is a Single-Phase Homogeneous Mixture
> **Hands-On Exploration: Overflowing Sweetness**

Learning Objectives
After studying Chapter 22, students will be able to:
• Recognize that most materials around them are mixtures of some sort.
• Understand how mixtures can be separated by physical means.
• Recognize that macroscopic samples cannot be classified as 100% pure.
• Distinguish solutions and suspensions from heterogeneous mixtures.
• Understand the concept of the mole.
• Use various terms associated with solutions.

Possible Misconceptions to Correct
• **Not so!** Fish breathe water.
• **Not so!** All impurities found in drinking water are bad for our health.
• **Not so!** Sugar no long occupies space upon dissolving in water.
• **Not so!** Solutes in boiling water evaporate along with the water.
• **Not so!** Natural orange juice is 100% pure.
• **Not so!** A solution must be in the liquid phase.

This chapter covers the basic concepts of mixtures, including the various definitions used in describing mixtures, how the components of a mixture can be separated, and how solutions are made. It is also where the concept of the mole is first introduced. What is missing are many of the details of what occurs between the molecules of a mixture. For that it is important the students first have a handle on how atoms are held together to form molecules, and then how some molecules are polar because of an uneven distribution of bonding electrons. The treatment of the submicroscopic details of molecular mixing, therefore, are not discussed until Chapter 24, which immediately follows Chapter 23 on chemical bonding.

In the **Explorations Practice Book:**
• Pure Mathematics.

In the **Next-Time Questions Book:**
• Solvent in Solution.

In the **Lab Manual:**
• Sugar and Sand (Involves the quantitative separation of a mixture).
• Sugar Soft (Students develop and use a calibration curve to measure sugar content of beverages).

Overhead Transparencies available for:
Figures 22.1, 22.4, 22.7, 22.14, 22.15

SUGGESTED PRESENTATION

22.1 Most Materials are Mixtures
In nature, it's rare that elements or compounds are found in a "purified state." Instead we find them mixed together. Challenge your students to think of a material that is NOT actually a mixture of elements, compounds, or both. Consider listing their replies in columns on the chalkboard. Be lenient with them and allow items such as aluminum foil, or diamond, to be listed in the non-mixture column. Then start getting nit-picky and point out how aluminum foil is hardly pure, consisting of small amounts of magnesium, with a coating of aluminum oxide. Or how it is that diamond's "color" (not refraction of light) results from the impurities it contains. Tell your students that you'll be getting into the technical definition of "pure" in this chapter, then proceed to discuss how it is that the air we breathe and the water we drink are example of mixtures and why. Consider using the overhead transparencies of Figures 22.1 and 22.4.

22.2 Mixtures Can Be Separated by Physical Means
The components of a mixture can be separated ("purified") based upon differences in physical properties.

DEMONSTRATION: Hold out a cup of water and add to it a piece of chalk. Announce that you have just created a mixture. Ask students how you might separate the components of this mixture. As you pour the water through your fingers alert students to the fact that you are separating based upon differences in physical properties—at room temperature water is a liquid while chalk is a solid. Show how this same principle applies to a distillation set-up. Distilling water away from food coloring works well.

DEMONSTRATION: Pour liquid nitrogen into an empty soda can held up by a clamp. The oxygen in the surrounding air will condense along the sides of the soda can much as water vapor condenses along the sides of a filled soda can just pulled from the refrigerator. Ask your students what evidence they see that the drips off of the liquid nitrogen filled soda can are *not* drips of water. Note that the drips are most visible only upon close inspection. Otherwise, the vapor they leave upon falling can be seen from farther back. Notably, as the drips hit a table top they make an audible sound.

DEMONSTRATION: Post 1982 pennies can be heated to separate the internal zinc from the copper coating. Heat the penny over a Bunsen burner or propane torch until blistering occurs and then "shake" the internally melted zinc into a crucible. After it cools, the sample should be passed around the class.

DEMONSTRATION: Before lecture, boil down a large glass of tap water in a clean beaker. Scrape the residual contents from the bottom of the beaker into a small vial. During lecture, hold out the vial and describe what you did. Encourage students to do the same at home using kitchenware (See Hands-On Explorations, page 376). Ask them if the contents represent "concentrated water" or "not concentrated water". A successful answer is: "That's not water at all. That's the material that was **in** the water. Eww!" You might label your vial as "'Your state' drinking water", for example, "California drinking water". Suggest to students the possibility of selling such vials abroad with the directions "Just add distilled water".

Regarding the Hands-On Exploration: Bottoms Up and Bubbles Out, on page 376, as is explored in Chapter 24, gases do not dissolve well in hot liquids. Air that is dissolved in room-temperature water, for example, will bubble out when the water is heated. Thus you can speed up step 3 by using warm water.

For further experimentation, have students perform step 3 in two pots side by side. In one pot, use warm water from the kitchen faucet. In the second pot, use boiled water that has cooled down to the same temperature. You'll find that boiling *deaerates* the water, that is, boiling removes the atmospheric gases. Chemists sometimes need to use deaerated water, which is made by allowing boiled water to cool in a sealed container. Ask students why a fish wouldn't live long in deaerated water.

22.3 Chemists Classify Matter as Pure or Impure

This section is useful for summing up many of the previous concepts presented in this chapter. The following important Ask Your Neighbor appears as a concept check in the textbook on page 379.

> ASK YOUR NEIGHBOR: Impure water can be purified by:
>   (a) removing the impure water molecules.
>   (b) removing everything that is not water.
>   (c) breaking down the water to its simplest components.
>   (d) adding some disinfectant such as chlorine.

Students have many misunderstandings about the term "pure", which is understandable considering how it is commonly used, often erroneously, in advertising. Contrast what is meant by 100% pure water versus 100% pure apple juice—one is fictional, and the other is set by definition. Contrast the terms "pure" and "purified".

> DEMONSTRATION: Separate orange juice into the pulp and the juice using a centrifuge. Talk about how the same technique is used to separated the components of blood.

Consider having the students work in groups on the Practice Page "Pure Mathematics", which was derived from the first several exercises of this chapter on page 386.

22.4 A Solution Is a Single-Phase Homogeneous Mixture

The following demonstration is simple, yet highly effective.

> DEMONSTRATION: Before lecture, fill a 500 mL graduated cylinder to the 500 mL mark, then find out how much sugar must be added so that the volume of solution reaches the brim of the cylinder. For this demonstration, add 500 mL of warm water to the graduated cylinder. Tell the students that you are going to dissolve a bunch of sugar in this water. Ask them to think about whether the volume should increase, decrease, or stay the same. Pour the water into a dry beaker (make a fuss about how it is that the beaker is bone dry and that you are not going to spill a drop of the water in your transfers). Mix in the sugar until it dissolves. Pour the solution back into the graduated cylinder. Slow down as you approach the 500 mL mark. Many students will be surprised as you reach the 500 mL mark. More surprise comes when you fill it exactly to the brim. Explain that matter does not cease to occupy volume even when it's dissolved.

Use the transparency of Figure 22.4 to remind students what happens when sugar dissolves in water.

A pitfall to this section is that there are many, many terms associated with solutions. Behind each term, however, lies a concept. Guide your students towards these concepts and away from memorization. There is much to see here on the molecular level.
The *mole* is introduced in this section. It is used to define *molarity*, a common unit of concentration. Molarity is used again in Section 25.3 for defining the pH of a solution.

Chapter 22 Answers and Solutions

Key Terms and Matching Definitions

_13_ concentration
_10_ dissolving
_4_ heterogeneous mixture
_5_ homogeneous mixture
_3_ impure
_1_ mixture
_15_ molarity
_14_ mole
_2_ pure
_11_ saturated solution
_9_ solute
_6_ solution
_8_ solvent
_7_ suspension
_12_ unsaturated solution

Review Questions

1. What defines a material as being a mixture?

   A material is a mixture if it is not pure.

2. Why is drinking water considered a mixture?

   Drinking water invariably contains small amounts of dissolved materials such as salts and atmospheric gases.

3. Why is sodium chloride not considered a mixture?

   Sodium chloride is a compound that has a set of characteristic properties that are uniquely different from the sodium and chlorine from which it is made. A mixture must contain two or more compounds. Sodium chloride by itself, therefore, is not considered to be a mixture.

4. How can the components of a mixture be separated from one another?

   Filtration or distillation can separate mixtures. These methods take advantage of differences in the components' physical properties.

5. How does distillation separate the components of a mixture?

   During distillation, one of the components of the mixture is boiled and the vapor is collected in another container.

6. The boiling point of oxygen, O_2, is 90 K (-183°C) and that of nitrogen, N_2, is 77 K (-196°C). What is the phase of oxygen, O_2, at 80 K (-193° C)? What is the phase of nitrogen, N_2, at this temperature?

   At 80 K (-193°C), oxygen, O_2, is a liquid and nitrogen, N_2, is a gas.

7. Why is it not practical to have a macroscopic sample that is 100 percent pure?

   Atoms and molecules are very small so if one atom or molecule out of a trillion is different then the sample is no longer pure.

8. Classify the following as (a) homogeneous mixture, (b) heterogeneous mixture, (c) element, or (d) compound:
   milk _____ steel _____
   ocean water _____ blood _____
   sodium _____ planet Earth _____

   Planet Earth and ocean water are a heterogeneous mixtures. Milk, blood, and steel are homogeneous mixtures. Sodium is an element.

9. How is a solution different from a suspension?

   In a solution all of the components are in the same phase whereas the components in a suspension are in different phases.

10. How can a solution be distinguished from a suspension?

    A centrifuge can be used to determine if a mixture is a solution or a suspension because it will separate the components of a suspension.

11. What happens to the volume of a sugar solution as more sugar is dissolved in it?

    The volume of a sugar solution gradually increases as more sugar is dissolved in it.

12. Why is a ruby gemstone considered to be a solution?

    A ruby gemstone is considered to be a solid solution because trace quantities of red chromium compounds in aluminum oxide are distributed evenly in a homogeneous mixture.

13. Distinguish between a solute and a solvent.

    A solute is the thing of lesser quantity in a solution (the thing being dissolved; e.g., salt in salt water). A solvent is the thing of greater quantity in a solution (e.g., water in salt water solution).

14. What does it mean to say a solution is concentrated?

    The larger quantity of solute per given volume of solvent the more concentrated a solution is.

15. Distinguish between a saturated solution and an unsaturated solution.

    A saturated solution has the maximum amount of solute allowed in the given amount of solvent. A saturated solution will hold no more solute in solution—as more solute is added, it will not all be dissolved into the solvent. An unsaturated solution has not reached its maximum amount of solute. More solute can be added, and it will continue to go into solution.

16. How is the amount of solute in a solution calculated?

    The amount of solute in a solution is calculated by multiplying the concentration of the solution by the volume of the solution.

17. Is 1 mole of particles a very large number or a very small number of particles?

    A mole is a very large number: 6.02×10^{23}. For example, a mole of marbles would be enough to cover the entire land area of the United States to a depth greater than four meters.

Solutions to Chapter 22 Exercises

1. A sample of water that is 99.9999 percent pure contains 0.0001 percent impurities. Consider from Chapter 21 that a glass of water contains on the order of a trillion trillion (1.3×10^{24}) molecules. If 0.0001 percent of these molecules were the molecules of some impurity, about how many impurity molecules would this be?

   a. 1,000 (one thousand: 1.3×10^3)

   b. 1,000,000 (one million: 1.3×10^6)

   c. 1,000,000,000 (one billion: 1.3×10^9)

   d. 1,000,000,000,000,000,000 (one million trillion: 1.3×10^{18})

   How does your answer make you feel about drinking water that is 99.9999 percent free of some poison, such as a pesticide? (See Appendix C for a discussion of scientific notation.)
   A percentage is transformed into a fraction by dividing by 100. To find 50% of something, for example, you multiply that something by 50/100 = 0.50. The percentage 0.0001% transforms into the fraction 0.000001, which when multiplied by 1×10^{24} equals 1×10^{18}. This is certainly a lot of pesticides molecules in your glass of water. The number of water molecules, however, far exceeds this number (see Exercise 2) and so these pesticides are not problematic. As an analogy, consider that there were about 12 billion pennies minted in 1990. This is certainly a lot of pennies, but they are still, nonetheless, relatively rare because the total number of pennies in circulation is far greater—on the order of over 300 billion.

2. Read carefully: Twice as much as one million trillion is two million trillion. One thousand times as much is 1,000 million trillion. One million times as much is 1,000,000 million trillion, which is the same as one trillion trillion. Thus, one trillion trillion is one million times greater than a million trillion. Got that? So how many more water molecules than impurity molecules are there in a glass of water that is 99.9999 percent pure?
   Find the number of water molecules in the glass and then compare them to the number of impurity molecules. According to Exercise 9, there are a trillion trillion water molecules in a glass of water. If this water is 99.9999% pure, then it also contains a million trillion impurity molecules. A trillion trillion is a million times more than a million trillion, therefore, there are a million times more water molecules than there are impurity molecules. In other words, for every million water molecules, there is only one impurity molecule. Thus, in a sample of water that is 99.9999% pure, the number of water molecules far exceeds the number of impurity molecules, even though there are trillions of each.

3. Someone argues that he or she doesn't drink tap water because it contains thousands of molecules of some impurity in each glass. How would you respond in defense of the water's purity, if it indeed does contain thousands of molecules of some impurity per glass?
   Study the answer to Exercise 2 to make a strong case that this sample of water is ultra ultra pure!

4. Explain what chicken noodle soup and garden soil have in common without using the phrase *heterogeneous mixture.*
   Chicken noodle soup and soil both consist of many different components all mixed together. In both of these materials one can visually distinguish many of these components.

5. Classify the following as element, compound, or mixture, and justify your classifications: salt, stainless steel, tap water, sugar, vanilla extract, butter, maple syrup, aluminum, ice, milk, cherry-flavored cough drops.

   Salt, sodium chloride; classification: compound. Flour, natural product; classification: mixture. Stainless steel, mix of iron and carbon; classification: mixture. Tap water, dihydrogen oxide plus impurities; classification: mixture. Sugar, chemical name: sucrose; classification: compound. Vanilla extract, natural product; classification: mixture. Butter, natural product; classification: mixture. Maple syrup, natural product; classification: mixture. Pepper, natural product; classification: mixture. Aluminum, metal; classification: in pure form—element (Sold commercially as a mixture of mostly aluminum with trace metals, such as magnesium.) Ice, dihydrogen oxide; classification: in pure form—compound; when made from impure tap water—mixture. Milk, natural product; classification: mixture. Cherry flavored cough drops, pharmaceutical; classification: mixture.

6. If you eat metallic sodium or inhale chlorine gas, you stand a strong chance of dying. Let these two elements react with each other, however, and you can safely sprinkle the compound on your popcorn for better taste. What is going on?

   Chemical compounds have physical and chemical properties that are different from the elements from which they are made. Oxygen, for example, is a gas at room temperature, as is hydrogen. These two elements combine, however, to make water, which is a liquid at room temperature. Similarly sodium and chlorine, although toxic by themselves, react to form a chemical compound, sodium chloride, that is uniquely different.

7. Which of the following boxes contains an elemental material? A compound? A mixture? How many different types of molecules are shown altogether in all three boxes?

   Box a: mixture. Box b: compound. Box c: element. There are three different types of molecules shown altogether in all three boxes: one with two open circles joined, one with a solid and open circle joined, and one with two solid circles joined.

8. Common names of chemical compounds are generally much shorter than the corresponding systematic names. The systematic names for water, ammonia, and methane, for example, are dihydrogen monoxide, H_2O; trihydrogen nitride, NH_3; and tetrahydrogen carbide, CH_4. For these compounds, which would you rather use: common names or systematic names? Which do you find more descriptive?

   Because they are commonly encountered, most people, including chemists, prefer to use the common names of these compounds. The systematic names, however, are more descriptive because they describe what elements are used to make these compounds.

9. What is the difference between a compound and a mixture?

   The atoms within a compound are chemically bonded together and do not come apart through the course of a physical change. The components of a mixture, however, may be separated from each other by physical means.

10. How might you separate a mixture of sand and salt? How about a mixture of iron and sand?

    Add the mixture of sand and salt to some water. Stir, and then filter the sand. Rinse the sand several times with fresh water to make sure that all of the salt has been removed. Collect all the salty water and evaporate away the water. The residue that remains will be the salt. After the sand dries, you've got just the sand. For a mixture of iron and sand, take advantage of the fact that only iron is attracted to a magnet.

11. Mixtures can be separated into their components by taking advantage of differences in the chemical properties of the components. Why might this separation method be less convenient than taking advantage of differences in the physical properties of the components?
The chemical property involves a chemical change. Through a chemical change, the material changes its fundamental identity. Thus, you may have separated it, but now it is something else, which means that you need to convert it back to what it was through a second chemical change. This can be an energy and time intensive process that is much less efficient than separating based upon differences in physical properties.

12. Why can't the elements of a compound be separated from one another by physical means?
The transformation of elements into a compound is necessarily a chemical change. To go backwards—from the compound back into the elements—would also be an example of a chemical change. The only way to separate an element from a compound, therefore, would be by chemical means.

13. Is the air in your house a homogeneous or heterogeneous mixture? What evidence have you seen?
A shaft of strong light, such as sunlight, passing through the air of your house reveals the presence of many floating dust particles. Because of these dust particles, we can say that the air inside your house is an example of a heterogeneous mixture. Fortunately, our nasal passage ways serve to filter out much of this dust.

14. Many dry cereals are fortified with iron, which is added to the cereal in the form of small iron particles. How might these particles be separated from the cereal?
Based upon the differences in physical properties. The iron filings are attracted to a magnet while the cereal is not. Try this with your next box of iron fortified cereal.

15. Why is half-frozen fruit punch always sweeter than the same fruit punch completely melted?
Fruit punch is a mixture and mixtures can be separated into their components by differences in physical properties. Initially, freezing water molecules selectively bind to themselves to form ice crystals. This excludes the sugar molecules. The effect is that the liquid phase loses water molecules to the ice crystals. The proportion of sugar molecules in the liquid phase, therefore, increases, which makes the liquid phase tastes sweeter. Upon complete freezing, the sugar become trapped within the ice crystals and the frozen juice can be used as a popsicle. Suck hard on a frozen popsicle, however, and you'll find that only the concentrated sugar solution pulls into your mouth.

16. Describe two ways to tell whether a sugar solution is saturated or not.
To tell whether a sugar solution is saturated or not, add more sugar and see if it will dissolve. If the sugar dissolves, the solution was not saturated. Alternatively, cool the solution and see if any sugar precipitates. If it precipitates then the solution was saturated. Because sugar forms supersaturated solutions so easily, however, neither of these methods are always successful.

23 Chemical Bonding

23.1 An Atomic Model Is Needed to Understand How Atoms Bond
23.2 Atoms Can Lose or Gain Valence Electrons to Become Ions
23.3 Ionic Bonds Result From a Transfer of Valence Electrons
> Hands-On Exploration: Up Close with Crystals
23.4 Covalent Bonds Result From a Sharing of Valence Electrons
23.5 Polar Covalent Bonds Result From an Uneven Sharing of Electrons
23.6 Molecular Polarity Results From an Uneven Distribution of Electrons

Learning Objectives
After studying Chapter 23, students will be able to:
• Apply the shell model of the atom to chemical bonding.
• Distinguish between an atom and an ion.
• Predict the formula of an ionic compound using the periodic table.
• Distinguish between ionic and covalent bonds.
• Understand how some molecules are polar.
• Understand how the polarity of molecules affects macroscopic properties.

Possible Misconceptions to Correct
• **Not so!** Atoms are held together by some sort of glue.
• **Not so!** The periodic table is not much more than a listing of known elements.
• **Not so!** Covalently bonded atoms are held together because they share electrons.
• **Not so!** Ionic and covalent bonds have nothing in common.
• **Not so!** Oil and water don't mix because their molecules are not attracted to each other.

A central theme for this chapter is how the periodic table can be used to gain insight into the nature of chemical bonding. Students who are familiar with the shell model of Section 18.4 will have an added advantage. The chapter is written, however, with the understanding that Section 18.4 may not have been covered. The necessary points of Section 18.4, therefore, are reviewed in the first section of this chapter.

Only ionic and covalent bonding are covered in this chapter, but not metallic bonding, which was cut for the sake of brevity. In the event you wish to go into metallic bonding, the following is an excerpt from *Conceptual Chemistry*, by John Suchocki, that you might find helpful:

> The outer electrons of most metal atoms tend to be weakly held to the atomic nucleus. Consequently, these outer electrons are easily dislodged, leaving behind positively charged metal ions. The many electrons easily dislodged from a large group of metal atoms flow freely through the resulting metal ions. This "fluid" of electrons holds the positively charged metal ions together in the type of chemical bond known as a **metallic bond.**
> The mobility of electrons in a metal accounts for the metal's ability to conduct electricity and heat. Also, metals are opaque and shiny because the free electrons easily vibrate to the oscillations of any light falling on them, reflecting most of it. Furthermore, the metal ions are not rigidly held to fixed positions, as ions are in an ionic crystal. Rather, because the metal ions are held together by a "fluid" of electrons, these ions can move into various orientations relative to one another, which is what happens when a metal is pounded, pulled, or molded into a different shape.

Two or more metals can be bonded to each other by metallic bonds. This occurs, for example, when molten gold and molten palladium are blended to form the homogeneous solution known as white gold. The quality of the white gold can be modified simply by changing the proportions of gold and palladium. White gold is an example of an **alloy**, which is any mixture composed of two or more metallic elements. By playing around with proportions, the properties of an alloy can be readily modified. For example, in designing the Sacagawea dollar coin, the U.S. Mint needed a metal that had a gold color—so that it would be popular—and also had the same electrical characteristics as the Susan B. Anthony dollar coin—so that the new coin could substitute for the Anthony coin in vending machines.

In the **Explorations Practice Book**:
• Chemical Bonds
• Shells and the Covalent Bond
• Bond Polarity and the Shell Model

In the **Next-Time Questions Book**:
• Ionic Bond

In the **Lab Manual**:
• Mystery Powders (Unknowns are identified through a series of physical and chemical tests)
• Molecules by Acme (Students build 3-D models of covalent compounds)

Overhead Transparencies available for:
Figures 23.1, 23.2, 23.4, 23.5, 23.6, 23.7, 23.8, 23.12, 23.13, 23.14, 23.15, 23.18, 23.19, 23.20, 23.21, 23.22. 23.23, 23.24, 23.25.

SUGGESTED PRESENTATION

23.1 An Atomic Model Is Needed to Understand How Atoms Bond
This first section is an important section especially for students who did not study the shell model of Chapter 18. This section introduces electron-dot structures and show how they relate to the shell model. Figure 6.2 shows the electron-dot structures for all the groups of atoms covered in this chapter.

23.2 Atoms Can Lose or Gain Electrons to Become Ions
In teaching this material my preference is to cover both Section 23.2 and 23.3 in one fell swoop showing the formation of sodium chloride. This deviates a tad from the textbook, which in Section 23.2 shows the formation of the fluoride ion.

Using colored chalk, draw the sodium atom with 11 electrons to the left of the chalkboard. You may or may not have them arranged by valence shells, as depicted in Figure 23.4. Ask the class what happens when you take one of the electrons away. Keep track of the net charge below the atom as shown in Figure 23.4. Show the symbol notation of the sodium ion, Na^{1+}, *above the diagram*. Consider adding field lines to show how the charge of this ion emanates outwards. Now would be a good time to give the class a formal definition of an ion. Similarly, draw a chlorine atom with all 17 electrons to the right of the sodium atom illustration. Ask the class what happens when you add an electron. Keep track of the net charge and then draw the symbol notation of the chloride ion, Cl^{1-} above your illustration just to the right of the Na^{1+}. Use different colored chalk for the sodium and chloride ions. I tend to use red for positive ions and blue for negative ions. Using the transparency for Figure

23.6, point out how elements to the left of the periodic table tend to form positively charged ions, while those to the right tend to form negatively charged ions. Furthermore, the number of electrons lost or gained is a function of the atomic group.

23.3 Ionic Bonds Result from a Transfer of Electrons

Continuing with the presentation from Section 23.2, erase your renditions of Figure 23.4 for both sodium and chlorine and have the students focus on the sodium, Na^+, and chloride, Cl^-, ions, which should have the field lines drawn around them. You may also note how the superscript of 1 is typically understood. Point out how these two oppositely charged ions are attracted to one another—there is an electrical force of attraction based upon the principle that opposite signs attract. We give this force a name. We call it the *ionic bond*. Define what is meant by an *ionic compound*.

ASK YOUR NEIGHBOR: Can a sodium ion be attracted to two chloride ions? [Some students may believe that the charges of two bonded ions cancel each other and so each sodium ion can only be attracted to one chloride ion. A good follow-up demonstration is to hold a bar magnet up to the class. Attach a second magnet to the tip of this magnet and ask if it would be possible to attach a third. How about a fourth? A fifth?]

A sodium ion can be attracted to a second chloride ion provided that the second chloride ion approaches from another angle. Draw the second chlorine ion on the opposite side of the sodium ion already drawn. Ask students if any additional chloride ions may be attracted to this sodium ion. As they answer "yes" draw chlorine ions above and below the sodium ion. You should mention that electric fields are three dimensional so chloride ions may also approach from outside the plane of the board. Ask then how sodium ions might feel about all these chloride ions. Answer: Pretty good! Oppositely charged ions packed together in such an orderly three dimensional fashion form an *ionic crystal*. Interestingly, the macroscopic dimensions of a crystal are the consequence of this ionic packing. Sodium and chlorine ions pack in a cubic orientation, hence, table salt crystals are cubic. (Salt manufacturers have discovered that under the proper conditions cubic salt crystals will coalesce into the shape of a hollow pyramid. This dietetic "flaked" salt occupies greater volume so that less salt is used per shake. Also, flaked salt is thought to be more easily tasted by the tongue because it has a greater surface area per crystal.)

Note the types of ions that elements tend to form relative to the periodic table. If you covered Section 18.4, consider asking your students why the trend? (The ion formed is related to the number of unpaired valence electrons.)

An important consideration is that the ions of any ionic bond must balance each other electrically—every electron lost by one atom is gained by another. For example, if one ion carries a double charge and the second ion carries a single charge, then the ratio of ions can no longer be 1:1. Rather, there will need to be twice as many of the singly charge ion. There is a Conceptual Physical Science—Explorations Practice Page covering this concept.

23.4 Covalent Bonds Result from a Sharing of Electrons

Illustrate how two kids may be held together by their mutual attraction for toys they share. In this analogy, the kids represent protons and the toys represent electrons. To keep it accurate, the kids should be nasty to each other (protons repel protons) and each have one toy (bonding electron) to share. Show how the analogy relates to the hydrogen molecule. Point out that in a covalent bond there are no ions involved but that the force holding the two atoms together is still electrical. This level of understanding satisfies most students. You may be asked, however, how it is that two repelling electrons can be squeezed together in between two hydrogen atoms. To answer this question you might refer the student to the shell model and note how it is that electrons tend to form electron-pairs. In such a case, the paired electrons are actually spinning about their axes (like the Earth spins on its axis) in opposite directions. This provides for oppositely aligned magnetic fields which allow the electrons to "tolerate" each other. A more accurate (and more detailed) explanation would require that you introduce the concept of quantum numbers.

Point out that covalent bonds primarily involve those elements toward the upper right hand side of the periodic table, with the exception of the noble gases. These are the elements with greatest electronegativities. Also address the unique feature of multiple covalent bonds. The term molecule should then be introduced as a group of atoms held together by covalent bonds. Check to see who was listening by announcing the following question:

ASK YOUR NEIGHBOR: Are atoms made of molecules or are molecules made of atoms?

The term "molecule" was introduced in the early 1800's by the French chemist Gay-Lussac in his work with the principle of combining volumes, which is not addressed in this textbook. During this time very few believed in the existence of atoms, and even fewer in the existence of groups of atoms—molecules. Ask students if its possible to see a single molecule. Note that a diamond is an example of a *macromolecule*. Show the molecular model of a diamond. A large model (>1 dm^3) built from miniature pieces should be placed on the overhead projector and twirled for a dramatic effect. Note the "tunnels" as they appear on screen.

23.5 Polar Covalent Bonds Result from an Uneven Sharing of Electrons
The applications of bond polarity are far reaching. They are discussed here and then explored much further in Chapter 24 Molecular Mixing.

See the Conceptual Physical Science—Explorations Practice Page entitled "Bond Polarity and the Shell Model". This practice page was developed out of a lecture skit that you may wish to apply here. You may or may not involve the shell model in your presentation. The two key points to address are:

1) Different atoms have different "pulling powers". This pulling power, also known as electronegativity, is a function of how strongly the atomic nucleus is able to pull on the valence electrons. The greater the pulling power of an atom, the greater its ability to pull bonding electrons closer to itself.

2) An atom that pulls electrons closer to itself will be slightly negative in charge because of the greater amount of time that electrons spend on that side of the bond.

Wrap up your discussion of covalent bond polarity by comparing it to the ionic bond. That all ionic bonds have some covalent character and that all polar covalent bonds have some ionic character is a useful unifying concept. Covalent bonds and ionic bonds are just two extremes of the same thing: atoms held together by some distribution of electrons.

23.6 Molecular Polarity Results From an Uneven Distribution of Electrons
A good order of examples to choose is as described in the text: carbon dioxide, CO_2, followed by water, H_2O. The overhead transparency of Figure 23.22 and Figure 23.23 may prove particularly useful for the vector addition involved in these two molecules.

The presentation assumes that students understand the concept of boiling. Be sure they do by presenting the following peer instruction question:

ASK YOUR NEIGHBOR: When water boils, water molecules
   (a) break down into hydrogen and oxygen.
   (b) separate from one another.
   (c) become lighter in mass.
   (d) All of the above. [b]

Consider finishing the chapter with the following demonstration, which—if you don't mind hiding some truth (see caveat)—makes for a great transition to the subsequent chapter on molecular interactions.

DEMONSTRATION: Charge a balloon by rubbing it on your hair. Hold the balloon to a thin stream of falling water (from a buret works nicely). The negative charge of the balloon attracts the dipoles of the water. Next pull out a balloon of a different color and lie by saying it is made out of a different type of polymer that actually forms a positive charge upon being rubbed over hair. Ask the class what will happen when you hold it up to the thin stream of water. Tease them jokingly. If you're in the mood, consider not answering this question until next time you meet. In my explanation for why the water is always attracted to any type of charge, I discuss how it is that water molecules are able to rotate so that the attractive side of the dipole is always closer to the charged balloon. Yes, there is a repulsion between the charged balloon and the opposite side of water's dipole, but when it comes to electrical forces, closeness wins. There is a Next-Time Questions pertaining to this particular demonstration.

An important caveat to the above demo is that the prime reason the water is attracted to the charged balloon is NOT because the water molecules are polar. Rather, any polarizable liquid—be it polar or nonpolar—behaves in much the same way. A stream of nonpolar hexanes, for example, is similarly attracted to the charged balloon.

Chapter 23 Answers and Solutions

Key Terms and Matching Definitions

__7__ covalent bond
__8__ covalent compound
_10_ dipole
__2__ electron-dot structure
_11_ electronegativity
__4__ ion
__5__ ionic bond
__6__ ionic compound
__9__ molecule
__3__ nonbonding pairs
_12_ nonpolar bond
_13_ polar bond
__1__ valence shell

Review Questions

1. How many shells are needed to account for the seven periods of the periodic table?
   Seven shells are needed to account for the seven periods of the periodic table.

2. How many electrons can fit in the first shell? How many in the second shell?
   Two electrons fit into the first shell. Six electrons fit into the second shell.

3. How many shells are completely filled in an argon atom, Ar (atomic number 18)?
   Three shells are filled in an argon atom.

4. Which electrons are represented by an electron-dot structure?
   Valence electrons are represented in an electron-dot structure.

5. How do the electron-dot structures of elements in the same group in the periodic table compare with one another?
   Electron dot structures of elements in the same group have the same number of valence electrons.

6. How many nonbonding pairs are there in an oxygen atom? How many unpaired valence electrons?
   Oxygen has two lone pairs of electrons and two unpaired valence electrons.

7. How does an ion differ from an atom?
   An ion has a charge and an atom does not.

8. To become a negative ion, does an atom lose or gain electrons?
   A gain of electrons causes a negatively charged ion.

9. Do metals more readily gain or lose electrons?
   Metals tend to lose electrons.

10. How many electrons does the calcium atom tend to lose?
    Calcium tends to lose two electrons.

11. Why does the fluorine atom tend to gain only one additional electron?
Fluorine only has room for one more electron in its outermost shell.

12. Which elements tend to form ionic bonds?
Elements on opposite sides of the periodic table tend to form ionic bonds.

13. What is the electric charge on the calcium ion in the compound calcium chloride, $CaCl_2$?
The electronic charge on Ca is +2 in $CaCl_2$.

14. What is the electric charge on the calcium ion in the compound calcium oxide, CaO?
The electric charge on Ca in CaO is +2.

15. Suppose an oxygen atom gains two electrons to become an oxygen ion. What is its electric charge?
The charge on the O atoms is –2.

16. What is an ionic crystal?
An ionic crystal is composed of a multitude of ions grouped together in a highly ordered three-dimensional array.

17. Which elements tend to form covalent bonds?
Elements that tend to form covalent bonds are primarily non-metallic elements.

18. What force holds two atoms together in a covalent bond?
Atoms in a covalent bond share electrons and are held together by mutual attraction.

19. How many electrons are shared in a double covalent bond?
Two electrons are shared per covalent bond.

20. How many electrons are shared in a triple covalent bond?
Six electrons are shared in a triple covalent bond.

21. How many additional electrons is an oxygen atom able to attract?
Oxygen is able to attract two extra electrons.

22. How many covalent bonds is an oxygen atom able to form?
Oxygen can form two covalent bonds.

23. What is a dipole?
A dipole is an uneven distribution of electrons in a bond caused by a difference in electronegativity between two atoms.

24. Which element of the periodic table has the greatest electronegativity? Which has the smallest?
Fluorine has the greatest electronegativity and Francium has the smallest electronegativity.

25. Which is more polar: a carbon–oxygen bond or a carbon–nitrogen bond?
A carbon – oxygen bond is more polar.

26. How is a polar covalent bond similar to an ionic bond?

Atoms close to each other on the periodic table have different electronegativities causing uneven sharing of electrons resulting in a bond that is still covalent but similar to an ionic bond

27. How can a molecule be nonpolar when it consists of atoms that have different electronegativities?

Dipoles that are equal and opposing each other cancel each other out.

28. Why do nonpolar substances tend to boil at relatively low temperatures?

A nonpolar substance tends to have weak attractions to itself, which causes a low boiling point.

29. Why don't oil and water mix?

Oil and water do not mix because water molecules are more attracted to themselves than to oil molecules.

30. Which would you describe as "stickier": a polar molecule or a nonpolar one?

A polar molecule is stickier because of greater electrical attractions.

Solutions to Chapter 23 Exercises

1. An atom loses an electron to another atom. Is this an example of a physical change or a chemical change?

This is an example of a chemical change involving the formation of ions, which are uniquely different from the neutral atoms from which they are made.

2. Why is it so easy for a magnesium atom to lose two electrons?

Magnesium has only two electrons in its valence shell and these two electrons are well shielded from the nuclear charge by inner shells of electrons.

3. Why doesn't the sodium atom gain seven electrons so that its third shell becomes the filled outermost shell?

The nuclear charge experienced by an electron in sodium's third shell is not strong enough to hold this many electrons. This is because there are 10 inner shell electrons shielding any third shell electron from the +11 nucleus. This means that it is able to hold at most one electron.

4. Magnesium ions carry a 2+ charge, and chloride ions carry a 1- charge. What is the chemical formula for the ionic compound magnesium chloride?

$MgCl_2$ (Two single negatively charged chlorine ions are needed to balance the one doubly positively charge magnesium ion)

5. Barium ions carry a 2+ charge, and nitrogen ions carry a 3- charge. What is the chemical formula for the ionic compound barium nitride?

Ba_3N_2

6. Does an ionic bond have a dipole?

Yes. The ionic bond is an example of a very strong dipole.

7. Why doesn't a neon atom tend to gain electrons?

Because there is no more room available in its outermost occupied shell.

8. Why doesn't a neon atom tend to lose electrons?
Neon's outermost electrons are held tightly to the atom by a relatively strong effective nuclear charge.

9. Why doesn't a hydrogen atom form more than one covalent bond?
The hydrogen atom has only one electron to share.

10. What drives an atom to form a covalent bond: its nuclear charge or the need to have a filled outer shell? Explain.
The force that causes any chemical bond to form is always electrical. Thus, it is an atom's nuclear charge that drives it to form a covalent bond. Be careful not ever to say that the atom "needs to have a filled outer shell". First of all, atoms are not living creatures and they don't "need" anything. Rather, there is a fundamental force that causes an attraction between oppositely charged particles such as electrons and the protons of the atomic nucleus. Strictly speaking, it is the electron's attraction to the nuclear charge that brings it to and holds it to an atom. When that electron is also held by another nucleus, the resulting dynamic is called a covalent bond.

11. Is there an abrupt change or a gradual change between ionic and covalent bonds? Explain.
There is a gradual change. We get this change by noting the relative positions of the bonding elements across the periodic table. If they are close together toward the upper right hand corner, then the bond is more covalent. When the elements are on opposite sides of the periodic table, the chemical bond between them is more ionic. For the bonding of atoms between these two extremes, the bonding tends to be a blend of both, which is also referred to as *polar covalent*.

12. Classify the following bonds as ionic, polar covalent, or nonpolar covalent (O, atomic number 8; F, atomic number 9; Na, atomic number 11; Cl, atomic number 17; Ca, atomic number 20; U, atomic number 92):
O with F   _____
Ca with Cl   _____
Na with Na   _____
U with Cl   _____
Oxygen with fluorine is covalent. Calcium with chlorine is ionic. Sodium with sodium is neither covalent nor ionic, but rather *metallic* (not discussed in the textbook). Uranium with chlorine is ionic.

13. Nonmetal atoms form covalent bonds, but they can also form ionic bonds. How is this possible?
When bonded to an atom with low electronegativity, such as any group 1 element, the nonmetal atom will pull the bonding electrons so closely to itself so as to form an ion.

14. Metal atoms can form ionic bonds, but they are not very good at forming covalent bonds. Why?
To form a covalent bond, an atom must have a fairly strong attraction for at least one additional electron. Metals atoms, however, tend not to have such an attraction. Instead, they tend to lose electrons to form positively charged metal ions.

15. Phosphine is a covalent compound of phosphorus, P, and hydrogen, H. What is its chemical formula?
The chemical formula for phosphine is PH_3, which is most similar to that of ammonia, NH_3. Note how phosphorus is directly below nitrogen in the periodic table.

16. Which bond is most polar: H-N, N-C, C-O, C-C, O-H, C-H?
O-H (The greatest difference in electronegativity is between oxygen and hydrogen.)

17. Which molecule is most polar: S=C=S, O=C=O, O=C=S?
O=C=S (The sulfur and oxygen pull on the bonding electrons with different strengths such that they don't cancel each other out.)

18. In each molecule, which atom carries the greater positive charge: H-Cl, Br-F, C-O, Br-Br?
The atoms found closer to the lower left-hand corner of the periodic table are those that will bare the positive charge: a) hydrogen b) bromine c) carbon d) neither!

19. List these bonds in order of increasing polarity: N-N, N-F, N=O, H-F

_____ , _____ , _____ , _____
(least polar)   (most polar)
In order of increasing polarity: N-N < N=O < N-F < H-F.

20. Which is more polar: a sulfur–bromine bond, S-Br, or a selenium–chlorine bond, Se-Cl?
A selenium-chlorine bond should be more polar. Observe their relative positions in the periodic table. Sulfur and bromine are more equidistant from the upper right-hand corner.

21. An individual carbon–oxygen bond is polar. Yet carbon dioxide, CO_2, which has two carbon–oxygen bonds, is nonpolar. Explain.
The two oxygen atoms in carbon dioxide are 180° apart from each another such that their electron-pulls on the central carbon atom are equal and opposite. The two dipoles, therefore, balance each other out making carbon dioxide a nonpolar compound.

22. Water, H_2O, is less than half as heavy as carbon dioxide, CO_2. Why then is the boiling point of water so much higher than that of carbon dioxide?
Water is a polar molecule because in its structure the dipoles do not cancel. Polar molecules tend to stick to one another, which gives rise to relatively high boiling points. Carbon dioxide, on the other hand, is nonpolar because of its symmetrical structure, which results in no net dipole and a relatively low boiling point. The boiling points of water and carbon dioxide are less a consequence the masses (or weights) of their molecules and more a consequence of the attractions that occur among their molecules.

24 Molecular Mixing

24.1 Submicroscopic Particles Electrically Attract One Another
24.2 Solubility Is a Measure of How Well a Solute Dissolves
| Hands-On Exploration: Circular Rainbows |
24.3 Solubility Changes with Temperature and Pressure
24.4 Soap Works by Being Both Polar and Nonpolar
| Hands-On Exploration: Crystal Crazy |

Learning Objectives
After studying Chapter 24, students will be able to:
• Distinguish between molecular attractions and chemical bonds.
• Compare and contrast the different types of molecular attractions.
• Understand and apply the concept of solubility.
• Articulate how soaps and detergents work.

Possible Misconceptions to Correct
• **Not so!** Molecular attractions and chemical bonds are fundamentally different.
• **Not so!** Nonpolar molecules are always nonpolar.
• **Not so!** All solutes dissolve better when the solvent is warmer.
• **Not so!** Styrofoam is always insoluble.
• **Not so!** Soaps and detergents are the same.

The chapter begins by defining and showing examples of three types of molecular attractions. They are presented in order of decreasing strength. Subsequent sections apply the concepts of molecular attractions to commonly encountered phenomena.

In the **Explorations Practice Book**:
• Atoms to Molecules to Molecular Attractions
• Solutions

In the **Next-Time Questions Book**:
• Oxygen in Water
• Bending Stream

In the **Lab Manual**:
• Radial Paper Chromatography (Separation of color components of ink)
• Pure Sweetness (Purification of brown sugar)

Overhead Transparencies available for:
Figures 24.1, 24.2, 24.3, 24.4, 24.13.

SUGGESTED PRESENTATION

24.1 Submicroscopic Particles Electrically Attract One Another
Start by distinguishing between a chemical bond and a molecular attraction. Both involve electrical forces of attraction, but chemical bonds are over 100 fold stronger. Be careful with some semantics: "what holds a molecule together" and "what holds molecules together"

may be easily confused. Review the concept of the molecular dipole to be sure your students understand it before going further. Use water as an example.

For the ion-dipole attraction, show the transparency of Figure 24.2 to show how many water molecules are required to break apart the sodium chloride ionic bond. Alert students to the fact that ionic bonds are broken as an ionic compound dissolves in water. When a covalent compound, such as sugar, dissolves in water, however, the covalent bonds remain intact.

Discuss the dipole-dipole attraction, which is fairly straight-forward—if students know what a dipole is, then they should understand how two dipoles may be attracted to each other. Note how the hydrogen bond is simply a relatively strong dipole-dipole attraction.

DEMONSTRATION: Fill two burets, one with 50.00 mL of water, and the other with 50.00 mL of 95% ethanol. Ask the students what volume will be obtained when the two liquids are combined. Drain the two liquids simultaneously into a 100 mL volumetric flask (use a permanent marker to calibrate the last three milliliters). A total of only 98.0 mL will be obtained. Tell the students to "Ask their neighbor" for an explanation. [One half of an answer (by analogy): At a dance hall 50 men by themselves and 50 women by themselves occupy a given amount of floor space. Bring the men and women together, however, and they occupy a total floor space that is less than the sum of the floor space they occupied while by themselves. Similarly, water and ethanol molecules are attracted to one another, hence, they are able to contract into a volume less than the sum of their volumes alone. The second half of an answer: The molecules are able to pack into a smaller combined volume. By analogy, the combination of 50 mL of marbles and 50 mL of sand does NOT result in 100 mL of mixture.]

24.2 Polar Molecules Can Induce Dipoles in Nonpolar Molecules

Electrons in a molecule are not static. Instead they are continually moving around. In a polar molecule, the electrons, on average, are found closer to one side. In a nonpolar molecule, the electrons, on average, are distributed evenly across the whole molecule. Because the electrons in a nonpolar molecule are not held in place they can be shuffled to one side or the other upon the application of an electric force. Draw Figure 26.4 on the chalkboard to show how the permanent dipole of a water molecule induces a temporary dipole in an oxygen molecule. Point out how the oxygen dipole exists only so long as the water is present. It is the dipole-induced dipole attraction that permits small quantities of nonpolar substances such as oxygen and carbon dioxide to dissolve in water.

ASK YOUR NEIGHBOR: There are dipole-induced dipole forces of attraction between oil and water molecules. So, why don't the two mix? [Answer: They do mix, but like oxygen and carbon dioxide, only to a very small extent because water molecules have such a great preference for other water molecules.]

Here is an analogy you might use to explain why oil and water form two different phases. Say at a party there are two kinds of people, those who like to talk and share ideas and those who are stone-faced and would rather say nothing. Mix these two types of people together and soon the talkative people are on one side and the stone-faced people on the other. It's not that there is a repulsion between the talkative people and the stone-faced people. In fact, there may be a weak attraction—some people need to be *induced* into a conversation. There is, nonetheless, a greater force of attraction between talkative people and this is what pulls them together to the point that they exclude most of the stone-faced people. Similarly, water is too attracted to itself by the stronger dipole-dipole attractions to the point that it excludes most of the oil molecules.

ASK YOUR NEIGHBOR: Due to ion-dipole attractions, a thin stream of water bends towards a charge balloon. Will a thin stream of hexanes, a nonpolar organic solvent, also bend towards the charged balloon? [Answer: Yes and it does so by way of ion-induced dipole attractions. This demonstration makes for a good follow-up to the demo where you show how a thin stream of water can be bent by a statically charged balloon.]

A fourth type of molecular attraction that is not discussed in this chapter is the induced dipole-induced dipole attraction. On the average, electrons in a nonpolar molecule or atom are distributed evenly. But electrons are perpetually moving around and at times more may be grouped to one side. This is the nature of a "momentary" dipole. A momentary dipole, albeit weak, is able to induce dipoles in neighboring molecules or atoms just as a permanent dipole can. The induced dipole can then, in turn, induce dipoles in other molecules or atoms. Because all the molecules or atoms are nonpolar, it is unclear as to who induced whom first. So, the interaction is simply called "induced dipole-induced dipole", rather than "momentary dipole-induced dipole."

The less volume electrons occupy in an atom, the less of a tendency they will have to congregate to one side of the atom—because of greater electrical repulsions. This means that smaller atoms, such as fluorine, exhibit weaker induced dipole-induced dipole attractions than do larger atoms, such as iodine. This explains why very few things stick to Teflon. It also explains why iodine, I_2, which is very nonpolar, is a solid at room temperature.

24.3 Solubility is a Measure of How Well a Solute Dissolves
The emphasis for this section should be on how the solublity of a solute depends upon the molecular attractions occurring between the solute and solvent. The more significant the molecular attractions, the greater the solubility. The old saying that "like dissolves like" arises from the fact that if two materials exert the same sorts of molecular attractions, then they are likely to mix together very finely, down to the level of molecules, which means that a solution will form.

DEMONSTRATION: Float a Styrofoam coffee cup in a petri dish full of acetone placed on the overhead projector. Flippantly ask the students if they can see the Styrofoam cup melting. Ask the question again and again until they realize it's not melting at all. So cried the Wicked Witch of the East "I'm dissolving! I'm dissolving!" For the pure humor of it cut out a small circle of yellow paper and place it in the middle of the remaining deformed Styrofoam. Use a spatula to place the "fried egg" on a paper towel while saying: "Chemistry is aiming to serve. How would you like your egg? Sunny side up?"

24.4 Solubility Changes with Temperature and Pressure
You may wish to demonstrate the making of a supersaturated solution of sugar. Set it up for the formation of crystals and set it aside so that the class can observe the crystal growth over the next several weeks. For quicker crystallization, prepare a solution of supersaturated copper sulfate pentahydrate, $CuSO_4 \cdot 5 H_2O$.

Perform the following demonstration to show that tap water does indeed contain dissolved gases.

DEMONSTRATION Fill a large beaker with warm tap water and let it stand at room temperature while you lecture. Note the bubbles that adhere to the inner sides of the beaker. Ask the students where the bubbles came from and what they contain? For further experimentation, perform the same demonstration in two beakers side-by-side. In one beaker use warm water from the faucet. In the second beaker, use boiled water that has cooled down to the same temperature. The process of boiling *deaerates* the water, that is, removes the atmospheric gases. Chemists sometimes need to use deaerated water, which is made simply by allowing boiled water to cool in a sealed container. Ask your students why don't fish live very long in deaerated water?

24.5 Soap Works by Being Polar and Nonpolar

Draw soap molecules surrounding grime to illustrate how soap works. Point out the induced dipole-induced dipole attractions between the nonpolar tail of soap and the grime, and the ion-dipole attractions between the polar head of soap and water. Note that your drawing is a cross-section of a spherical conglomeration, also known as a *micelle*. Time permitting, you might take this a step further and draw a lipid bilayer in the shape of a circle. Note that this is a cross-section of a 3-dimensional conglomeration known as a *cell*. Point out the aqueous inner chamber. Add proteins to the bilayer and call it a membrane. Throw in a cellular nucleus some organelles and call it living tissue.

You might consider showing how soap molecules bind to calcium ions and discuss the disadvantages of hard water, which is water that contains relatively high concentrations of calcium and magnesium ions. In brief, two soap molecules will bind to a single Ca^{2+} ion (or the Mg^{2+} ion) to form a complex that is insoluble in water and comes out as "scum". It's the material of the "ring-around-the-bathtub." This scum limits the cleaning ability of soaps, which makes hard water not so desirable.

Chapter 24 Answers and Solutions

Key Terms and Matching Definitions

_ 1 _ hydrogen bond
_ 2 _ induced dipole
_ 4 _ insoluble
_ 6 _ precipitate
_ 3 _ solubility
_ 4 _ soluble

Review Questions

1. What is the primary difference between a chemical bond and an attraction between two molecules?

   A chemical bond is many times stronger than an attraction between molecules.

2. Which is stronger, the ion–dipole attraction or the induced dipole–induced dipole attraction?

   Ion-dipole attraction is stronger than an induced dipole-induced dipole attraction.

3. Why are water molecules attracted to sodium chloride?

   The positive sodium ions are attracted to the negative side of a water molecule and negative chloride ions are attracted to the positive side of a water molecule.

4. How are ion–dipole attractions able to break apart ionic bonds, which are relatively strong?

   A multitude of ion-dipole attractions with water can break apart the ionic bonds of sodium chloride and pull the ions apart.

5. Are electrons distributed evenly or unevenly in a polar molecule?

   No, electrons congregate at one side of a molecular dipole to give it a slight negative charge, and the opposite side will be slightly positive.

6. What is a hydrogen bond?

   A hydrogen bond is an extremely strong dipole-dipole attraction.

7. How are oxygen molecules attracted to water molecules?

   Oxygen molecules are attracted to water molecules when the oxygen molecules are brought close to the water molecules. The negative side of a water molecule pushes oxygen's electrons farthest from water and results in a temporary uneven distribution of electrons in the oxygen molecule known as an induced dipole.

8. Are induced dipoles permanent?

   No, induced dipoles are only temporary. They only occur (are induced) when they are in close proximity to a water molecule or another dipole.

9. Why does oxygen have such a low solubility in water?

   Oxygen has a low solubility in water because the only attractions occurring between oxygen and water molecules are weak dipole-induced dipole attractions. Water's attraction for itself is stronger than its attraction for oxygen molecules.

10. By what means are ethanol and water molecules attracted to each other?

Ethanol and water molecules are attracted to each other by means of hydrogen bonding.

11. What does it mean to say that two materials are infinitely soluble in each other?

Two materials are infinitely soluble in each other when there is no practical point of saturation. The submicroscopic attractions of the solute are comparable to those occurring within the solvent.

12. What kind of electrical attraction is responsible for oxygen dissolving in water?

The electrical force responsible for oxygen dissolving in water is weak dipole-induced dipole attraction.

13. What effect does temperature have on the solubility of a solid solute in a liquid solvent?

A change in temperature most often results in a change in the solubility of a solute in a solvent. In most known cases, a higher temperature results in an increase in solubility. There are some cases, however, in which a higher temperature actually results in a decrease in solubility.

14. What effect does temperature have on the solubility of a gas solute in a liquid solvent?

Higher temperatures will decrease the solubility of a gas in a liquid because the gas will have a higher kinetic energy and be less able to stay in solution. Gas molecules will be more likely to leave a liquid solvent at higher temperatures.

15. What is the relationship between a precipitate and a solute?

A solute is a solid or gas that is mixed into a solution. A precipitate is a solid that forms within a solution. A solute becomes a precipitate when too much solute is added to a solution and the solute falls out of solution.

16. Why does the solubility of a gas solute in a liquid solvent decrease with increasing temperature?

The solubility of a gas decreases with increasing temperatures because the gas molecules will have more kinetic energy and be more likely to escape from solution.

17. Which portion of a soap molecule is nonpolar?

The tail of a soap molecule that contains carbon and hydrogen atoms is the nonpolar portion of the molecule.

18. Water and soap are attracted to each other by what type of electrical attraction?

Water and soap are attracted to each other by strong ion-dipole attractions between each water molecule and the polar head of each soap molecule.

19. How many soap molecules can be made from a single fat molecule?

Three.

20. What is the difference between a soap and a detergent?

A detergent is a synthetic soap that has stronger grease penetration. Detergents are cheaper than soaps.

Solutions to Chapter 24 Exercises

1. Why are ion–dipole attractions stronger than dipole–dipole attractions?
Because the magnitude of the electric charge associated with an ion is much greater.

2. Explain why, for these three substances, the solubility in 20°C water goes down as the molecules get larger but the boiling point goes up.
The boiling points go up because of an increase in the number of molecular interactions between molecules. Remember, when we talk about the "boiling point" of a substance we are referring to a pure sample of that substance. We see the boiling point of 1-pentanol (the molecule on the far right) is relatively high because 1-pentanol molecules are so attracted to one another (by induced dipole-induced dipole as well as by dipole-dipole and dipole-induced dipole attractions). When we refer to the "solubility" of a substance we are referring to how well that substance interacts with a second substance—in this case water. Note that water is much less attracted to 1-pentanol because most of 1-pentanol is non-polar (its only polar portion is the OH group). For this reason 1-pentanol is not very soluble in water. Put yourself in the point of view of a water molecule and ask yourself how attracted you might be to a methanol molecule (the one on the far left) compared to the pentanol molecule (the one on the far right).

3. The boiling point of 1,4-butanediol is 230°C. Would you expect this compound to be soluble or insoluble in room-temperature water? Explain.
A high boiling point means that the substance interacts with itself quite strongly. Put yourself in the point of view of a water molecule and you will see that you are attracted to both ends of 1,4-butanediol. In fact 1,4-butanediol is infinitely soluble in water!]

4. Why are noble gases infinitely soluble in other noble gases?
Two substances that can be mixed homogeneously in any proportion are said to be infinitely soluble. By this definition noble gases are infinitely soluble in noble gases.

5. Which solute in Figure 24.10 has a solubility in water that changes the least with increasing temperature?
Sodium chloride, NaCl.

6. At 10°C, which is more concentrated: a saturated solution of sodium nitrate, $NaNO_3$, or a saturated solution of sodium chloride, NaCl? (See Figure 24.10.)
At 10°C a saturated solution of sodium nitrate, $NaNO_3$, is more concentrated than a saturated solution of sodium chloride, NaCl.

7. Suggest why salt is insoluble in gasoline. Consider the electrical attractions.
Salt is composed of ions that are too attracted to themselves. Gasoline is non-polar so salt and gasoline will not interact very well.

8. Which would you expect to have a higher melting point: sodium chloride, NaCl, or aluminum oxide, Al_2O_3? Why?
The aluminum oxide has a higher melting point because of the greater charges of the ions, and hence the greater force of attractions between them.

Conceptual Physical Science—Explorations **Teaching Guide**

9. Hydrogen chloride, HCl, is a gas at room temperature. Would you expect this material to be very soluble or not very soluble in water?

Although oxygen gas, O_2, has poor solubility in water, there are many other examples of gases that have good solubility in water. From the concepts discussed in Chapter 6, you should be able to deduce that hydrogen chloride is a somewhat polar molecule. This gaseous material, therefore, has a good solubility in water by virtue of the dipole/dipole attractions occurring between the HCl and H_2O molecules.

10. Would you expect to find more dissolved oxygen in ocean water around the North Pole or tropical ocean water close to the equator? Why?

No, because of the warmer temperatures. The solubility of oxygen in water *decreases* with increasing temperature.

11. What is the boiling point of a single water molecule? Why does this question not make sense?

Boiling involves the separation of many molecules (plural). With only one molecule, the concept of boiling is meaningless.

12. Account for the observation that ethanol, C_2H_5OH, dissolves readily in water but dimethyl ether, CH_3OCH_3, which has the same number and kinds of atoms, does not.

The arrangement of atoms within a molecule makes all the difference as to the physical and chemical properties. Ethyl alcohol contains the -OH group, which is polar. This polarity, in turn, is what allows the ethyl alcohol to dissolve in water. The oxygen of dimethyl ether, by contrast, is bonded to two carbon atoms: C-O-C. The difference in electronegativity between oxygen and carbon is not as great as the difference between oxygen and hydrogen. The polarity of the C-O bond, therefore, is less than that of the O-H bond. As a consequence dimethyl ether is significantly less polar than is ethyl alcohol and is not readily soluble in water.

13. Why are the melting points of most ionic compounds far higher than the melting points of most covalent compounds?

When an ionic compound melts, the ionic bonds between the ions are overcome. When a covalent compound melts, the molecular attractions between molecules are overcome. Because ionic bonds are so much stronger than molecular attractions, the melting points of ionic compounds are typically much higher.

14. How necessary is soap for removing salt from your hands? Why?

Soap is not at all necessary for removing salt from your hands. The strong ion-dipole interactions between fresh water and the salt are most sufficient to lift the salt away from your hands.

15. When you set a pot of tap water on the stove to boil, you'll often see bubbles start to form well before boiling temperature is reached. Explain this observation.

These initial bubbles are the gases that were dissolved in the water coming out of solution. Because the solubility of gases in water decreases with increasing temperature, a standing warm pot of water will show more bubbles forming on the inner sides than will a standing cold pot of water.

16. Fish don't live very long in water that has been boiled and brought back to room temperature. Why?

The boiling process removes the air that was dissolved in the water. Upon cooling the water is void of its usual air content, hence, the fish drown.

25 Acids and Bases

Learning Objectives
After studying Chapter 25, students will be able to:
• Identify acids and bases found in their daily living.
• Understand acid/base as a behavior of chemicals.
• Identify the hydronium and hydroxide ions.
• Recognize a salt as the product of the reaction of an acid and a base.
• Understand what is meant by acidic, neutral, and basic solutions.
• Describe and explain the concept of pH.
• Find the log of simple exponential numbers.
• Apply the concepts of acids and bases to our atmosphere.
• Apply the concepts of acids and bases to our oceans.

Possible Misconceptions to Correct
• **Not so!** It would be lethal to ingest an acid or a base.
• **Not so!** All salt is made of sodium chloride.
• **Not so!** Base-10 logarithms are difficult.
• **Not so!** pH's cannot be less than zero.
• **Not so!** Atmospheric carbon dioxide is necessarily bad news.
• **Not so!** Humans don't have an impact on levels of atmospheric carbon dioxide.
• **Not so!** Rainwater is not naturally acidic.

In the **Explorations Practice Book**:
• Donating and Accepting Hydrogen Ions

In the **Next-Time Questions Book**:
• Soda Water
• pH of Zero
• In a Neutral Solution

In the **Lab Manual**:
• Sensing pH (Extracting and using red cabbage pH indicator)
• Upset Stomach (acid/base microtitration to evaluate antacid effectiveness)

Overhead Transparencies available for:
Figures 25.3, 25.4, 25.7, 25.8, 25.11, 25.14, Table 25.1.

SUGGESTED PRESENTATION

25.1 Acids Donate Protons, Bases Accept Them
Begin by discussing the many commercial applications of acids and bases. Point out how economists judge the economic strength of nations based upon the quantities of these materials produced.

FYI, emphasis is placed on the Bronsted-Lowry definition of acids and bases. This definition is more general than is the Arrhenius definition, though not as general as the Lewis definition. The acronym BAAD given by the cartoon character on page 427 is useful tool for many students.

My thinking is that it is best not to say that a chemical <u>is</u> an acid or that it <u>is</u> a base. Students may get confused when they find that in one instance a chemical, such as water, is an acid, and in another it is a base. It is far better to say that a chemical <u>behaves</u> as an acid, or that it <u>behaves</u> as a base. When a chemical donates a hydrogen ion it behaves as an acid, when the same chemical accepts a hydrogen ion it behaves as a base.

On the chalkboard it is useful to show the movement of the hydrogen ion from one molecule to the other. Draw the symbol for hydrogen on a piece of paper, which may be taped to the board. Show how the acid donates the hydrogen ion by transferring the paper between reactants. Likewise, note how the base accepts the hydrogen ion. For example:

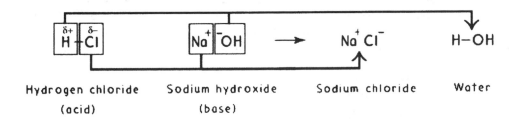

This visualization helps students to recognize which chemicals in an equation are behaving as acids and which are behaving as bases. Also, students get the sense that products are, in fact, made from the reactants, despite that they are both seen at once in the chemical equation. The reversibility of acid/base reactions can be visualized by using two pieces of paper containing the symbol for hydrogen. For example:

Define the chemist's use of the terms "salt" and "neutralization reaction." Draw an illustration such as the following on the chalkboard while emphasizing how it is that, upon neutralization, negative and positive atoms come together.

25.2 Some Acids and Bases Are Stronger Than Others

Different chemicals have different personalities. Some are quite forceful about donating the hydrogen ion (strong acid), while others are more timid (weak acid). What determines the strength of an acid is complicated and not discussed in the text. It's more important that the student focus on the effect acid strength has on the number of ions formed. With a strong acid, ionic products predominate. With a weak acid, non-ionic reactants predominate.

DEMONSTRATION: Use a light bulb equipped with electrodes as seen in Figure 25.9 to demonstrate the proportion of ions found in solutions of strong and weak acids. Begin with distilled water. Pour sodium chloride into the distilled water to show how the intensity of light increases with the number of ions. Draw the equation for HCl reacting with water on the board and have students predict the brightness of the bulb. Repeat the same for acetic acid. (Use 1 M solutions.) Follow up by showing that tap water is a weak conductor of electricity. Warning: Do not stir the solution with a metal rod while the electrodes are submerged.

25.3 Solutions Can be Acidic, Basic, or Neutral

Water is such a weak acid and weak base that the concentration of hydronium and hydroxide ions in "pure" water is very small, about 10^{-7} M. Although the concentration of these ions is very small, what students can be brought to understand is that, in pure water, for every one hydroxide ion that forms, there will be one hydronium ion that forms. It's analogous to a room full of people with one hat each. If suddenly a number of the people gave their hat to some on with one hat, the consequence would be that the number of people with no hat would be equal to the number of people with two hats. For water, the hydrogen ion is the hat—for every hydronium ion that gets formed from the donation of a hydronium ion, there will also be a hydroxide ion that gets formed. Thus, in pure water, the concentration of hydronium and hydroxide ions are the same. Once this concept is established, you can define a neutral solution as one in which the hydronium and hydroxide ion concentrations are equal. When an acid is added, the hydronium ion concentration will be greater than the hydroxide ion concentration and this makes for an acidic solution. Likewise, when a base is added, the hydroxide ion concentration will be greater than the hydronium ion concentration and this makes for a basic (or alkaline) solution.

Spend a few minutes reviewing the logarithm. Most students wince at the sight of the log function on the chalkboard. Turn this around and have fun by stating that "logs are dirt easy." Declare that logs are so easy that you can teach them logs in 45 seconds. Boast a pretend previous record and then the bet is on! Wait for the second hand on the clock to get to a 12, 3, 6 or 9 then begin. "When one is asking for the log of a number, they are really asking 'to what power is ten raised?' Thus if one wanted to know the log of 10^3 as in $\log 10^3 = ?$, you would simply ask 'To what power is 10 raised?' We see here plainly that the answer is 3. So, if I've really taught you about logs, you should be able to answer this: 'What is the log of 10^2?'" Then solicit the response of "2" from the students, whereupon you can speedily look to the clock and declare victory...in record time! The follow-up is to show them how it is that the log of 100 also equals 2. Then draw a table on the chalkboard that shows the relationship between the power of ten and the decimal value. For example:

10^3	=	1000	(three zeros)
10^2	=	100	(two zeros)
10^1	=	10	(one zero)

10^{-1}	=	0.1	(one zero to the left)
10^{-2}	=	0.01	(two zeros to the left)
10^{-3}	=	0.001	(three zeros to the left)

The hydronium ion concentrations we usually deal with are very small. This means taking the log of negative exponents. Chemists use the negative sign in the definition of pH to change these negative numbers to positive numbers. It is then helpful to show students what's happening when the [log] button gets pressed on their calculators and how the calculators are very useful for concentrations that don't begin with the numeral 1.

ASK YOUR NEIGHBOR: What's the pH of a 0.5 M solution of HCl? How about a 1.0 M solution? A 2.0 M solution? [Answers: 0.301; 0; -0.310. Students may be surprised that negative pH values are possible. The lower limit of pH depends on the solubility of acid. A saturated solution of hydrochloric acid is 12.0 M, which corresponds to a pH of -1.08.

Many chemicals change color with pH. These chemicals, which are usually organic, can serve as pH indicators. You'll note that pH indicators are not discussed in the text. The stage is set, however, to present pH indicators as a demonstration, which you might also assign as a Hands-On Exploration: Rainbow Cabbage.

Some dyes used to make color paper are also pH sensitive. Certain brands of goldenrod colored paper, for example, turn bright red when dipped in a solution of sodium hydroxide.

DEMONSTRATION: Submerge a pH electrode in a glass of water and then using a straw, blow bubbles into the water. The carbon dioxide of your breath will bring the water to a pH of 5. Ask the class whether they think you really have acid breath. While the pH meter is set up, be sure to submerge the electrode in a glass of cola. Another favorite is to stir campfire ashes into water and see the pH rise to above 10. As was discussed in Chapter 17, alkaline ashes were once used to make soap. Recall that the term alkaline is derived from the Arabic term for ashes: al-qali.

25.4 Rainwater is Acidic and Ocean Water is Basic
Having studied through Sections 25.1 through 25.3, students should have little difficulty in understanding and appreciating this environmentally-oriented section.

The following demonstration serves as a nice introduction. After showing how your breath is acidic because of the CO_2 it contains, students will appreciate how the atmosphere is acidic for the same reasons.

DEMONSTRATION: Add a drop of phenolphthalein to a few milliliters of water in a test tube. Make the solution slightly alkaline by adding a small amount of sodium carbonate, Na_2CO_3. The solution will turn pink. Point out that by adding an acid the pH drops and the pink color will disappear (Phenolphthalein indicator changes color at about a pH of 7). Demonstrate by adding a drop of acid, such as hydrochloric acid or vinegar. Repeat the same procedure in a second test tube this time using a straw to blow in carbon dioxide from your breath.

Interestingly, according to Michael Mottl, a geochemist at the University of Hawaii, prior to the industrial revolution, the ocean was a net emitter of carbon dioxide rather than the net absorber it is today. (Michael's wife and daughter appear on page 361.)

Chapter 25 Answers and Solutions

Key Terms and Matching Definitions

__1__ acid
__8__ acidic solution
__7__ amphoteric
__2__ base
__9__ basic solution
__3__ hydronium ion
__4__ hydroxide ion
_10__ neutral solution
__6__ neutralization
_11__ pH
__5__ salt

Review Questions

1. What is a hydrogen ion?

   The hydrogen ion discussed in this chapter is a hydrogen atom minus its single electron. This ion is the same thing as a lone proton.

2. When an acid is dissolved in water, what ion does the water form?

   Dissolving an acid in water causes the formation of a hydronium ion.

3. When a chemical loses a hydrogen ion, is it behaving as an acid or a base?

   A chemical that loses a hydrogen ion is behaving as an acid.

4. Does a salt always contain sodium ions?

   A salt does not always contain sodium ions.

5. What two classes of chemicals are involved in a neutralization reaction?

   Acids and bases are involved in a neutralization reaction.

6. What does it mean to say that an acid is strong in aqueous solution?

   A strong acid will completely dissociate in water.

7. What happens to most of the molecules of a strong acid when the acid is mixed with water?

   Most of the molecules of a strong acid are broken apart when it is put in water.

8. Why does a solution of a strong acid conduct electricity better than a solution of a weak acid having the same concentration?

   A solution of a strong acid has more ions in solution and can conduct electricity better than a weak acid.

9. Which has a greater ability to accept hydrogen ions: a strong base or a weak base?

   A strong base has a greater ability to accept hydrogen ions.

10. When can a solution of a weak base be more corrosive than a solution of a strong base?

    A concentrated solution of a weak base could have more corrosive power than the dilute solution of a strong base.

11. Is it possible for a chemical to behave as an acid in one instance and as a base in another instance?

Yes, a chemical that can behave as either an acid or a base is amphoteric.

12. Is water a strong acid or a weak acid?

Water is a weak acid.

13. What does the pH of a solution indicate?

The pH of a solution indicates the acidity of the solution.

14. As the hydronium ion concentration of a solution increases, does the pH of the solution increase or decrease?

As the hydronium ion concentration increases the pH of the solution will decrease.

15. What is the product of the reaction between carbon dioxide and water?

The product of the reaction between CO_2 and H_2O is H_2CO_3.

16. How can rain be acidic and yet not qualify as acid rain?

Acid rain has a pH of less than 5.

17. What does sulfur dioxide have to do with acid rain?

Sulfur dioxide combines with oxygen and water in the air to make sulfuric acid.

18. How do humans generate the air pollutant sulfur dioxide?

The burning of fossil fuels contributes to SO_2 in the air.

19. How does one lime a lake?

Calcium carbonate is added to the lake to neutralize the acid.

20. Why aren't atmospheric levels of carbon dioxide rising as rapidly as might be expected based on the increased output of carbon dioxide resulting from human activities?

The ocean absorbs the CO_2 where it is neutralized and is not re-released.

Solutions to Chapter 25 Exercises

1. Suggest an explanation for why people once washed their hands with ashes.
The potassium carbonate found in ashes acts as a base and reacts with skin oils to produce slippery solutions of soap.

2. What is the relationship between a hydroxide ion and a water molecule?
A hydroxide ion is a water molecule minus a hydrogen nucleus.

3. An acid and a base react to form a salt, which consists of positive and negative ions. Which forms the positive ions: the acid or the base? Which forms the negative ions?
The base accepted the hydrogen ion, H$^+$, and thus gained a positive charge. The base thus forms the positively charged ion. Conversely, the acid donated a hydrogen ion and thus lost a positive charge. The acid thus forms the negatively charged ion.

4. Water is formed from the reaction between an acid and a base. Why is water not classified as a salt?
A salt is the *ionic compound* produced from the reaction of an acid and a base. Water is a covalent compound.

5. Identify the acid or base behavior of each substance in these reactions:
   a. $H_3O^+ + Cl^- <=> H_2O + HCl$
   b. $H_2PO_4 + H_2O <=> H_3O^+ + HPO_4^-$
   c. $HSO_4^- + H_2O <=> H_3O^+ + SO_4^{2-}$

   For (a) note that the H$_3$O$^+$ transforms into a water molecule. This means that the H$_3$O$^+$ loses a hydrogen ion, which is donated to the Cl$^-$. The H$_3$O$^+$, therefore, is behaving as an acid while the Cl- is behaving as a base. In the reverse direction we see the H$_2$O gaining a hydrogen ion (behaving as a base) to become H$_3$O$^+$. It gets this hydrogen ion from the HCl, which in donating is behaving as an acid. You should be able make similar arguments for (b) and (c) to arrive at the following answers:
   a) acid, base, base, acid
   b) acid, base, acid, base
   c) acid, base, acid, base.

6. Identify the acid or base behavior of each substance in these reactions:
   a. $HSO_4^- + H_2O <=> OH^- + H_2SO_4$
   b. $O^{2-} + H_2O <=> OH^- + OH^-$

   a) base, acid, base, acid

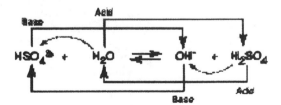

b) base, acid, base, acid

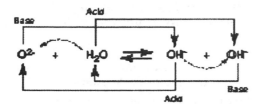

7. Sodium hydroxide, NaOH, is a strong base, which means it readily accepts hydrogen ions. What products are formed when sodium hydroxide accepts a hydrogen ion from a water molecule?
    Sodium hydroxide, NaOH, accepts a hydrogen ion from water to form water and sodium hydroxide! In solution, of course, this sodium hydroxide is dissolved as individual sodium ions and hydroxide ions.

8. What happens to the corrosive properties of an acid and a base after they neutralize each other? Why?
    The corrosive properties are no longer present because the acid and base no longer exist. Instead they have chemically reacted with each other to form completely new substances—salt and water—that are not so corrosive.

9. What is true about the relative concentrations of hydronium and hydroxide ions in an acidic solution? How about a neutral solution? A basic solution?
    If the hydronium ion concentration of a solution is higher than the hydroxide ion then the solution is acidic. If the opposite is true then the solution is basic.

10. Why do we use the pH scale to indicate the acidity of a solution rather than simply stating the concentration of hydronium ions?
    The concentration of hydronium ions is typically so small it needs to be stated using scientific notation. The pH scale, therefore, is one of convenience.

11. When the hydronium ion concentration of a solution equals 1 mole per liter, what is the pH of the solution? Is the solution acidic or basic?
    $$pH = -\log[H_3O^+] = -\log(1) = -(-0) = 0$$
    This an acidic solution. Yes, pH can be equal to zero!

12. When the hydronium ion concentration of a solution equals 10 moles per liter, what is the pH of the solution? Is the solution acidic or basic?
    Use a calculator to find the log of 2 (it's 0.301).
    $$pH = -\log[H_3O^+] = -\log(2) = -(0.301) = -0.301$$
    This a very acidic solution. Yes, pH's can be negative!!

13. What is the concentration of hydronium ions in a solution that has a pH of -3? Why is such a solution impossible to prepare?
    This solution would have a hydronium ion concentration of 10^3 M, or 1000 moles per liter. The solution would be impossible to prepare because only so much acid can dissolve in water before the solution is saturated and no more will dissolve. The greatest concentration possible for hydrochloric acid, for example, is 12 M. Beyond this concentration, any additional HCl, which is a gas, added to the water simply bubbles back out into the atmosphere.

14. When the pH of a solution decreases by 1, say from pH = 4 to pH = 3, by what factor does the hydronium ion concentration increase?
    The hydronium increases by a factor of 10.

15. What happens to the pH of an acidic solution as pure water is added?
    As pure water is added to an acidic solution, the hydronium ions (and anything else that is dissolved in this acidic solution) become more dilute, that is, less concentrated. Thus, the pH increases.

16. Why might a small piece of chalk be useful for alleviating acid indigestion?
    If the chalk is made of calcium carbonate, $CaCO_3$, it is made of the same active ingredient found in many antacids. The calcium carbonate is a base that reacts to neutralize any excess acids. Be careful, though, never to take too much calcium carbonate because the stomach is designed to always be somewhat acidic.

17. How might you tell whether or not your toothpaste contained calcium carbonate, $CaCO_3$, or perhaps baking soda, $NaHCO_3$, without looking at the ingredients label?
    Add it to some vinegar. If the toothpaste starts to bubble, there's a good chance it contains calcium carbonate.

18. Why do lakes lying in granite basins tend to become acidified by acid rain more readily than lakes lying in limestone basins?
    It is the alkaline character of limestone (also known as calcium carbonate) that serves to neutralize waters that might be acidified in the Midwestern United States.

19. Cutting back on the pollutants that cause acid rain is one solution to the problem of acidified lakes. Suggest another.
    Add a neutralizing substance such as limestone.

20. How might warmer oceans accelerate global warming?
    The warmer the ocean, the lower the solubility of any dissolved gases such as carbon dioxide, CO_2. Less CO_2 would be absorbed and more of it would remain to perpetuate global warming.

26 Oxidation and Reduction

Learning Objectives
After studying Chapter 26, students will be able to:
• Identify oxidation as the loss of electrons.
• Identify reduction as the gain of electrons.
• Understand how a battery works.
• Understand how fuel cells work and their significance for the future.
• Explain what happens as iron rusts.
• Compare and contrast combustion with respiration.

Possible Misconceptions to Correct
• **Not so!** A half-reaction can occur on its own.
• **Not so!** Silver tarnish can only be cleaned by polishing.
• **Not so!** Batteries run out because they lose charge.
• **Not so!** Playing the car radio has no effect on fuel efficiency.
• **Not so!** Fuel cells have few practical applications.

In the **Explorations Practice Book**:
• Loss and Gain of Electrons

In the **Next-Time Questions Book**:
• Fuel

In the **Lab Manual**:
• See Hands-On Exploration: The Silver Lining on p. 447 of the textbook

Overhead Transparencies available for:
Figures 26.2, 26.4, 26.5, 26.6, 26.9, 26.18, 26.19

SUGGESTED PRESENTATION

26.1 Oxidation Is the Loss of Electrons and Reduction Is the Gain of Electrons
Consider beginning this chapter with the "Potato Clock" demonstration in which copper and zinc electrons inserted into two potato halves generate a current that drives an LCD clock. Show how the clock is not plugged into any wall outlet and how there is no hidden battery. Instead, there is a simplified battery that drives the clock—a battery made of copper and zinc electrodes and an electrolyte solution. Lead students into how the mystery of how batteries work will be revealed to them by studying this chapter. As a segue into this first

section, state that the principle behind a battery is actually quite simple—one material that prefers to give up electrons is placed in a circuit with another material that prefers to accept electrons.

Some elements tend to lose electrons, while others tend to gain them. Note how this tendency to lose or gain electrons is a periodic trend as is depicted in Figure 26.2. To help students remember which is oxidation and which is reduction you might introduce the mnemonic: LEO the lion goes GER (Loss of Electrons is Oxidation and Gain of Electrons is Reduction). That a reducing agent is oxidized and an oxidizing agent is reduced can be remembered by the lion that went "ROOR!"

26.2 The Energy of Flowing Electrons Can be Harnessed
Start by defining electrochemistry and then immediately jump into the following demonstrations.

> DEMONSTRATION: Place a shiny iron nail halfway into a solution of copper sulfate. Wait for a minute or two before pulling out a copper coated nail. This is most impressive. Note what is going on by referring to Figure 26.3 (Sorry, no transparency of Fig 26.3 was made available.)

> DEMONSTRATION: Continue on the lines of the previous demo by building a crude galvanic cell in class. A sensitive amp meter, zinc and copper electrodes, beakers, and a copper sulfate solution work quite well. For the salt bridge you can use a paper towel wet with the copper sulfate solution.

26.3 The Electricity of a Battery Comes from Oxidation-Reduction Reactions
Walk students through the two transparencies for Figures 26.4 and 26.5. They should then be ready to look at the various designs of batteries, fuel cells, and electrolysis. The take-home message is that putting chemicals that like to lose electrons in contact with chemicals that like to gain electrons generates an electric current provided the electric circuit is complete.

26.4 Fuel Cells Are Highly Efficient Sources of Electrical Energy
Fuels cells are an important application of electrochemistry, and they appear to be destined to become even more important in our immediate future. Thus, you may wish to spend some extra time discussing the chemistry behind fuel cells. Alert students to the idea that perhaps before not too long, rather than recharging their cell phone batteries, they'll be purchasing little ampules of methanol from the grocery store. When the cell phone power runs low, they'll open a tiny port and squirt in some of the methanol and the phone will be good to go for another month! Super large fuel cells will be used to light up skyscrapers, which will thus be independent of a centralized power system. Miniaturized fuel cells will be used to power just about any electronic gizmo that is today powered by batteries.

26.5 Electrical Energy Can Produce Chemical Change
If you haven't yet demonstrated the electrolysis of water, you have yet another chance to do so for this section. That the hydrogen and oxygen collect in a 2:1 ratio by volume is to be noted! If you have some platinum wire available, using this wire to extend the electrodes of a 9-V battery makes this demonstration "oh so convenient".

26.6 Oxygen Is Responsible for Corrosion and Combustion
This section provides a great opportunity to wrap up concepts learned in this and in previous chapters, such as periodic trends. Encourage students to work through the accompanying Practice Page on oxidations and reductions. Consider creating an overhead transparency of this Practice Page helping students work through it during class.

Another way in which metals are protected from corrosion is called cathodic protection. In this technique, iron structures are protected from oxidation by placing them in contact with metals, such as zinc or magnesium, which have a greater tendency to oxidize. This forces the iron to accept electrons, which means it behaves as a cathode. As can be seen in Figure 26.15, rusting occurs only where iron behaves as an anode. Ocean tankers, for example, are protected from corrosion by strips of zinc affixed to their hulls. Similarly, outdoor pipes are protected by being connected to magnesium rods inserted into the ground.

A good final note to make for this section (and chapter) is the similarities between respiration and combustion. Oxygen has a great affinity for electrons. This, in turn, has led to the fascinating chemistry of life.

Chapter 26 Answers and Solutions

Key Terms and Matching Definitions
_ _7_ _ anode
_ _6_ _ cathode
_10_ _ combustion
_ _9_ _ corrosion
_ _4_ _ electrochemistry
_ _5_ _ electrode
_ _8_ _ electrolysis
_ _3_ _ half reaction
_ _1_ _ oxidation
_ _2_ _ reduction

Review Questions

1. Which elements have the greatest tendency to behave as oxidizing agents?
   The elements in the upper right of the periodic table (except for noble gases) have the greatest tendency to behave as oxidizing agents.

2. Write an equation for the half reaction in which a potassium atom, K, is oxidized.

   $$K \rightarrow K^+ + 1e^-$$

3. Write an equation for the half reaction in which a bromine atom, Br, is reduced.

   $$Br_2 + 2e^- \longrightarrow 2Br^-$$

4. What happens to a reducing agent as it reduces?
   A reducing agent is oxidized as it reduces.

5. What is electrochemistry?
   Electrochemistry is the study of electrical energy and chemical changes.

6. What is the purpose of the salt bridge shown in Figure 26.5?
   To allow for a balance of charge between the two chambers.

7. What is the purpose of the manganese dioxide in a dry-cell battery?
   Manganese oxide in a dry cell battery aids in the removal of ammonia (NH_3) and hydrogen (H_2) gases to avoid the build-up of pressure and potential leakage or explosions.

8. What chemical reaction is forced to occur while a car battery is being recharged?

A reversed oxidation-reduction reaction is forced to occur while a car battery is recharged.

9. Why don't the electrodes of a fuel cell deteriorate the way the electrodes of a battery do?

As long as fuel is supplied, fuel cells don't run down, but car batteries die when the electron-producing chemicals are consumed.

10. What are the chemical emissions of a hydrogen/oxygen fuel cell?

Primarily water vapor but also some unreacted hydrogen and oxygen.

11 What is a major technological hurdle to the development of the hydrogen fuel cell?

Hydrogen fuel is a gas at room temperature and pressure, which makes it difficult to store and transport.

12. What is electrolysis, and how does it differ from what goes on inside a battery?

Electrolysis uses electrical energy to produce a chemical change whereas a battery uses a chemical change to produce electrical energy.

13. What ore is used in the manufacture of aluminum?

Bauxite.

14. Why is oxygen such a good oxidizing agent?

Oxygen is a good oxidizing agent because it has such a strong effective nuclear charge and room for extra electrons (See Chapter 5), as is indicated by its location to the upper right of the periodic table. It readily accepts electrons from many other types of elements.

15. What do the oxidation of zinc and the oxidation of aluminum have in common?

After oxidation, zinc and aluminum both form water-insoluble oxidized coats that prevent further oxidation.

16. What is electroplating, and how is it accomplished?

Electroplating is the process in which one metal is coated with another by electrolysis. The net effect is that desirable metal atoms from the positively charged electrode are deposited on the negatively charged object.

17. What are some differences between corrosion and combustion?

Corrosion is the deterioration of a metal by oxidation. Combustion is a redox reaction between a nonmetal and oxygen.

18. What are some similarities between corrosion and combustion?

Corrosion and combustion are both redox reactions, and they both require oxygen as a reactant.

Solutions to Chapter 26 Exercises

1. Which atom is oxidized?
The atom that loses an electron and thus gains a positive charge (the red one) is the one that was oxidized.

2. In the previous exercise, which atom behaves as the oxidizing agent?
The atoms that gains an electron and thus a negative charge (the blue one) is the one that behaves as an oxidizing agent.

3. What correlation might you expect between an element's electronegativity (Section 23.5) and its ability to behave as an oxidizing agent? How about its ability to behave as a reducing agent?
An oxidizing agent causes other materials to lose electrons. It does so by its tendency to gain electrons. Atoms with great electronegativity tend to have a strong attraction for electrons and, therefore, also behave as strong oxidizing agents. Conversely, a reducing agent causes other materials to gain electrons. It does so by its tendency to lose electrons. Atoms with great electronegativity, therefore, have little tendency to behave as reducing agents.

4. Based on their relative positions in the periodic table, which might you expect to be a stronger oxidizing agent, chlorine or fluorine? Why?
Fluorine should behave as a stronger oxidizing agent because it has a greater effective nuclear charge in its outermost shell.

5. Iron is a better reducing agent than the copper ion Cu^{2+}. In which direction do electrons flow when an iron nail is submerged in a solution of Cu^{2+} ions?
The electrons flow from the submerged nail to the copper ions in solution.

6. Why is the anode of a battery indicated with a minus sign?
The anode is where oxidation takes place and free roaming electrons are generated. The negative sign at the anode of a battery indicates that this electrode is the source of negatively charged electrons. They run from the anode, through an external circuit, to the cathode, which bares a positive charge to which the electrons are attracted. (When a battery is recharged energy is used to force the electrons to go in the opposite direction. In other words, during recharging, the electrons move from the positive electrode to the negative electrode—a place where they would not ever go without the input of energy. Electrons are thus gained at the negative electrode, which is now classified as the cathode because the cathode is where reduction occurs and the gain of electrons is reduction. Look carefully to Figure 26.8b to see how this is so.

7. Is sodium metal oxidized or reduced in the production of aluminum?
The sodium is oxidized as it loses its electron to the aluminum ions.

8. Why is the formation of iron hydroxide, $Fe(OH)_2$, from Fe^{2+} and OH^- not considered an oxidation–reduction reaction?
According to the chemical formula for iron hydroxide, there are two hydroxide groups for every one iron atom. Each hydroxide group has a single negative charge. This means that the iron of iron hydroxide must carry a double positive charge, which is no different from the free Fe^{2+} ion from which it is formed. This reaction is merely the coming together of oppositely-charged ions.

9. Your car lights were left on while you were shopping, and now your car battery is dead. Has the pH of the battery fluid increased or decreased?
As a car battery produces electricity it consumes various chemicals including sulfuric acid. As this sulfuric acid is consumed, the concentration of hydronium ions decreases and so the pH rises.

10. Jewelry is often manufactured by electroplating an expensive metal such as gold over a cheaper metal. Sketch a setup for this process.
Attach a wire to the jewelry to make it an electrode and dip it into a solution of gold ions. In the same container place a gold electrode. U$ a battery to drive a current between the two electrodes to force ions from the solution onto th jewelry.

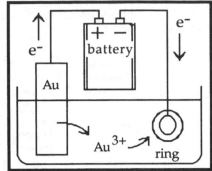

11. Some car batteries require the periodic addition of water. Does adding the water increase or decrease the battery's ability to provide electric power to start the car? Explain.
How much power a battery can deliver is a function of the number of ions in contact with the electrodes—the more ions, the greater the power. Assuming the lead electrodes (seen as a grid within the battery) are completely submerged both before and after the water has been added, then diluting the ionic solution of the car battery will decrease the number of ions in contact with the electrode and thus decrease the power of the battery. This effect is only temporary because more ions are soon generated as the battery is recharged by the generator. If the water level inside the battery, however, is so low that the internal lead electrodes are no longer completely submerged, then adding water increases the surface area of the electrode in contact with the solution. This counterbalances the weakening effect of diluting the ionic solution.

12. Why does a battery that has thick zinc walls last longer than one that has thin zinc walls?
The zinc walls are transformed into zinc ions as the battery provides electricity. Once this supply of zinc runs out, the battery can no longer operate. A battery with thicker zinc walls, therefore, has more "starting material" for the chemical reactions that occur within the battery and thus has the potential for lasting longer.

13. The oxidation of iron to rust is a problem structural engineers need to be concerned about, but the oxidation of aluminum to aluminum oxide is not. Why?
Aluminum oxide is insoluble in water and thus forms a protective coating that prevents continued oxidation of the aluminum.

14. Why are combustion reactions generally energy releasing?
Combustion reactions are generally exothermic because they involve the transfer of electrons to oxygen, which of all atoms in the periodic table has one of the greatest tendencies for gaining electrons.

15. Which element is closer to the upper right corner of the periodic table, [art] or [art]:
The one that gains a negative charge (the red one) is more likely the one that is located closer to the upper right hand corner of the periodic table.

16. Water is 88.88 percent oxygen by mass. Oxygen is exactly what a fire needs to grow brighter and stronger. So why doesn't a fire grow brighter and stronger when water is added to it?
The oxygen is chemically bound to hydrogen atoms to make water, which is a completely different from oxygen, O_2, which is what is required for combustion. Another way to phrase an answer to this question would be to say that the oxygen in water is already "reduced" in the sense that it has gained electrons from the hydrogen atoms to which it is attached. Being already reduced, this oxygen atom no longer has a great attraction for additional electrons.

17. Clorox is a laundry bleaching agent used to remove stains from white clothes. Suggest why the name begins with *Clor-* and ends with *-ox*.
The active ingredient contains chlorine atoms, which behave as strong oxidizing agents.

18. Iron has a greater tendency to oxidize than does copper. Is this good news or bad news for a home in which much of the plumbing consists of iron and copper pipes connected together? Explain.
This is very bad news to have iron and copper pipes in contact with each other. The iron atoms will lose electrons to the copper atoms, which will pass those electrons onto oxygen atoms that are in contact with the surface, much like is indicated in Figure 26.15.

19. Copper has a greater tendency to be reduced than iron does. Was this good news or bad news for the Statue of Liberty, whose copper exterior was originally held together by steel rivets?
If copper has a greater tendency to become reduced than iron, that means that electrons will preferentially flow from the iron to the copper (and then onto oxygen as indicated in the answer to Exercise 18). Corrosion is thus accelerated around the interface of these two metals. This was one of the prime reasons that the Statue of Liberty required a full restoration back in 1976.

20. One of the products of combustion is water. Why doesn't this water extinguish the combustion?
This water is in the gaseous phase and merely floats away from the fire.

27 Organic Compounds

27.1 Organic Chemistry Is the Study of Carbon Compounds
27.2 Hydrocarbons Contain Only Carbon and Hydrogen
27.3 Unsaturated Hydrocarbons Contain Multiple Bonds
> **Hands-On Exploration: Twisting Jellybeans**

27.4 Organic Molecules Are Classified by Functional Group

Learning Objectives
After studying Chapter 27, students will be able to:
• Recognize why carbon is such a unique element.
• Identify how fossil fuels are a valuable source for material goods.
• Explain how petroleum is refined into various products.
• Appreciate the diversity of carbon compounds.

Possible Misconceptions to Correct
• **Not so!** Organic chemistry is not related to organic farming.
• **Not so!** Organic structures should be memorized.
• **Not so!** Higher octane fuels burn faster.
• **Not so!** Double covalent bonds can rotate.
• **Not so!** All organic compounds smell terrible.

The structures of organic compounds and their physical and chemical properties are introduced in this chapter. Much of the chapter is descriptive, however, you will also find the application of previously learned concepts such as molecular attractions and acid/base chemistry. This chapter also sets the stage for Chapters 28 and 29, both of which include discussions of organic compounds.

In the **Explorations Practice Book:**
• Structures of Organic Compounds

In the **Next-Time Questions Book:**
• Diversity with Carbon

In the **Lab Manual:**
• Molecules by Acme (Students build 3-D models of organic compounds)
• Smells Great! (Microsynthesis of various aromatic esters)

Overhead Transparencies available for:
Figures 27.1, 27.2, 27.3, 27.7, 27.8, 27.12, 27.13, 27.14, 27.15, 27.16, 27.18, 27.19, 27.21.

SUGGESTED PRESENTATION

27.1 Organic Chemistry Is the Study of Carbon Compounds
That carbon atoms are able to bond with themselves repeatedly can be related to the strength of the carbon-carbon single bond. The C—C bond energy is 347 kJ/mole. Compare this to the bond energies of N—N (293 kJ/mole), O—O (138 kJ/mole), and

S—S (213 kJ/mole), and Si—Si (176 kJ/mole). Another vital characteristic of carbon is its ability to form 4 covalent bonds. Point out to students how this is a "peak" in terms of the periodic trend of valence—neon forms zero bonds, fluorine forms 1, oxygen forms 2, nitrogen forms 3, carbon forms 4, boron forms 3, and so on.

Using a molecular modeling kit show the wide variety of structures possible from six carbon atoms alone (leave out the hydrogen atoms to facilitate switching between structures). Note how each configuration has a different set of physical and chemical properties. Introduce an oxygen atom to show an even greater variety of compounds. That carbon forms strong covalent bonds with "heteroatoms" is another important aspect of carbon's versatility. The number of possible carbon-based compounds is truly endless.

With organic chemicals, carbon and hydrogen atoms provide a relatively inert framework to which reactive atoms, such as nitrogen and oxygen, may attach. These added atoms give the organic chemical much of its character—much like ornaments on a tree. This chapter begins by studying the carbon-hydrogen framework.

27.2 Hydrocarbons Contain Only Carbon and Hydrogen
Hydrocarbons come in all three phases. Blow some soap bubbles using methane (or propane) to demonstrate the gaseous phase (methane bubbles will rise, but propane bubbles will sink). Bring in some hexanes or gasoline to show the liquid phase. The solid phase is seen with plastics such as high or low density polyethylene, polypropylene, or polystyrene. The phase of a hydrocarbon is a function of its molecular mass. Consider creating a hand-out or an overhead transparency of the "Properties of Hydrocarbons" table on the following page.

Show what is meant by a structural isomer. Introduce the term *conformation* and contrast it to what is meant by *configuration*, which refers to how the atoms are connected. Use the human body as an analogy. The configuration of the arm is such that the wrist bone is connected to the ulna bone, the ulna bone is connected to the elbow bone, etc. The conformation refers to how the bonds are oriented within a particular configuration. Again, using the human body as an analogy, the whole arm is one configuration, which can have a wide variety of different conformations (extend your arm and twist it about). Go through examples so that students can recognize when two structures are either different configurations, or different conformations of the same configuration.

ASK YOUR NEIGHBOR: How many different configurations are shown below? Which ones, if any, are different conformations of the same configuration?

A   B   C   D

Properties of Hydrocarbons

Molecular Formula	Name	Melting Point (°C)	Boiling Point (°C)	Phase at Room Temp.
CH_4	Methane	-184	-161	
C_2H_6	Ethane	-183	-88	Gas
C_3H_8	Propane	-188	-42	
C_4H_{10}	*n*-Butane	-138	-0.5	
C_5H_{12}	*n*-Pentane	-130	36	
C_6H_{14}	*n*-Hexane	-94	69	
C_7H_{16}	*n*-Heptane	-91	98	Liquid
C_8H_{18}	*n*-Octane	-57	126	
$C_{16}H_{34}$	*n*-Hexadecane	18	288	
$C_{17}H_{36}$	*n*-Heptadecane	23	303	
$C_{18}H_{38}$	*n*-Octadecane	28	317	Solid
$C_{2000}H_{4002}$*	Polyethylene	136	dec.**	

----
* The number of carbon atoms per molecule in polyethylene varies greatly but is generally a large number not more than 100,000.
** decomposes before boiling

27.3 Unsaturated Hydrocarbons Contain Multiple Bonds

When students hear the term "unsaturated" they are likely to think of unsaturated fats. "Saturated" means that a carbon atom is saturated with hydrogen atoms, that is, bonded to a maximum number. Only single covalent bonds appear in saturated hydrocarbons. The hydrocarbons discussed in the previous section are all saturated. "Unsaturated" means that there are fewer than a maximum number of hydrogen atoms bonded to carbon. This occurs when double or triple bonds are present. Relating this to one's diet, the hydrocarbon portion of saturated fat molecules consists of only single bonds. The hydrocarbon portions of unsaturated fats, however, contain multiple bonds, usually the one or more double bond. One reason unsaturated fats may be better for our health is that double bonds are more chemically reactive, hence, easier to metabolize. You might tell your students that the double bond is like a handle that the body grabs to help move the molecule through the digestion process. In general, the better an organic molecule flows through your body, the less harmful it is.

Consider looking up the review article by Gary Taubes in the 30 March 2001 issue of *Science*. This article, entitled "The Soft Science of Dietary Fat", points out that there is little to no evidence correlating dietary saturated fats to coronary heart disease. The article explores in depth the history of how we have come to assume that saturated fats are necessarily bad and ought to be avoided at all expense. It makes for an interesting expose on what happens with science and politics come together. If not available through your library, it may be found on the web for a cost of $5 to the AAAS through:

http://www.sciencemag.org/content/vol291/issue5513/index.shtml#newsfocus

27.4 Organic Molecules Are Classified by Functional Group

Heteroatom" is the common term used by organic chemists to describe nitrogen, oxygen, chlorine, or any other non-carbon/non-hydrogen atoms in an organic molecule. In introducing the various heteroatom containing functional groups, you might wish to emphasize that these structures are presented as a display of the diversity of carbon, more than for memorization.

In society, the words "alcohol" and "ethanol" are used interchangeably. From a chemical point of view, however, alcohols are a class of organic compounds, of which ethanol is one example. Define the alcohol as an organic molecule containing the hydroxyl functional group.

> ASK YOUR NEIGHBOR: Because water consists of a hydroxyl group bonded to a hydrogen atom can it be classified as an alcohol? [No. Alcohols are organic molecules, which by definition contain carbon. Since there is no carbon in water, it cannot be classified as an alcohol.]

Alcohol molecules are attracted to one another primarily by the dipole-dipole attractions between hydroxyl groups. The more hydroxyl groups in an alcohol, the greater the molecular attractions.

> DEMONSTRATION: Write on the chalkboard the chemical structures for ethanol, ethylene glycol, and glycerol. Ask students to predict the order of boiling points. Then produce three unlabeled glass vials, each containing one of the above alcohols. Ask students to identify them. Point out how viscosity is also a function of the strengths of molecular attractions.

Show how ethers are structurally related to alcohols. You might do this with a molecular modeling kit. It is interesting to note that a new class of compounds is produced simply by changing the arrangement of atoms. Since they lack the oxygen-hydrogen dipole, ethers are much less soluble in water and their boiling points are lower.

DEMONSTRATION: Contrast the miscibility of ethanol and diethyl ether with water. First define miscibility as the ability of two substances to form a single phase. Pour equal amounts of water into two graduated cylinders. Have the class note the volume levels. Mix in a drop of water soluble food coloring. Pour the same quantity of ethanol to one of the containers and the same quantity of diethyl ether to the other. Cover the tops with parafilm and shake (You will note a pressure build up as you mix the water and ether). The water and ethanol form a single liquid phase. The water and ether, however, form two liquid phases. Note the volume level of the water in the water/ether cylinder and ask the class to explain any discrepancies. That some of the ether has dissolved in the water can be demonstrated by pouring the two phases into a separatory funnel and collecting the lower aqueous phase. Have a student volunteer note the odor of this ether containing water.

Low molecular mass amines have a characteristic bad odor. Inform your students that this is why you have not brought any samples to show them. Higher molecular mass amines, however, do not have such characteristic odors.

ASK YOUR NEIGHBOR: Higher molecular mass amines do not give off the characteristic bad odor released by lower molecular mass amines. Why not? [We can only smell that which reaches our nose. In order for a scent to reach our nose it must be in a gaseous phase. Lower molecular mass amines have fewer molecular attractions, hence, they are more volatile, which means that the molecules readily escape into the gaseous phase. Higher molecular mass amines, on the other hand, have strong molecular attractions that hold the molecules to the solid or liquid phases, which we cannot smell.]

Show how amines can act as bases by accepting the hydrogen ion. The hydrogen ion is attracted to the lone pair of electron on the nitrogen atom. You might show where these electrons come from by drawing the shell model for nitrogen.

DEMONSTRATION: Show how to extract caffeine from coffee. Pour a strong cup of coffee into a separatory funnel. Bring the coffee to a pH of about 9 or 10 by adding drops of a solution of sodium hydroxide. Pour some diethyl ether (about a third the volume of the coffee) into the funnel. Stopper the funnel, invert it and open the stopcock to release any pressure. Close the stopcock and shake the contents. After the two layers settle collect the lower aqueous layer in a beaker. Collect the ether layer in a second beaker. Add some anhydrous sodium sulfate to the ether to absorb any water. Decant some of the ether into a watch glass and let it evaporate. The residues left behind contain caffeine. Be careful not to let too many of the ether fume migrate towards the students. If possible, perform this demo in a fume hood, or at least cover the open beaker containing the ether layer with parafilm or with a larger beaker inverted over it. If not much residue is collected, consider rotovapping an ether layer prior to the class so that you can show what the residue looks like after all of the ether is evaporated. Brewed coffee contains from 18-15 milligrams of caffeine per oz. Decaffeinated coffee is made by extracting whole coffee beans with organic solvents, usually supercritical carbon dioxide. The beans are then roasted to bring out flavor.

DEMONSTRATION: Bring to class samples of some of the more pleasantly fragrant aldehydes such as the ones listed in Figure 27.19, which is also available as a transparency.

ASK YOUR NEIGHBOR: Most of the aspirin consumed today is synthetically produced from crude oil. How is this aspirin different from aspirin derived from the willow tree? [There is no difference. They are exactly the same. Neither one is either better or worse.]

DEMONSTRATION: In the event your students are not performing the Smells Great! lab activity, add a couple grams of salicylic acid to a watch glass. State how this material is a precursor to aspirin, then ask for a volunteer to attest to the fact that it doesn't have much of an odor. Dissolve the salicyclic acid in a couple milliliters of methanol. Follow up by adding a couple drops of concentrated sulfuric acid. Stir and set it aside to evaporate. Alternatively, set it atop an overhead projector. The heat of the projector lamp will speed up the evaporation and the shadows of the crystal formations can be seen on the projection screen. Note that crystal formation upon the evaporation of the methanol is sometimes quite beautiful. After the methanol has evaporated ask for a volunteer to attest to the fact that wintergreen (methyl salicylate) has been formed. Show the equation for the reaction on the board. FYI: The sulfuric acid helps this reaction move forward by making it easier for the oxygen of the methanol molecule to attack the carbon of the carbonyl. It does so by donating a hydrogen to the oxygen of the carbonyl. This in turn makes the carbon of the carbonyl more positive in character, which makes it susceptible to an attack by the lone pair on the oxygen of the methanol molecule.

Chapter 27 Answers and Solutions

Key Terms and Matching Definitions
_10_ alcohol
_15_ aldehyde
_16_ amide
_12_ amines
_7_ aromatic compound
_13_ carbonyl group
_17_ carboxylic acid
_4_ conformations
_18_ ester
_11_ ethers
_9_ functional group
_8_ heteroatom
_2_ hydrocarbons
_14_ ketone
_1_ organic chemistry
_5_ saturated hydrocarbons
_3_ structural isomers
_6_ unsaturated hydrocarbons

Review Questions
1. Why is carbon able to form a limitless number of compounds?

   Carbon is able to form a limitless number of compounds because carbon atoms can link together and also form bonds with other types of atoms, such as oxygen and nitrogen.

2. What organic molecule gives rise to the flavor of vanilla?
   Vanillin.

3. How do two structural isomers differ from each other?

   Structural isomers have different arrangements of their carbon atoms, but the number of carbon atoms they each have is the same.

4. How are two structural isomers similar to each other?
   Structural isomers have identical chemical formulas.

5. What physical property of hydrocarbons is used in fractional distillation?
   Boiling points of hydrocarbons are used for fractional distillation.

6. To how many atoms is a saturated carbon atom bonded?
   A carbon atom in a saturated hydrocarbon is bonded to 4 atoms.

7. What is the difference between a saturated hydrocarbon and an unsaturated hydrocarbon?
   Saturated hydrocarbons have only single bonds. Unsaturated hydrocarbons have multiple bonds.

8. How many multiple bonds must a hydrocarbon have in order to be classified as unsaturated?

A hydrocarbon must have at least one multiple (double or triple) bond to be classified as unsaturated.

9. Aromatic compounds contain what kind of ring?
Aromatic compounds contain a 6-membered ring system called a benzene ring.

10. What is a heteroatom?
A heteroatom is any atom other than carbon or hydrogen in an organic molecule.

11. Why are low-formula-mass alcohols soluble in water?
Small alcohols are soluble in water because they have polar oxygen-hydrogen bonds similar to water. Like dissolves like.

12. What distinguishes an alcohol from an ether?
An alcohol has a hydroxyl (oxygen bonded to hydrogen) group, but an ether contains an oxygen atom bonded to two carbon atoms.

13. Why do ethers typically have lower boiling points than alcohols?
Ethers typically have lower boiling points than alcohols because there is no hydrogen bonding in an ether. The ether's weaker intermolecular forces give them lower boiling points than alcohols.

14. Which heteroatom is characteristic of an amine?
Nitrogen is found in all amines.

15. Do amines tend to be acidic, neutral, or basic?
Amines tend to be basic. The lone electron pair located on nitrogen atoms makes them basic because this lone pair is able to accept a hydrogen ion.

16. Are alkaloids found in nature?
An alkaloid is a naturally occurring amine.

17. What are some examples of alkaloids?
Morphine and caffeine are two examples of alkaloids.

18. Which elements make up the carbonyl group?
Carbon and oxygen make up a carbonyl group.

19. How are ketones and aldehydes related to each other? How are they different from each other?
Both contain carbonyl groups. Ketones have the carbonyl carbon bonded to two adjacent carbon atoms, but aldehydes have the carbonyl carbon bonded to either one hydrogen and one carbon or to two hydrogens.

20. How are amides and carboxylic acids related to each other? How are they different from each other?
Amides and carboxylic acids both contain carbonyl groups. Amides have the carbonyl carbon bonded to a nitrogen atom, but carboxylic acids have the carbonyl carbon bonded to a hydroxyl group.

Solutions to the Chapter 27 Exercises

1. Which contains more hydrogen atoms: a five-carbon saturated hydrocarbon molecule or a five-carbon unsaturated hydrocarbon molecule?
   A saturated hydrocarbon with 5 carbon atoms will have 12 hydrogen atoms. An unsaturated hydrocarbon with 5 carbon atoms will have 10 or fewer hydrogen atoms.

2. Why does the melting point of hydrocarbons increase as the number of carbon atoms per molecule increases?
   Because of greater induced dipole-induced dipole molecular interactions.

3. Draw all the structural isomers for hydrocarbons having the molecular formula C_4H_{10}.

4. Draw all the structural isomers for hydrocarbons having the molecular formula C_6H_{14}.

5. How many structural isomers are shown here:
   There are only two structural isomers drawn. The one in the middle and the one on the right are actually two conformations of the same isomer.

6. Which two of these four structures are of the same structural isomer:
   The structures on the upper right and the lower left are different conformations of the same structural isomer.

7. The temperatures in a fractionating tower at an oil refinery are important, but so are the pressures. Where might the pressure in a fractionating tower be greatest, at the bottom or at the top? Defend your answer.
   The pressure is greater at the bottom of the fractionation tower because of a higher temperature and because of a greater number of vaporized molecules.

8. Heteroatoms make a difference in the physical and chemical properties of an organic molecule because

a. they add extra mass to the hydrocarbon structure.
b. each heteroatom has its own characteristic chemistry.
c. they can enhance the polarity of the organic molecule.
d. all of the above.
d, all of the above.

9. What is the percent volume of water in 80-proof vodka?
The 80 proof vodka is 40 percent ethanol by volume, hence 60 percent water.

10. How does ingested methanol lead to the damaging of a person's eyes?
Ingesting methanol is indirectly harmful to one's eyes because in the body it is metabolized to formaldehyde—a chemical most toxic to living tissue. Methanol, just like ethanol, however, also has inherent toxicity and is thus also directly harmful.

11. The phosphoric acid salt of caffeine has the structure [p. 486, Ex 11]. This molecule behaves as an acid in that it can donate a hydrogen ion, created from the hydrogen atom bonded to the positively charged nitrogen atom. What are all the products formed when 1 mole of this salt reacts with 1 mole of sodium hydroxide, NaOH, a strong base?

Caffeine
(free base) $+ H_2O + Na^+H_2PO_4^-$

12. The solvent diethyl ether can be mixed with water but only by shaking the two liquids together. After the shaking is stopped, the liquids separate into two layers, much like oil and vinegar. The free-base form of the alkaloid caffeine is readily soluble in diethyl ether but not in water. Suggest what might happen to the caffeine of a caffeinated beverage if the beverage was first made alkaline with sodium hydroxide and then shaken with some diethyl ether.
Bring the beverage to an alkaline pH by adding a base such as sodium hydroxide and the caffeine salt it contains will be transformed into the caffeine free base (see Exercise 11), which is more soluble in the organic solvent diethyl ether than it is in water. If the caffeinated beverage is made alkaline with sodium hydroxide and then shaken with some diethyl ether, most of the caffeine free base will thus dissolve into the diethyl ether layer while the polar components of the beverage will remain in the aqueous phase.

13. Alkaloid salts are not very soluble in the organic solvent diethyl ether. What might happen to the free-base form of caffeine dissolved in diethyl ether if gaseous hydrogen chloride, HCl, were bubbled into the solution?
The HCl would react with the free base to form the water-soluble, but diethyl ether-insoluble hydrochloric acid salt of caffeine. With no water available to dissolve this material, it precipitates out of the diethyl ether as a solid that may be collected by filtration.

14. Draw all the structural isomers for amines having the molecular formula C_3H_9N.

15. Explain why caprylic acid, $CH_3(CH_2)_6COOH$, dissolves in a 5 percent aqueous solution of sodium hydroxide but caprylaldehyde, $CH_3(CH_2)_6CHO$, does not.

The caprylic acid reacts with the sodium hydroxide to form a water soluble salt, which dissolves in the water. The aldehyde, on the other hand, is not acidic so it will not form a water soluble salt.

16. In water, does the molecule [p 484, Exercise 16, structure of LSD] act as an acid, a base, neither, or both?
Don't let the name fool you. Look to the structure to deduce its physical or chemical properties. Because of the nitrogens this alkaloid molecule contains, it behaves as a base.

17. If you saw the label phenylephrine ? HCl on a decongestant, would you worry that consuming it would expose you to the strong acid hydrochloric acid? Explain.
No! This label indicates that it contains the hydrogen chloride salt of phenylephrine, but no acidic hydrogen chloride. This organic salt is as different from hydrogen chloride as is sodium chloride (table salt), which may also go by the name of "the hydrogen chloride salt of sodium." This of it this way: assume you have a cousin named George. Now, you may be George's cousin, but in no way are you George. In a similar fashion, the hydrogen chloride salt of phenylephrine is made using hydrogen chloride, but it is in no way hydrogen chloride. A chemical substance is uniquely different from the elements or compounds from which it is made.

18. Suggest an explanation for why aspirin has a sour taste.
Aspirin's chemical name is acetyl salicylic acid. It is the acidic nature of aspirin that gives rise to its sour taste.

19. An amino acid is an organic molecule that contains both an amine group and a carboxyl group. At an acidic pH, which structure is most likely:
At an acidic pH, the structure shown in (c) is the most likely. This is because the amine group behaves as a base, which means that it will react with the hydronium ions (which are abundant at low pHs) to form the positively charged nitrogen ion.

20. Identify the following functional groups in this organic molecule—amide, ester, ketone, ether, alcohol, aldehyde, amine:

1. ether
2. amide
3. ester
4. amide
5. alcohol
6. aldehyde
7. amine
8. ether
9. ketone

28 The Chemistry of Drugs

28.1 There Are Several Ways to Classify Drugs
28.2 The Lock-and-Key Model Guides Chemists in Creating New Drugs
28.3 Chemotherapy Cures the Host by Killing the Disease
28.4 The Nervous System Is a Network of Neurons
28.5 Psychoactive Drugs Alter the Mind or Behavior
28.6 Pain Relievers Inhibit the Transmission or Perception of Pain

Learning Objectives
After studying Chapter 28, students will be able to:
• Describe how drugs are classified.
• Explain the lock-and-key model of drug action.
• Identify where drugs come from.
• Describe how nerve impulses travel through neurons.
• Describe how various drugs effect nerve transmissions.
• Distinguish between stimulants and depressants.
• Explain how certain pain relievers relieve pain.

Possible Misconceptions to Correct
• **Not so!** All drugs are bad for us.
• **Not so!** Each drug exerts a singular effect.
• **Not so!** All neurons are physically connected to each other.
• **Not so!** The body is unable to counter the effect of a drug.
• **Not so!** Alcohol is a stimulant.
• **Not so!** Heroin is more addicting than nicotine.
• **Not so!** Medicines are a good alternative to a healthy lifestyle.

Drugs have had such a great impact on our lives. This includes the medicines we take to cure our ills, as well as the illicit drugs that people take illegally for recreation. We've done our best to maintain a tone of the real dangers of illicit drug use. However, what students need and expect most from this textbook is accurate information based upon scientific study and evidence. We trust you will find the discussions here fair and unbiased.

Students will need to have covered Chapter 27 prior to working with this chapter.

There are many new exciting developments occurring in the development of medicines. The recent development of the anti-leukemia drug Gleevac is an important example. After studying this chapter, your students should have a strong background with which to understand and appreciate such developments as they arise.

In addition to your formal presentations, consider allowing students to research various classes of drugs on their own. Forewarn them about all the junk one can find on the web. Refer them to specific web sites or more traditional resources, such as the *Physician's Desk Reference* or the *Merck Index*. Students might be encouraged to develop "posters" that present information on drugs to a general public audience. One day may be dedicated as a "poster session" where all the students' posters are set up around the classroom. Students can then read and grade each other's posters. Half of each student's grade come from the average of all the evaluations he or she received (with your quality control) plus a score that reflects how well that student graded all of the other posters. This idea also works well for Chapter 29 Plastics.

Be sure also to consider using the Discussion Topics listed in the endmatter for possible class discussions.

In the **Explorations Practice Book**:
• Neurotransmitters

In the **Next-Time Questions Book**:
• Aspirin

Overhead Transparencies available for:
Figures 28.2, 28.4, 28.5, 28.6, 28.8, 28.9, 28.10, 28.11, 28.13, 28.14, 28.15, 28.20, 28.21, 28.22, 28.23, 28.25.

SUGGESTED PRESENTATION

28.1 There are Several Ways to Classify Drugs
Start class by asking students for their definitions of a drug. List possible definitions on the board and lead the class to a distinction between a drug and a medicine. While all medicines are drugs, not all drugs are medicines. Point out the different ways that drugs are classified by rendering elements of Tables 28.1 and 28.2 on the chalkboard. Finish up by noting the dangers of combining drugs that have similar effects.

28.2 The Lock-and-Key Model Guides Chemists in Creating New Drugs
To illustrate the lock-and-key model, take a piece of paper and crumple it up. The resulting wad will have numerous nooks and crannies. Explain to students how these nooks and crannies are analogous to certain regions of their bodies, especially on the surface of cells. Show how it is that a piece of chalk, or some similar prop, is able to fit within one of these nooks and crannies. As the chalk is nestled into the nook, show how it is that the paper is not static, rather, it may contort once the chalk binds to its site. The contortion of the paper wad opens up other nooks (on the opposite side, for example), that other molecules might able to fit into.

This is the essence of the lock-and-key model of drug action: a drug works as it binds to some receptor site in the body. As it binds, it causes the surface to contort, which then influences other receptor sites, and hence other biochemical reactions that might be occurring.

In explaining the similar actions of morphine, codeine, and heroin, it is very useful to have their molecular models on hand. One suffices. Simply change the functional groups accordingly to transform from one compound to the next. Although the functional groups change, the overall shape of the molecules are the same. This helps us to visualize the important relationship between the structure of a drug molecule and its biological effect.

Be sure not to miss out on the opportunity of stressing yet another reason that the world's tropical rainforests should be preserved. Plants are often in mortal combat against other plants, insects, fungi, and animals. From this combat arises a multitude of biologically active compounds that serve the plant some evolutionary advantage. These compounds are the very ones that chemists look for in the search for new medicines.

28.3 Chemotherapy Cures the Host by Killing the Disease
Sulfa drugs were really the first general antibiotics ever made available to humans. They were invented in the 1930s and resulted in the saving of millions of lives, including the grandparents or great grandparents of many of your students. To be put another way: Had

these drugs not been invented then, many of us (including your students) would not have been born.

Penicillins and related antibiotics quickly replaced the sulfa drugs for most infections after they were developed in the late 1930s and they became a vital resource during World War II.

28.4 The Nervous System Is a Network of Neurons

This is the most concept intensive section of this chapter because it digs into the mechanisms of neuron transmissions. This is prerequisite information, however, for understanding the actions of the drugs discussed in subsequent sections.

Here is an interesting aside: Neurons aren't the only type of cells that tend to eject sodium ions. In fact, the preferential ejection of sodium ions is a behavior found with most cells, especially with the cells of plants. Interestingly, plants absorb potassium ions from the soil, but in most instances the route for sodium ions is in the other direction—plants give off sodium ions to the soil and so ultimately to the groundwater, streams, rivers, and then the oceans. So, while sodium and potassium ions are about equally abundant in the Earth's crust, seawater contains about 2.8 percent NaCl, but only about 0.8 percent KCl. Some scientists believe that it is cell's low tolerance for sodium ions that led to the mechanisms for selectively pumping these ions out of cells, which, in turn, led to the evolution of the nervous system, and hence, animals.

28.5 Psychoactive Drugs Alter the Mind or Behavior

Be sure to highlight the structural similarities between many of the drugs discussed in this section and the neurotransmitters discussed in the previous section. You might, for example, overlap the transparencies for Figures 28.10 and 28.13 to show how the amphetamines resemble the neurotransmitters norepinephrine and dopamine.

Some detail is provided regarding the mechanism of actions for ethyl alcohol and benzodiazepines. These are *concepts*, however, and so should take precedence over requiring students to memorize individual structures (yuk!). Furthermore, it is our belief that allowing students to learn the mechanism for drug actions is one of the best ways of helping them decide against the use of potentially harmful illicit drugs.

28.6 Pain Relievers Inhibit the Transmission or Perception of Pain

Distinguish between anesthetics (prevent nerve transmissions to the brain) and analgesics (enhances our ability to tolerate pain). Show how it is that over-the-counter analgesics, such as aspirin, prevent the synthesis of pain and inflammation generating prostaglandins.

Students are always interested in the placebo effect. Studies suggest that every one in three of us is a "placebo responder."

Due to the need for brevity, there are many other classes of drugs that are not covered in this chapter. This includes, the antiviral agents, anticancer agents, hallucinogens, antidepressants, drugs for the heart, allergies, and birth control. For reference, you will find discussions of these drugs in the drug chapter of *Conceptual Chemistry* by John Suchocki. You might also consider directing students toward choosing these drugs as topics for a poster session as described earlier.

Chapter 28 Answers and Solutions

Key Terms and Matching Definitions

_10_ _ analgesic
_9_ _ anesthetic
_3_ _ chemotherapy
_2_ _ lock-and-key model
_4_ _ neuron
_6_ _ neurotransmitters
_7_ _ physical dependence
_8_ _ psychological dependence
_5_ _ synaptic cleft
_1_ _ synergistic effect

Review Questions

1. What are the three origins of drugs?
   Drugs originate from plants, animals, or are synthesized.

2. Are a drug's side effects necessarily bad?
   A drug's side effects are not necessarily bad.

3. What is the synergistic effect?
   When one drug enhances the effect of another it is called a synergistic effect.

4. In the lock-and-key model, is a drug viewed as the lock or the key?
   The drug is viewed as the key.

5. What holds a drug to its receptor site?
   Molecular attractions, such as hydrogen bonding, hold a drug to its receptor site.

6. Why do bacteria need PABA but humans can do without it?
   Bacteria need PABA to produce folic acid because they cannot utilize folic acid from outside sources while humans can utilize folic acid from outside sources.

7. How does penicillin G cure bacterial infections?
   Penicillin G inhibits the growth of bacterial colonies by binding to receptor sites that the bacteria need for building their cell walls.

8. How does a neuron maintain an electric potential difference across its membrane?
   Neurons maintain electrical potential across a membrane by pumping sodium ions from their inner hollow channels.

9. What are the symptoms that a person's stress neurons have been activated?
   The symptoms of the stimulation of stress neurons are the mind becoming more alert, opening of the air passages, the heart beats faster and nonessential activities are stopped.

10. What are some of the things going on in the body when maintenance neurons are more active than stress neurons?
    Maintenance neurons are responsible for digestion, intestinal muscle function, sharpening vision, and maintaining heart rate.

11. What neurotransmitter functions most in the brain's reward center?

Dopamine functions most in the brain's reward center.

12. What is the role of GABA in the nervous system?

GABA inhibits the output of nerve impulses.

13. How is psychological dependence distinguished from physical dependence?

Physical dependence involves physical symptoms such as depression, fatigue, and desire to eat. Psychological dependence symptoms can exist long after the physical dependence symptoms disappear and can lead to renewed drug-seeking behavior.

14. What is one mechanism for how caffeine stimulates the nervous system?

Caffeine facilitates the release of norepinephrine into the synaptic cleft.

15. What neurotransmitter does nicotine mimic?

Nicotine mimics neurotransmitter acetylcholine.

16. What drugs enhance the action of GABA?

Alcohol and benzodiazepines affect the action of GABA.

17. What is an anesthetic?

An anesthetic blocks pain by preventing nerves from transmitting sensations.

18. What is an analgesic?

Analgesics enhance our ability to tolerate pain without abolishing nerve sensations.

19. Where are the major opioid receptor sites located?

Opioid receptor sites are located in the brain.

20. What biochemical is thought to be responsible for the placebo effect?

Endorphines are thought to be responsible for the placebo effect.

Solutions to Chapter 28 Exercises

1. Aspirin can cure a headache, but when you pop an aspirin tablet, how does the aspirin know to go to your head rather than your big toe?

The aspirin doesn't "know" to go to your head rather than your big toe. In fact, once the aspirin enters the bloodstream it is distributed throughout the body, which is why the aspirin is good for alleviated headaches as well as toe aches.

2. Which is better for you: a drug that is a natural product or one that is synthetic?

Whether a drug is isolated from nature or synthesized in the laboratory makes no difference as to "how good it may be for you". There are a multitude of natural products that are downright harmful, just as there are many synthetic drugs that are also harmful. The effectiveness of a drug depends on its chemical structure, not the source of this chemical structure.

3. Would formulating a sulfa drug with PABA be likely to increase or decrease its antibacterial properties?

Sulfa drugs are transformed into sulfanilamide, which binds to the PABA receptor site on an enzyme that bacteria use to produce folic acid, a vital nutrient. In this sense, the sulfanilamide "competes" with the PABA for this receptor site and is thus said to be an inhibitor. If PABA were provided along with the sulfa drug, then there would be a greater chance that PABA, rather than the sulfanilamide, would bind first, thus helping the bacteria to produce the folic acid that they need. Formulating PABA with sulfa drug, therefore, is likely to decrease its antibacterial properties.

4. What is an advantage of synaptic clefts between neurons rather than direct connections?
The synaptic cleft allows the body to regulate the passage of a nerve impulse from one neuron to the next or from a neuron to a target tissue, such as muscle.

5. How is a drug addict's addiction similar to our need for food? How is it different?
If the drug addict doesn't get the drug, he or she will experience a number of undesirable withdrawal symptoms that prompt the addict into drug-seeking behavior. Similarly, when we haven't eaten for a while, we experience undesirable hunger pangs, fatigue, and sometimes a shakiness that prompts us into food-seeking behavior. Thus, in a sense, we are addicted to food in much that same way that a drug addict is addicted to a drug—there is a bodily dependence. There is a fundamental difference, however, in that we can live without the drugs that get abused, but we cannot live without the food we eat.

6. Nicotine solutions are available from lawn and garden stores as an insecticide. Why must gardeners handle this product with extreme care?
Gardeners must exercise extreme care when using solutions of nicotine because nicotine is extremely poisonous to humans.

7. A variety of gaseous compounds behave as general anesthetics even though their structures have very little in common. Does this support the role of a receptor site for their mode of action?
Recall that a molecule must have a certain structure in order to be able to bind to a receptor site. That the structures of these general anesthetics have very little in common suggests that there is no specific structure responsible for the general anesthetic effect and, furthermore, that there is no specific receptor site on which they are acting.

8. How might the structure of benzocaine be modified to create a compound having greater anesthetic properties?
Of course, once the structure of benzocaine is modified, it is no longer benocaine but some other chemical. Extend the ester group so that there is a nitrogen atom two carbons away from the ester's lower oxygen atom as seen in Figure 28.23, and you'll end up with a compound, such as procaine, which has much greater anesthetic properties.

9. Which is the more appropriate statement: Opioids have endorphin activity, or endorphins have opioid activity? Explain your answer.
Endorphins likely came first, and then humans made the discovery of how opium contains compounds that mimic the effect of endorphins. Thus, "opioids have endorphin activity". Why this is so is something you should be sure to discuss with your instructor.

10. A person may feel more relaxed after smoking a cigarette, but his or her heart is actually stressed. Why?
Initially, the nicotine of the cigarette may relax the users' muscles and it does so by binding the maintenance motor neurons. The nicotine, however, remains bound to the receptor sites on these neurons, which are thus depressed. This has the effect of enhancing the stress motor neurons, which can be detrimental to one's heart tissue causing the tissue to be overworked.

29 Plastics

Learning Objectives
After studying Chapter 29, students will be able to:
• Describe and explain the formation of synthetic polymers.
• Distinguish between addition and condensation polymers.
• Appreciate the recent history of the development of plastics.
• Describe where plastics come from.

Possible Misconceptions to Correct
• **Not so!** Polymers are not found in nature.
• **Not so!** Plastics have been around for many centuries.
• **Not so!** Plastics had only a marginal impact on World War II.
• **Not so!** There is an unlimited supply of plastics.

This chapter is divided into two parts. The first part consisting of the first three sections, is an overview of the chemistry of polymers. This includes the different types of polymers and how they are formed. The second part consisting of the latter three sections, is a brief history of the development of plastics. While the first three sections may require some formal lecture presentations, the latter three sections pretty much stand on their own as assigned reading.

As with the previous chapter on drugs, this chapter lends itself well to a poster session assignment. Look back to the Chapter 28 description in this Teacher's Guide for some ideas on how you might organize such a poster session with your students.

In the **Explorations Practice Book:**
• Polymers
• History of Plastics

In the **Next-Time Questions Book:**
• Waterproofing Spots

In the **Lab Manual:**
• Name That Recyclable (Unknown plastics are identified by their densities)

Overhead Transparencies available for:
Figures 29.1, 29.2. 29.9.

SUGGESTED PRESENTATION

29.1 Organic Molecules Can Link To Form Polymers

A good theme to carry through this chapter is how the physical properties of a polymer are a consequence of the chemical structure of its component monomers. Properties to focus on include density, hardness, and melting point (Note: glass transition temperature is not defined).

You should touch upon the idea of biopolymers, such as starches, proteins, and nucleic acids. These are the polymers that we eat and our bodies are made of. With an understanding of the synthetic polymers discussed in this chapter, students will have a good handle for understanding biopolymers in their life science courses.

29.2 Addition Polymers Result from the Joining Together of Monomers

Show the formation of polyethylene using the overhead transparency for Figure 29.2. You can then use this same transparency to show the formation of other addition polymers. Using a transparency marker, simply write in -CH_3 groups on every other carbon, or benzene groups on every other carbon to show the formation of polypropylene and polystyrene, respectively. Different monomer starting materials, but the chemistry is the same. Let students in on the excitement that early polymer developers must have experienced—all they had to do was play around with the starting materials and, voila, a wide variety of different polymers could be formed with applications limited only by our imaginations.

29.3 Condensation Polymers Form with the Loss of Small Molecules

Use the transparency of Figure 29.9 and discuss the formation of Nylon. You might insert some tidbits about its history found in this section and also in Section 29.5. If possible, perform the synthesis of Nylon for your students. It is an unforgettable experience for them. As with all demo, be sure to experiment with the conditions on you own before performing in front of the group.

> DEMONSTRATION: Here is a procedure for the synthesis of Nylon. Prior to class, prepare two solutions as follows:
>
> Solution A: Place 5.81 g of hexamethylenediamine (1,6-diaminohexane) in a beaker. Warm until it melts and dilute to 100 mL with 0.5 M NaOH (20 g NaOH per liter).
>
> Solution B: Dilute 4.58 g of adipoyl chloride with cyclohexane to a volume of 100 mL. Caution: The adipoyl chloride is corrosive releasing hydrogen chloride fumes. Prepare in a fume hood.
>
> During class, place about 5 mL of solution A in a 50 mL beaker. Slowly add the same quantity of solution B to the same beaker. Beware of the hydrogen chloride fumes that form upon the reaction. The role of the sodium hydroxide in Solution A is to react with this HCl, but some still invariably escapes as fumes. Hold some litmus paper to the fumes to show the students the formation of this gas. A film will form at the interface of the two solutions. Do not stir this mixture. Instead, wearing gloves, carefully hook the film with a paper clip bent at the tip and pull the film from the beaker. It works well to hold the beaker at a slight angle and pull the nylon off the wet lip of the beaker. Carefully guide the nylon out of the beaker. Continue pulling until the solutions are exhausted. The nylon can be spooled around a large beaker. Pop any bubbles that formed during the pulling process. Rinse the nylon thoroughly before passing it around for the class to examine more closely.

Students will comment on how "weak" the strand of Nylon is. In other words, it is fairly easy to break. You might bring out some fine nylon rope. Pull it apart carefully so as to collect some single strands. Note that "yes" these single strands are weak, but that together they form a very strong rope.

29.4 The Development of Plastics Involved Experimentation and Discovery
Relate the stretching of a rubber band to Figure 29.13, which shows the orientation of polyisoprene strands upon stretching. Interestingly, as the rubber band is stretched, polymer strands become aligned, which means a decrease in entropy. This has the effect of the release of heat. Another way to think of it is that the energy you put into stretching the rubber band is released as heat. Alternatively, you can say that there are more molecular attractions that form between the strands and this releases heat. In short, the actual physics and chemistry of this phenomenon is not so straight-forward. Nonetheless, you can feel the heat released by putting the rubber band up to your lips. Relax the rubber band and the entropy decreases and there is a consequent absorption of energy—the rubber band feels cool. You might consider passing rubber bands out to each student for them to try on their own. It's a most interesting phenomenon.

Consider obtaining flash paper from a local magician's supply store. Discuss the chemistry of the flash paper, nitrocellulose, with your students before igniting it. Mention how it is that this same material was once used to make motion picture film. As the film would come close to the hot projector lamp, it had a tendency to catch fire. After a number of well-known movie theaters burnt to the ground in 1920's, there arose the tradition of "emergency exits".

29.5 Polymers Win in World War II
This section is a good example of the great impact chemistry has had on society. The polymers discussed in this section were developed "just in time" for World War II (as were the antibiotics discussed in Chapter 28). Nations who had greatest access to these polymers (and antibiotics) were at a great advantage. Note how it's the little things that can make all the difference—a big fancy World War II bomber is no good if there is no rubber available to make its tires. These "little things," therefore, are not so little!

Point out how it was that after World War II that plastics were quite revered. It was only several decades later that plastics began to take on the persona of being "cheap", "disposable" and "widely available". It's upon us now to change this persona. Plastics are now a vital resource and our supply of the petroleum used to make these materials is finite.

29.6 Attitudes About Plastics Have Changed
After a brief discussion on the virtues of recycling plastics, take the issue a step further by surveying the students on what they believe to be the top three problems/concerns currently faced by the human race. Human population growth is usually a popular choice, but it's not likely that it will be voted unanimously by students as the number one problem or concern facing us. The follow-up of showing them how most all other problems hinge on this one is not difficult.

There is cause for hope. Remarkable treatments for diseases such as AIDS have been developed and drug companies are doing what they can to provide these medicines to those who can't afford them. Chlorofluorocarbon concentrations are coming down. Many nations have established zero population growth and many developing nations have shown dramatic drops in their population growths. Air pollution control measures do work to give us cleaner air to breathe. Sustainable energy resource technologies are being embraced by developing nations. The list of optimistic notes goes on. Perhaps, most significant, however, is the integration occurring as more and more people from different nations become connected to one another by electronic media, telecommunications, and the worldwide web. Perhaps by these global communications, exploits of nations and peoples over other nations and peoples will diminish. The power of human voices speaking in unison is not to be underestimated. A major concern is that these voices are voices of both compassion and reason. We are not born with compassion or reason—these are traits that develop as we mature. As teachers, helping our students mature in these traits is perhaps our greatest service.

Chapter 29 Answers and Solutions

Key Terms and Matching Definitions

_ 3 _ addition polymer
_ 4 _ condensation polymer
_ 2 _ monomer
_ 1 _ polymer

Review Questions

1. Are monomers made of polymers or are polymers made of monomers?

   Polymers are made out of the joining of monomers.

2. Are all polymers made by humans?

   Not all polymers are made by humans. There are a multitude of naturally occurring polymers including the biopolymers found in living organisms, such as DNA.

3. What happens to the double bond of a monomer participating in the formation of an addition polymer?

   One of the bonds in the multiple bond of a monomer opens to form a new bond with a neighboring monomer molecule.

4. Which has more branching in its polymer chains: HDPE or LDPE?

   The low density polyethylene has more branching. This branching makes the polymer strands occupy a greater volume, which is why it is less dense.

5. Which has more chlorine atoms per polymer stand: polyvinyl chloride, or polyvinylidene chloride?

   The polyvinylidene chloride has twice as many chlorine atoms per polymer strand as compared to the polyvinyl choride.

6. Why is polyvinylidene chloride a stickier plastic than polyethylene?

   The large chlorine atoms in Saran wrap help it to stick to surfaces such as glass via induced dipole molecular attractions that are absent in polyethylene.

7. What is released in the formation of a condensation polymer?

   Upon formation of a condensation polymer, a small molecule (i.e., water or hydrochloric acid) is released from each monomer.

8. What is a copolymer?

   A copolymer is a polymer composed of two or more different monomers.

9. What is a thermoset polymer?

A thermoset polymer is a polymer that cannot be remelted or reshaped after it has been formed. Thermoset polymers are hard plastics that are good for countertops and durable dishes.

10. How did Schobein discover nitrocellulose?

Schobein discovered nitrocellulose in 1846 when he spilled nitric acid and sulfuric acid on the floor and wiped it up with a cotton rag.

11. What chemical is used to make celluloid a workable material?

Camphor is added to collodion to make celluloid a workable material.

12. What is one of the major drawbacks of celluloid?

Celluloid is highly flammable.

13. Who provided Baekeland with the financial resources to develop Bakelite?

Baekeland sold his photographic paper to Eastman, the founder of the Kodak camera, which allowed him enough money to work on the development of Bakelite.

14. What prompted Brandenberger to seek a way to make thin sheets of viscose?

Brandenberger was upset that attendants at a restaurant had to throw away fine linens and he wanted a way to make them easy to wipe off.

15. How did chemists transform cellophane into a vaporproof wrap?

DuPont added small amounts of nitrocellulose and wax to make cellophane moisture proof.

16. What was one of the prime motivations for the Japanese to invade Malaysia at the beginning of World War II?

Malaysia supplied the U.S. with 90% of its rubber. Without rubber the U.S. would not have tires for its vehicles.

17. What polymer proved useful in the development of radar equipment lightweight enough to be carried on airplanes?

Polyethylene was used to carry radar equipment because it was light and an electrical insulator.

18. What role did Teflon play in World War II?

Teflon was used to line the valves and ducts of an apparatus they were building to make nuclear weapons.

19. What is an environmental drawback of plastics?

An environmental drawback of plastics is that they are not biodegradable. They can, however, be recycled. This is an advantage because creating plastic-ware from recycled plastic requires less energy and resources than does creating plastic-ware from petroleum.

20. What raw material are plastic made from?

The raw material used to make plastics today is petroleum.

Solutions to Chapter 29 Exercises

1. Would you expect polypropylene to be denser or less dense than low-density polyethylene? Why?

   Polypropylene consists of a polyethylene backbone with methyl groups attached to every other carbon atom. This side group interferes with the close packing that could otherwise occur among the molecules. As a consequence, we find that polypropylene is actually less dense than is polyethylene—even low-density polyethylene.

2. Many polymers emit toxic fumes when burning. Which polymer in Table 29.1 produces hydrogen cyanide, HCN? Which two produce toxic hydrogen chloride, HCl, gas?

   The combustion of polyacrylonitrile produces hydrogen cyanide. Any of the chlorine containing polymers will produce hydrogen chloride upon combustion. This would include polyvinyl chloride and polyvinylidene chloride.

3. One solution to the problem of our overflowing landfills is to burn plastic objects instead of burying them. What would be some of the advantages and disadvantages of this practice?

   The plastics, along with other combustible trash, could be burned at a power plant for the generation of electric energy. As discussed in the previous exercise, however, the burning of some plastics produce toxic chemicals, such as hydrogen cyanide, or hydrogen chloride. All polymers when burned produce carbon dioxide, which is harmful in that it contributes to global warming. The technology is available, however, to minimize these emissions. Perhaps, though, the ultimate solution is to recycle the plastics. Don't forget that plastics are presently derived from fossil fuels, which are one of nature's finite resources.

4. Which would you expect to be more viscous, a polymer made of long molecular strands or one made of short molecular stands? Why?

   A polymer made of long chains is likely to be more viscous because of the tendency of longer chains to get tangled among themselves.

5. Hydrocarbons release a lot of energy when ignited. Where does this energy come from?

   Ultimately, this is the energy that was captured from the sun by photosynthetic plants that turned into fossil fuels after decaying under anaerobic conditions.

6. What type of polymer would be best to use in the manufacture of stain-resistant carpets?

   A fluorine containing polymer such as Teflon.

7. As noted in the Concept Check of Section 29.3, the compound 6-aminohexanoic acid is used to make the condensation polymer nylon-6. Polymerization is not always successful, however, because of a competing reaction. What is this reaction? Would polymerization be more likely in a dilute solution of this monomer or in a concentrated solution? Why?

   The carboxylic acid side of the molecule reacts not with a nitrogen atom from a neighboring molecule, but with the nitrogen atom within the same molecule to form the following cyclic structure:

The greater the concentration of reactants, the greater chance of them colliding with each other. Therefore, in order to favor the carboxylic acid reacting with a nitrogen from a neighboring molecule, it works to increase the number of those neighboring molecules, which is what happens when the concentration of this monomer is increased. Polymerization, therefore, is more favored in a concentrated solution than it is in a dilute solution.

8. Why does a Styrofoam cup insulate better than a transparent plastic cup, even though they are both made of the same material, which is polystyrene?

The air pockets that are found within the Styrofoam are what serve to insulate, not the polystyrene of which the Styrofoam cup is made.

9. What role did chance discovery play in the history of polymers? Cite some examples.

As with any scientific endeavor, chance discovery played an important role in the development of polymers. In all cases, however, there was a scientist with an open and innovative mind that was ready to recognize and take advantage of a chance observation. Charles Goodyear accidentally tipped sulfur into heated natural rubber to discover vulcanized rubber. Christian Schobein inadvertently wiped up a nitric acid spill with a cotton rag to discover nitrocellulose. Jaque Brandenberger thought of cellophane as he observed the accidental stains on tablecloths. Teflon was discovered upon the unexpected disappearance of a chemical in a gas cylinder that Roy Plunkett was compelled to saw in half.

10. What is the difference between collodion and celluloid?

Both collodion and celluloid are forms of nitrocellulose. They differ in that celluloid is nitrocellulose that has been made more moldable by the addition of camphor.

11. What is the chemical difference between celluloid and cellophane?

Celluloid and cellophane are both derived from cellulose. The celluloid, however, has nitrate groups where each hydroxyl group appears in cellulose. Cellophane has the same chemical composition of cellulose, but it has been transformed to a film by both chemical and mechanical processing.

12. Why does a freshly cut Ping-Pong ball smell of camphor?

Because it is made using camphor.

13. Why are Ping-Pong balls so highly flammable?

They are made of nitrocellulose, which is the same highly combustible material used to make gun cotton.

14. How are the chemical structures of Bakelite and Melmac similar to each other? How are they different?

Both Melmac and Bakelite are thermoset polymers consisting of a three-dimensional network of cross-linking polymers. Although their structures are similar, they differ greatly in their chemical compositions. Melmac contains a high proportion of nitrogen atoms and is made from the combination of melamine and formaldehyde. Bakelite has no nitrogen atoms is made from the combination of phenol and formaldehyde.

15. List these plastics in order of the year in which they were developed: cellophane, celluloid, collodion, nylon, parkesine, PVC, Teflon, viscose yarn.

Collodion, Parkesine, Celluloid, Viscose Yarn, Cellophane, PVC, Nylon, Teflon.

30 Minerals And Their Formation

30.1 Minerals Can Be Identified by Their Properties
      Crystal Form Expresses the Arrangement Of Atoms in a Mineral
      | Crystal Power |
      Hardness is the Resistance of a Mineral To Scratching
      Cleavage And Fracture Are Ways in Which Minerals Break
      | Hands-On-Physical Science: Salt Crystals |
      Luster Is the Appearance of a Mineral's Surface in Reflected Light
      A Mineral's Color may Vary, but it's Streak Is Always the Same
      Specific Gravity Is a Ratio of Densities
      Chemical Properties – The Taste Test And The Acid Test
      | Asbestos: Friend and Foe |
30.2 Minerals That Form Rock Fall into Five Main Groups
      Silicates Make up Nearly Ninety Percent of the Earth's Crust
      Oxides Are Important Ore Minerals
      Carbonate Minerals Make Limestone
      Sulfides And Sulfates Are Also Important Ore Minerals
30.3 On The Way To Rocks
      Minerals and Rock Formed from Magma
          Melting
          Crystallization
      Minerals and Rock Formed from a Water Solution
      Minerals—The Link To Rocks

Learning Objectives
After studying Chapter 30, students will be able to:
• Define a mineral.
• Describe the six physical and two chemical properties used to identify minerals.
• Describe that only about two dozen of the thousands of minerals are common.
• State the relationship between minerals and rocks.
• Name the five main mineral groups.
• Describe how materials valuable to modern society come from minerals.
• Define magma and state how types of magma are classified.
• Describe partial melting relative to the different types of magma and igneous rock.
• State how crystallization forms different minerals.

Possible Misconceptions to Correct
• **Not so!** Specific gravity is the same as density.
• **Not so!** All asbestos is bad.
• **Not so!** Crystals have unique energies that promote healing.
• **Not so!** A single mineral always has the same color.

This chapter introduces the subject of Earth Science. Some instructors have found that it is worthwhile to take a few minutes to allow students to discuss what aspects of Earth Science are of interest to them. Many students become interested in Earth Science because of their love for the outdoors or concern for the environment. The study of minerals is based on methods drawn from mineralogy, geology, chemistry, and physics, and the first step in their study requires the precise identification of their components — the minerals present in them.

This chapter has an emphasis on definitions and description of processes. The specialized vocabulary may mean some memory work. We suggest that memorization be kept to a minimum (open book exams will prompt this). More important than the introduced basic vocabulary, is the appreciation of the more interesting aspects of minerals. Nurturing a wide overview should not be hampered by definitions and memorization. How you till your soil determines where student effort is placed.

Instill in your students that minerals or the products of minerals can be found just about everywhere. In fact, minerals have contributed greatly to our present technologic culture—practically every manufactured product contains materials obtained from minerals. The world of human-made articles depends on the elements obtained from minerals. Ask your students to think of some common articles made up of minerals, ask them to list the articles. Suggest a survey of their immediate surroundings—the classroom, home, or work place. Have a class discussion about the common articles they have found.

In the **Explorations Practice Book**:
• Chemical Structure and Formulas of Minerals

In the **Next-Time Questions Book**:
• Difference between a rock and a mineral
• Mineral Production

In the **Lab Manual**:
• Crystal Growth
• What's that Mineral?

Overhead Transparencies available for :
Figures 30.4 and 30.11

SUGGESTED PRESENTATION

Begin by citing how physical science has been taught thus far by considering ideal cases. In the physics of falling objects, the air was neglected; in the chemistry of molecular interactions, molecules were treated in isolation, which is seldom the case in the real world. And now we study rocks and the minerals that compose them. We see minerals in collections and in textbook photographs as individual crystals, showing all of the form, luster, and other properties we will study. But most minerals are actually irregular blobs in rocks. Onward!

Remind students that recall of definitions learned in physics and chemistry is assumed, e.g. element and a compound, solid, liquid and gas, acid and base, density, pressure, heat and hydraulics.

30.1 Minerals Can Be Identified by Their Properties
Atoms make up molecules; minerals make up rocks. Formation of minerals depends on the pressure and temperature at the time of formation. Hence minerals can be indicators of conditions at the time and place of origin.

Key concepts are: The difference between a rock and a mineral is somewhat like that between a compound and an element, but more like the difference between a mixed and a pure substance. Minerals are commonly thought of as metals: the single elements gold, silver, lead, copper, zinc and aluminum. Most minerals, however, are compounds of different elements. When a mineral is considered to be of economic value, a rock rich in that mineral is considered to be an ore body.

Composition of a mineral depends on what's available at the time of formation. Greatest effect of composition on physical properties is ion size, which affects packing and so affects structure.

Packing of atoms in a mineral depends on the relative size of atoms. Closer packing leads to stronger bonds which influence the physical properties of the mineral.

Overall **charge** must be zero. For example, halite: Na^{+1} and Cl^{-1} must be combined 1:1. Fluorite: Ca^{+2} and F^{-1} must be combined 1:2.

Rate of mineral growth depends on how often the right atom can get to a spot where it is likely to stay. This depends on concentration and mobility of components—viscosity and flow restriction.

Instructors have saved time, kept it simple, and involved students in hands-on activities by using a few readily available materials; e.g. pieces of chalk, candy, china, coal, glass, metal, wood, and so on. Involving students encourages their imagination and creativity, but avoid busy work.

Cleavage and Fracture
Involve your students in the discussion of cleavage and fracture by doing the Hands-On Physical Science Exploration with Salt Crystals—large grain sea salt crystals work great. The calcite demonstration is also a must!

DEMONSTRATION: Check the cleavage properties of calcite, which exhibits perfect cleavage in three directions. Align a screwdriver in direction of a cleavage plane and hit with a hammer. The calcite should break into two pieces, each piece displaying rhombohedral cleavage planes. Then wrap one piece of calcite in cloth or newspaper. Hit with hammer. Unwrap and show the numerous pieces each displaying the rhombohedral cleavage planes. Be careful not to hit the calcite too hard, for calcite will crumble.

DEMONSTRATION: Do you know how pencils are made? A box of pencils can show cleavage by splitting, fracture by breaking the wood splines and graphite core, hardness by the label (2B, 4H, etc.).

Crystal **shape** reflects internal structure—this can provide a link to the Chemistry section.

CHECK QUESTION: In how many ways can we tell a genuine diamond from an imitation? [By determining cleavage, hardness, density, and any of the many physical and chemical properties].

Specific Gravity
While on the subject of precious minerals, distinguish between 10 and 24 karat gold. The proportion of pure gold in an alloy is thus: Pure gold is 24 karat; 10 karat is 10/24 pure, or 10 parts pure gold by weight and 14 parts of other metals.

When running water is available, challenge a student to demonstrate the concept behind panning for gold using a pie-tin, some sand, some mud, some iron filings, some bits of lead cut from a fishing sinker or a wheel balancing lead slug.

Asbestos: Friend and Foe
The box on Asbestos merits elaboration. Humans have been ingesting asbestos since time zero. It has always been in the air and water, the amounts being little different today than

centuries ago. The prevalent form of asbestos, relatively harmless chrysotile, is tarred with association to the dangerous amphibole crocidolite. The two minerals differ in composition, color, shape, solubility, and persistence in human tissue. Chrysotile, $Mg_6Si_4O_{10}(OH)_8$, is a white serpentine mineral that tends to be soluble and disappears in tissue. Crocidolite, $Na_2(Fe^{3+})_2(Fe^{2+})_3SiO_{22}(OH)_2$, is blue in color, is relatively insoluble, and persists in tissue. Only about 5% of the asbestos in place in the United States is crocidolite. Much of North American asbestos comes from chrysotile mines in Quebec, which have been operating since before 1900 and have produced about 40 million tons of chrysotile. Needless to say, lax mining practices resulted in large amounts of chrysotile dust in the surrounding air. Wives of miners who lived near the mines were heavily exposed. But four epidemiological studies of Quebec chrysotile mining localities show that lifelong exposure of women to dust from nearby mines caused no statistically significant excesses in asbestos related disease. The panic to remove all types of asbestos reflects the absence of science. A multibillion dollar program is in full swing, without starting with an accurate assessment of the problem. (Check the Yellow Pages for the alarmingly large numbers of lawyers in the asbestos claim business.) More about this in the March 1990 *Science* editorial, "The Asbestos Removal Fiasco", October 1995 *Environmental Geology* article "The Schoolroom Asbestos Abatement Program" and July 1997 *Scientific American* article "Asbestos Revisited".

30.2 Minerals That Form Rock Fall into Five Main Groups

Begin this Section by referring to Table 30.4 and the Periodic Table of Elements in the Chemistry section. For example, are you going to refer to silicates, oxides, carbonates, sulfides, and sulfates primarily by name, or primarily by formula, or by both? Formulas can be very complicated.

Refer back to the chapters in chemistry and the different bonding mechanisms of the chemical elements. Illustrate that the internal arrangement of atoms in a mineral is determined by the charges on the atoms and more importantly by the size of the atoms involved. The atoms need to fit with one another in order to form a stable bond.

The two most abundant elements, oxygen and silicon, combine with other cations to form the most common mineral group, the silicates. The silicon-oxygen (SiO_4) tetrahedron is the common building block of the silicates. It has four oxygen atoms (O^{2}) with a single silicon atom (Si^{4+}) at the center. The tetrahedron has an excess charge of -4 and is not stable. To satisfy the charges, the tetrahedron acts as a simple anion (-) and forms a bond to a cation (+). Another way to satisfy the negative oxygen charge is by polymerization, the linking of tetrahedra to form chains, sheets, and various network patterns.

> CHECK QUESTION: If a particular mineral has a consistent shape, why don't all crystals of a given mineral look the same? [Different growth rates may be in different directions. Many crystals run out of room to grow, and fill whatever space is available. Well-formed crystals develop only when space is available, OR when a particular mineral's "crystallizing power" is much greater than the surrounding minerals (e.g. garnets surrounded by muscovite in a schist).]

Most silicate minerals form when molten rock cools. Thus with minor exceptions, all the igneous rock forming minerals are silicates. In addition, some silicate minerals may represent the weathered products of pre-existing silicate minerals. Still other silicate minerals are formed under the extreme pressures associated with metamorphism. Silicate minerals are divided into two groups based on the presence or absence of iron. Minerals containing iron and/or magnesium in their structure are referred to as ferromagnesium silicates, whereas minerals with an absence of iron and/or magnesium are simply referred to as non-ferromagnesium silicates. To help in lecture and lab work the following information is provided. This information is not included in the text — too much information may lead to overload.

Ferromagnesian Silicates (the dark-colored minerals)

Olivine and garnet are the two chief groups of silicates built of isolated tetrahedra. Olivine, predominant in basaltic rocks of the oceanic crust and rocks of the upper mantle, is olive-green to yellowish brown in color, has a glassy luster, and a conchoidal fracture. Garnet, characteristically found in metamorphic rocks of the continental crust, is most often brown to deep red in color. Both have a glassy luster and conchoidal fracture.

Pyroxenes and amphiboles are silicates made of continuous chains of silicate tetrahedra. Pyroxenes are built from single chains; amphiboles are built of double chains. Most are dark green to black in color and have good cleavage parallel to the silicate chain. The bonds are weaker across these surfaces than the bond between silicon and oxygen. The two differ in cleavage angle, pyroxenes cleave at a 90° angle, and amphiboles at 60° and 120° angles. Pyroxene is dominant in dark colored igneous rocks formed by basaltic lavas and intrusives. Pyroxene commonly alters to amphibole during late stages of crystallization of igneous rocks and during metamorphism.

Biotite, a member of the mica family, has a sheet-like silicate tetrahedra as a basic building unit. The bond between the sheets is weaker than the bond holding the tetrahedra together within the sheet. Hence biotite, like other micas, has excellent cleavage in one direction. Biotite is black due to its iron content, and occurs in a variety of geologic environments. Biotite is a characteristic mineral in igneous rocks such as granite and granitic pegmatites.

Non-ferromagnesian Silicates (the light-colored minerals)

Muscovite, also a member of the mica family, has the same sheet-like structure of biotite, but has a lighter color. Muscovite occurs in a variety of geologic environments from igneous, metamorphic, and sedimentary. It is a common-to-abundant mineral in almost every type of metamorphic schist.

Quartz is the only mineral consisting entirely of silicon and oxygen. Quartz belongs to a network in which all the oxygen atoms in each SiO_4 tetrahedron are shared with neighboring tetrahedra, producing a stable, strongly bonded structure. As a result, quartz is hard, resistant to weathering, and displays no cleavage—quartz has a conchoidal fracture. Generally colorless unless affected by impurities, quartz characteristically forms six sided, hexagonal, crystals. Quartz is a common and abundant mineral occurring in a great variety of geological environments. It is present in many igneous and metamorphic rocks where it is a major constituent of granitic pegmatites. In sedimentary rocks, quartz is the major constituent of sandstone.

Feldspar is the most common mineral in the Earth's crust. It accounts for about 60 percent of all minerals in the continental crust, and together with quartz comprises about 75 percent of the volume of the continental crust. The structure of feldspar is very similar to the shared oxygen network found in quartz, except that some silicon atoms are replaced by aluminum atoms. Feldspars are relatively hard, have two planes of cleavage meeting at 90° angles, and vary in composition. There are two types of feldspars, alkali-feldspars ($KAlSi_3O_8$ to $NaAlSi_3O_8$) and plagioclase-feldspars ($NaAlSi_3O_8$ to $CaAlSi_3O_8$). Members of both of these groups are given individual names. Most alkali-feldspars are light in color (for example the alkali-feldspar orthoclase is usually light to salmon pink in color). Most plagioclase feldspars range in color from white to gray. The only sure way to distinguish between the two types of feldspars is by looking for parallel lines, striations, on the cleavage faces. Only plagioclase feldspar has striations. As rock-forming minerals, feldspars are widely distributed and very abundant. They are found in igneous, metamorphic, and, more rarely sedimentary rocks.

30.3 On The Way to Rocks
The Lab on Crystal Growth would be a great way to introduce the material in this section. The lab can be done by student groups, or if need be, as an instructor demonstration. The lab on Mineral Identifcation can then conclude the chapter and get students ready for the lab on Rock Identification.

In Conclusion:
For your own information, the USGS compiles a list of *Selected references on rocks, minerals, and gemstones* Write to:

U.S. Geological Survey
Geologic Inquiries Group
907 National Center
Reston, VA 22092
(703) 648-4383

or use the following Web sites:

http://www.usgs.gov/education

http://minerals.usgs.gov/

The USGS provides selected guides for rockhounds and hobbyists, general references for all ages, elementary school to adult, and periodicals.

An identification book on rocks and minerals is very helpful for this chapter. I like *Simon & Schusters Guide To Rocks and Minerals*. Another very interesting book is *The Practical Geologist* by Dougal Dixon. This book contains helpful hints for things to do.

Chapter 30 Answers and Solutions

Key Terms and Matching Definitions

_12__ chemical sediments
__5__ cleavage
__2__ crystal form
_10__ crystallization
__6__ fracture
__7__ luster
_13__ magma
__1__ mineral
__4__ Mohs scale of hardness
_11__ partial melting
__3__ polymorphs
__9__ specific gravity
__8__ streak

Review Questions

1. What is a mineral?
    A mineral is a naturally formed, inorganic, crystalline solid composed of an ordered array of atoms and having a specific chemical composition.

2. What physical properties are used in the identification of minerals?
    The physical properties used to identify minerals include crystal form, hardness, cleavage, luster, color, streak, and specific gravity.

3. All minerals are defined by an orderly internal arrangement of their atoms—the crystal form. Yet, most mineral samples do not display their crystal form. Why not?
    Well-shaped crystals are rare in nature because minerals typically grow in cramped spaces.

4. What are two of the classifications for mineral luster?
    Two of the classifications are: vitreous—bright, glassy and adamantine—diamond-like, brilliant. There are others, see Table 30.2.

5. Although color is an obvious feature of a mineral, it is not a very reliable means of identification. Why not?
    Although some minerals may have a distinctive color, most minerals occur in a variety of colors due to chemical impurities, and many minerals are colorless. The streak, the color of a mineral in its powdered form, is a better tool for mineral identification as the color of the streak is constant.

6. Will the mineral topaz scratch quartz, or will quartz scratch topaz? Why?
    Look at Mohs Scale of Hardness and you will see that topaz (H=8) will scratch quartz (H=7).

7. The minerals calcite, halite, and gypsum are all nonmetallic, light and softer than glass, and all have three directions of cleavage. In what ways can they be distinguished from one another?
    Let's use the process of elimination. Halite has a salty taste, and can be distinguished from calcite and gypsum by a simple taste test. Calcite, a carbonate mineral, will fizz when exposed to HCl. If the mineral does not taste salty, and does not fizz when exposed to HCl, the mineral is most likely gypsum.

8. Silver has a density of 10.5 g/cm³. What is its specific gravity?

The specific gravity of silver is 10.5.

9. What is the relationship of density to specific gravity?
Density is a ratio—weight/volume; how heavy a mineral is for its size. Specific gravity is a ratio of densities—density of a substance/ density of water. Specific gravity has the same numerical value as density, without units.

10. What is the most abundant element in the Earth's crust? What is the second most abundant element?
Oxygen accounts for 46.60 percent of the Earth's crust; thus it is the most abundant element. After oxygen, the second most abundant element in the Earth's crust is silicon (27.72 percent by mass).

11. What is the most abundant mineral in the Earth's crust? What is the second most abundant mineral?
Feldspars are the most common and abundant minerals. Quartz is the second most common mineral.

12. Name the five most common mineral groups found in most rocks.
The silicates, oxides, carbonates, sulfides, and sulfates.

13. What is meant by *partial melting*?
Partial melting is, as the name implies, incomplete melting in which different minerals with their different melting points result in magmas of different compositions.

14. How are partial melting and crystallization similar?
In partial melting, solid minerals melt to form magma. In crystallization, solid crystals form out of a liquid mixture. The processes are similar but occur in the reverse order. For partial melting, the magma generated is made up only from those minerals that have melted, the ones having the lowest melting points—which means those having a high silicon content. For crystallization, minerals that have the highest melting points—which means those that have the lowest silicon content—crystallize first, followed by minerals with lower melting points (those containing larger amounts of silicon).

15. If a rock contains mineral A and mineral B, which would melt first, mineral A with 30% silicon, or mineral B with 25% silicon?
Mineral A because high silicon-content minerals are the first to melt.

16. What are three common chemical sediments?
Calcite, gypsum, and halite.

17. When water evaporates from a body of water, what type of sediment is left behind?
Just like the name implies, evaporation leads to evaporites—minerals and rocks that are precipitated when a restricted body of seawater or the water of a saline lake evaporates. (Examples of evaporites include gypsum, anhydrite, and halite.)

18. What is the most common chemical sediment?
Carbonates.

19. What is the most abundant carbonate rock?
Limestone is the most abundant carbonate rock.

20. How are most of the carbonate minerals and rocks formed?
Carbonates are minerals and rocks composed mostly of calcite, $CaCO_3$, or dolomite, $CaMg(CO_3)_2$. Most carbonates are formed biologically as a result of shell growth.

Some, such as cave dripstones, are an example of calcium carbonate precipitating inorganically from dripping water.

Solutions to Chapter 30 Exercises

1. Clearly distinguish between physical and chemical properties, and give examples of each.
    The properties of minerals are determined by their compositions and their crystal structure. Physical properties include crystal shape, luster, color and streak, specific gravity, hardness, and cleavage and fracture. Chemical properties are less obvious and may require some knowledge and or expensive equipment. Simple chemical tests include reaction to acid (dilute HCl) and the taste test for halite.

2. Describe the difference between a mineral and an element.
    An element is a material that cannot be decomposed into other substances except by radioactive decay. Although a few minerals are composed of single elements, the majority of minerals are composed of a combination of elements.

3. Why is color not always the best way to identify a mineral?
    Chemical impurities affect color. Most minerals contain such impurities.

4. What does a colorless streak tell you about a mineral?
    That the mineral has a nonmetallic luster.

5. What makes gold so soft (easily scratched) while quartz and diamond are so much harder?
    Small atoms can pack closer together than large atoms because their electrons are closer to their nucleus. Closely packed atoms have a smaller distance between one another, and thus form stronger bonds than do minerals in which the atoms are not so closely packed. Gold, because of its large atomic size, is relatively soft (hardness less than 3), and diamond, with its small carbon atoms and tightly packed structure, is relatively hard (hardness = 10).

6. Imagine that we have a liquid with a specific gravity of 3.5. Knowing that objects of higher specific gravity will sink in the liquid, will a piece of quartz sink or float in the liquid? How about a piece of chromite?
    The quartz, specific gravity of 2.65, will float. The chromite, specific gravity of 4.6, will sink.

7. Does the fact that carbon dioxide is given off in the fizz when HCl touches a mineral mean that the mineral contains carbon?
    Yes, all carbonate minerals contain carbon. The carbon in the CO_2 comes from the carbonate mineral.

8. Is cleavage the same as crystal form? Why or why not?
    No, the planar surfaces we see in cleavage are where a mineral breaks due to a weakness in crystal structure or bond strength. The planar surfaces in a crystal form are the external shape from the crystals internal arrangement of atoms.

9. Silicon is essential for the computer industry in making microchips. Can silicon be mined directly from the Earth?
    Remember, the tendency of silicon to bond with oxygen is so strong that silicon is never found in nature as a pure element; it is always combined with oxygen.

10. What mineral groups provide most of the ore that we, as a society, need?
    The sulfides and oxides make up the majority of ore minerals.

11. What two minerals make up most of the sand in the world?
Feldspar is the most common and abundant mineral, and quartz is the second most common mineral. Both minerals are relatively hard, so they make up most of the world's sand deposits.

12. What class of minerals does Galena (PbS) belong to?
Galena is a sulfide.

13. What class of minerals does Anglesite (PbSO$_4$) belong to?
Anglesite is a sulfate.

14. Is it possible for crystallization to enrich a magma in more than just silicon?
Yes. Just as minerals with lower melting temperatures contain more silicon than higher melting-temperature minerals, there are other elements that are more prevalent in minerals with lower melting temperatures.

15. If high silicon-content magma is the last to cool, why aren't high silicon rocks the last to melt?
Remember, partial melting is the reverse order of crystallization. Minerals that have the highest melting points (those that have the lowest silicon content) are the last to melt and the first to crystallize. Minerals with lower melting points (those containing larger amounts of silicon) are the first to melt and the last to crystallize.

16. Why is halite the last mineral to precipitate from evaporating seawater?
As evaporation proceeds, the minerals that are the most difficult to dissolve precipitate first, followed by the minerals that dissolve more easily. Halite dissolves easily and is thus the last mineral to precipitate.

17. Would you expect to find any fossils in limestone? Why or why not?
Yes, limestone is formed predominantly from the accumulation of dead sea organisms.

18. How do chemical sediments produce rock? Name two rock types that form by chemical sedimentation.
Chemical sedimentary rocks are formed from the precipitation of minerals from a solution, usually water. The process can occur directly, as a result of inorganic processes, or indirectly, as a result of a biochemical reaction. Carbonates are the best example of rocks formed by biochemical reactions, whereas evaporites are good examples of rocks formed by inorganic processes.

19. Why is asbestos in drinking water not particularly harmful to humans, whereas asbestos particles in air is very harmful?
Ingesting asbestos is primarily harmful to the lungs, not to the stomach and intestines. Furthermore, harm depends on the type of asbestos. Whereas the crocidolite variety, blue in color, is harmful, the more abundant white chrysotile asbestos is not. This is the kind found in drinking water. Data from the EPA show that in a liter of drinking water there are often millions of fibers of chrysotile asbestos—deemed safe to drink.

20. Make an argument that the removal of asbestos products such as ceiling tile and pipe coverings, may be more hazardous to humans than simply covering them up.
Chrysotile, is generally not harmful to humans. Left undisturbed, chrysotile fibers typically occur in air at concentrations of 0.001 fibers per cubic centimeter. After a removal process, however, chrysotile fiber content in the air increases to about 40 fibers per cubic centimeter—a 40,000 times increase!

31 Rocks

Learning Objectives

After studying Chapter 31, students will be able to:
- Describe the three main groups of rocks.
- Describe the physical and chemical conditions that give rise to different igneous rocks.
- Describe how sedimentary rocks offer clues to geologic history.
- Describe the importance of fossils.
- Describe the physical and chemical conditions that give rise to different metamorphic rocks.
- Differentiate between two kinds of volcanoes: one kind with violent eruptions producing steep slopes and the other kind with voluminous lava flows producing gentle slopes.
- Describe how rocks are never truly destroyed, but are part of the *Rock Cycle*.

Possible Misconceptions to Correct

- **Not so!** Magma flows from volcanoes.
- **Not so!** Sedimentary rocks are formed solely from sediment grains.
- **Not so!** Every pre-existing life form has left fossils.
- **Not so!** Metamorphic rocks are the end of the rock cycle.
- **Not so!** Crystallization and recrystallization are synonymous.

In the **Explorations Practice Book:**
- The Rock Cycle
- Igneous Rock Differentiation: How to Make Granite

In the **Next-Time Questions Book:**
- Petroleum geologists

Overhead Transparencies available for:
Figures 31.7 and 31.19

In the **Lab Manual**:
- What's that Rock?
- Rock Hunt

SUGGESTED PRESENTATION

31.1 Rocks Are Divided Into Three Main Groups
Point out that the igneous, metamorphic and sedimentary rock classifications are not mutually exclusive, because, over long periods of time, the same material may be subjected repeatedly to all the different processes. Refer students to the plate tectonic application of the rock cycle.

31.2 Igneous Rocks Form When Magma Cools
This is a good place to show *Fire Under the Sea*. Remind students that the key concepts of composition, structure, and process of formation are identical to those introduced in the physics and chemistry parts of this text. Students often have a way of mistakenly thinking that, because each scientific discipline has its own vocabulary and area of concern, science courses have little in common. This not only makes learning more difficult, but also may prevent students from enjoying the beauty and majesty of science as a single universe of knowledge and process.

Six minerals make up the great bulk of all igneous rocks—the minerals are quartz, feldspars, micas, amphiboles, pyroxenes, and olivine. Therefore, the chemical elements contained in these minerals are the principal chemical elements in magmas. They are Si, Al, Ca, Na, K, Fe, Mg, H, and O. With O as the most abundant anion, we express the compositional variations in terms of oxides with SiO_2 as the most abundant oxide for controlling the properties of magma. In a general sense, there are three compositionally distinct types of magma. The first type, basaltic, contains 50% SiO_2, the second type, andesitic, about 60%. The third type, rhyolitic, referred to in the text as granitic to avoid introducing extra terms, contains about 70% SiO_2. Of all igneous rocks in the crust (oceanic and continental combined) approximately 80% forms from basaltic magma, 10% from andesitic magma, and 10% from granitic magma.

Of note for the water content of the different magmas: From the text, water content of a rock affects its melting point. Rocks with a high water content have a lower melting point because water dissolves in the magma. Rocks with a low water content have a higher melting point and therefore require higher temperatures to melt.

CHECK QUESTION: Can buildings that are constructed of granite be called fireproof? Why or why not? [No. Although granite will not ignite like wood, granite has a high water content. So if heat steams away the moisture, the stone may weaken and crumble.

NEXT-TIME QUESTION: When a volcano erupts under the sea, does all the lava freeze instantly when it hits the sea water. If not, why not? [Everything we learned about latent heat, thermal conductivity and convection applies for both the water and the rock. The tremendous changes in location and temperature of a lot of rock and water take a lot of time!]

31.3 Sedimentary Rocks Blanket Most Of The Earth's Surface
An interesting thing about sediment is that it takes time for grains in water to settle. In general, smaller grains settle slower; larger grains settle faster; grains don't settle when water moves fast. Relate the settling of grain particles to inertia. Larger grains have more

mass and thus more inertia; larger grains are the first to settle out. Large grains get broken into small ones; small grains coalesce into big ones.

> DEMONSTRATION: An inexpensive small package of concrete mix consisting of cement, sand and gravel, and a pan can show interesting properties of a rock mix. A home owner doing a little patching of a wall may want to separate the gravel and have just sand and cement left. (This is known as a "neat" mix.) We can do this easily; no water required. Just cover the pan bottom with an inch or more of mix, and tap the pan sharply. Will the gravel go to the bottom, stay where it is, or go to the top, where it can easily be removed? Why? [Gravel goes to the top, due to mean density and sufficient impact.]

The process of weathering occurs by mechanical means, chemical means, or both together. The process of erosion is simply transportation of sediment.

The section on fossils is of interest to many students. Lectures on fossilization are better off as a hands-on approach. If you have samples of fossils let the students learn by observation.

31.4 Metamorphic Rocks are Changed Rocks
Metamorphic rocks are rocks that have been changed from their original state. Mechanical deformation by itself produces the least significant type of metamorphism. The general effect of mechanical deformation produces rocks that are flattened and elongated with a decrease in grain size. Recrystallization usually produces a change in mineral assemblage. The general effect of recrystallization produces rocks with an increase in grain size.

Once again the study of metamorphic rocks can be highlighted depending on your location. Students in Pennsylvania may know what a slate roof is like, and be interested in knowing that old-time blackboards were made of a big slice of slate. Billiard table tops were made that way too!

The vocabulary of metamorphic rock types and their characteristics is covered in the laboratory section on identification of rocks. Use your discretion as to its importance for text material. Students often learn better by hands-on experience.

31.5 The Rock Cycle, A Descriptive Key
Use OHT Figure 31.19. This section is a summary and review of this chapter. Should a situation arise when there is just not enough time available to cover all the material, careful reading of this section should give students the key concepts.

Chapter 31 Answers and Solutions

Key Terms and Matching Definitions

_10_ chemical weathering
_11_ erosion
__4_ extrusive rocks
__1_ igneous rocks
__5_ intrusive rocks
__6_ lava
_14_ mechanical deformation
__9_ mechanical weathering
__3_ metamorphic rocks
_12_ metamorphism
__8_ pluton
_13_ recrystallization
_15_ rock cycle
__2_ sedimentary rocks
__7_ volcano

Review Questions

1. Name the three major types of rocks, and describe the conditions of their origin.
    Igneous, sedimentary, and metamorphic. Igneous rocks are formed by the cooling and crystallization of magma. Sedimentary rocks are formed from weathered material (sediments) carried by water, wind, or ice. Metamorphic rocks are formed from preexisting rocks that are transformed by high temperature, high pressure, or both—without melting.

2. What are the most common igneous rocks and where do they generally occur?
    On the continents, the most common igneous rocks are granite and andesite. On the ocean floor, the most common igneous rock is basalt.

3. What percentage of the Earth's crust is composed of igneous rocks?
    About 95% of the Earth's crust is composed of igneous rock.

4. Where on the Earth's surface are lava flows most common?
    Lava flows are most common on the ocean floor.

5. What are the three major types of volcanoes?
    Shield volcanoes, cinder cones, and composite cones.

6. Which type of volcano produces the most violent eruptions? Which type produces the quietest eruptions?
    Composite volcanoes tend to erupt explosively because they usually have very gooey magmas and lavas.
    Shield volcanoes generally erupt more quietly due to a steady supply of very fluid basaltic lava.

7. What are three common types of plutons?
    Dikes, sills, and batholiths

8. Are the Sierra Nevada mountains presently losing or gaining height?
    Sierra Nevada mountains are presently gaining height with time because the upward push of the batholiths is faster than erosion can wear them down.

9. How does weathering produce sediment? Distinguish between weathering and erosion.
    Weathering breaks down and decomposes surface rock. Mechanical weathering physically breaks rocks into smaller and smaller pieces. Chemical weathering, which involves reactions with water, decomposes rock into smaller pieces. As rock is weathered, it erodes. Erosion is the process by which weathered rock particles are removed and transported away by water, wind, or ice.

10. What does roundness tell us about sediment grains?
    When sediment grains are first produced, they are normally quite angular and jagged. During transportation, especially by water, the grains are continuously chipped by impacts, which decreases their size and rounds off their sharp edges. Thus roundness can tell us the manner and relative distance sediment grains traveled.

11. Relate the shape and sorting of sand grains to the way they were probably transported.
    In general, poorly sorted, angular grains of various shapes imply a short transportation distance, whereas well-sorted, well-rounded grains imply a greater transportation distance. Glacial deposits, tend to be very poorly sorted and angular, whereas wind-blown deposits tend to be very well sorted and fine-grained.

12. What is a clastic sedimentary rock?
    A clastic sedimentary rock is composed of small fragments of preexisting rocks. Clastic sedimentary rocks are classified by grain size.

13. In what two ways does sediment turn into sedimentary rock?
    The transformation of sediments to sedimentary rock occurs in two ways—compaction and cementation. As the weight of overlying sediments presses down upon deeper layers, sediment grains are squeezed and compacted together. This compaction squeezes water out of the spaces between sediment particles. This water often contains in solution compounds such as silicon dioxide, calcite, and hematite. These compounds, which are chemically precipitated from solution, partially fill the pore spaces with mineral matter and thereby act as cementing agents.

14. What are the three most common clastic sedimentary rocks?
    The most common clastic sedimentary rocks are shale, composed of very fine particles too small to be visible with a magnifying hand lens, sandstone, composed of medium sized particles such as those found in typical beach sand, and conglomerate, composed of a variety of larger particles, ranging from pebbles to boulders.

15. What is a fossil? How are they used in the study of geology?
    Fossils are the remains of preexisting life forms. They are used to interpret the Earth's geologic past. They play an important role as time indicators and in the matching up of rocks from different places of similar age.

16. What is metamorphism? What causes metamorphism?
    Metamorphism occurs when preexisting rocks undergo a change. The agents of metamorphism are heat and pressure.

17. What are the two processes by which rock is changed?
    Recrystallization and mechanical deformation. (The first occurs when rocks subjected to high temperatures and pressures go through a change in mineral assemblage. Mechanical deformation, which may or may not involve elevated temperatures, occurs when a rock is subjected to stress.)

18. What patterns of alteration are characteristic of contact metamorphism?
    One of the most common changes is an increase in grain size due to recrystallization. The grain size is greatest at the contact, and decreases with distance from that point. The

water content of the rock also changes with distance from the contact. At the contact, where temperature is high, water content is low. So we find dry, high-temperature minerals such as garnet and pyroxene at the contact. Farther away, we find water-rich, low-temperature minerals such as muscovite and chlorite.

19. What changes are characteristic of regional metamorphism?
Deformation, as seen in folded and faulted rock layers in many mountain ranges. Also, distinctly foliated and layered textures and zonal sequences of minerals and textures.

20. List the different cycles of rock formation.
(a) Magma to igneous rock. (b) Igneous rock to metamorphic rock or sediment. (c) Sediment to sedimentary rock. (d) Sedimentary rock to metamorphic rock or sediment. (e) Metamorphic rock to magma or sediment.

Solutions to Chapter 31 Exercises

1. Name at least one other national park, besides Yellowstone National Park, that was formed by volcanic or plutonic activity.
Volcanic activity: Hawaii Volcanoes National Park, Hawaii; Haleakuala National Park, Hawaii; Crater Lake National Park, Oregon; Katmai National Park, Alaska; Lassen National Park, California; Mount Rainier National Park, Washington; Craters of the Moon National Monument, Idaho.
Plutonic activity: Yosemite National Park, California; Mount Rushmore National Park, South Dakota; Acadia National Park, Maine.

2. What type of rock is formed when magma rises slowly and solidifies before reaching the Earth's surface? Give an example.
Intrusive igneous rock. If the magma cuts across rock layers, the pluton is referred to as a dike. If the magma spreads out parallel to layering, the pluton is either a sill or a laccolith. The largest pluton is a batholith. Batholiths are generally formed by numerous intrusions over time. Basalt and granite, among others, are igneous rocks.

3. Where on the Earth's crust do we find the two most common igneous rocks, basalt and granite?
Although basalt can form on both the oceanic crust and continental crust, basalt is most common on the ocean floor. Granite is common on the continental crust.

4. Are the Hawaiian Islands primarily made up of igneous, sedimentary, or metamorphic rock?
The Hawaiian Islands are predominantly made up of igneous rock of volcanic origin.

5. Can metamorphic rocks exist on an island of purely volcanic origin? Explain.
Yes. In order for rock to become metamorphosed it needs to be subjected to heat and/or pressure. The heat source on a volcanic island lends itself to produce either contact metamorphism (rocks surrounding magmas are changed by the heat of the igneous body) or hydrothermal metamorphism (hot fluids that percolate through the rock, changing the rock).

6. What accounts for the differences in lava composition of the two volcanoes that have erupted in recent times, Mauna Loa in Hawaii, and Mount St. Helens in Washington?
Mauna Loa in Hawaii is formed from basaltic magma, which is very fluid. The fluidity allows gases to migrate upward and escape with relative ease. Basaltic eruptions therefore are not very explosive. The eruption of Mount St. Helens is a different story. Composite cone volcanoes are composed of thick, slow-moving magmas (andesitic magma). Such thickness impedes the upward migration of gases. The gases collect as bubbles and pockets that increase in size and pressure until they explode, ejecting lava and rock fragments from the volcano.

7. Can a sequence of plutonic rocks be both intrusive and extrusive ?
   Yes. Lava flows originate underground, and the lava is extrusive. The part of the rock sequence that fed the lava flow may cool and solidify underground, and would be called intrusive.

8. What types of minerals are clastic sedimentary rocks commonly made of?
   Clastic sedimentary rocks are composed primarily of quartz, feldspar, and clay minerals.

9. What general rock feature does a geologist look for in a sedimentary rock to determine the distance the rock has traveled from its place of origin?
   The smoothness of the grains that make up the rock indicates travel time, and hence, distance. If its grains are angular, then a short travel time is indicated. Small rounded grains indicate a longer travel time, and hence longer distance.

10. What feature of clastic sedimentary rock enables the flow of oil after it has been formed?
    Clastic sedimentary rock's connected pore spaces between individual sediment grains permits the movement of oil.

11. Of the rocks (a) granite (b) sandstone (c) limestone (d) halite, which is the first to weather in a wet (humid) climate? Which is the last to weather? Why.
    Halite (d) weathers first. It is composed of NaCl which dissolves easily in a humid environment. Granite (a) weathers last since it is very resistant to all types of mechanical and chemical breakdown.

12. Which type of rock is most sought by petroleum prospectors—igneous, sedimentary, or metamorphic? Why?
    Sedimentary rock. Petroleum formation begins with the accumulation of sediment from areas rich in plant and animal remains. As the buried organic-rich sediment is heated over a sufficient period of time, chemical changes take place that create oil. Under pressure of the overlying sediments the minute droplets are squeezed out of the source rocks and into overlying porous rocks that become reservoirs.

13. What kind of weathering is imposed on a rock when it is smashed into small pieces? When dissolved in acid?
    Rock smashed to pieces is a form of mechanical weathering. Subjecting a rock to acid is chemical weathering.

14. What type of rock is made of previously existing rock whose formation does not involve high temperature and pressure?
    Sediments, and then sedimentary rock, forms when the previously existing rock is subjected to forces of weathering and erosion.

15. What properties of slate make it good roofing material?
    The characteristic of slate that makes it good for roofing is its excellent rock cleavage. Also, the small crystal size helps make it watertight.

16. Name two mica minerals that can give a metamorphic rock its foliation.
    Muscovite and biotite.

17. How is foliation different than sedimentary layering?
    Foliation is the realignment of minerals so that they are perpendicular to the direction of compressive forces. Sedimentary layering is the laying down of sediments one on top of the other.

18. Can metamorphism, caused solely by elevated temperature occur without the presence of magma? Why or why not?
    Yes, by burial metamorphism. As rocks are buried they slowly heat up due to the geothermal gradient until they are in equilibrium with the temperatures surrounding

them. This process alters the mineralogy and appearance of the rock. So although metamorphism, both contact and regional, usually involves magma, burial metamorphism can also occur without the presence of magma. If buried deep enough, the mineralogy and appearance will also be affected by pressure.

19. Each of the following statements describes one or more characteristics of a particular metamorphic rock. For each statement, name the metamorphic rock being described.
    (a) Foliated rock derived from granite.
    (b) Hard, nonfoliated, single mineral rock, formed under high to moderate metamorphism.
    (c) Foliated rock possessing excellent rock cleavage. Generally used in making blackboards.
    (d) Nonfoliated rock composed of carbonate minerals.
    (e) Foliated rock containing about 50 percent platy minerals; named according to the major minerals in the rock.
    (a) Gneiss (b) Quartzite (c) Slate (d) Marble (e) Schist

20. Explain the different cycles of rock formation.
    Igneous rock is formed when the molten magma beneath the Earth's crust cools and crystallizes. Magma can crystallize into many different kinds of igneous rock. Sedimentary rock is the result of the decomposition and disintegration of igneous (or other) rocks by weathering and erosion. When sedimentary rock is buried deep within the Earth or is involved in mountain building, great pressures and heat can transform it into metamorphic rock. When subjected to still greater heat and pressure, metamorphic rock melts and turns to magma, which eventually solidifies as igneous rock to complete the rock cycle. The rock cycle varies in its routes.

32 The Architecture of the Earth

Learning Objectives
After studying Chapter 32, students will be able to:
• Describe the different types of seismic waves.
• Identify the Earth's different internal layers.
• State how the Earth's internal layers were discovered by the use of seismic waves.
• Describe the differences and relationship between the asthenosphere and the lithosphere and how they affect the Earth's surface features.
• Explain that heat-driven convection currents operate within the Earth.
• Describe the differences between oceanic and continental crust.
• Describe that motion in the outer core drives Earth's magnetic field.
• Describe the different types of faults and the forces that cause them.
• Describe how and why earthquakes occur and the scales used to measure their intensity and magnitude.

Possible Misconceptions to Correct
• **Not so!** The Earth has three distinctly uniform layers—the crust, the mantle, and the core.
• **Not so!** The Earth's interior is molten.
• **Not so!** The crustal surface is uniformly thick.
• **Not so!** The Earth's crust rides on the mantle.

Demonstration Equipment
• Throw rug
• Foam rubber pad

In the Explorations Practice Book:
• Faults
• Structural Geology

In the Next-Time Questions Book:
• Hot Spring
• Radioactive Granite

In the Lab Manual:
• Over and Under
• Top This

Overhead Transparencies available for :
Figures 32.1, 32.4, 32.5, 32.6, 32.9, 32.11, 32.12, and 32.13

This chapter and the next are the most "physical" of the Earth Science chapters. Waves have their application in seismology and the study of the Earth's interior. Mechanics and thermodynamics are the foundations of convection in the core and mantle, plate tectonics, and structural geology. Even though some of the physics isn't mentioned by name, here's your opportunity to tie in earlier parts of the course and show how a great deal of geology is applied physics.

The U.S. Geological Survey has a wealth of information for teachers and students:

http://www.usgs.gov/tracks/teachers.html

SUGGESTED PRESENTATION

32.1 Earthquakes Make Seismic Waves

CHECK YOUR NEIGHBOR: Except for the observations in deep mines, how do we know any details about the Earth's interior? [How we know about the details of the Earth's interior is not altogether different than how a bat knows about the details of a dark cave. Onward to seismic waves.]

Not only does a bat know details of caves it can't "see", dolphins sense the details of the ocean bottom in the middle of the night. In the same way, Earth scientists probe the Earth's interior. They do so by studying seismic waves. In your lectures, consider picking up on the distinction between transverse and longitudinal waves, but going further into the details of seismic waves is getting away from the essence of the chapter, and should be avoided (the text conveys enough material on seismic waves for a physical science class). An interesting point to make is that one of the ways in which Earth scientists learned so much about the Earth's interior was the Cold War. During the height of the Cold War numerous underground tests conducted by the former Soviet Union were of great concern to the free world. To more closely monitor these tests, an extensive network of sensitive seismographs was installed around the world. The seismograms from this monitoring allowed a closer examination of the Earth's interior — a boon to Earth scientists. Thus political conflict resulted in a tremendous gain in science.

32.2 Seismic Waves Show the Earth has Layers
The Core The core-forming process has a name that I have always found amusing, "the iron catastrophe." The story goes like this: A popular theory of the formation of the terrestrial planets is called *cold accretion*. The planets formed when many stony and metallic meteorites, gases, dust, etc. clumped together due to gravitational attraction. Heat from radioactive decay initiated melting. Molten rock and molten metal are largely immiscible, so the Earth's own gravity resulted in the migration of denser molten metal toward the center of the planet. A hypothesized consequence of this is that the speed of the Earth's rotation increased due to more mass in the center, much like a spinning ice skater increases her speed when she draws her arms close to her body. This increase in speed provides a mechanism for the *daughter theory* of our moon. The theory states that the moon was formed from molten Earth material that was either thrown off the Earth during this increase in rotational speed or from one or more "splashes" caused by large meteorites crashing into the still-molten Earth. Nice story! (Other theories for the moon include (1) the *sister theory* (formed at the same time), and, (2) capture of "wandering" celestial body.)

CHECK YOUR NEIGHBOR: Do Earth scientists REALLY KNOW that the Earth's center is iron? [No, they don't really know, with the assurance they know the composition of the Earth's crust. But all studies of the Earth's interior support the hypothesis that the center of the Earth is indeed iron. We assume it is and go from there. If it turns out we are wrong, then we make adjustments and update our knowledge base. Science progresses by assuming a hypothesis that is consistent with all the known data while holding the door open to other theories if it turns out that a better explanation comes up.]

The Mantle Convection in the mantle is and has been the driving force of plate tectonics, which in turn has created every mountain range on Earth. Very dynamic indeed. Also, the mantle is "a girl's best friend" (really a jewelry store's best friend!) because all gem quality diamonds are formed in the intense pressure environment of the mantle. The diamonds are later brought near the Earth's surface by rare, explosive volcanic eruptions called *kimberlite pipes*.

CHECK YOUR NEIGHBOR: How big are the molecules that make up a diamond? [A diamond is an example of one molecule — as big as the particular diamond itself!]

The Crust The crustal surface is where we see the dynamics of our planet. The concept of isostasy, which is described not defined in the text, can be explained by a floating iceberg. Most of the mass of an iceberg is below the water line much like the mass of continental land. Tall mountain ranges have most of their mass below the surface.

CHECK YOUR NEIGHBOR: If you wish to drill a hole through the Earth's crust, where would you drill to succeed with the shortest hole? [The ocean floor.]

32.3 Folds, Faults, and Earthquakes
Structural Geology Here's where mechanics comes into the picture — compression (reverse faults and folds), tension (normal faults), and shearing (strike-slip faults). The rug example in the text is an easy demonstration in the classroom, and it gets students involved. To repeat the text here a bit, suppose you had a throw rug on your floor, with your friend standing on one end. If you push the rug toward your friend while keeping it on the floor, a series of ripples, or **folds**, develop in the rug. This is what happens to the Earth's crust when it is subjected to compressive stress. We can compare the ripples created on the rug to folding of rocks on the Earth's surface—both are generated by compressive stresses. Explain that if the compressive force overcomes the mechanical strength of the rock, thrust or reverse faults form to accommodate the compression. Blocks of foam rubber can also be used for this demonstration.

Chapter 32 Answers and Solutions

Key Terms and Matching Definitions

_11_ anticline
__3_ asthenosphere
__2_ core
__4_ crust
__6_ fault
_10_ lithosphere
__9_ mantle
__8_ Mohorovicic discontinuity (Moho)
__7_ primary waves
__1_ secondary waves
__5_ syncline

Review Questions

1. P-waves and S-waves move through the Earth's interior in two ways. What is the difference in their mode of propagation?
   P-waves are longitudinal waves; they compress and expand the rock as they move through it. P-waves can travel through any type of material—solid granite or magma or water or air. They are the fastest of all seismic waves and the first to register on a seismograph. S-waves are transverse—they vibrate the particles of their medium up and down and side to side. S-waves can travel only through solids—not in fluids, and are the second to register on a seismograph.

2. Can S-waves travel through liquids? Explain.
   No. Fluids cannot support transverse motion, as solids can. S-waves can travel only through solids.

3. Name the two types of surface waves and describe the motion of each.
   Rayleigh waves and Love waves. Rayleigh waves move in an up-and-down motion, and Love waves move in a side-to-side, whiplike motion. Both surface-wave types travel at lower speeds than P- and S-waves and so are the last to register on a seismograph.

4. What was Andrija Mohorovicic's major contribution to geology?
   Mohorovicic presented the first convincing evidence that the Earth's "innards" are layered—discovered from observed changes in seismic wave speeds below the surface. He concluded that the observed speed increase was due to variation in the density of the Earth. With data he drew a map of the upper boundary of the Earth's mantle, known as the Mohorovicic discontinuity ("Moho"), which separates the Earth's crust from the rocks of different composition in the mantle below.

5. List the different properties of the 4 types of seismic waves. How did seismic waves contribute to the discovery of the Earth's internal boundaries?
   Body waves. P-waves are longitudinal and can travel through any type of material. S-waves are transverse and can travel only through solids. Surface waves. Rayleigh waves move in an up-and-down motion, and Love waves move in a side-to-side, whiplike motion. Both P- and S-waves are strongly influenced by a pronounced boundary 2900 kilometers deep. When P-waves reach that boundary, they are reflected and refracted casting a wave shadow (no direct penetration of seismic waves). This infers a significant change in the density of the materials present,

which identifies the boundaries between the mantle, outer, and inner core. The measured speed of P-waves in the core suggests it to be solid.

6. What does the wave shadow that develops 105–140° from the origin of an earthquake tell us about the Earth's composition?
The P-wave shadow allows no direct penetration of seismic waves, inferring a significant change in the density of the materials present. The materials that make up the crust are different than those that make up the mantle.

7. What is the evidence for the solidity of the Earth's inner core?
P-wave reflection from a boundary within the core shows another layer. P-waves passing through the inner portion of the core have a greater speed than those passing through the outer core do. Therefore, the inner core must be solid.

8. Even though the inner and outer cores are both composed predominantly of iron and nickel, the inner core is solid and the outer core is liquid. Why?
Although the inner core is very hot, intense pressure from the weight of the rest of the Earth prevents the material of the inner core from melting. Because less weight is exerted on the outer core, the pressure is less here, with the result that the iron and nickel are liquid.

9. What is the evidence that the Earth's outer core is liquid?
The speeds at which seismic waves travel through the core suggest that the core is composed of metallic iron. The boundary at the core casts an S-wave shadow that is even more extensive than the P-wave shadow, suggesting that S-waves are unable to pass through the core. Because S-waves cannot travel through liquids, we infer that the outer portion of the core is liquid.

10. Describe the asthenosphere and the lithosphere. In what way are they different from each other?
The upper portion of the mantle, extending from the crust-mantle boundary down to a depth of about 350 kilometers, has two zones: The first is the lower part, the *asthenosphere*, which is plastic-like. Internal thermal convection currents contribute to its gradual flow, which greatly affect the surface features of our planet. The *lithosphere* is situated above the asthenosphere; it is about 100 km thick and includes the entire crust and the uppermost portion of the mantle. It is relatively rigid and brittle and resists deformation. The lithosphere is, in a sense, floating on top of the asthenosphere. The lithospheric plates are continuously in motion as they float on the circulating asthenosphere.

11. What convectional movement is responsible for the motion of lithospheric plates?
Internal thermal convection currents in the asthenosphere greatly affect the lithosphere, and hence the surface features of our planet. The lithospheric plates are continuously in motion as they float on the circulating asthenosphere.

12. How does continental crust differ from oceanic crust?
They differ in density, composition, and thickness. The crust of the ocean basins is compact. It's only about 10 kilometers thick and is composed of dense basaltic rocks. The part of the crust we know as continents is between 20 and 60 kilometers thick. Continental crust is composed of less dense granitic rocks.

13. Why does continental crust float higher on the Earth's surface than oceanic crust?
The continental crust floats higher than the oceanic crust because it is less dense.

14. What are folds?
A fold is buckled rock that has been subjected to compressive stress.

15. Are folded rocks the result of compressional or tensional forces?
    Compressional force.

16. Distinguish between anticlines and synclines.
    The rocks in an anticline are oldest at the core, and as you move horizontally away from the axis, the rocks get younger. In anticlines, the rocks tilt away from the fold axis. The rocks at the core off a syncline are the youngest, and as you move horizontally away from the axis, the rocks get older and older. In synclines, the rocks tilt away from the fold axis.

17. Two major types of faults are reverse faults and normal faults. What is the difference between them?
    Reverse fault: **created by compressional forces which cause rocks in the hanging wall to be pushed upward along the fault plane relative to rocks in the footwall.** *Normal fault*: **created by tensional forces which cause rocks in a hanging wall to drop downward along the fault plane relative to those in the adjacent footwall.**

18. How are strike-slip faults different from normal or reverse faults?
    Strike-slip faults show horizontal relative motion. Normal and reverse faults show vertical relative motion.

19. What type of fault is associated with the 1964 earthquake in Alaska?
    The 1964 earthquake in Anchorage, Alaska was caused by a reverse fault. (The earthquake registered 8.5 on the Richter scale, and caused 131 deaths and $300 million in damage.)

20. The Mercalli Scale measures earthquake intensity. The Richter Scale measures earthquake magnitude. Which scale is the more precise measurement? Why?
    The Richter Scale is more precise. The Richter Scale measures quake severity in terms of the amount of energy released and the amount of ground shaking at a standard distance from the quake by measuring the amplitude of seismic waves. The scale is logarithmic; each increase of 1 unit on the scale is equal to an increase of 10 in the amplitude of shaking.

Solutions to Chapter 32 Exercises

1. Compare the relative speeds of primary and secondary seismic waves, and relate speeds of travel to the medium in which the waves travel.
    The speed of a wave depends on the type of material it travels through. P-waves (primary waves) are the fastest seismic waves and travel through all mediums—solids and fluids. The denser the material, the faster the movement. S-waves (secondary waves) are slower and can only travel through solids.

2. Explain how seismic waves indicate whether regions within the Earth are solid or liquid.
    A P-wave goes through both solids and liquids, whereas an S-wave goes only through a solid. So when S-waves fail to traverse part of the Earth's interior, a liquid phase is indicated. By studying the passage of both P- and S-waves through the Earth, solid and liquid layers can be identified.

3. How do seismic waves indicate layering of materials in the Earth's interior?
    When a seismic wave encounters a boundary between different layers, reflection and refraction of the wave occur. The reflected part of the wave tells us the location of the boundary, and as it continues into the layer and is once again reflected it reveals the boundary between the next layer. Parts that continue without reflection are encountered at another location on the Earth. The relative reflections and refractions

reveal a solid inner core, a liquid outer core, a rocky plastic-like mantle, and a rigid and brittle crust.

4. What is the evidence for the Earth's central core being solid?
The Earth's solid inner core is revealed by the differences in P- and S- wave propagation through the Earth's interior. As these waves encounter the mantle-core boundary at 2900 km, a very pronounced wave shadow develops. P-waves are both reflected and refracted at the boundary, but S-waves are only reflected. S-waves cannot travel through liquids, implying a liquid outer core. At a certain depth, as P-waves propagate through the outer core, they refract and increase in speed as they enter a new medium. The faster traveling wave indicates a solid inner core.

5. What is the evidence for distinguishing a boundary at the base of the crust?
The speed of seismic waves increases abruptly at a certain depth beneath the surface. The increase in speed marks the boundary at the base of the crust—the Moho.

6. Speculate on why the lithosphere is rigid and the asthenosphere plastic, even though they are both part of the mantle.
The lithosphere contains the crustal surface—continental and oceanic. The lithosphere is rigid because it is composed of material that has cooled and solidified. The deeper asthenosphere, however, is hotter and is semi-molten. It flows as a semi-liquid. Hence, the lithosphere rides above and "floats" on the asthenosphere.

7. If the Earth's mantle is composed of rock, how can we say that the crust floats on the mantle?
Part of the Earth's mantle is rigid and part is hot enough to be semi-molten. The crust is embedded in the rigid lithosphere, which floats on the semi-molten asthenosphere.

8. Is the lithosphere part of the mantle? Explain the relationships of the crust to the lithosphere and the lithosphere to the mantle.
The lithosphere contains both the uppermost part of the mantle and the entire crust. Thus, part of the lithosphere is part of the mantle.

9. Which extends farther into the mantle, the continental or the oceanic crust? Why?
The continental crust certainly stands higher because it is composed of buoyant granitic material. Like an iceberg, the thicker it is, the further it extends downward. As a mountain range forms it slowly sinks and extends downward as the crust bends downward. Because the oceanic crust is thinner, it doesn't extend as deep into the mantle.

10. How does erosion and wearing away of a mountain affect the depth to which the crust right below mountain extends into the lithosphere?
Just as shaving off the top of an iceberg would lighten the iceberg, and cause it to float higher, the erosion and wearing away of mountains lightens them and causes them to float higher on the mantle. This causes the depth to which the crust extends into the mantle to decrease.

11. Describe how the presence of faults and folds supports the idea that lithospheric plates are in motion.
Faults and folds are the strain that result from stress. Stress builds up in the lithosphere because it is rigid, broken into plates, and is in motion, just as two cars that crash into each other results in crumpled, broken cars.

12. What kind of force creates reverse faults? Where in the United States do we find evidence of reverse faults?

Compression creates reverse faults. The Rocky Mountain foreland, the Canadian Rockies, and the Appalachian Mountains, to name a few, were formed in part by reverse faulting.

13. What kind of force creates normal faults? Where in the United States do we find evidence of normal faults?
Tension creates reverse faults. Virtually the entire state of Nevada, and eastern California, southern Oregon, southern Idaho, and western Utah are greatly affected by normal faulting.

14. Strike-slip faults show horizontal motion. Where in the United States do we find strike-slip faulting?
The San Andreas Fault along the west coast of the United States is a famous strike-slip fault.

15. If you found folded beds of sedimentary rock in the field, what detail would you need to know in order to tell if the fold was an anticline or a syncline?
You would need to know the ages of the different rock layers. If the rocks at the center, or *core*, of a fold are the youngest, and as you move horizontally away from the axis, they get older, the fold is a syncline. If the rocks in the fold are oldest at the core, and as you move horizontally away from the axis, they get younger, the fold is an anticline.

16. Does the fact that the mantle is beneath the crust necessarily mean that the mantle is denser than the crust? Explain.
The separation of elements during the Earth's formation resulted in heavier elements migrating toward the center of the planet and lighter elements floating to the surface of the planet. So yes, the greater density of the mantle contributes to its position beneath the crust.

17. The weight of ocean floor bearing down upon the lithosphere is increased by the weight of ocean water. Relative to the weight of the 10-km-thick basaltic ocean crust (specific gravity 3), how much weight does the 3-km-deep ocean (specific gravity 1) contribute? Express your answer as a percent of the crust's weight.
The comparison is the weight of ocean 3 km deep (the number 3) with the weight of 10 km of crust 3 times as dense (the number 30). How big is 3 compared with 30? One tenth as much. The ocean contributes 10% of the crust's weight.

18. The Richter scale is logarithmic, meaning that each increase of 1 on the Richter scale corresponds to an increase of 10 in the amplitude of the seismic waves created by an earthquake. An earthquake that measures 8 on the Richter scale has how many times more ground shaking than a quake that measures 6 on the Richter scale?
Each log unit is an order of magnitude, i.e. one log unit is 10 (10^1), two log units is 100 (10^2), three log units is 1000 (10^3), etc. So an Earthquake of magnitude 8 has 100 times the amplitude of a magnitude 6 quake, and has likewise 100 times more ground shaking.

19. What is a very likely cause for the existence of the Earth's magnetic field?
Motion in the liquid outer core is most probable cause for the existence of the Earth's magnetic field.

33 Our Restless Planet

Learning Objectives

After studying Chapter 33, students will be able to:
- Identify the pieces of evidence to support continental drift.
- Define paleomagnetism and its relationship to continental drift.
- Describe the theory of seafloor spreading.
- Understand that features of the ocean floor (magnetic patterns, age, and sea-floor topography) provide evidence of plate tectonics.
- Describe the theory of plate tectonics.
- Recognize, differentiate between, and provide examples of the three types of plate boundaries
- Describe the principal structures (mountains, volcanoes, deep-sea trenches, and faults) that form at the three different kinds of plate boundaries.
- Describe how the formation of the different rock types relates to plate tectonics.
- Explain the location and properties of volcanoes that are due to hot spots and the explanation for those that are due to subduction.

Possible Misconceptions to Correct

- **Not so!** The theories of continental drift and plate tectonics were readily accepted by the scientific community.
- **Not so!** Continental drift and the theory of plate tectonics are the same thing.
- **Not so!** The Earth is shrinking or expanding.
- **Not so!** The continents and oceans are static and unmoving.

Demonstration Equipment

- Various maps that may be available at your school.

In the **Explorations Practice Book:**

- Plate Boundaries
- Sea-floor Spreading

In the **Next-Time Questions Book:**

- Warmth of a natural hot spring

In the **Lab Manual**:
There are no labs for Chapter 33

Overhead Transparencies available for :
Figures 33.1, 33.3, 33.6, 33.9, and 33.11

SUGGESTED PRESENTATION

Depart from the order of the chapter and begin in high gear with the idea of the continents floating over the globe like ice floes in the Arctic Sea. Where the ice sheets rise highest above the sea, is where they're also the thickest and where they extend deepest into the water. Likewise for the continents, which in a sense are floating upon the mantle. We are all certainly aware of changes that occur suddenly, like during an earthquake or the collapse of a building. But we aren't as aware of these changes if they occur in slow motion. The changes in geology that build mountains and wear them down to nubs are more spectacular than those of the greatest earthquakes — the change simply eludes us because it extends over long periods of time.

> MOTIVATIONAL QUESTION: We understand that coal deposits are the ancient remains of vegetation trapped beneath the Earth's surface. And we find coal deposits in Antarctica, a place certainly too cold for vegetation. How can coal deposits exist in this cold place? [Antarctica wasn't always at the south pole. It was at one time far from the poles, where the climate was warm enough for vast vegetated regions. Onward to continental drift.]

33.1 The Theory of Continental Drift
Many people have looked at a world map and noticed how South America and Africa look like they "fit" together like jigsaw puzzle pieces. (I remember noticing this as a child—and that the idea created my initial interest in science.) This is also where Alfred Wegener started his theory of continental drift, and a good place to begin a lecture because it starts the student thinking from the point of discovery. The fact that Wegener backed this up with geologic, climatic, and biologic evidence didn't help him convince his contemporaries. However, when the theory of sea-floor spreading arrived in the 1960s Wegener's original lines of evidence were revived, and he was shown to be one of the great creative thinkers and synthesizers of our time.

33.2 The Theory of Plate Tectonics
Have your students refer to Figure 33.8.

> CHECK YOUR NEIGHBOR: Is the Earth expanding? [No.] As lithospheric plates diverge at spreading centers, why doesn't the radius of the Earth increase? [Subduction occurs also.] What happens when the leading edge of a diverging plate collides with the leading edge an adjacent plate? [Subduction occurs.]

33.3 There are Three Types of Plate Boundaries
H.H. Hess provided the missing piece, the driving force, by showing that sea floor spreads at **divergent** boundaries. Later work by others hinted at subduction zones (**convergent** boundaries). Because mid-ocean ridges are quite long, and, since they are on a sphere, spreading cannot occur at equal rates along the whole ridge. Hence, the ridge becomes "offset" and segmented. **Transform faults** provide the mechanism that accommodates the different spreading rates by "transforming" motion between ridge segments. Interestingly, it was first thought that these transform faults were actually the cause of the offset ridge segments. This makes the transform fault appear to have the opposite sense of strike-slip motion that they really do (see practice sheet on plate boundaries).

CHECK YOUR NEIGHBOR: Okay, so the continents drifted long ago. How do we know whether or not they are still drifting? [Ask people who live along the plate boundaries, where earthquakes are quite common, and they will attest to the fact that the plates are still moving.]

Showing a map of the Hawaiian Islands and the Emperor Seamounts chain as an excellent way to illustrate the effects of a plate moving over a hot spot. Another great one is the Yellowstone-Snake River Plain hot spot. For a very long time North America has been riding over this hot spot and it has produced the volcanic rocks of the Snake River Plain and the amazing Yellowstone National Park. This can be clearly seen on a geologic map of the region.

One of the most amazing things about geology is geologic time and the power of erosion. The Appalachian mountains were produced by the same process that formed the Himalayas: continental collision. The Himalayas formed when India crashed into Asia, and they are still rising. The Appalachians formed about 250 million years ago when North America collided with Gondwanaland (an amalgamation of Africa, South America, Antarctica, India, Australia, New Zealand, and southeast Asia). The Appalachians were likely as high and grand as the Himalayas, but now look at them! Two hundred and fifty million years has worn them down to a nub.

CHECK YOUR NEIGHBOR: Floating icebergs often collide and crunch into one another. Do the Earth's plates similarly collide? [Yes. Ask inhabitants of the Himalaya and Andes regions this question. If they don't know the answer, it's because the events that produced the high mountains occurred over long periods of time, and in "slow motion" as discussed earlier.]

33.4 The Theory That Explains Much
Try to be as local as possible with this section. Use examples from where you and your students live and relate them to plate tectonics. Some of the well known examples from the text are applicable anywhere.

Chapter 33 Answers and Solutions

Key Terms and Matching Definitions

__2__ Alfred Wegener
__7__ convergent boundary
__5__ divergent boundary
__4__ H.H. Hess
__3__ Pangaea
__1__ paleomagnetism
__6__ sea-floor spreading
__8__ transform fault boundary

Review Questions

1. What key evidence did Alfred Wegener use to support his idea of continental drift?
   Wegener's theory of continental drift proposed that continental land was not static—the continents moved. The theory was well supported by the "jig-saw" fit of continental land masses at their margins, and by data in paleo-climatology and paleontology. Although the evidence was quite remarkable, a suitable driving mechanism to produce such crustal movement was lacking.

2. How does evidence of prehistoric glaciation found in parts of South America, southern Africa, India, and southern Australia support the concept of a supercontinent?
   Glacial evidence indicates that if these continents were in their present positions, the ice sheet would have had to cover the entire S. Hemisphere, and in some places, cross the equator. Such an extensive ice sheet would have made the world climate very cold. But there is no evidence of glaciation in the N. Hemisphere at that time. In fact, the time of glaciation in the S. Hemisphere was a time of subtropical climate in the N. Hemisphere. Wegener proposed that Pangaea had been in existence 300 million years ago, with South Africa located over the Earth's South Pole. This reconstruction brings all the glaciated regions into close proximity in the vicinity of the South Pole and places the modern northern continents nearer the tropics.

3. What was the stated reason for the scientific community rejecting Wegener's idea of Continental Drift?
   Although Wegener's evidence was quite remarkable, a suitable driving mechanism to produce such crustal movement was lacking.

4. What information can be learned from a rock's magnetic record?
   Three essential bits of information are contained in the preserved magnetic record: (1) the polarity of the Earth's magnetic field at the time the rock was formed, (2) the direction to the magnetic pole from the rock's location at the time the rock was formed, and (3) the magnetic latitude of the rock's location at the time the rock was formed. Once the magnetic latitude of a rock and the direction of the magnetic poles are known, the position of the magnetic pole at the time of formation can be determined.

5. What role did paleomagnetism play in supporting continental drift?
   Using paleomagnetism, a plot of the position of the magnetic north pole through time revealed that, over the past 500 million years, the position of the pole had wandered extensively throughout the world. There were two possible ways to explain this occurrence, either the magnetic poles migrated through time or the continents had drifted. Because the apparent path of polar movement varied from continent to continent, it was more reasonable that the continents had moved.

6. Where are the deepest parts of the ocean?
The deepest parts of the ocean occur in the deep ocean trenches that form at subduction zones.

7. What major discovery at the bottom of the ocean did H. H. Hess make?
Sea-floor spreading. (Hess proposed that the seafloor is not permanent but is constantly being renewed. He theorized that the ocean ridges are located above upwelling convection cells in the mantle. As rising material from the mantle oozes upward, new lithosphere is formed. The old lithosphere is simultaneously destroyed in the deep ocean trenches near the edges of continents. Thus in a conveyor belt fashion new lithosphere forms at a spreading center, and older lithosphere is pushed from the ridge crest to be eventually recycled back into the mantle at a deep ocean trench.)

8. How is the ocean floor similar to a gigantic slow-moving tape recorder?
Paleomagnetic analysis of the ocean floor reveals that as new basalt is extruded at an oceanic ridge, it is magnetized according to the existing magnetic field. Alternating strips of normal and reversed polarity paralleling sides of the rift areas are akin to a very slow magnetic tape recording, showing the magnetic history of the Earth and a continuous record of the movement of the seafloors.

9. What does the Earth's crust have in common with a conveyor belt?
As rising material from the mantle oozes upward, new lithosphere is formed. The old lithosphere is simultaneously destroyed in the deep ocean trenches near the edges of continents. Thus in a conveyor belt fashion new lithosphere forms at a spreading center, and older lithosphere is pushed from the ridge crest to be eventually recycled back into the mantle at a deep ocean trench.

10. In what way does seafloor spreading support continental drift?
Sea floor spreading allows for the movement of the continents. With the ocean floor moving in a conveyor belt fashion, new lithosphere is formed at a spreading center, and older lithosphere is pushed from the ridge crest to be eventually recycled back into the mantle at a deep ocean trench.

11. Why does most geologic activity occur near plate boundaries?
Most geologic activity occurs near plate boundaries because the boundaries are places where huge slabs of rigid lithosphere are interacting.

12. What are hot spots? How are they useful for understanding plate movements?
Hot spots are fixed locations of upwelling in the mantle. The upwelling causes magma production, which breaks through the lithosphere to form volcanic islands (if beneath an ocean) like the Hawaiian Islands. The sequence of islands and seamounts traces out the path that a plate moved.

13. Name and describe the three types of plate boundaries.
***Divergent boundaries* are where two plates are moving apart from one another, i.e.: spreading centers. *Convergent boundaries* are where two plates are moving toward one another. There are three types of convergent boundaries: oceanic-oceanic, oceanic-continental, and continental-continental. *Transform fault boundaries* are where two plates are sliding horizontally past one another.**

14. What is a rift?
A rift, or rift valley, is a long, narrow trough that forms as a result of the divergence of two plates.

15. What kind of boundary separates the South American Plate from the African Plate?
A spreading center, or divergent boundary, separates the two plates.

16. Describe the three types of plate collisions that occur at convergent boundaries.
One type is between two oceanic plates, resulting in the subduction of one plate beneath the other to produce a deep ocean trench. Another type is between an oceanic plate and a continental plate, where the denser oceanic plate is subducted beneath the lighter continental plate, producing a deep ocean trench. A third type is the collision of two continental landmasses, which is always preceded by oceanic-continental convergence. Because continental crust, being light and buoyant, does not undergo appreciable subduction, convergence between two continental plates is more like a head-on collision, responsible for the formation of mountain ranges.

17 The Appalachian Mountains were produced at what type of plate boundary?
Convergent boundary. The Appalachian Mountains were produced from a continental-continental collision that ultimately resulted in the formation of the supercontinent Pangaea.

18. What is a transform fault?
A transform fault is a plate boundary that occurs where two plates are neither colliding nor pulling apart but rather sliding horizontally past one other. (The fault "transforms" the motion from one ridge segment to the other.) Because contact forces are neither tensional nor compressional, there is no creation or destruction of the lithosphere. A transform fault is a zone of horizontal accommodation of movement, with neither side of the fault moving up or down relative to the other.

19. What kind of plate boundary separates the North American Plate from the Pacific Plate?
There are actually two responsible agents: A convergent boundary coupled with a transform fault boundary.

20. At what type of plate boundary is regional metamorphism found?
Regional metamorphism is found at convergent plate boundaries.

21. Do you think it is likely to find andesitic rocks close to regionally metamorphosed rock, or should these two rock types be widely separated? Why?
Andesitic rocks are volcanic in origin and occur at convergent plate boundaries. Convergent plate boundaries are also host to regional metamorphism. So, yes, the two rocks are often found near each other.

Solutions to Chapter 33 Exercises

1. Describe how the different paths of polar wandering helped establish that continents move over geologic time.
The apparent path of polar wandering as determined from North American rocks, is different than the path determined from European rocks. If North America and Europe had been stationary the polar wander paths would overlie each other.

2. Why are most earthquakes generated near plate boundaries?
Most of the stress that builds up in the lithospheric plates does so where two (or three) plates are touching. They touch at their boundaries. When the stress reaches a critical threshold, rocks break, slide past each other, and earthquakes are generated.

3. Why do mountains tend to form in long narrow ranges?
Mountain ranges are the result of plate convergence. Since plate margins are typically rather long, the mountains that form along them are long. They are relatively narrow

because most of the deformation related to plate interaction occurs close to the plate boundaries.

4. Relate the formation of metamorphic rocks to plate tectonics. Would you expect to find metamorphic rocks at all three types of plate boundaries? Why or why not?
One could find metamorphic rock at all three types of plate boundaries. At convergent boundaries, we expect regional metamorphism involving mechanical deformation and elevated temperatures. At divergent boundaries we might expect to find thermally metamorphosed rocks. At transform boundaries, we might find mechanically deformed rocks. By far the majority of metamorphic rocks are associated with convergent boundaries. Metamorphic rocks at the other two types of boundaries represent a small fraction of the total.

5. Cite one line of evidence that suggests subduction once occurred off the coast of California.
Possible answers include: The granitic Sierra Nevada range, which are the batholiths left over from subduction-derived partial melting. The occurrence of trench deposits along the coastal areas of Northern California. The occurrence of metamorphic rocks both in the Sierra Nevada and near the trench deposits.

6. Distinguish between continental drift and plate tectonics.
Continental drift proposed that continental land was not static—the continents moved. The theory was well supported by the "jig-saw" fit of continental land masses at their margins, and by data in paleo-climatology and paleontology. Although the evidence was quite remarkable, a suitable driving mechanism to produce such crustal movement was lacking. The theory of plate tectonics states that the lithosphere is broken up into about a dozen rigid moving plates that move in response to convection within the planet's interior. The boundaries between these plates—divergent, convergent, and transform boundaries—are the sites where crust is formed (seafloor spreading) and destroyed (subduction zones). Continental drift provided the idea supported by later findings related to plate tectonics.

7. Are the present ocean basins a permanent feature on our planet? Discuss why or why not.
The oceans on our planet have been around since very early in Earth's history. The present ocean basins, however, are not a permanent feature. The present day Atlantic Ocean did not exist when Pangaea was in existence. Then it was a tiny rift area between continental lands. With a spreading center in the middle of the Atlantic, the floor of the Atlantic Ocean is constantly growing.

8. Are the present continents a permanent feature on our planet? Discuss why or why not.
The present day arrangement of continents is not a permanent feature. Hence, the way a map of the world looks has changed drastically over geologic time. Many continents have increased in size over geologic time. Partial melting and crystallization act to increase the silicon content of rocks, which decreases their density. The continental crust is made of these less dense rocks. In general, continental crust is not subducted, due to its buoyant nature.

9. Why is it that the most ancient rocks are found on the continents, and not on the ocean floor?
The ocean floors are the sites of crustal formation. New crust is generated at a spreading center, as the new crust is formed the older crust moves away. Older oceanic crust has been subducted, while older continental crust has not. In general, continental crust does not get subducted because of its lower density.

10. Upon crystallization, certain minerals (the most important being magnetite) align themselves in the direction of the surrounding magnetic field, providing a magnetic fossil imprint. How does the Earth's magnetic record support the theory of continental drift?

As new rock is extruded on the seafloor, the newly formed magnetic minerals are aligned in the direction of the magnetic field. When the field changes, and new rock is extruded, newly formed minerals align with the new direction. Thus paleomagnetic data on pole reversals provide a record of seafloor spreading, which in turn accounts for the motions of the continents and continental drift.

11. How is the theory of seafloor spreading supported by paleomagnetic data?
    There are two supporting theories: Apparent polar wandering and magnetic surveys of the ocean floor. Studies during the 1950s used paleomagnetism to show that the position of the magnetic poles had gradually wandered around the globe. Since the geographic poles do not wander, it is hard to conceive that the related magnetic poles had wandered. To explain the apparent movement of the magnetic poles it was suggested that it was the continents that had moved and not the poles. This idea was supported by the theory of seafloor spreading and magnetic surveys of the ocean floors. The surveys showed alternating strips of normal and reversed polarity, paralleling either side of the spreading rift areas.

12. What kind of boundaries are associated with seafloor spreading centers?
    Divergent boundaries are the dominant feature associated with seafloor spreading. Transform fault boundaries connect offset segments of the divergent boundary.

13. What is meant by magnetic pole reversals? What useful information do they tell us about the Earth's history?
    Magnetic pole reversals have to do with the fact that the polarity of the Earth's magnetic field periodically reverses—the north magnetic pole becomes the south magnetic pole and vice versa. Because certain minerals align themselves with the magnetic field, rocks have a preserved record of the Earth's magnetism. Pole reversals and paleomagnetism provide strong evidence for the concept of seafloor spreading. As new basalt is extruded at the oceanic ridge, it is magnetized according to the existing magnetic field. Magnetic surveys of the ocean's floor show alternating strips of normal and reversed polarity, paralleling either side of the rift area. Thus, the magnetic history of the Earth is recorded in spreading ocean floors as in a very slow magnetic tape. The dates of pole reversal can be determined by dating rocks that come from the ocean floor. Thus the rate of seafloor spreading can also be determined.

14. Using a photocopy of Figure 33.8, mark the different boundaries of plate interaction. Draw arrows showing direction of plate movement for convergent, divergent and transform fault boundaries.
    Self explanatory.

15. Earthquakes, the result of sudden motion in the Earth caused by abrupt release of slowly accumulated stress, cause rock to fracture or fault. Relate such faulting to horizontal movement of plates. Where does this type of movement occur?
    A fault is defined as a fracture in the Earth's crust along which appreciable movement has taken place. Horizontal movement occurs when two plates slide past one another with little upward or downward movement. This typically occurs along transform faults, which connect offset spreading ridge segments. The most famous horizontal movement in a fault zone is the San Andreas Fault in California.

16. Lithospheric material is continuously created and destroyed. Where does this creation and destruction take place? Do the rates of the two processes balance each other?
    Lithosphere is created at spreading centers (divergent plate boundaries) and destroyed at subduction zones (convergent plate boundaries). The theory of plate tectonics states that the Earth is neither expanding nor contracting. Thus the rate of production of new lithosphere must equal the rate of destruction of old lithosphere.

17. Subduction is the process of one lithospheric plate descending beneath another. Why does the oceanic portion of the lithosphere undergo subduction while the continental portion does not? **Oceanic crust is more dense than continental crust, so buoyancy inhibits the subduction of continental crust.**

18. What geologic features are explained by plate tectonics? **Mountain ranges, volcanoes, plutonic rocks, metamorphic rocks, folded and faulted rocks are all explained by plate tectonics. The deposition of marine sedimentary rocks on continental crust is explained by higher stands of sea level, which can often be attributed to faster sea floor spreading rates. Virtually all geologic processes can be tied back to plate tectonics, although sometimes the link is quite indirect. For example, consider the formation of a stream valley. As a mountain is growing, the stream gradient increases, which affects the development of the stream valley. The growth of mountains is a result of plate tectonics. There are many interesting examples!**

19. In 1964, a large tsunami struck the Hawaiian Islands without warning, devastating the coastal town of Hilo, Hawaii. Since that time a tsunami warning station has been established for the coastal areas of the Pacific. Why do you think these stations are located around the Pacific rim? **The Pacific rim is also known as the "ring of fire" because the Pacific Plate has the most subduction zones, and thus the highest potential for tsunami-generating earthquakes. In such a seismically active zone, a reliable warning system is a must.**

20. Where is the world's longest mountain range located? **The Mid-Atlantic ridge, running essentially north-south in the middle of the Atlantic Ocean, is the world's longest mountain range.**

21. If the mid-Atlantic ocean is spreading at 2 cm per year, how many years has it taken for it to reach its present width of 5000 km? **From distance = speed $\times$ time, time = distance/speed. For a numerical value we convert km to cm. In 1 km there are 1000×100 cm. So,**

$$\text{time} = \frac{(5000 \text{ km})\,(1000 \text{ m} / \text{km})\,(100 \text{ cm} / \text{m})}{2 \text{ cm} / \text{year}} = 250 \text{ million years}$$

Answer to Calculation Corner

1. **The distance between Los Angeles is:**

$$600 \text{ km} \times \frac{1000 \text{ m}}{1 \text{ km}} \times \frac{100 \text{ cm}}{1 \text{ m}} = 6 \times 10^7 \text{ cm.}$$

2. **The rate of movement along the San Andreas Fault is 3.5 cm/yr, so:**

$$6 \times 10^7 \text{ cm} \times \frac{1 \text{ yr}}{3.5 \text{ cm}} = 17{,}142{,}857 \text{ years}$$

which rounds off to 17 million years.

34 Water on Our World

Conceptual Physical Science—Explorations

Learning Objectives
After studying Chapter 34, students will be able to:
- Define and describe the hydrologic cycle.
- Define groundwater and describe how it flows underground.
- Define and distinguish permeability from porosity.
- Name the three variables that affect stream flow velocity.
- Locate, on a map, the North American Continental Divide and describe where water on each side of the divide will flow.
- Describe the similarities and differences of glaciers and rivers.
- Describe the terms accumulation and ablation.
- Explain how ocean waves form and move.
- Name several sources of man-made water contamination.
- Name several ways to conserve water on a daily basis.

Possible Misconceptions to Correct
- **Not so!** Most of Earth's freshwater is in rivers and lakes.
- **Not so!** The ground under our feet is solid, non-porous rock.
- **Not so!** Stream flow velocity always increases as a stream progresses downstream.
- **Not so!** A stationary glacier is a glacier without flow.

Demonstration Equipment
- Sugar cubes
- Beakers
- Various sizes of sand and pebbles (separated)

In the **Explorations Practice Book**:
- Groundwater Flow and Contaminant Transport
- Stream Velocity
- Glacial Movement

In the **Next-Time Questions Book**:
- Why don't ponds and lakes seep away?
- Permeability and Porosity

In the **Lab Manual**:
• Water Below Our Feet

Overhead Transparencies available for:
Figures 34.2, 34.4, and 34.7

SUGGESTED PRESENTATION

Begin with the following observation and questions: If we dig a hole in the ground and then fill it with water, the water soon seeps into the ground and is gone. Then we look at a lake or pond. Why doesn't water there similarly seep into the ground? Is there plastic or something beneath the bottom that prevents draining? State that these questions are not correctly answered by most people — who are only vaguely aware of what groundwater and water tables are about. One with a knowledge of water tables realizes the interesting reason that lakes don't (ordinarily) drain and a hole dug in the ground that is then filled with water (ordinarily) does. The pond or lake doesn't drain simply because it intersects the water table. When you dig a hole in the ground that is above the water table, of course the water soon drains downward. Knowing about groundwater changes the way we look at our surroundings. The person educated in Earth Sciences sees the world quite differently.

34.1 The Hydrologic Cycle
Remind students that water is a finite resource. No new water has entered Earth's natural systems since the planet formed (except for tiny amounts from comets and comet dust). Earth's water simply is cycled and recycled. Water is constantly moving—even in glaciers.

34.2 Water Below the Surface
Point out that most of the Earth's fresh water (aside from water tied up in the polar ice caps) resides underground. These underground "reservoirs" of water account for about 98.56% (0.80% of which is soil moisture) of the Earth's fresh water, or about 0.62% of the Earth's total water. However, if we consider groundwater that is economically available (shallow groundwater; certainly no deeper than one kilometer) groundwater plus soil moisture equals 97.04% of the Earth's freshwater resources. Since soil moisture isn't exploitable as a water resource, about 95.39% of our available fresh water is beneath the ground. Students may wonder why the groundwater percentage goes down when we consider only shallow groundwater. Remind them that we changed our focus to "available" freshwater. The percentage of surface freshwater has not changed but the total has, so the fraction that is underground is now smaller. Groundwater is an important source of fresh water for people, agriculture, livestock, and industry. As the population grows so will dependence on groundwater. Groundwater can be found just about anywhere below the Earth's surface.

CHECK YOUR NEIGHBOR: Why aren't soil moisture and deep groundwater available as a freshwater resource? [Soil moisture resides in the unsaturated zone under negative pressure (i.e. less than atmospheric pressure). If a pump were operating in the unsaturated zone it would pump only air. Deep groundwater is simply too expensive to bring to the surface (due to pumping costs). It is cheaper to get water from other sources.]

DEMONSTRATION: Absorption of water by different soil or rock materials. Have a student dip a sugar cube half way into colored water. Explain that the sugar cube is not completely solid and contains many open pore spaces. These pore spaces become saturated when a cube is dipped in water. Have four students fill four beakers with different soil/rock materials—sand, clay, small pebbles, and garden soil. Fill the beakers with measured amounts of water. The amount of water added gives the porosity of the soil/rock material.

In the western United States groundwater is the primary source of water for drinking, domestic use, and agriculture. In many areas groundwater literally brings life to the region.

34.3 Streams Come in Different Shapes and Sizes

Rivers and streams are greatly affected by their gradient. The steeper the gradient the faster the flow, the greater the energy. The obvious role of gravity has led to a widespread misconception—that rushing mountain streams flow swiftly, while broad rivers roll along slowly. In fact, water velocity often increases downstream despite the loss of steep gradient. One reason has to do with friction and efficiency. In the headwater regions, where the gradient is steep, water moves through small narrow boulder strewn channels. Although the water moves swiftly it is slowed down both externally, by the force of friction from contact with boulders and the narrow channel, and internally within the turbulent water itself. As the water moves downstream, the channel widens and deepens as it accommodates more water. Deepening and widening of the channel thereby reduces some of the factors of friction and increases the streams efficiency. Wider and deeper channels permit water to flow more freely and hence more rapidly. As pointed out in the text, another reason is that the number of tributaries to the mainstream increases as we move downstream. If the cross-sectional area of the main stream doesn't increase much, the water velocity will increase.

34.4 Glaciers are Flowing Ice

Glaciers and the polar ice caps account for about 77 percent of the Earth's total fresh water supply. Most of this glacial ice (98%) is found in the polar regions where the intensity of solar radiation is greatly reduced as the Sun's rays strike the Earth at an oblique angle. Since the energy is dispersed over a great area, it does not act to effectively heat the Earth's surface. The remaining 2 percent of the Earth's glacial ice is distributed around the world in locations of high elevations.

34.5 Most of Earth's Water is in the Oceans

I think it is fascinating that most of the relief on Earth is actually underwater. The deepest part of the ocean is much deeper than the tallest mountain. I've heard the analogy that a pool cue ball, if magnified to the same scale as the Earth, would show more relief than the visible surface of the Earth. That is, compared with its radius, the "bumps" around the circumference of the Earth are insignificant.

Students don't often realize that when a wave moves through the ocean, the water itself is not displaced very much. It is only the orbital component of the wave that causes much water movement. The rest of the ocean wave—like waves in general—is the transmitted disturbance, not moving water. Ocean waves and wave refraction also provide a link to physics and the study of waves discussed earlier in the book.

34.6 Can We Drink the Water

Population growth and industrial and agricultural production produce quantities of waste that are frequently greater than the environment can handle. The contamination of subsurface waters is of primary concern. Have students research articles about waste disposal techniques. Two widely used techniques include deep-well injection of liquid wastes and sanitary landfills for solid wastes. Your class can discuss the pros and cons of the different techniques. Contamination is also caused by leakage from ponds and lagoons used by larger waste-disposal systems, and by leaching of animal wastes, fertilizers, and pesticides from agricultural soils.

In discussing the problems of groundwater and surface water contamination, end on a positive note. Try to get into what can be done to better the situation. Encourage students to look for the solutions to the problems in their readings.

Get the students involved in a discussion about conserving water. Most classes can come up with many more ways to save water than is mentioned in the text. Make it a fun, in-class exercise for them.

Chapter 34 Answers and Solutions

Key Terms and Matching Definitions

__9__ ablation
__8__ accumulation
_10__ continental Margin
__7__ glacier
__2__ groundwater
__1__ hydrologic cycle
__6__ leachate
__4__ permeability
__3__ porosity
__5__ water table

Review Questions

1. Describe the hydrologic cycle.
   The natural circulation of water from the oceans to the air, to the ground, then to the oceans and then back to the atmosphere is called the hydrologic cycle.

2. Distinguish between *porosity* and *permeability*.
   Porosity is the volume of open space, or voids, in a soil or rock sample compared to the total volume of solids plus voids. The ability of a material to transmit fluid is its permeability.

3. What soil, or soil type, can have high porosity but low permeability?
   Clay, or clayey soils, because the pores are small and poorly connected.

4. A kitchen table is usually flat, but the water table is generally not flat. Why?
   The water table tends to rise and fall with the contours of the surface topography.

5. Compare and contrast the zone of aeration with the zone of saturation.
   The *zone of aeration* is an unsaturated zone, where pore spaces in the Earth are filled mainly with air. Deeper is the *zone of saturation*, where water percolating down from the surface has filled (saturated) all pore spaces. The upper boundary of this saturated zone is called the water table.

6. What type of soils allow for the greatest infiltration of rainfall?
   Sandy soils.

7. How does an aquitard differ from an aquifer?
   Aquifers transmit water; aquitards inhibit the flow of water.

8. What factors affect the rate of groundwater movement?
   The permeability of the aquifer and the slope of the water table determine the rate of groundwater movement.

9. What is meant by stream gradient, and how does it affect stream velocity?
   The *gradient* of a stream is the ratio of the vertical drop to the horizontal distance for that drop. Because of gravity, stream speed tends to be greater where the gradient is steep, but downstream, discharge and channel geometry also influence stream speed.

10. What happens when (a) the discharge of a stream increases, and (b) the speed of a stream increases?
    Increased discharge always means larger volumes of water can be transported by a stream, but increased discharge doesn't always means that the stream speed increases. Increases in discharge and speed do not always correlate directly because changes in channel geometry and the cross-sectional area of the channel might also occur.

11. How does the shape of a stream channel affect flow?
    Consider two streams that have the same cross-sectional area. Water flowing in the channel touches the channel bottom and sides. Friction between the water and channel slows water speed. The greater the contact area, the greater the friction. The cross-sectional shape of a channel determines the amount of water in contact with the channel and hence the amount of frictional drag. If the stream channel is rounded and deep, as opposed to flat-bottomed and relatively shallow, the stream speed will be faster because there is less channel contact.

12. What is the significance of the Continental Divide in North America with respect to water flow to the Atlantic and Pacific Oceans?
    The *Continental Divide* separates the Pacific basin on the west from the Atlantic basin on the east. Water west of the Divide eventually flows to the Pacific Ocean, and water east of the Divide flows to the Atlantic Ocean.

13. What conditions are necessary for a glacier to form?
    A large amount of snow that cannot melt is needed for a glacier to form. The ice of a glacier is formed from recrystallized snow. After snowflakes fall, their accumulation slowly changes the individual flakes to rounded lumps of icy material. As more snow falls, the pressure exerted on the bottom layers of icy snow compacts and recrystallizes it into glacial ice.

14. What distinguishes a huge block of ice from a glacier?
    Ice does not become a glacier until it moves under its own weight. This occurs when the ice mass reaches a critical thickness of approximately 50 meters and the weight of the overlying ice causes the ice at the base to deform plastically and flow downslope.

15. What two main ways do glaciers flow?
    Plastic flow from the slippage of ice crystals and basal sliding.

16. Why do crevasses form on the surface of glaciers?
    The uppermost portion of the glacier, carried along both by basal sliding and by internal plastic deformation, behaves like a rigid, brittle mass that may fracture. Huge, gaping cracks called *crevasses* may develop in this surface ice.

17. Under what conditions does a glacier front advance?

The amount of snow added to a glacier annually is termed accumulation. The total amount of ice lost annually is called ablation. When accumulation exceeds ablation, the glacier advances—it grows.

18. Under what conditions does a glacier front retreat?
    The amount of snow added to a glacier annually is termed accumulation. The total amount of ice lost annually is called ablation. When ablation exceeds accumulation, the glacier retreats—it shrinks.

19. Why do waves become taller as they approach shore?
    As waves approach the shore, they slow down. The wave period remains unchanged because the swells from deeper waters continue to advance. As a result, incoming waves gain on leading slower waves and the distance between waves decreases. This concentration of water in a narrower zone produces higher, steeper waves.

20. What is wave refraction? Why does it happen in ocean waves?
    Wave refraction is the bending of a wave due to differences in wave speeds. It occurs in ocean waves when they approach the shore at an oblique angle (the portion nearest the shore slows first, causing the bend) or where landforms, such as headlands, protrude into the open water, slowing some portions of a wave before others.

21. List three ways our water supply is being contaminated.
    The groundwater supply can be adversely affected by a variety of sources, including septic tank disposal systems and sewage treatment facilities, agricultural fertilizers, municipal landfills, toxic-waste and hazardous-waste landfills, leaking underground storage tanks, and chemical and petroleum product spills.

Solutions to Chapter 34 Exercises

1. Look at a map of any part of the world and you'll see the locations of older cities where rivers occur, or have occurred. What is your explanation?
   Fresh water provides the sustenance of life. This includes drinking water, agricultural uses, sanitation, and transportation,

2. How much of the Earth's supply of water is fresh water, and where is most of it located?
   Less than 3% of the Earth's water is fresh water. Most of it is locked up on the polar ice caps and in glaciers.

3. Where does most rainfall on Earth finally end up before becoming rain again?
   The oceans.

4. If the water table at location X is lower than the water table at location Y, does groundwater flow from X to Y or from Y to X?
   Groundwater flows from areas where the water table is high to areas where the water table is low. So, groundwater would flow from Y to X.

5. Is the infiltration of water into the ground greatest on steep, rocky slopes or on gentle, sandy slopes? Defend your answer.
   Gentle, sandy slopes. There are two issues here: 1) runoff vs. infiltration and 2) permeability. Steep slopes tend to have more consolidated material than gentle slopes, which gives them a lower permeability. The steepness enhances runoff, reducing the chance of infiltration. Gentle slopes enhance infiltration (versus runoff) and sandy material is likely to have a relatively higher permeability, which also enhances infiltration.

6. How is the local hydrologic cycle affected by the practice of drawing drinking water from a river, then returning sewage to the same river?

   The overall mass balance is not affected much. The only possible affect is evaporation. Water quality is certainly affected, however.

7. Why is pollution of groundwater a greater environmental hazard than pollution of surface waters?

   The pollution of groundwater is more difficult to detect. The cleaning of groundwater pollution is very time consuming and extremely expensive. In most cases the groundwater is never cleaned back to its original precontaminated state.

8. Some metals can be extremely dangerous to water supplies. Aluminum has been linked to Alzheimer's and Parkinson's disease; cadmium is known to cause liver damage; and lead affects the circulatory, reproductive, nervous, and kidney systems. What are the likely ways these metals can get into our water supply?

   Metals occur naturally in the ground. In most cases heavy metals that enter the water supply naturally, do so in limited quantities. When the quantities increase it is usually because of human interaction with the environment. Mining tears up the Earth. The desired minerals and materials are stripped from the area, and the garbage is left behind. This garbage is an unnatural accumulation of loosened heavy metals and minerals that are now free to enter the water supply. Industry uses heavy metals, minerals, and chemicals for various stages of production. Once used they become waste, which with improper management enters the environment.

9. Is water in the unsaturated zone called groundwater? Why or why not?

   No, water in the unsaturated zone is not groundwater. The open pore spaces between sediment grains must be completely filled with water for the water to be called groundwater. In the unsaturated zone, open pore spaces are filled with water *and* air.

10. By what means can Earth scientists predict the discharge of a stream after a rainstorm?

    Discharge is the volume of water flowing past a certain point in a given amount of time. Discharge will increase in proportion to the amount of rain that falls. By knowing the area of the drainage basin and the amount of rainfall the change in discharge of a stream can be estimated.

11. As a population increases so does the amount of garbage produced by that population. In many areas the way to deal with increasing wastes is by burial in a landfill or underground storage facilities. What principal factors must be considered in the planning and building of such sites?

    In order for a site to be considered safe it must be located where waste products and their containers cannot be affected chemically by water, physically by Earth movements, or accidentally by people.

12. What effect does a dam have on the water table in the vicinity of the dam?

    A dam acts to hold back water. In a lake the water table intersects the land surface. When a dam is built there is an influx of water from the reservoir into the groundwater. Thus the water table rises.

13. What effect does the accumulation of sediments behind a dam have on its capacity for storing water?

    As water enters a reservoir it abruptly slows down and drops its load of sediment. In time the reservoir may fill up with sediment making the dam useless.

14. In an aquifer, if the water table next to a stream is lower than the water level in the stream, does groundwater flow into the stream or does stream water flow into the ground? Explain.

    Water flows from areas of high water table to areas of low water table. The water flows from the stream into the ground. We say that the stream is recharging (adding water to) the aquifer.

15. As runoff into streams increases, what variables of stream flow (as discussed in the text) increase?

If the cross sectional area of the stream remains constant, discharge and stream speed increase as runoff into the stream increases. If the cross sectional area of the stream changes, then stream discharge will increase but stream speed may or may not increase. (Speed increase depends on how big the increase in area is compared to the increased discharge.)

16. How is a glacier formed?

Glaciers are formed from recrystallized snow. Accumulation of snow slowly changes the individual flakes to rounded lumps of icy material. As more snow falls, the pressure exerted on the bottom layers of icy snow compacts and recrystallizes it into glacial ice. This ice does not become a glacier until it moves under its own weight. This occurs when the ice is approximately 50 meters thick.

17. How does "frictional drag" play a role in the external movement of a glacier? How about the internal movement?

Frictional drag slows down a glacier's external movement. The glacier experiences this drag as it encounters the bedrock. So, movement is slowest at the base and at the sides of the glacier. Inside the glacier, ice flows plastically. The weight of the ice above causes the glacial ice molecules to slide over one another. The internal flow of a glacier exceeds the external flow (due to frictional drag) as the glacier slides over itself without cracking or breaking.

18. As waves approach shallow water, those with longer wavelengths slow down before those with shorter wavelengths. Why?

When water depth approaches half a wave's wavelength, the bottom of the wave's circular path flattens, slowing the wave.

19. How does leachate form?

Precipitation infiltrating a landfill site may dissolve a variety of compounds from the solid waste. The resulting liquid, known as leachate, can move vertically downward from the landfill to the water table and contaminate the groundwater.

20. What is a continental divide?

Drainage basins are separated from one another by *divides*, lines tracing out the highest ground between streams. A drainage basin can cover a vast area or be as small as 1 square kilometer. A continental divide is the largest type of divide; it separates flow on one side of a continent from another (e.g., the Continental Divide in the Rocky Mountains of North America).

35 Our Natural Landscape

Conceptual Physical Science—Explorations

35.1 The Work of Air
35.2 The Work of Groundwater
        Pumping Can Cause Land Subsidence
        Some Rocks are Dissolved by Groundwater
            Caverns and Caves
            Sinkholes
35.3 The Work of Surface Water
        Erosion, Transport, and Deposition of Sediment
        Stream Valleys and Floodplains
        Deltas are the End of the Line for a River
        Even Dry Places are Affected by SurfaceWater
35.4 The Work of Glaciers
        Glacial Erosion and Erosional Landforms
        Glacial Sedimentation and Depositional Landforms
35.5 The Work of Oceans

Learning Objectives

After studying Chapter 35, students will be able to:
• Describe the main forces (wind, groundwater, surface water, glaciers, and oceans) that do work on the landscape.
• Describe the formation and movement of a sand dune.
• Describe the formation of an underground cave (cavern).
• Name several landforms created by groundwater (caves, caverns, karst, and/or areas of subsidence).
• Describe surface water flow (laminar and turbulent flow).
• Describe the processes of erosion, transport and deposition.
• Name several landforms created by surface water (V-shaped valleys, floodplains, and deltas).
• Describe how glaciers erode and deposit sediments and rock.
• Name some landforms (erosional and depositional) associated with glaciers.
• Describe several ways in which the ocean shapes the land.
• Name several landforms associated with oceans (beaches, spits, wave cut platforms, etc.).

Possible Misconceptions to Correct

• **Not so!** Land subsidence only occurs during times of drought.
• **Not so!** Land subsidence is reversible, as water is taken out of the ground the land subsides, but if water is reintroduced the land will return to its original position.
• **Not so!** Underground rivers are common.
• **Not so!** In desert areas, the sun's intense heat is the main cause of erosion.

Demonstration Equipment

• 3 feet of 6 inch diameter nonporous, flexible, plastic tubing
• Coarse sand

In the **Explorations Practice Book**:
• Stream Flow

In the **Next-Time Questions** book.
• Groundwater

In the **Lab Manual**:
There are no labs for Chapter 35.

Overhead Transparencies available for :
Figures 35.11 and 35.12

SUGGESTED PRESENTATION

35.1 The Work of Air
Although a minor player in the overall movement of sediment, remind students of the role wind plays. Analogies to things like sandblasters (that remove paint and graffiti) should be useful.

35.2 The Work of Groundwater
The work done by groundwater that we discuss focuses on land subsidence and development of karst-like features. Many students have probably visited picturesque caves and caverns. Such familiar experiences should be used to generate student interest. Land subsidence examples like the Leaning Tower of Pisa and Mexico City are particularly interesting. Can you imagine the building you live in actually sinking?

35.3 The Work of Surface Water
This section concentrates on the effect of stream flow on the land surface. It is the erosive work of rivers that gouges out canyons and whittles away solid rock. Rivers shape the landscape. Emphasize that rivers do their work by three processes: erosion, transportation, and deposition.

You may refer back to the Rock Cycle to show the process of erosion. Use the term WETS—Weathering, Erosion, Transportation, Sedimentation. (Note: Sedimentation = deposition—the physical process of laying down sediment, and precipitation—the chemical and biochemical means of sediment cementation.)

In general, erosion is extensive where rivers move swiftly and transport great quantities of sediment; and deposition takes place where the streams slow down. The amount of sediment the river can carry depends on the speed of the current, which in turn determines the erosive power of the river. Running water can swiftly carry off soil as well as uncompacted sand and gravel. Water rich in dissolved substances can also chemically erode river channels. A river can carry a great amount of sediment in a short period. The Mississippi River transports more than 440 million tons of silt, clay, and sand in an average year. It is no wonder that over a course of a few million years, the Mississippi River Delta has moved from Cairo, Illinois to its present location near the city of New Orleans, Louisiana. The Mississippi River transports enough debris to move its delta six miles seaward every century!

More recently, the great flood of 1993 has altered the map of the Midwest. Flooding of the Mississippi River has erased towns, made islands out of peninsulas, and forged new river channels. The 1993 flood event is excellent for class discussion. Students can research effects of flooding on the land, groundwater, wells, and transportation links. A question to ponder—How does this affect sedimentation in the Mississippi River Delta? Is there a noticeable increase in the delta's extension?

DEMONSTRATION: Purchase 3 feet of 6 inch diameter nonporous, flexible, plastic tubing (similar to the type used for drainage). Cut the tube to make a U-shaped trough. Fill the trough with coarse sand. Step 1: Hold the trough in a slanted position over a large empty pan. Pour water, a trickle at a time, on the sand at the upper end. Water flowing at a slow steady rate carries small grains of sand with it to the pan. The larger, heavier sand grains remain in the trough. Step 2: Repeat step 1 but pour the water at a faster rate (more force). Both the small and large grains should wash down into the pan. Step 3: Raise and lower the trough to see the effect of slope. Step 4: Place a large rock in the middle of the flow of water to see the effect it has on the deposition of sediments. Step 5: Bend the trough into gentle and tight curves to see the effect of stream velocity, erosion, and deposition.

35.4 The Work of Glaciers
Depending on where you live, there may be many interesting examples of the work of glaciers. The Great Lakes, Bunker Hill, Yosemite National Park, Glacier National Park are but a few spectacular examples of how glaciers have modified our natural landscape.

35.5 The Work of Oceans
This section on oceans focuses on landforms — landforms on the ocean floor as well as land forms adjacent to the shoreline. If previous chapters have already been covered, students should have little difficulty in discussing land features of the ocean basins. Because waves dominate beach processes, the section on waves relates directly to shoreline landforms.

Chapter 35 Answers and Solutions

Key Terms and Matching Definitions

__3__ cavern
__8__ cut-bank
__7__ delta
_ 10__ drift
__6__ laminar flow
__9__ point bar
__1__ sand dune
__4__ sinkhole
__2__ subsidence
__5__ turbulent flow

Review Questions

1. How are sand dunes formed?
   Sand dunes are formed when air flow is blocked by an obstacle. As the wind sweeps over the obstacle, wind speed slows and sand grains fall out of the air to be deposited in the wind shadow. As more sand falls, a mound forms which further blocks the flow of air. With more sand and more wind a dune forms.

2. How are ripple marks formed?
   In the desert, winds move over surfaces of dry sand, picking up the small, more easily transported particles but leaving the large, harder-to-move particles behind. The small particles bounce across the desert floor, knocking more particles into the air, to form *ripple marks*, which are actually tiny sand dunes.

3. What are the consequences of overpumping groundwater?
   In areas where groundwater withdrawal has been extreme, the land surface is lowered—it *subsides*. Also, depletion of groundwater resources can occur if the pumping rate exceeds the recharge rate from natural occurrences such as rainfall.

4. How does rainwater become acidic? How does this affect groundwater?
   Rainwater naturally reacts with carbon dioxide in the air and soil to produce carbonic acid. When this slightly acidic rainwater comes in contact with carbonate rocks, the carbonic acid partially dissolves the rock, which is then carried away in solution. As groundwater steadily dissolves the limestone and other carbonate rocks, it creates unusual erosional features. It is in carbonate rocks that we find the only true underground rivers.

5. What is karst topography? Where on Earth is it found?
   When sinkholes, caves, and caverns define the land surface, the terrain is called *karst topography*. Karst regions can be found throughout the world: in the Mediterranean basin; in sections of the Alps and the Pyrenees; in southern China; and in Kentucky, Missouri, and Tennessee.

6. How does a stalactite form? How does a stalagmite form?
   Dripping water, rich in dissolved calcium carbonate, trickles down from the cave ceiling, creating icicle-shaped stalactites as water evaporates and carbonate precipitates. Some solution drips off the end of the stalactites to build corresponding cone-shaped stalagmites on the floor.

7.   What is the greater transporter of sediment, a laminar flow or a turbulent flow? Why?
     Turbulent flow, because in turbulent flow the water motion is irregular and sediments have a greater tendency to remain in suspension. In laminar flow, water moves steadily in a straight-line path with no mixing of sediment in the channel.

8.   Name three ways the movement of water erodes the stream channel. Which one creates potholes?
     Chemical weathering, hydraulic action, and abrasion. The most powerful is abrasion, which can produce potholes.

9.   What factors are responsible for the formation of a stream valley?
     As rainfall hits the ground, it loosens soil and washes it away. As more and more rain falls and the ground continues to lose soil, a gully forms. Once water and soil particles funnel into such a gully, a stream channel is created. Its erosive power enables a stream to widen and deepen its channel, transport sediment, and, in time, create a valley.

10. Under what conditions do curvy, meandering rivers form along a floodplain?
     As a stream flows downhill and its gradient becomes gentler, the focus of its energy changes from eroding downward to eroding laterally in a side-to-side motion. As a result of this lateral action, the stream develops a more curvy (sinuous) form.

11. What type of streams and stream valleys do we generally find in high mountainous regions?
     In high mountain areas, the erosive action of a stream cuts down into the underlying rock to form a narrow V-shaped valley. Fast-moving rapids and beautiful waterfalls are characteristic of V-shaped mountain stream valleys.

12. What is a delta?
     A delta forms where a river ends as it enters a sea, bay, or lake. As a river encounters a standing body of water, it dumps its load of sediment due to a decrease in the river's speed. The dumped sediment is referred to as a *delta*.

13. Deserts are generally dry areas. Why is water still a major factor of erosion in the desert environment?
     Although water is rare in the desert, when a heavy rain falls, water does not have time to soak into the ground and causes flash floods. These flash floods transport and then deposit great quantities of debris and sediment.

14. What are striations? What is their significance?
     Striations are parallel scratches created by large rock fragments carried at the bottom of a glacier that scrape the underlying bedrock. They are aligned in the direction of ice flow, and thus tell us the past movement of a glacier that has long since receded. By mapping striations on land once covered by continental glaciers, geologist can decipher the flow direction of the ice.

15. What erosional features might you find in an area of alpine glaciation? See Figure 35.21.
     Erosional features in alpine glaciation can include a cirque (a bowl-shaped depression), a tarn (a cirque that has become filled with water), an arête (where two cirques have converged), a horn (a jagged peak), moraines (lateral, medial, and terminal), hanging valleys (a suspended valley above the main valley floor) and a characteristic U-shape valley.

16. What are the two types of glacial deposits? Discuss their depositional features.
     Glacial deposits are collectively called *drift*. Drift is deposited in two principal ways. When glacial sediment is released into meltwater, it is carried and deposited like any other waterborne sediment; thus it is well sorted. This type of drift is called outwash. Material deposited directly by melting ice—an unsorted mixture of clayey and bouldery rock debris—is called till. The most common glacial deposit landform is the moraine

(lateral, median, and terminal), a ridge-shaped landform that marks the boundaries of ice flow. Other distinctive landforms include drumlins, kames, eskers and kettle lakes.

17. Describe how a sea stack forms.
Along some rocky coastlines, sea caves form along with cliffs. Sea arches can form if two caves, usually on opposite sides of a headland, unite. When an arch collapses, an isolated remnant called a sea stack is left behind.

18. What types of land features are associated with transport of sand from a longshore current?
Longshore currents move sand down the length of the coast and may cause the formation of spits. When sand ridges form parallel to the coast, they eventually grow into barrier islands. Barrier islands form where ridges of sand break the surface of the water for a long enough period of time that vegetation begins to take hold.

Solutions to Chapter 35 Exercises

1. In the formation of a river delta, why is it that coarser material is deposited first, followed by medium and finer material farther out? Defend your answer.
    The deposition of sediment in a delta environment is due to a stream's inability to transport sediment indefinitely. The settling of grain particles is directly related to inertia. Larger grains have more mass and more inertia; thus larger grains are the first to settle out. Smaller grains have less mass and less inertia and are the last to settle out.

2. What causes the formation of branches off the main channel of a river delta?
    As a delta grows, the distance traveled by water in the main channel to reach a bay becomes so great that the stream shifts its course and begins cutting new shorter pathways to the bay. This accounts for the radiating branching fingers of a delta. When the fingers get too long, the process begins again. As streams continue to flow to the sea, and as successive beds are deposited one on top of the other, the delta builds itself outward.

3. What is a sinkhole? What factors contribute to its formation?
    A sinkhole is a large cavity open to the sky. It can form as a cave with a collapsed roof or from the dissolution of carbonate rock by acidic rain or groundwater. So, the factors that contribute to a sinkhole's formation include acidic rain or groundwater, an existing cave or any type of opening that allows the seepage of water.

4. The Mississippi Delta has moved south from near Cairo, Illinois, to its present location in Louisiana. Other than the length of time, why has the delta moved so far?
    The Mississippi River has a huge water and sediment capacity. With an annual load of 440 million tons of sediment it is no wonder that the Mississippi Delta is moving southward. Each episode of deposition acts to lengthen the course of the river and extend the delta. The Mississippi Delta continues to grow.

5. Which of the three agents of transportation—wind, water, or ice—transports the largest boulders? Why?
    Ice has the greatest competence (the ability to transport sediment particles) and thus can carry the largest loads. Glaciers moving across a landscape loosen and lift up blocks of rock and incorporate them into the ice. They literally pick up everything in their path. As the ice melts the rock debris is deposited.

6. Which of the three agents of transportation is limited to transporting small size rocks? Why?
    Wind has the lowest competence. Wind has a low density and is not capable of picking up and transporting heavy sediments. Sand grains transported by wind move by skipping and bouncing along the surface. Silt and clay sediments are easily transported by the wind, but are not easily lifted by the wind. These types of particles tend to lie flat on the

surface. In order to be carried by wind currents they must first be lifted or ejected into the current. For example, wind blowing across a desert road. There is very little dust raised on a quiet road but a road with traffic generates a lot of dust.

7. In what way does a glaciated mountain valley differ from a nonglaciated mountain valley? See Figure 35.22.
A glaciated mountain valley begins its formation in a previously formed stream valley. The glacier carves out the existing features and further accentuates them. A glaciated valley is characterized by sharp, angular features, it is deep and wide with a characteristic U-shape. A non-glaciated mountain valley is characterized by a narrow V-shaped valley.

8. Are underground rivers ever found in nature? Explain.
Yes. Underground rivers are often found where groundwater flows through limestone. In most other sediments and rocks, there are no underground rivers; groundwater usually flows through pores.

9. Describe the formation of caves and caverns in limestone.
Groundwater flow in limestone aquifers occurs mostly through fractures in the rock, rather than through pores. As rainwater (enriched in carbonic acid) soaks into limestone, it moves through these fractures. As the groundwater flows toward a stream, as shown in Figure 35.4a, the slightly acidic water dissolves the surrounding limestone, causing the fractures to become larger. This eventually creates an underground channel. The stream that the groundwater is flowing toward also dissolves and erodes its stream channel, causing the water level in the stream and the water table to drop. This lowering of the water table drains the water from the underground, forming caves.

10. Do you think a stream in which the flow is laminar can become turbulent without increasing the volume of water in the stream?
Yes, because the speed of a stream can increase without increasing the volume of water in the stream. As we learned in Chapter 34 and in this chapter, stream speed can increase in many ways. If stream speed increases, a laminar flow can become turbulent.

11. Why is it that water is the main cause of erosion in the desert, even though there is very little water?
Rare as water is in the desert, when a heavy rain falls, the water does not have time to soak into the ground and causes flash floods. These flash floods transport and then deposit great quantities of debris and sediment

12. Why is it that the sand of some beaches is composed of small pieces of sea shells?
Sand-sized fragments from coral reefs and carbonate platforms make up the white-sand beaches in many island areas, such as Hawaii. Look carefully at the sand in such tropical beaches, and you'll see it is predominantly composed of shell fragments. The shell fragments come from the erosion of the nearby reefs and carbonate platforms.

13. Describe the formation of stalactites.
Water dripping down from cave ceilings, which is rich in dissolved calcium carbonate, creates icicle-shaped stalactites as water evaporates and the calcium carbonate precipitates.

14. Why do we say that surface water is both a creator and destroyer of sediments and sedimentary rocks?
Surface water erodes rocks and sediments and transports them from their original locations. Surface water also deposits sediments as a stream's ability to carry sediments declines with speed.

15. Why do point bars form on the inside bends of meandering streams?

Point bars are depositional features that form because stream speed is slowest on the inside bend of a curve. Stream speed is greatest on the outside bends, which causes cut banks to form.

16. Name three environments that favor evaporite deposits. What, if anything, do they have in common?
Modern-day and ancient evaporites are found in desert basins, tidal flats, and restricted sea basins. They all are environments where the evaporation of water dominates over the accumulation of water.

17. What can we learn from glacial striations? In the context of modern continental glaciation, is there any other way to get the same information about the direction of glacial movement? Would that method work to learn about ancient continental glaciation?
Glacial striations tell the direction of ice movement. For modern continental glaciers, we could simply infer that the glacier moved from cold areas to warm areas during glacial advances, and the reverse for glacial retreats. However, as we learned in Chapter 33, landmasses have shifted around over geologic time, and what was once a "cold" region may no longer be so. Therefore using the current climate to infer the direction of ancient glaciers would not work.

18. How is a roches moutonee different from a drumlin?
Roche moutonees are an erosional feature in which the steep side points in the direction of glacial advance. Drumlins are depositional features in which the steep side points in the direction of glacial retreat.

36 A Brief History of the Earth

Learning Objectives
After studying Chapter 36, students will be able to:
• Describe the concept of the Geologic Time Scale.
• State the assumption of uniformitarianism.
• Describe the five principals used for relative dating.
• Define radiometric dating and state its importance.
• Describe the relationship between relative dating and radiometric dating.
• Name some of the radioactive isotopes used for radiometric dating.
• Describe several important aspects and events for each of the eras in the Geologic Time Scale.
• Name the current era, period and epoch.
• Describe how it is that we are now currently in an ice age.
• Describe the role of humans in geologic time.

Possible Misconceptions to Correct
• **Not so!** The Earth is not very old.
• **Not so!** Humans and dinosaurs coexisted with one another.
• **Not so!** All life forms now in existence evolved recently.
• **Not so!** Extinctions occur only because of catastrophic events.

In the **Explorations Practice Book:**
• Relative Time
• Age Relationships
• Radiometric dating
• Our Earth's Hot Interior

In the **Next-Time Questions Book:**
• The age of the Earth

In the **Lab Manual**:
There are no labs for Chapter 36.

Overhead Transparencies available for :
Figure 36.5

SUGGESTED PRESENTATION

It has been said that children can't really appreciate history, because their own experience of time is too limited for them to have an appreciation of any time scale. A fully conscious insect with a few-hour life span similarly would have no idea that the plant or tree it feeds upon has a "short" life cycle that fits in the life cycles of other life forms that utilize trees. "Short" to us, that is. Upon casual observation, even we are not fully aware of the actions of plants and trees. Because their activities are in "slow motion" we do not see that vegetation is every bit as violent as animals in maintaining their hierarchical positions in the food chain. Even slower and more violent are the Earth's geological processes. Like the insect with the few-hour life span, we are not aware of long-term changes—unless we study our surroundings very carefully—which is what this course is about!

Early (European) thoughts about geologic history
Before ~ 1500 (pre-Renaissance)—strictly biblical.
~ 1500   **DaVinci** (Italy) —Questioned the flood as the cause of fossils.
~1670   **Nicolaus Steno** —Superposition, Original Horizontality, Lateral Continuity
              Robert Hooke —Looked at fossils with a microscope; suggested fixed life span for species; questioned flood.
~1785   **James Hutton/John Playfair** (Scotland) —Uniformitarianism, etc.
~1800   **William Smith** (England)—Map completed in 1815, plus table of strata; general ideas about correlation of fossils.
              W. Smith/G. Cuvier (France) Principle of faunal succession (oldest fossils are in lowest strata). Principle of faunal assemblages (strata with similar fossils are similar age).

Principles plus lots of detailed descriptive work led to relative time scales (which are always in the process of being revised).

Early attempts at establishing absolute time scale
1654   **Archbishop Ussher** (Ireland): Added up life spans of old testament characters; Earth was created in 4004 B.C., on October 26 at 9 a.m. (apparently he wasn't into significant figures!). Very influential for about 150 years, and is still cited.
~1760   **Buffon** (>100 years later) 75,000 years based on cooling rate of Earth's iron core.
~1850   **Kelvin** (Scotland) 20-40 million years, based on cooling of Earth.
              Kelvin ~ 18 million years, and **Helmholtz** 20-40 million years, both based on radiation from Sun, assuming energy from gravitational contraction.
~1893   **Walcott** ~75 million years, based on total thickness of strata.
1899   **Joly** ~90 - 100 million years, based on salt accumulation in the ocean.

During this time radioactivity was discovered by Becquerel (France), x-rays by Roentgen (Germany), and radium was isolated by Curie (France). In 1905 Rutherford suggested the use of radioactivity for dating. In 1950 Libby (USA) developed C-14 dating.

36.1 The Geologic Clock

We begin by looking into the Earth's time scale. Draw a long line on the chalkboard. Then segment the line into twelve equal pieces to represent the months of the year, going from January to December. In the various sections mark off the time for the different events. Some of the dates used are not known with great precision (especially early dates). So I am providing the dates used in developing this time line.

Jan 1—the origin of the Earth. (4.5 billion years ago)
Feb 26 —Earliest Earth rocks. (3.8 billion)
Mar 23—first simple life and photosynthesis. (3.5 billion)
July 22—free oxygen begins to accumulate in the atmosphere. (2.0 billion)
Sept 1—first green algae and organisms with a nucleus. (1.5 billion)
Nov 17—the proliferation of life—the beginning of the Paleozoic Era. (544 million)
Nov 21—first fish; the first vertebrate. (505 million; Cambrian-Ordovician boundary)
Nov 27—life on land (plants). (423 million; mid-Silurian)
Dec 2—amphibians move to land. (360 million; Devonian-Carboniferous boundary)
Dec 13—first mammals. (226 million; mid-Triassic)
Dec 14 to Dec 26—the age of the dinosaur. (215 to 66 million; mid-Triassic to end of Cretaceous)
Dec 31 at 11:49 p.m.—Humans emerge. (90,000 years ago)
Dec 31, fourteen seconds before midnight—the birth of Christ. (33 B.C.)
Dec 31, two seconds before midnight—the Declaration of Independence. (1776)
Dec 31, about one second before midnight—the start of the Industrial Revolution. (1800)

Follow this up with the analogy: If the age of the Earth is the length of the Golden Gate Bridge (about 6000 ft long), then 600 years of civilization is 0.1 inch (about the thickness of a car key)! Whereas most fields of study are concerned with no more than the car key, geologists are concerned with the whole bridge! (Or carrying this further, cosmologists are concerned with the bridge and its more than 2-mile long on ramp!)

36.2 Relative Dating-The Placement of Rocks in Order

Relative Dating tells us the sequence that events occurred—if one event happened before another event. Generalizations concerning contacts of rock masses —where two rock masses are in contact with one another, the younger rock mass is the one that 1) contains fragments of the other, 2) sends tongues or branches into the other, 3) bakes or alters the other, 4) cuts across the layers or structures of the other, 5) overlies the other. Point out that an object must exist before anything can happen to it.

36.3 Radiometric Dating Reveals the Actual Time of Rock Formation

Radiometric Dating gives us the absolute age of rock. Radiometric dating is a refinement of relative time. This section can be tied to the earlier material on radioactivity. Point out that the age of the Earth is not estimated by analyzing rocks that formed 4.5 billion years ago. Instead scientist have dated certain meteorites which presumably coalesced at the same time as the Earth. The processes of erosion, volcanism and plate tectonics have effectively obliterated all traces of the Earth's early history.

CHECK YOUR NEIGHBOR: The Earth is some 4.5 billion years old, yet the oldest rocks only date back to 3.7 billion years. Why don't we find rocks dated at 4.5 billion years? [The material that may have formed any rocks 4.5 billion years ago has been mixed back into the stew that made up the Earth's surface that long ago.]

36.4 The Precambrian Era, the Time of Hidden Life

The Precambrian comprises over 85 percent of the Earth's history. In this time the Earth's surface cooled, which allowed the formation of lithospheric plates. The development of photosynthesis generated free oxygen and the beginning of primordial life forms.

CHECK YOUR NEIGHBOR: From where did the oxygen that makes a large part of the Earth's early atmosphere originate? [Mainly from the waste products of plant life.]

CHECK YOUR NEIGHBOR: From where did the oxygen that makes a large part of today's atmosphere originate? [Mainly from the waste products of plant life.]

36.5 The Paleozoic Era, a Time of Life Diversification

The Paleozoic Era marks the first abundant fossil evidence of life. The significant occurrences of the Paleozoic include the emergence of many diverse life forms and the formation of the supercontinent of Pangaea.

36.6 The Mesozoic Era, When Dinosaurs Ruled the Earth

The Mesozoic Era is the age of the reptile. The subject of dinosaurs has always been of general interest. If there is a natural history museum in your area, try to get a field trip together. Even the movie "Jurassic Park" generates interesting discussions. For instance, were dinosaurs warm blooded or cold blooded? The main goal is to get students interested — a spark may lead to a fire. Science is an ongoing process and at present we don't know all the answers. The world is like a big puzzle, with each piece an answer to a question. The puzzle is incomplete. The main points of the Mesozoic Era include the rise and fall of the dinosaurs, the appearance of the first mammals, and the break up of Pangaea.

36.7 The Cenozoic Era, the Time of the Mammal

The Cenozoic Era is the age of the mammals, and is the Era in which humans evolved. For a more biological and cultural approach (integration) discuss how people from various areas around the world are different.

Point out that humans, like other species from previous geologic time, adapt to the environment to survive. But humans do more than adapt — they also change the environment. Humans can be a geologic force. This ties in to the problems of water contamination discussed in Chapter 34.

Relate your discussion about the Pleistocene to the effects of glacial erosion. Point out that there have been several glacial and interglacial periods in the present ice age. Many people do not realize that we are still in an ice age. An ice age can be defined as a time period when continental scale glaciers (such as the polar ice caps) are present. You may remark about the Little Ice Age—the period of cold between the 15th and 19th Century. The Little Ice Age is depicted in the paintings of ice skaters by Flemish artists. Point out that glacial advances are accompanied by a drop in sea level, due to water taken up by glacial ice.

Chapter 36 Answers and Solutions

Key Terms and Matching Definitions

__7__ angular unconformity
_11__ Cenozoic
__3__ cross-cutting
__5__ faunal succession
__4__ inclusions
_10__ Mesozoic
__1__ original horizontality
__9__ Paleozoic
_12__ Precambrian
__8__ radiometric dating
__2__ superposition
__6__ unconformity

Review Questions

1. Suppose we find a certain type of sediment deposit in all modern streams. On a geologic expedition in unknown territory, we find the same type of deposit in ancient rocks. What can we say about the ancient rocks? What assumption are we making?
We can assume that the ancient rocks represent the location of an ancient stream. This assumption is called *uniformitarianism*.

2. What five principles are used in relative dating? Describe each one.
1. Original horizontality. Layers of sediment are deposited evenly, with each new layer laid down nearly horizontally over older sediment.
2. Superposition. In an undeformed sequence of sedimentary rocks, each layer is older than the one above and younger than the one below.
3. Crosscutting. An igneous intrusion or fault that cuts through preexisting rock is younger than the rock through which it cuts.
4. Inclusion. Any inclusion is older than the rock containing it.
5. Faunal succession. Fossil organisms succeed one another in a definite, irreversible time sequence.

3. When a granitic dike is found in a bed of sandstone, what can be said about the relative ages of the dike and the age of the sandstone? What is this principle called?
If a granitic dike is cutting across a bed of sandstone, the sandstone must be older than the granite, because the sandstone had to there in order for the granite to cut through it. This is the principle of cross-cutting relationships.

4. Why aren't all rock formations found with a continuous sequence from the beginning of time to the present?
Weathering and erosion, crustal uplifts, and other geologic processes interrupt the normal sequence of deposition, creating breaks or gaps in the rock record.

5. Explain how fossils of fishes and other marine animals occur at high elevations such as the Himalayan Mountains.
Such a find is evidence of crustal uplift. The rocks that contain the fossils used to be at the bottom of the sea.

6. In an undeformed sequence of rocks, fossil X is found in a limestone layer at the bottom of the formation, and fossil Y is found in a shale layer at the top of the formation. What can we say about the ages of fossils X and Y?

Using the principles of inclusion and superposition, we can say that fossil X is older than fossil Y.

7. What is the definition of half-life?
The time required for half the atoms in a sample of a radioactive isotope to decay.

8. What isotope is best for dating very old rocks?
Radiometric dating with uranium-238 is best for dating very old rocks. (This isotope shows the oldest rocks on the Earth are 3.8 billion years old. Rocks containing micas and feldspars are often dated by measuring the amounts of parent potassium-40 and daughter argon-40.)

9. What isotope is commonly used for dating sediments or organic material from the Pleistocene?
Carbon-14.

10. Which of the geologic time units spans the greatest length of time?
The Precambrian era.

11. How old is the Earth?
Approximately 4.5 billion years.

12. The Paleozoic era experienced several fluctuations in sea level. What effect did this have on life forms?
When shallow seas covered the continent, marine life flourished. Changing sea levels greatly influenced the progression and diversification of life forms—from marine invertebrates to fishes, amphibians, and reptiles.

13. What is the Silurian period best known for?
The Silurian brought the emergence of terrestrial life, the earliest known being terrestrial plants that had a well-developed circulatory system (vascular plants).

14. The Devonian is known as "the age of fishes." What were some of the Devonian life forms?
Lowland forests of seed ferns, scale trees, and true ferns flourished in the Devonian. In the seas, the fishes diversified into many new groups. Some, such as the shark and bony fishes, are still present today. The first amphibians made their appearance during the late Devonian.

15. Why do many geologists consider the lobe-finned fishes to be especially significant?
The lobe-finned fishes are of particular interest because of their development of internal nostrils, which enabled some species to breathe air. Another important characteristic of the lobe-finned fishes is that their fins were lobed and muscular with jointed appendages that enabled the animals to walk.

16. During what time period were most coal deposits laid down? Why was this period unique?
Most coal deposits were laid down in the Carboniferous period. The warm, moist climatic conditions brought about lush vegetation and dense swampy forests. These swamps were the source of the extensive coal beds that now lie under North America, Europe, and northern China.

17. What group evolved from the amphibians with the development of the amniote egg?
The reptiles.

18. What is the Mesozoic era known as?
The age of reptiles.

19. What is the most likely cause of the Cretaceous extinction that wiped out the dinosaurs?
A meteorite impact.

20. What Pangaean landmass survives to this day?
    Only that of Europe and Asia has survived to the present time.

21. What geologic event allowed the development of many mammals in the early Cenozoic?
    The extinction of the dinosaurs and other Mesozoic reptiles left many biological niches vacant. The mammals were able to evolve and fill these empty niches.

22. What role did tectonic activity play in the formation of the San Andreas Fault?
    The collision between the westward moving North American Plate and the Pacific ridge system occurred about 30 million years ago, giving birth to the San Andreas Fault.

Solutions to Chapter 36 Exercises

1. Suppose you see a group of sedimentary rock layers overlain by a basalt flow. A fault displaces the bedding of the sedimentary rock but does not intersect the basalt flow. Relate the fault to the ages of the two rock types in the formation.
   The fault is clearly older than the basalt and younger than the sedimentary rock. The sedimentary rock had to be there before the fault in order for the fault to displace it. The reverse argument holds for the basalt.

2. If a sedimentary rock contains inclusions of metamorphic rock, which rock is older?
   The metamorphic rock had to have been in existence before the sedimentary rock in order for there to be pieces of it in the sedimentary rock.

3. Refer to the following figure. Using the principles of relative dating, determine the relative ages of the rock bodies and other lettered features. Start with the question: What was there first?
   From oldest to youngest the sequence is: G, A, B, C, D, I, H, F, E

4. Which isotopes are most appropriate for dating rocks from the following ages: (a) the early Precambrian; (b) the Mesozoic; (c) the late Pleistocene?
   a) Uranium-238 (or possibly Potassium-40, depending on how early)
   b) Uranium-235 or Potassium-40 are best, but Uranium-238 will work too (not as precise).
   c) Carbon-14 is the only reasonable isotope to use.

5. Has the amount of uranium in the Earth increased over geologic time? Has the amount of lead increased? Explain.
   Uranium has decreased and lead increased (via radioactive decay).

6. Granitic pebbles within a sedimentary rock have a radiometric age of 300 million years. What can you say about the age of the sedimentary rock? Nearby, a dike having a radiometric age of 200 million years intrudes an outcrop of the same sedimentary rock. What can we say about the age of the sedimentary rock?
   Since the pebbles are clearly older than the sedimentary rock, the rock is no more than 300 million years old. Since the dike is younger than the sedimentary rock, the age of the sedimentary rock can now be bracketed between 200 and 300 million years.

7. Geologists often refer to the early Paleozoic as the "Cambrian Explosion". What do you think is meant by this phrase?
   The phrase refers to the great diversity of life found in the fossil record that was not apparent in the Precambrian. Almost all major groups of marine organisms came into existence during the Cambrian period, as evidenced by abundant fossils. The Cambrian saw the development of organisms having the ability to secrete calcium carbonate and calcium phosphate for the formation of outer skeletons, or shells. The preservation of these shells as fossils is why so much more is known about the Paleozoic than the Precambrian.

8. What is the difference between a nonconformity and an angular unconformity?

A nonconformity is a gap in the rock record represented by sedimentary rocks overlying the eroded surface of intrusive igneous or metamorphic rocks. This type of unconformity represents large amounts of uplift and an enormous amount of "missing" time. An angular unconformity is tilted or folded sedimentary rocks overlain by younger, relatively horizontal rock layers. This represents a deformational event, such as mountain building, followed by a period of subsidence and deposition.

9. What key developments in life occurred during the Precambrian era?
The first atmosphere developed, the ozone layer developed, stromatolites appeared. Stromatolites and certain algae developed photosynthesis, which put free oxygen into the atmosphere.

10. What factors are believed to have contributed to the generation of free oxygen during the early Precambrian? In what way did the increase in oxygen affect our planet?
Stromatolites and certain algae developed photosynthesis, which uses sunlight and carbon dioxide and produces oxygen as a byproduct. With the release of free oxygen, a primitive ozone layer began to develop above the Earth's surface. The ozone layer reduced the amount of harmful ultraviolet radiation reaching the Earth. This protection and the accumulation of free oxygen in the Earth's atmosphere permitted the emergence of new life.

11. What evidence do we have of Precambrian life?
Stromatolites and other fossils in rocks that are known to be Precambrian in age.

12. Why can we find Paleozoic marine sedimentary rocks, such as limestone and dolomite, widely distributed in the continental interiors?
Several times during the Paleozoic the continents were flooded by shallow seas.

13. Coal beds are formed from the accumulation of plant material that becomes trapped in swamp floors. Yet coal deposits are found on the continent of Antarctica, where no swamps or vegetation exists. How can this be?
At the time of deposition, the climate of Antarctica was mild enough to support swamps.

14. A radiometric date is determined from mica that has been removed from a rock. What does the date signify if the mica is found in granite? What does the date signify if the mica is found in sedimentary rock?
If found in granite, the date signifies the age of the granite (when the mineral crystallized from magma). If found in sedimentary rock, it tells us that the rock can be no older than the date of the mica mineral.

15. How does iridium relate to the time of the extinction of the dinosaurs?
The cause of the extinction is still a source of some debate among scientists. Luis and Walter Alvarez hypothesize that the extinction was caused by the impact of a large meteorite. This hypothesis is supported by an abundance of iridium in sediments that mark the boundary between the Cretaceous and Tertiary periods. In general, the composition of large meteorites is similar to the composition of the Earth, including similar concentrations of iridium. Because most of the Earth's iridium is deep in its interior, the concentration of iridium in a meteorite is higher than the iridium concentration in the Earth's crust. All over the world the concentration of iridium in sediments at the K/T boundary is much greater than in sediments above or below the boundary. The K/T boundary layer was deposited about 65 million years ago—the time of the great dinosaur extinction.

16. During the Earth's long history, life has emerged and life has perished. Briefly discuss the emergence of life and the extinction of life for each era.
<u>Precambrian</u> — first life; stromatolites, bacteria, algae; soft-bodied animals.

<u>Paleozoic</u> — trilobites, shelled animals, first life on land, first fish, first amphibians, first reptiles; major extinctions in the Ordovician and Permian.

<u>Mesozoic</u> — age of the reptiles, dominance and diversification of dinosaurs, first mammals, first bird, first flowering plants; major extinction at the end of the Cretaceous (bye-bye dinosaurs!!)

<u>Cenozoic</u> — age of mammals, diversification of mammals, expansion of flora, emergence of humans; extinction of many large mammals.

17. In what ways could sea level be lowered? What effect might this have on existing life forms?
Sea level could be lowered if the climate turned colder, causing more water to be tied up in glacial ice. This could drastically affect shallow water creatures (habitat destruction) and cause many extinctions. The colder climate could also cause the demise of some species through habitat destruction and scarcity of food. Sea level could also be lowered if seafloor spreading rates decreased.

18. What could cause a rise in sea level? Is this likely to happen in the future? Why or why not?
Melting of the polar ice caps. This could easily happen if the grim predictions of global warming due to greenhouse gasses were to occur. An increase in seafloor spreading rates could also cause sea level to rise. It is likely that sea level will rise in the future, as it has done in the past.

19. What general assumption must be made to understand the processes that occurred throughout the Earth's history?
The assumption of uniformitarianism states that processes and natural laws that we observe today also occurred or were valid throughout the Earth's history. If we did not make this assumption, we wouldn't know where to start in our mission to decipher the Earth's exciting history.

20. If fine muds were laid down at a rate of 1 cm per 1000 years, how long would it take to accumulate a sequence 1 km thick?
100 million years.

37 The Atmosphere, The Oceans, and Their Interactions

Learning Objectives

After studying Chapter 37, students will be able to:

- Describe how latitude, elevation, topography, and proximity to large bodies of water and cold or warm ocean currents affect temperature.
- Describe how the ozone layer formed and state its importance.
- Relate the different atmospheric gases that absorb the Earth's thermal radiation to the greenhouse effect.
- Name the six layers of the atmosphere in order.
- Describe the thermal and chemical structure of the atmosphere.
- Describe how the differential heating of the Earth results in circulation patterns in the atmosphere and oceans that globally distribute the heat.
- Describe how the angle of the sun affects seasons.
- Describe how heating of the Earth's surface and atmosphere by the sun drives convection within the atmosphere and oceans, producing wind and ocean currents.
- Describe the Coriolis effect and why it exists.
- Describe the interaction of wind patterns, ocean currents, and mountain ranges results in the global pattern of rain forests and deserts at specific latitudes.
- Describe the properties of ocean water, such as temperature and salinity, can be used to explain the layered structure of the oceans and the generation of horizontal and vertical ocean currents.

Possible Misconceptions to Correct

- **Not so!** Areas of the Earth that are closest to the sun are warmer than areas that are away from the sun.
- **Not so!** Distance from the sun determines Earth's surface temperatures.
- **Not so!** Solar radiation directly warms the Earth's lower atmosphere, and hence, the Earth's surface.
- **Not so!** Of all the greenhouse gases, carbon dioxide plays the largest role in confining the Earth's heat.
- **Not so!** An at-home observance of the Coriolis effect can be seen in the direction water spirals down a sink drain.

   351

In the **Explorations Practice Book**:
- Driving Forces of Air Motion
- Short and Long Wavelengths
- The Earth's Seasons

In the **Next-Time Questions Book**:
- Evaporation and Precipitation

In the **Lab Manual**:
- Solar Power I
- Solar Power II

Overhead Transparencies available for:
Figures 37.4 and 37.7

The Earth is powered by the radiant energy of the sun. For more than 4.6 billion years, the sun's radiant energy has traveled across space to the Earth, where a small portion of its solar output is intercepted. Because of the Earth's curvature, the energy at the top of the atmosphere is unevenly distributed, creating an imbalance of energy from the equator to the poles. This unevenness of energy generates circulations in the atmosphere and on the surface below. Because of the Earth's tilt and corresponding uneven distribution of energy during the year, our planet undergoes seasonal change.

Filtering harmful UV radiation, charged particles, and space debris from reaching the Earth's surface, the atmosphere protects our planet as it balances the amount of energy the Earth receives. These surface energy balances give rise to global patterns of temperature, winds and ocean currents—the topics covered in this chapter.

SUGGESTED PRESENTATION

Begin by asking your class where the atoms come from that make up the material that composes a tree? Many think that tree material originates from the ground. [So a massive tree should be in the middle of a hole?] Not so, except for a few minerals and much of the water it takes into its substance, trees get most of their building material from the *air*. When CO_2 impinges on a tree leaf, it is pulled in. The leaf is able to pull the carbon from the molecule and discharge the refuse — the oxygen. How is it able to pull this feat off? By the energy of sunlight! So the next time you take a breath of air, be thankful for the existence of trees. No trees, no oxygen! Wood is composed of mainly hydrogen and carbon. Wood, like us, is a hydrocarbon. And where does the tree get its hydrogen? From water. Again, sunlight provides the energy to make the separation. And what happens when you burn the wood of the tree? It cycles back to its original form, CO_2, which forms when oxygen is energetically slammed against the carbon as in a fire. So the energy of the fire is simply the stored energy of sunlight. Interesting stuff.

37.1 Earth's Atmosphere and Oceans
So where did the early atmosphere come from? Trees? No, from miniature trees of a sort — from green algae — which dates back to the late Precambrian. Like all higher forms of green plants that followed, the algae developed the ability of photosynthesis, the byproduct of which is guess what? Oxygen!

Evidence of early atmospheric compositions are obtained by core samples from the polar ice caps. Tiny air bubbles trapped within the ice are then analyzed for composition. By taking samples from different layers Earth scientists can determine when the air was last floating around in the atmosphere (analogous to dating layers of sedimentary rock!)

Tie in the evolution of the Earth's atmosphere and oceans to the eruption of surface volcanoes and the outside bombardment of interplanetary comets—for both processes contributed. Once the atmosphere and oceans formed, life emerged on the Earth.

37.2 Components of the Earth's Atmosphere
If we make a tall stack of foam-rubber bricks, the bricks at the bottom will be more squashed than the bricks at the top. So it is with the atmosphere. The densest part of the atmosphere is at the Earth's surface (or in mines below). Most of the atmosphere is near the Earth's surface because of gravity. So it is the force of gravity on molecules of air that holds most of the atmosphere from going off into space. (If gravity were less, like on the Moon, molecular speed caused by solar energy would be greater than escape velocity and no atmosphere would be maintained.) The atmosphere thins with altitude and ultimately becomes indistinguishable from the background gas in space. So there is no upper "surface" of the "ocean of air" like there is on the ocean of water.

CHECK QUESTION: When a helium-filled balloon is released in the air, how high does it go? Does it leave the Earth's atmosphere? [It doesn't get very high before it bursts, usually within sight. Why does it burst? Because surrounding air pressure decreases with height allowing the balloon to grow until it ruptures. Special balloons for high-altitude measurements can achieve altitudes into the stratosphere without bursting — another story.]

37.3 Solar Energy
Do the flashlight demonstration suggested in the text. Take the demonstration one step further by bringing in a globe and showing the wide distribution of light at the poles and the concentration of light at the equator. Relate seasons to the Earth's tilt. New Englanders who revel in the fall foliage and others who enjoy the seasonal cycle can be thankful that the polar axis is inclined at 23.5 degrees to the orbit plane (the ecliptic). Use the OHT for Figure 37.7 or draw the sketch on your black board, first with only the two positions of the Earth at the far left and far right. Ask which of these two positions represents winter months and which represents summer months. Encourage neighbor discussion.

Once it is clear that winter is at the left, show the position of the Earth in autumn and in spring. Shift the position of the sun closer to the Earth in winter, for this is actually the case. From your drawing, your class can see why Northern Hemisphere types enjoy an extra week of spring and summer! Southern Hemisphere types are compensated by a somewhat milder climate year round due to the greater amount of ocean in the Southern Hemisphere (80% as compared to about 60% for the Northern Hemisphere).

The Greenhouse Effect
Compare the window glass of the florist's greenhouses to the water vapor and carbon-dioxide window glass of the Earth's atmosphere. Relate the section on solar and terrestrial radiation back to concepts covered in Physics. Short waves easily penetrate the Earth's atmosphere whereas long waves do not (they are reflected back to the Earth thus they warm the Earth). Emphasize that among the atmospheric gases, water vapor plays the largest role in confining the Earth's heat. Although increased levels of carbon dioxide have impacted the Earth's atmosphere, more information is needed before we can identify the major causes of global warming. Recent studies, for example, indicate that hurricanes kick appreciable amounts of carbon dioxide from the ocean into the atmosphere. Emphasize and reemphasize that the Earth has undergone many climatic changes during her long history (see box on global

warming). How much human activities affect these changes is usually overestimated in the media.

State that terrestrial radiation rather than solar radiation is directly responsible for the warmth of the air around us. Air is primarily warmed by the Earth, which is an important reason we don't freeze at night when we're not in the sun's light. Three cheers for terrestrial radiation!

Interesting point: The Earth is always "in equilibrium" whether it is overheating or not. At a higher temperature, as global warming produces, the Earth simply radiates more terrestrial radiation. Income and outgo match in any case; the important consideration is the temperature at which this income and outgo match.

As an interesting side point that has to do with adjusting to heating, cite how a frog cannot discern small changes in temperature, and if sitting comfortably in a pan of water that is slowly heated on a stove, it will make no effort to jump out as the water as temperature increases. It will just sit there and be cooked. But this is not limited to frogs. According to accounts given by cannibals who cook their victims in large pots of water, the same is true of humans. This was a sad fact some 25 years ago in Mill Valley, CA, where water in a hot tub gradually overheated (due to a faulty heater) and resulted in the death of the unsuspecting and drowsy occupants. You can compare this to other cases where if adverse conditions are increased gradually, humans will tolerate what otherwise would be completely unacceptable to them: smog, noise, pollution, crime, and so on.

37.4 Driving Forces of Air Motion
Consider a non spinning world with a uniform surface and without clouds. Then you have a world with very little air and water movement and a world without weather. For it is the unequal heating of the Earth's surface that produces the fluctuations in the atmosphere. Give the world a spin and you'll get meandering waves moving west-east just below the poles. You now have a world with jet streams.

The processes of the pressure gradient force, Coriolis force, and frictional force operate on both the atmosphere as well as the ocean. Emphasize the connections between these two fluids—what effects one effects the other. Atmospheric circulation assists in the important transfers of energy and mass on Earth Together, Earth's atmospheric and oceanic circulations represent a vast heat engine powered by the sun.

37.5 Global Circulation Patterns
Similar to the atmosphere, the ocean can be divided into layers—the surface layer, the transitional layer, and the deep layer. In each of these layers salinity, temperature, and density vary. Although these variations contribute to the flow of water, the underlying cause of water movement relates back to the atmosphere and the uneven distribution of solar energy.

DEMONSTRATION: Fill a large basin with fresh water. Fill a large container (clear soda bottles work nicely) with fresh water, fill another large container with salt water (salt concentration can vary, but keep track of amount of salt added.) One at a time, submerge the water filled containers into the basin. Measure the amount of water displaced by the fresh water filled container. Measure the amount of water displaced by the salt water filled container. Compare the amount of displacement. The salt water filled container should displace the volume of the salt added.

Chapter 37 Answers and Solutions

Key Terms and Matching Definitions

__8__ Coriolis effect
__6__ greenhouse effect
__9__ gyre
__5__ ionosphere
__3__ mesosphere
__7__ salinity
__2__ stratosphere
__4__ thermosphere
__1__ troposphere

Review Questions

1. What were the main components of the Earth's first atmosphere? What happened to this atmosphere?
   Hydrogen and helium, along with a few simple compounds such as ammonia and methane. When the sun was born, the blast from the sun's formation likely produced a strong outflow of charged particles—strong enough to sweep the Earth of its earliest atmosphere.

2. The Earth's present atmosphere likely developed from gases that escaped from the interior of the Earth during volcanic eruptions. What were the three principal atmospheric gases produced by these eruptions?
   Probably much like the gases found in the volcanic eruptions of today—about 85% water vapor, 10% carbon dioxide, and 5% nitrogen, by mass. (The early atmosphere had no free oxygen and therefore was inhospitable to the type of life we have today.)

3. Explain the importance of photosynthesis in the evolution of the atmosphere.
   The production of free oxygen did not occur until the primitive plants known as stromatolites and green algae appeared. These plants used photosynthesis to convert CO_2 and H_2O to hydrocarbon and free oxygen. With the production of free oxygen, an ozone (O_3) layer formed in the upper atmosphere, which reduced the amount of UV radiation reaching the Earth's surface. The surface therefore became more hospitable to life. The evolution of oxygen in this global envelope was a vital step in the history of Earth and its life.

4. What elements make up today's atmosphere?
   Primarily nitrogen and oxygen, with small amounts of water vapor, argon, and carbon dioxide.

5. Being that our atmosphere developed as a result of volcanic eruptions, why aren't there higher traces of atmospheric carbon dioxide, one of the principal volcanic gases?
   CO_2 Dissolves in the ocean.

6. Does temperature increase or decrease as one moves upward in the troposphere? As one moves upward in the stratosphere?
   Decreases; increases.

7. What causes the fiery displays of light called the *auroras*?
   High-speed ions ejected from the sun stir up the ionosphere.

8. What does the angle at which the sun strikes the Earth have to do with the temperate and polar regions?

The lower angle in the sky spreads light over a larger area, reducing the temperature.

9. What does the tilt of the Earth have to do with the change of seasons?
   The tilt of the Earth is what is responsible for the seasons.

10. Why are the hours of daylight equal all around the world on the two equinoxes?
    See Fig. 37.7. Only at those times does the Earth's axis point neither toward nor away from sun.

11. How does radiation emitted from the Earth differ from that emitted by the sun?
    Lower temperature Earth radiates lower frequency radiation; high temperature sun emits higher frequency radiation.

12. How is the atmosphere near the Earth's surface heated from below?
    It is heated by terrestrial radiation as well as by solar radiation.

13. What are the three main driving forces of air motion?
    Temperature differences, pressure differences, and surface friction.

14. What is the underlying cause of air motion?
    The underlying cause of general air circulation is the unequal heating of the Earth's surface.

15. How does the Coriolis effect determine the general path of air circulation?
    The Coriolis deflects winds toward the right in the N. Hemisphere and toward the left in the S. Hemisphere. The magnitude of the Coriolis effect varies according to 1) the speed of the wind: the faster the speed, the greater the deflection, 2) latitude: deflection is greatest at the poles and decreases to zero at the equator.

16. What is the characteristic climate of the doldrums and why does it occur?
    At the equator, direct heat causes air to flow vertically upward with very little horizontal movement, resulting in a vast low-pressure zone. The rising motion creates a narrow, windless realm of air that is still, hot, and stagnant. When the moist air rises, it cools and releases torrents of rain. Over land areas these frequent rains give rise to the tropical rain forests that characterize the equatorial region.

17. In summer, Southeast Asia, India, and Africa experience heavy flooding. Why?
    The subtropical jet stream. The formation of this jet stream is related to the warming of the air above the Tibetan highlands. During the summer, the air above the continental highlands is warmer than the air above the ocean to the south. Thus temperature and pressure gradients generate strong on-shore winds that contribute to the region's (rainy) climate. During winter, the winds change direction to produce a dry season.

18 What factors set surface ocean currents into motion?
   The forces that drive the winds also impact the movement of seawater: Temperature differences, pressure differences, and surface friction.

19. How does the Coriolis effect influence the movement of surface waters?
    Friction is a primary force that sets surface waters into motion. If distances are short, the surface waters move in the same direction as the wind. For longer distances, however, the deflective Coriolis effect causes surface waters to spiral in a gyre. The circular motion is clockwise in the N. Hemisphere and counterclockwise in the S. Hemisphere.

20. Explain the circulation pattern of the Gulf Stream.
    In the North Atlantic Ocean, warm equatorial water flows westward into and around the Gulf of Mexico then northward along the eastern coast of the United States. This warm-

water current is called the *Gulf Stream*. As the Gulf Stream flows northward along the North American coast, the prevailing westerlies steer the warm current eastward toward Europe. As the warm current encounters Europe, it is diverted southward toward the equator where it is once again picked up by the trade winds to move westward into the Gulf of Mexico and once again become part of the Gulf Stream.

21. How does the density of seawater vary with changes in temperature? How does density change with salinity?
Cold water is denser than warm water, cold seawater sinks below warmer seawater. Salinity also affects density: The greater the salinity, the greater the density.

Solutions to Chapter 37 Exercises

1. It being true that a gas fills all the space available to it, why doesn't the atmosphere go off into space?
It does! The atmosphere is mostly concentrated near the surface because of gravity. Gravity is what holds most of the atmosphere from going off into space. It does, however, thin out as you move away from the Earth's surface until it becomes indistinguishable from the background gas in space. This is why there is no upper limit placed on the atmosphere.

2. Why do your ears pop when you ascend to higher altitudes? Explain.
The air pressure at higher altitudes is less than at the surface. Time is required for your body to adjust to this new pressure, so the air inside your body pushes outward more than the atmosphere pushes inward, producing that popping feeling.

3. The Earth is closest to the sun in January, but January is cold in the Northern Hemisphere. Why?
In January the Northern Hemisphere on the Earth is tilted away from the sun, so it receives less solar radiation per unit area.

4. How do the total number of hours of sunlight in a year compare for tropical regions and polar regions of the Earth? Why are polar regions so much colder?
The total hours of sunlight (and solar energy) are dependent on the incidence of the sun's rays on the Earth's surface. In tropical regions the sun's rays are concentrated as they strike perpendicular to the Earth's surface. As such, tropical regions receive twice as much solar energy as in polar regions. In polar regions, the sun's rays are at an angle and solar energy is spread out and dispersed. As such, polar regions are cool. The tilt of the Earth allows polar regions to receive nearly 24 hours of sunlight (albeit, dispersed sunlight) for half the year, and nearly 24 hours of darkness the other half of the year.

5. How do the wavelengths of radiant energy vary with the temperature of the radiating source? How does this affect solar and terrestrial radiation?
High temperature sources radiate short wavelengths and cooler sources radiate longer wavelengths. The hot sun emits waves of much shorter wavelengths than the waves emitted by Earth (terrestrial radiation). Radiation from the sun is mainly in the visible region of electromagnetic waves, whereas terrestrial radiation is infrared.

6. How is global warming affected by the relative transparencies of the atmosphere to long- and short-wavelength electromagnetic radiation?
The Earth absorbs short-wavelength radiation from the sun and reradiates it as long-wavelength terrestrial radiation. Incoming short wave-length solar radiation easily penetrates the atmosphere to reach and warm the Earth's surface, but outgoing long-wavelength terrestrial radiation cannot penetrate the atmosphere to escape into space. Instead, atmospheric gases (mainly water vapor and carbon dioxide) absorb the long-wave terrestrial radiation. As a result, this long-wave radiation ends up keeping the Earth's surface warmer than it would be if the atmosphere were not present.

7. Why is it important that mountain climbers wear sunglasses and use sunblock even when the temperature is below freezing?

Air temperature is not the factor. Solar radiation is. At high elevations there is less atmosphere above you to filter UV rays, so you are exposed to more high-energy radiation.

8. If there were no water on the Earth's surface, would weather occur? Defend your answer.

Yes, without oceans there would still be weather. Unequal heating of the Earth's surface is responsible for weather, and this is greatly affected by the presence of oceans, but by no means completely dependent upon oceans. Winds and other weather conditions occur on other planets, all without oceans. And on the Earth, far inland away from bodies of water, weather conditions such as Chinook winds and tornadoes occur.

9. If the Earth were not spinning, what direction would the surface winds blow where you live? What direction does it blow on the real Earth at 15° S latitude and why?

Although directions are variable, on a non-spinning Earth surface winds would still blow from areas of high pressure to low pressure. On the real Earth at 15° S latitude we are in the region of the doldrums where the air is warm and the winds are light. In this region the light winds blow from east to west.

10. What is the relationship between global atmospheric circulation and ocean currents? Relate oceanic gyres to patterns of subtropical high pressure.

Cell-like circulation patterns set up by atmospheric temperature and pressure differences are responsible for the redistribution of heat across the Earth's surface and global winds. Because the winds set the surface waters into motion, atmospheric circulation and oceanic circulation are interrelated. What affects one affects the other. Ocean currents do not follow the wind pattern exactly however; they spiral in a circular whirl pattern—a gyre. In the Northern Hemisphere as prevailing winds blow clockwise and outward from a subtropical high, the ocean currents move in a more or less circular, but clockwise, pattern. The Gulf Stream, a warm water current in the North Atlantic Ocean, is actually part of a huge gyre.

11. Relate the jet stream to upper-air circulation. How does this circulation pattern relate to airline schedules from New York to San Francisco and the return trip to New York?

Jet streams are usually found between elevations of 10 and 15 kilometers, although they can occur at higher and lower elevations. As a swiftly flowing westerly wind, the jet streams greatly influence upper-air circulation as they transfer heat from polar regions to tropical regions. As a westerly wind, air travel is faster from west to east and slower from east to west. Thus, flights from San Francisco to New York are shorter in time than the return trip from New York to San Francisco.

12. What are the jet streams and how do they form?

The high-speed winds of the upper troposphere. With wind speeds averaging between 95 and 190 km per hour, the jet streams play an essential role in the global transfer of thermal energy from the equator to the poles.

    There are two important jet streams, the *polar jet* and the *subtropical jet*. Both form in response to temperature and pressure gradients. The polar jet forms as a result of a temperature gradient at the polar front, where cool polar air meets warm tropical air. The subtropical jet is generated as warm air is carried from the equator to the poles, producing a sharp temperature gradient along the boundary (subtropical front).

13. Why are temperature fluctuations greater over land than water? Explain.

Water has a high heat capacity thus it retains heat longer than a substance with a low heat capacity (like sand or soil). The fact that water takes a long time to cool and that it resists changes in temperature affects the climate of areas close to the oceans. Look at a

globe and notice the high latitude countries of Europe. If water did not have a high specific heat capacity, the coastal countries of Europe would be as cold as the northeastern regions of Canada, for both are at the same latitude.

14. How does the ocean influence weather on land?
The ocean acts to 1) moderate the temperature of coastal lands; and 2) provide a reservoir for atmospheric moisture.

15. What happens to the salinity of seawater when evaporation at the ocean surface exceeds precipitation? When precipitation exceeds evaporation? Explain.
When evaporation exceeds precipitation salinity increases. In ocean water it is the water that evaporates, the salt is left behind. When precipitation exceeds evaporation salinity decreases as a new influx of fresh water dilutes the salt solution.

16. Water denser than surrounding water sinks. With respect to the densities of deeper water, how far does it sink?
It will sink until it reaches a point of equilibrium—the point where it encounters water of the same density.

17. What effect does the formation of sea ice in polar regions have on the density of seawater? Explain.
When seawater in polar regions freezes only the water freezes and the salt is left behind. The seawater that does not freeze experiences an increase in salinity, which in turn brings about an increase in density. The cold, denser, saltier seawater sinks, producing a pattern of vertical movement. Movement is also horizontal as cold dense water flows along the bottom to the deeper parts of the ocean floor.

18. Why are most of the world's deserts found in the area known as the horse latitudes?
As air from the sweltering doldrums rises, it divides and spreads out either to the north or south. At about 30° N and 30° S latitudes, the air has cooled enough to descend toward the surface. As it descends it compresses and warms resulting in a high-pressure zone—a belt of hot, dry surface air. On land, these high-pressure zones account for the world's great deserts.

19. As a volume of seawater freezes, the salinity of the surrounding water increases. Explain.
Seawater does not freeze easily but when it does, only the water freezes, and the salt is left behind. Thus the seawater that does not freeze experiences an increase in salinity, which in turn brings about an increase in density. The cold, denser, saltier seawater sinks, setting up a pattern of vertical movement.

20. Why do the temperate zones have unpredictable weather?
The midlatitudes are noted for their unpredictable weather. Although the winds tend to be westerlies, they are often quite changeable as the temperature and pressure differences between the subtropical and polar air masses at the polar front produce powerful winds.

Answers to Calculation Corner

Dense as Air

1. The density of the air in the tank is 1.25 kilograms/cubic meter. The mass of this air is found by multiplying by the tank volume:

$$\frac{1.25 \text{ kg}}{\text{m}^3} \times 0.0100 \text{ m}^3 = 0.0125 \text{ kg}$$

2. **The mass of the air is found by multiplying the density of the air in the tank by the tank volume:**

$$\frac{240 \text{ kg}}{\text{m}^3} \times 0.0100 \text{ m}^3 = 2.4 \text{ kg}$$

38 Weather

Learning Objectives
After studying Chapter 38, students will be able to:
• Distinguish between humidity and relative humidity.
• State the relationship between dew, frost, and fog.
• Describe the three variables that control weather.
• Name some ways in which heat is exchanged with the air.
• Define adiabatic process and differentiate it from heat exchange.
• Understand temperature inversions and the relationship to smog.
• Describe the formation of a cloud.
• List and describe the different types of clouds.
• Define the term air mass and describe the characteristics of different air masses.
• Understand and describe the three different atmospheric lifting mechanisms.

Possible Misconceptions to Correct
• **Not so!** When the air is saturated, it is raining.
• **Not so!** Weather forecasting is guesswork.
• **Not so!** Smog only occurs because of human pollution.
• **Not so!** All clouds produce precipitation.

Demonstration Equipment
None

In the **Explorations Practice Book**:
• Air Temperature and Pressure Patterns
• Surface Weather Maps

In the **Next-Time Questions Book**:
• Why don't all the water droplets in a cloud fall to the ground?
• Which is more dense: dry air or humid air?
• Evaporation
• Foggy sunglasses (summer)
• Foggy sunglasses (winter)

In the **Lab Manual**:
• Indoor Clouds

Overhead Transparencies available for:
Figures 38.4, 38.5, 38.6, and 38.10

What do most people talk about in casual conversations? The weather, of course. This chapter provides some scientific insights that underlie the weather.

SUGGESTED PRESENTATION

38.1 Water in the Atmosphere
The textbook discusses the energy release that accompanies the condensation of water in the atmosphere. It doesn't discuss the mechanism for this energy release. Interestingly enough, H_2O molecules simply give most of their KE to the air during their last collision before condensation. The details are shown in the three sketches below.

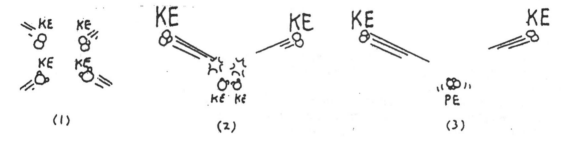

Consider two pairs of molecules, say with equal KEs before collision (Sketch 1). After collision, individual KEs may be quite unequal, for molecules that transfer much of their KE to others are left with corresponding less KE of their own (Sketch 2). So far, there is no change in the air's total KE score. But if the slower molecules happen to be H_2O, they are candidates for condensation if their next collisions are with other H_2Os that have similarly just given most of their KE to neighboring molecules (Sketch 3). Upon condensation of the slow-moving H_2Os, other molecules remaining in the air have an increase in average KE. Voila! *H_2O molecules transfer KE to the surrounding air during their last collision while in the gaseous phase*—the collision that immediately precedes condensation. The energy gained by the air is the well-known heat of vaporization—about 540 calories per gram of condensed H_2O for an ambient temperature of 100°C. It's greater for lower temperatures (molecules bopped to high speeds in a low-speed environment gain more energy than molecules bopped to the same high speeds in higher-speed environments). So all things being equal, a rainy day really is warmer than a cloudy day.

Condensation in the Atmosphere An interesting way to present the condensation of water vapor to droplets is the following: Ask why a glass containing an iced drink becomes wet on the outside, and why a ring of moisture is left on the table. You can inject a bit of humor here and state that the reason has to do with—then pause and write a big 38.1 on the board. Then ask why the walls of the classroom would become wet if the temperature of the room were suddenly reduced. State that the answer is—then underline your 38.1 . Ask why dew forms on the morning grass, and state the answer is—another underline for 38.1. Ask why fog forms, and how the clouds form, and back to your 38.1. By now your class is wondering about the significance of 38.1. Announce you're discussing Figure 38.1, and with class attention and interest go on to discuss the formation of fog and clouds (and even rain, hail, and snow). [Snow crystallizes from vapor; hail is rain that freezes when tossed upward, often repeatedly, by strong updrafts.]

Condensation is enhanced by the presence of ions, dust, or tiny particles that act as the nuclei of droplets. London became much foggier when coal burning provided more particles in the air to initiate condensation.

Evaporation Here we consider the effects of phase changes in the atmosphere. Phase change infers a corresponding energy change. Interesting examples are:

Cooling produced by an air conditioner
Warming produced by a heat pump (an air conditioner "turned backward")
Spraying of crops when frost threatens
Freeze-dried products (including coffee)

CHECK QUESTION: s evaporation greater over warm water or cold water? [Evaporation is greater above warm water, for greater molecular motion pops more of them from the water. Thus evaporation is greater over oceans in warm regions (warm air holds more moisture than cool air) than over oceans in cold polar regions (which is also one reason why there is little snowfall in the polar regions).

It is interesting to note that raindrops evaporate as they fall toward the Earth's surface, so they need to be relatively large in order to reach the Earth's surface. If they are not large enough, they evaporate in the atmosphere forming *virga* (streams seen under clouds).

There are two interesting effects of energy transfer in rainfall. The key concept is that energy is absorbed by something that changes phase from solid Æ liquid Æ gas, and energy is released by something that changes the other way; from gas Æ liquid Æ solid. Consider water vapor condensing to form raindrops. Energy is released by the H_2O, tending to warm the air. But when rain falls, considerable evaporation occurs. If drops evaporate entirely on the way down, then no net energy transfer occurs. When rainfall does reach the ground, which wins, cooling or warming? Pose this as a check question. [For rain that reaches the ground, the net effect is warming—until it again evaporates. Interesting material!]

38.2 Air Masses—Movement and Temperature Changes
Ask if it would be a good idea on a hot day when going for a balloon ride to only wear a T-shirt. Or would it be a good idea to bring warm clothing? A glance at Figure 38.3 will be instructive. You're into the *adiabatic expansion* of rising air in our atmosphere.

But better than words, have your students blow on their hands and feel the warmth of their breath. Then repeat, with lips puckered so the air expands on the way to their hands. Coolness! Likewise for rising air, which cools by about 10°C for each 1-km rise. And what happens to air that descends? Warmness! The air is compressed and its temperature rises (Chinooks).

Discuss the check question in the text about yanking down a giant dry-cleaner's garment bag from a high altitude and the changes in temperature it undergoes. (It's helpful to consider parcels of air as if they were blobs in giant plastic tissue bags—good for visualizing processes.) Then follow this with the second footnote about aircraft heating, which is of considerable interest: but don't assume that because it's in the text that you can't introduce it to your class as if it were brand new information. (We're past that stage, thinking that everything really interesting in the text is absorbed by our students in their reading—or are our students really less scholarly than yours?)

There is more to Chinook winds than is cited in the text. As Figure 38.4 suggests, warm moist air that rises over a mountain cools as it expands, and then undergoes precipitation where it gains latent heat energy as vapor changes state to liquid (rain) or solid (snow). Then when the energetic dry air is compressed as it descends on the other side of the mountain, it is appreciably warmer than if precipitation hadn't occurred. Without the heat gain by the air in precipitation, air would cool in expanding and warm the same amount in compressing, with no net increase in temperature.

Discuss temperature inversion and the role it plays in air pollution; or at least in confining air pollution. On the matter of pollution, we find now that even rain is polluted. Acid rain has wreaked havoc with the environment in many parts of the world. Interestingly enough, pure rain water is naturally acidic. Ever-present carbon dioxide dissolves in water vapor to form carbonic acid. Decomposing organic matter, volcanoes, and geysers can release sulfur dioxides that form sulfuric acid. Lightning storms can cause nitric acid formation. The environmental problem of acid rain, however, is not the small amount caused by natural sources. Fossil fuel combustion is the largest single source of acid-producing compounds. Interestingly enough, it isn't the destruction of vast forests or poisoning of wildlife that has evoked the loudest public outcry—acid rain dulls the high-tech finishes on automobiles, and *that*, for John Q. Public, is going too far!

38.3 There are Many Different Clouds

So air expands as it rises, and therefore cools. What happens to the water molecules in air that cools? Condensation! If it happens high up in the sky, it's called a cloud. If it happens down near the ground, it's called fog. So remember the three Cs—Cools Condenses Clouds.

CHECK QUESTION: Why does cooling air condense? [See Figure 38.1, or recall that the polar characteristics of water molecules makethem tend to stick to one another, as seen when water drops bead on a surface. In warm air they are moving too fast to stick when they collide. Like a couple of magnets thrown at each other, they fly off in different directions when they bounce. But toss the magnets slowly and they'll stick when they meet. Likewise for H_2O molecules in the air. Slow-moving water molecules stick—condensation.]

CHECK QUESTION: Why are clouds predominantly over mountain ranges, rather than above adjoining valleys? [Any moist air that blows against the mountains is swept upward, and then it's the three Cs!]

CHECK QUESTION: Why are clouds so prevalent over islands—even those without mountains to provide updrafts? [When exposed to sunshine, land warms more than water (recall water's high specific heat capacity). So moist air blowing over the relatively warm land is heated. When it warms it expands and becomes buoyant and rises. Then it's the three Cs!]

(Hey, three CHECK QUESTIONS IN A ROW — by now you've likely noticed that some of your most successful lectures occur when you pose intriguing questions instead of professing! Most of the questions you pose pop up spontaneously, and those appearing here are merely samples.)

38.4 Air Masses, Fronts, and Storms
38.5 Weather can Be Violent
38.6 Weather—Number One Topic of Conversation
These three sections tie the former discussions together. Assign your students to watch the Weather Report on their local television station, the Weather Channel, or bring in the daily weather report from the newspaper. Use the information to discuss where the air masses in your area originate. Look up the suggested Web sites to download weather maps for different locations. Talking about the weather with an understanding of the various processes involved can certainly enlighten the conversation!

Conclude Earth Science with your best shots on *storms* — thunderstorms, tornadoes, hurricanes — the works!

Chapter 38 Answers and Solutions

Key Terms and Matching Definitions

__4__ clouds
__5__ convectional lifting
__7__ front
__8__ frontal lifting
__1__ humidity
__6__ orographic lifting
__2__ relative humidity
__3__ temperature inversion

Review Questions

1. Distinguish between humidity and relative humidity.
   Humidity is a measure of the amount of water vapor in the air. Relative humidity is a ratio of the amount of water vapor divided by the maximum amount that can be in the air at a given temperature.

2. Why does relative humidity increase at night?
   First, relative humidity can change without changing the air's water vapor content. As air temperature drops, such as occurs at night, the relative humidity increases because the air is approaching its saturation point.

3. As air temperature decreases, does relative humidity increase, decrease, or stay the same?
   As air temperature decreases, the relative humidity increases because the air is approaching its saturation point.

4. What does saturation point have to do with dew point?
   Dew point is the temperature at which air is saturated with water vapor, which causes dew to form (condensed water vapor).

5. What happens to the water vapor in saturated air as the air cools?
   It condenses.

6. Explain why warm air rises and cools as it expands.
   Warm air rises because it is less dense. It expands because less atmospheric pressure squeezes on it as it rises. It cools due to adiabatic expansion.

7. Does a rising parcel of air get warmer, get cooler, or stay the same temperature?
   Gets cooler due to adiabatic expansion.

8. What is an adiabatic process?
   One that happens quickly enough for no heat input or output to occur.

9. What is a temperature inversion? Give examples of where these inversions may occur.
   Condition wherein upper regions of air are warmer than lower regions. An example is Los Angeles basin where warmer air is above colder air; Denver also, at times.

10. What happens to the air pressure of an air parcel as it flows up the side of a mountain?
    Air pressure always decreases with increasing height. So, as an air parcel flows up the side of a mountain, air pressure within the parcel decreases, allowing it to expand and cool.

11. Explain how clouds form.

As warm moist air rises, it cools and becomes less able to contain water vapor. As the water vapor condenses into tiny droplets, clouds are formed.

12. Rain or snow is most likely to be produced by which of the following cloud forms? a) cirrostratus, b) nimbostratus, c) altocumulus, d) stratocumulus
(a) cirrostratus, (b) nimbostratus, and (c) altocumulus.

13. Are clouds having vertical development characteristic of stable air, stationary air, unstable air, or dry air?
Unstable air.

14. Which type of clouds can become thunderheads?
Cumulonimbus clouds.

15. Explain how convectional lifting plays a role in the formation of cumulus clouds?
First, Earth's surface is heated unequally with some areas heating up more quickly. Air in contact with these surface "hot spots" rises, expands, and cools. This rising of air is accompanied by the sinking of cooler air aloft. This circulatory motion produces convectional lifting. When cooling occurs close to the air's saturation temperature, the condensing moisture forms a cumulus cloud. Air movement within the cumulus cloud moves in a cycle: Warm air rises, cool air descends.

16. Does a rain shadow occur on the windward side of a mountain range or on the leeward side? Explain.
The leeward side. As an air mass moves down the leeward slope, it warms. The descending air is dry because most of its moisture was removed in the form of clouds and precipitation on the windward (upslope) side of the mountain.

17. Differentiate between a cold front and a warm front.
If a cold air mass moves into an area occupied by a warm air mass, the contact zone between them is called a *cold front*, and if warm air moves into an area occupied by cold air, the zone of contact is called a *warm front*.

18. What cloud form is associated with thunderstorms?
Cumulus.

19. How do downdrafts form in thunderstorms?
As particles of precipitation grow larger and heavier within a cloud, they eventually begin to fall as rain, which drags some of the cool air along with it to create a downdraft. (Together, the rising warm updraft and the sinking chilled downdraft make up a storm cell within the cloud.)

20. Briefly describe how thunder and lightning develop.
As water droplets in a cloud rub against one another, the cloud becomes electrically charged—usually positive at the top and negative at the base. As electrical stress builds up, the charge becomes great enough that electrical energy is released and passed to other points of opposite charge, which quite often is the ground. The electrical energy flow from cloud to ground is lightning. As lightning heats up the air, the air expands and we hear lightning's noisy companion, thunder.

21. What information must be known to predict the weather?
Knowing present weather conditions including temperature, air pressure, humidity, type of clouds, level of precipitation, and wind direction and wind speed.

22. The accuracy of weather forecasts depends on great quantities of data and thousands of calculations. If the number of data points were decreased, would accuracy also decrease?
The more data, the better the forecast. So yes, accuracy would decrease.

Solutions to Chapter 38 Exercises

1. Why do clouds tend to form above mountain peaks?
   As moist air is lifted or pushed upslope against a mountain it cools adiabatically. As rising air cools, its capacity for containing water vapor decreases, increasing the relative humidity of the rising air. If the air cools to its dew point, the water vapor condenses and a cloud forms. Stable air that is forced upward forms stratus type clouds whereas unstable air tends to form cumulus type clouds.

2. Why does warm, moist air blowing over cold water result in fog?
   Warm air is able to hold more water vapor before becoming saturated than can cold air. As warm moist air blows over cold water it cools which causes the water vapor to condense into tiny droplets of fog.

3. Why does dew form on the ground during clear, calm summer nights?
   The ground and objects on the ground are often cooler than the surrounding air. As air comes into contact with these cold surfaces it cools and its ability to hold water vapor decreases. As the air cools below its dew point, water vapor condenses onto the nearest available surface.

4. Why does a July day in the Gulf of Mexico generally feel appreciably hotter than a July day in Arizona?
   The air around the Gulf of Mexico is more humid. Arizona, in contrast, has no large body of water to wet the air. Even though both regions may have the same temperature, the inhibiting effect of humidity on bodily evaporation finds one feeling considerably warmer in the Gulf States.

5. Would you expect a glass of water to evaporate more quickly on a windy, warm, dry summer day or a calm, cold, dry, winter day? Defend your answer.
   Warm, dry air holds more water vapor than cold dry air. The wind keeps the air above the glass dry by blowing away the moist air formed from evaporation. Hence, a glass of water will evaporate more readily on a windy, warm, dry summer day.

6. Why does surface temperature increase on a clear, calm night as a low cloud cover moves overhead?
   The low cloud cover acts as an insulation blanket inhibiting the outflow of terrestrial radiation.

7. During a summer visit to Cancun Mexico, you stay in an air-conditioned room. Getting ready to leave your room for the beach, you put on your sunglasses. The minute you step outside your sunglasses fog up. Why?
   The change in environment from cold to warm. Remember, both environments have the same number of water vapor molecules. As you leave the air-conditioned room the warm air outside comes into contact with the cold surface of the sunglasses. During contact the cold surface cools the air by conduction and the warm air's ability to hold water vapor decreases. As the air cools to its dew point water vapor condenses onto the sunglasses.

8. After a day of skiing in the Rocky Mountains, you decide to go indoors to get a warm cup of cocoa. As you enter the ski lodge, your eyeglasses fog up. Why?
   The change in environment from cold to warm. Remember, both environments have the same concentration of water vapor molecules. As we leave the cold outdoors the warm air inside comes into contact with the cold surface of the eyeglasses. As the air touching the eyeglasses cools to its dew point, water vapor condenses onto the eyeglasses.

9. Is it possible for the temperature of an air mass to change if no heat is added or subtracted? Explain.

Yes! The temperature of an air mass can change without the addition or subtraction of thermal energy— this is adiabatic expansion or compression. Blow on your hand and feel the warmth of your breath. When you pucker your lips and blow, the air expands and when it reaches your hand it is considerably cooler (try it now and see). But no thermal energy was subtracted in this case. Likewise for air that rises and cools. And when air is compressed, like in pumping a bicycle tire, the air is warmed without the addition of thermal energy. So it is with Chinook winds. If an air mass is lifted up a mountain slope, the temperature will drop because the pressure drops. If an air mass sinks down a slope it's temperature and pressure will go up.

10. Why is it necessary for an air mass to rise if it is to produce precipitation?

The production of cloud droplets into water droplets. Recall that water droplets in clouds are so small that they evaporate before reaching the ground. Rising air allows the water droplets more time in the cloud where they can grow in size. Once the weight of the drop is greater than the force of the rising air, the drop descends growing larger as it falls through the moist air, yielding precipitation.

11. As an air mass moves first upslope and then downslope over a mountain, what happens to the air's temperature and moisture content?

As an air mass is pushed upward over a mountain the rising air cools, and if the air is humid, clouds form and precipitation occurs. As the air mass moves down the other side of the mountain (the leeward slope), it warms. This descending air is dry because most of its moisture was removed in the form of clouds and precipitation on the windward (upslope) side of the mountain.

12. The sky is overcast, and it is raining. What type of cloud is above you, nimbostratus or cumulonimbus? Defend your answer.

Nimbostratus. Nimbostratus clouds are a wet-looking low cloud layer associated with light to moderate rain or snow. They are generally dark gray, which makes visibility of the sun or moon quite difficult. Although cumulonimbus clouds are also associated with precipitation, they do not produce an overcast sky. You can generally see the top of a cumulonimbus cloud.

13. What accounts for the large spaces of blue sky between cumulus clouds?

The fact that warm air rises and cool air sinks. As cool air sinks, the expansion of warm air beneath it is inhibited, so we usually see single cumulus cloud with a great deal of blue sky between them.

14. Why don't cumulus clouds form over cool water?

The formation of cumulus clouds requires hot spots of air. Over cool water the air is cool; there is an absence of warm thermals.

15. What is the difference between rainfall that accompanies the passage of a warm front and rainfall that accompanies the passage of a cold front?

In a warm front warm air slides upward over a wedge of cooler air near the ground. Gentle lifting of the warm moist air produces stratus and nimbostratus clouds and drizzly rain showers. In contrast, cold fronts occur as warm moist air is forced upward by advancing cold air. As the air lifts, it expands and cools to the dew-point temperature to a level of active condensation and cloud formation. This abrupt lifting produces cumulonimbus clouds, which are often, accompanied by heavy showers, lightning, thunder, and hail.

16. How do fronts cause clouds and precipitation?

When two air masses make contact, differences in temperature, moisture, and pressure can cause one air mass to ride over the other. Such differences are usually accompanied by wind, clouds, rain, and storms.

17. Explain why freezing rain is more commonly associated with warm fronts than with cold fronts.
The gradual rise of air means an extended period for the generation of different types of precipitation. In a warm front, less-dense warm air gradually rides up and over colder, denser air producing widespread cloudiness and precipitation way before the actual front. In many respects, a warm front is like a temperature inversion. As the front advances rain or snow develops, and as winds become brisk, the rain or snow changes to freezing rain. At the front, the air gradually warms, and the rain or snow turns to drizzle. Behind the front, the air is warm and the clouds scatter. Change occurs as the air temperature climbs.

18. How does a rain-shadow desert form?
When an air mass is pushed upward over a mountain range the rising air cools, and if it is humid, clouds form. As the air mass moves down the leeward slope of the mountain, it warms. This descending air is dry because most of its moisture was removed in the form of clouds and precipitation on the windward side of the mountain. Because the dry leeward sides of mountain ranges are sheltered from rain and moisture, rain shadow deserts often form.

19. Why are clouds that form over water more efficient in producing precipitation than clouds that form over land?
They simply have more moisture.

20. What is the source of the enormous amount of energy released by a hurricane?
Moisture from the warm ocean provides the reservoir of energy. When the moisture condenses it releases heat, which provides the energy that the hurricane releases. This is why hurricanes die out over land—they are cut off from their fundamental source of energy — warm, moist air.

Hands-On Exploration

Atmospheric Can-Crusher

When the molecules of water vapor come in contact with the room-temperature water in the saucepan, they condense, leaving a very low pressure in the can. The much greater surrounding atmospheric pressure crushes the can. Here you see dramatically how pressure is reduced by condensation. This occurs because liquid water occupies much less volume than does the same mass of water vapor. As the vapor molecules come together to form the liquid, they leave a void (low pressure).

This activity also shows how the atmospheric pressure surrounding us is very real and significant.

39 The Solar System

Learning Objectives

After studying Chapter 39, students will be able to:
• Describe how the moon goes through its cycle of phases.
• Describe how solar and lunar eclipses occur.
• Explain why one side of the moon always faces the Earth.
• Describe characteristic features about the sun.
• Explain current thinking about how the solar system formed.
• Describe features of the planets of the solar system.
• Distinguish between asteroids, meteoroids, and comets.

Possible Misconceptions to Correct

• **Not so!** The moon does not spin about a polar axis.
• **Not so!** Eclipses are rare events, occurring only every few years.
• **Not so!** The sun shines only during daylight hours.
• **Not so!** Asteroids are rare in the solar system.
• **Not so!** Meteoroids are rare in the Earth's atmosphere.
• **Not so!** Falling stars are stars that race across the sky.
• **Not so!** Comets travel around the sun indefinitely, without burning up.

Demonstration Equipment
None

Consider writing this on the board when you begin your study of astronomy:

> "Man must rise above the Earth, to the top of the atmosphere, and beyond; for only then will he fully understand the world in which he lives."
> *Socrates*

This is the time to bring your class to a planetarium, if possible. Or give a slide show and invite your colleagues in astronomy to give an illustrated guest lecture with his or her best slides. If you are lucky enough to have one or two portable telescopes and the time in the evening, you might consider a class "star party" and discuss the universe out-of-doors. Some teachers do this with telescopes, hot dogs, and soft drinks.

A superior 10-minute film that makes an excellent tie from the solar system, galaxies, and the universe, discussed briefly in the preceding chapter, to the atom—comparing sizes as powers of ten is the oldie-but-goody *Powers of Ten*, by Charles and Ray Eames, and narrated by Philip Morrison. (Pyramid Films, 1978).

A worthwhile class activity to consider is constructing a sundial.

In the **Practice Book:**
• Earth-Moon-Sun Alignment

In the **Next-Time Questions** book:
• Red Lunar Eclipse
• Earth-Rise from the Moon

Overhead Transparency available for:
Figure 39.4

SUGGESTED PRESENTATION

Begin by challenging your class to give convincing information to support the notion that the world is not flat, but round. Students "know" the Earth is round and in motion around the sun, but how many are prepared to defend these beliefs? Their belief is usually based on faith in a teacher, in a book, in an astronomer, or in programs they have watched on TV—but rarely upon evidence. Interestingly, there is much evidence that the Earth is flat, and not in motion at all!

What is the direct evidence for a round Earth? Does it appear round when you drive across the country? Does it appear round from a high-flying plane? And how does one know whether or not pictures taken from space are authentic? How does one know whether or not the space ventures by astronauts were not "Hollywood?"

39.1 The Moon—Our Closest Celestial Neighbor
Don't be disheartened if you find that there are students in your class who don't know that the moon can be seen in the daytime. Suggest they look for it during the daytime near the first or third quarter. Ask on which side of the moon should they look for the sun at these times. Be sure all your students make observations of the moon for several weeks. Observations night after night will show that at the same time each evening the moon is farther to the east among the stars.

39.2 Phases of the Moon—Why Appearance Changes Nightly
Be prepared to discover (if you haven't already) that many students in your class think the crescent moon is so because of the Earth's shadow on it. A survey before the chapter is covered may reveal this. (If the survey shows the same students believing this after you have covered the chapter, then...egad!)

DEMONSTRATION: Play flashlight tag. Suspend a large ball above your lecture table, turn off the lights, and illuminate the ball with a flashlight from different parts of the room. Phases of the ball are easily seen, and the phases of the moon forever understood by those who disappointed you on your survey. Learning has occurred! Or toss Styrofoam balls, about 6 cm in diameter or larger, to your class. Let them move the balls around their heads to see the changing phases as you shine the light on them.

CHECK YOUR NEIGHBOR: Often when viewing the crescent of the moon, the shadowed part is not completely dark, but is quite visible. What is the explanation? [Earthshine! The dark face of the moon is basking in earthshine, the reflection of which is why we see the dark part of the moon. Is this dark part the hemisphere we don't ordinarily see? No, it's the same hemisphere that faces us as always, but simply in the shade.]

Cratering is a notable feature of the lunar surface. Point out that the craters are often many times larger than the meteorites that caused them. A unit of energy from a munitions explosion causes the same size crater as the same unit of kinetic energy from a falling object. If you toss a baseball into mud, you'll produce crater shapes not unlike those seen on the moon. Different impact speeds will produce different shaped craters, with depth-to-width ratios much the same as those produced by meteorites. Of course, the many craters made on the Earth when those on the moon were occurring have long since been obliterated by weathering and other geologic processes.

39.3 Eclipses—The Shadows of the Earth and the Moon
Use Figures 39.5 and 39.7 to explain eclipses. Stress the idea that like everything in the sunshine, a shadow is cast. Imaging the shadow cast by the huge Earth will be challenging to many students. Those in a total solar eclipse experience the shadow of the moon first hand. The shadow of the Earth is seen on the moon during a lunar eclipse. Interesting lesson!

Color of the Moon
The redness of the eclipsed moon is an interesting extension of the redness of sunsets. Understandably, the red is most predominant near the edge of the Earth's shadow, and in the center may be completely dark. Hence we say the eclipsed moon sometimes appears red. The phases of a lunar eclipse are nicely shown in the photo on page 697, with Paul Hewitt's granddaughter Grace.

In discussing moon color, the question often arises about the "Blue Moon". The term "Blue Moon," for what it's worth, is the name given to the second full moon that appears in a calendar month. Since the lunar cycle is 29.5 days and the average month is 30 days, there will be times when the 29.5-day cycle fits within a calendar month. This happens every 2.7 years, on the average. So the blue moon doesn't have to do with physics or astronomy. However, the term "Blue Moon" also refers to the different phenomenon that does involve physics: That's when the moon's disk appears bluish, which occurs when the Earth's atmosphere contains particles 0.8 to 1.8 microns in diameter, slightly larger than the wavelength of visible light. Such particles, produced by forest fires or volcanoes, scatter red light while allowing the blue through (just the opposite of red getting through blue scattering to produce red sunsets).

39.4 Why One Side of the Moon Always Faces Us
The gravity lock of the moon on the Earth such that one side always faces us may need further explanation, for the explanation of Figure 27.5 cites two concepts not covered earlier in the text: torque and center of mass. The center of mass of the moon is in its geometric center (assuming symmetrical structure). The center of gravity, with respect to the Earth, is displaced toward the Earth from its center of mass. This is because the nearer side of the moon interacts with more force than the far part—it "weighs" more. So like a compass, any off-axis orientation with the force field results in a torque that tends to line it on-axis.

39.5 The Sun—Our Nearest and Most-Loved Star
Sunspots are dark because they are cooler than the surrounding regions. Their darkness has to do with the contrast of hotter regions. If you put a 75-watt light bulb and a 100-watt light bulb at the ends of your lecture table, they both look rather bright. Bring them together, and the 75-watt bulb looks darker when held in front of the brighter 100-watt bulb. (In a similar way, the black you see on a TV screen is actually no blacker than the "gray" face when not lit up. It looks black in contrast to the brightness of the illuminated part.)

39.6 How Did the Solar System Form?
Scale of the Solar System. Consider scaling the solar system down to the size of a football field, where the sun is on the goal line and Earth on the 2-yard line (leaving some room for Mercury and Venus). Mercury would then be on the 2-foot line, and Venus on the 4-foot line. Beyond Earth, Mars would be on the 3-yard line, Jupiter on the 10-yard line, Saturn on the 20-yard line, Uranus on the 40-yard line, Neptune on the 60-yard line, and Pluto on the 80-yard line. On this scale, the nearest star would be 1000 miles away!

39.7 Planets of the Solar System

ACTIVITY: You can integrate planetary sizes and distances into the student's experience by scaling 1 foot = one million miles. Then the sun is close to the size of a basketball. The planets are small objects that can be held in the hand. Calculate the sizes and distances of one or two planets with your students, and let them calculate others. The Earth, for example, would be 93 feet away from the basketball, easy to set off as paces. Ask for a volunteer for each of the other planets. Whoever volunteers for Pluto (average distance some 3800 million miles) will have to pace 3800 feet away across town!

39.8 The Inner Planets—Mercury, Venus, Earth, and Mars

People who talk about visiting Mars usually have no idea of how far away it is. They may remember that it is supposed to take two years to reach it, but how far away is it? It is not a short hop away on a spaceship. Scaling of the solar system is a worthwhile activity.

39.9 The Outer Planets—Jupiter, Saturn, Uranus, and Neptune

Uranus is barely perceptible to the naked eye in a clean dark sky. In ancient times, without photographic film and time exposures that betray movement in the skies, Uranus went unnoticed as a planet. Nobody noticed that it wandered.

39.10 Asteroids, Meteoroids, and Comets

Meteorites

How have scientists established the age of the Earth as 4.5 billion years? By rock samples? No, any rocks that existed in early Earth have long ago subducted to magma and to become part of the rock cycle (Chapter 31). We date the Earth not by Earth rocks, but by dating meteors, which presumably coalesced at the same time as the Earth. Geologists love meteors!

Meteor showers dump an estimated 360 to 6000 tons of cosmic dust on the Earth each year. Annual meteor showers occur when the Earth passes through streams of material formed from the outgassing of a comet's nucleus as it nears perihelion. Micrometeorites do not incandesce like larger meteorites because their large surfaces compared to their masses allows them to radiate heat very rapidly. So they pass through the atmosphere relatively unchanged. It turns out the Earth appears to be under a constant rain of micrometeorites. Collecting them can be done by the sticky side of ordinary Scotch tape upon a rooftop exposed to the clear sky. Investigation of the tape after several hours of exposure can be done by microscope, where the tape is sandwiched between microscope slides. At a magnification of about 100, airborne dust, pollen, and various types of industrial pollution are evident on the tape. Micrometeorites appear as metallic nickel-iron spheres. You'll need to be proficient at identifying nickel-iron compounds to increase the likelihood of extraterrestrial origin. More of these should be found, of course, during times of meteor showers. To learn more about this technique, see the article *Chasing Meteors with a Microscope* in the *Junior College Science Teacher*, May 1993.

Comets. How long does a comet live? Answer: Until it runs out of gas. The text states that the orbits of comets extend far beyond the orbit of Pluto. This is true for most comets, but not the shorter periodic comets like Halley's (76 years), which orbits the sun well within the solar system. The majority of comets discovered each year are the long-period comets that take 100,000 to 1 million years to complete a solar orbit. Most of their times are beyond the orbit of Pluto, at distances of 40,000 to 50,000 AU from the sun—about one-fifth the way to the nearest star. The textbook does not treat the Oort cloud, the proposed reservoir of cometary nuclei.

Answers and Solutions to Chapter 39

Key Terms and Matching Definitions

__5__ asteroid
_10__ comet
__3__ lunar eclipse
__8__ meteor
__9__ meteorite
__6__ meteoroid
__1__ moon phases
__2__ solar eclipse
__4__ sunspots

Review Questions

1. How does the Moon's rate of rotation about its own axis compare with its rate of revolution around the Earth?
The rates are the same.

2. Where is the sun when you view a full moon?
Directly in back of you.

3. In what alignment of sun, moon, and Earth does a solar eclipse occur?
When all three are aligned with the moon between the sun and Earth.

4. In what alignment of sun, moon, and Earth does a lunar eclipse occur?
When all three are aligned with the Earth between the sun and moon.

5. Why is totality during a lunar eclipse not altogether dark?
The atmosphere acts as a lens and refracts sunlight onto the dark moon.

6. What does the spin rate of the moon have in common with its orbital rate about the Earth?
They are the same, which results in one side always facing Earth.

7. What happens to the amount of the sun's mass as it "burns?"
It is converted into radiant energy.

8. What is the solar wind?
A hurricane of high-speed protons and electrons ejected by the sun.

9. How does the rotation of the sun differ from the rotation of a solid body?
Equatorial regions spin faster than regions at higher latitudes.

10. How old is the sun?
Nearly 5 billion years.

11. What happens to the speed of a spinning mass of gas when it contracts?
It speeds up.

12. Why did the ancients call planets "wanderers"?
Because they move differently than the stars in the sky.

13. Why are days on Mercury very hot and nights very cold?
Closeness to the sun and very long days and nights due to slow rotation.

14. Why is Earth called the *blue planet*?
Because of the blue oceans that dominate its surface.

15. What gas makes up most of the Martian atmosphere?
    Carbon dioxide.

16. What surface feature do Jupiter and the sun have in common?
    All parts do not rotate in unison, and both lack a hard surface.

17. Why does Jupiter bulge at the equator?
    Because it rotates rapidly.

18. Which move faster, Saturn's inner rings or the outer ones?
    Inner rings (like the greater speed of inner planets or any close-orbiting satellites).

19. What is a falling star?
    A meteor visible in the sky as it burns in the atmosphere.

20. Why do the tails of comets point away from the sun?
    They are swept away from the sun because of the solar wind.

Solution to Chapter 39 Exercises

1. Which is larger, the radius of the sun or the distance between moon and Earth? (See the inside front cover.)
The sun (7 × 10⁸ m) is much larger than the distance between the Earth and the moon (3.8 × 10⁸ m).

2. Why does the moon lack an atmosphere? Defend your answer.
Gravitation at the moon's surface is too small; escape velocity at the moon's surface is less than the speeds that molecules of gas would have at regular moon temperatures, so any gases on the moon escape.

3. In what ways would a telescope mounted on the moon produce better views into space than telescopes mounted on Earth?
There would be no atmospheric refraction because of no atmosphere.

4. Is the fact that we see only one side of the moon evidence that the moon spins or that it doesn't rotate? Defend your answer.
The fact we see one side is evidence that it rotates; if it didn't rotate, we'd need only wait until it completed a half orbit to see its opposite side.

5. Photograph (a) shows the moon partially lit by the sun. Photograph (b) shows a Ping-Pong ball in sunlight. Compare the positions of the sun in the sky when each photograph was taken. Do the photos support or refute the claim that they were taken on the same day? Defend your answer.
In both photos the sun if off to the right, at about 2:30 o'clock, slightly in back. If it were exactly to the right the moon and ball would be half lit.

6. Why are there a lot more craters on the surface of the moon than on the surface of the Earth?
Erosion hasn't occurred on the moon, so craters have not been covered up. Another way of saying the same thing is that the moon wears no makeup.

7. Why is it not totally dark in the location where a total solar eclipse occurs?
Brightness of the solar corona somewhat lights up the Earth.

8. Because of the Earth's shadow, a partially eclipsed Moon looks like a cookie with a bite taken out of it. Explain with a sketch how the curvature of the bite indicates the size of the Earth relative to the size of the moon. How does the tapering of the sun's rays affect the curvature of the bite?
Extend the bite to complete a circle, and the patch of the Earth's shadow appears to be a circle with a diameter 2.5 moon diameters. Does this mean the Earth's diameter is 2.5 moon diameters? No, because the Earth's shadow at the distance of the moon has tapered. How much? According to the tapering that is evident during a solar eclipse, by 1 moon diameter. So add that to the 2.5 and we find the Earth is 3.5 times wider than the moon.

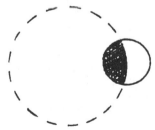

9. What energy processes make the sun shine? In what sense can it be said that gravity is the prime source of solar energy?
The sun's output of energy is that of thermonuclear fusion. Because fusion in the sun is the result of gravitational pressure, we can say the prime source of solar energy is gravity. Without the strong gravity, fusion wouldn't occur.

10. Where are elements heavier than hydrogen and helium formed?
In star interiors.

11. What is the cause of winds on Mars (and on almost every other planet, too)?
Unequal heating of the surface and therefore the atmosphere.

11. What is the major difference between the terrestrial and Jovian planets?
Except for Pluto (which may not be a planet at all) they have rings, and are large gaseous low-density worlds.

12. Why was Jupiter once thought to be a failed star?
Its composition resembles that of the sun.

13. Why are the seasons on Uranus different from the seasons on any other planet?
A planet like Earth rotates through an axis that is slightly non-perpendicular to the orbital plane. This means that the angle that the sun's rays make with a given part of its surface depends on the time of the planet's year. A slight tilt results in slight changes of season. Uranus, however, is enormously tilted, with its polar axis nearly in the plane of its orbit. Its seasons are very exaggerated, so that when the polar axis is aligned with the sun, a full summer is at one pole and a full winter at the opposite pole.

14. What were the similar historical circumstances that link the names of the planets Neptune and Pluto with the elements Neptunium and Plutonium?
Neptune was the name given to the first planet to be discovered beyond Uranus, and Pluto the second. Likewise, Neptunium was the name given to the first element discovered beyond uranium, and plutonium the second.

15. By what investigative method was Pluto discovered?
Examination of photographic plates that over time showed moving objects.

16. Why are meteorites so much more easily found on Antarctica than on other continents?
Antarctica, because so many would be imbedded in ice. On regular ground, they are not so obvious. Atop ice means they came from above.

17. A meteor is visible only once, but a comet may be visible at regular intervals throughout its lifetime. Why?
A comet continually orbits the sun.

18. What would be the consequence of a comet's tail sweeping across the Earth?
Almost none except for spectacular meteor showers high in the atmosphere.

19. Chances are about 50-50 that in any night sky there is at least one visible comet that has not been discovered. This keeps amateur astronomers busy looking night after night, for the discoverer of a comet gets the honor of having it named for him or her. With this high probability of comets in the sky, why aren't more of them found?
Quite simply, the sky is BIG. A faraway comet occupies a pin-point in the sky, and there are oodles of pin-points!

20. In terms of the conservation of energy, describe why comets eventually burn out.
On each pass around the sun, material and the energy that is associated with it is swept away. This material and energy comprise the comet tails. Since the comet is composed of a finite amount of material, sooner or later it is dissipated entirely.

40 The Stars

40.1 The Constellations

The Big Dipper and the North Star

40.2 Birth of Stars
40.3 Life and Evolution of Stars
40.4 Death of Stars

Astrology—Link to Pseudoscience

40.5 The Bigger They Are, the Harder They Fall—Supernova
40.6 Black Holes—The Fate of the Supergiants
40.7 Galaxies
40.8 The Big Bang

Learning Objectives
After studying Chapter 40, students will be able to:
• Explain that constellations are local views of star groups flavored by history.
• Describe how stars are born, how they live, and how they die.
• Distinguish between astronomy and astrology.
• Describe how big stars have relatively short lives, and why.
• Explain current thinking about black holes.
• Describe features of galaxies.
• Describe the concept of the Big Bang.

Possible Misconceptions to Correct
• **Not so!** The constellations do not circle a stationary Earth.
• **Not so!** The sun is much different from ordinary stars.
• **Not so!** Astronomy and astrology are two words for the same thing.
• **Not so!** Giant stars should be more stable than small stars.
• **Not so!** Black holes are like vacuum cleaners in outer space, to be feared by space-faring
    visitors.
• **Not so!** Black holes are formidable entities.
• **Not so!** The Big Bang is a weak theory of the beginning of the universe.

Demonstration Equipment
None

Great website on black holes: http://hubble.stsci.edu/fun_.and._games

This chapter is a brief overview of the life of stars, galaxies, with some flavor of black holes and brief mention of quasars—standard stuff. Although most all scientists accept astronomy and condemn astrology, it is embarrassing to note that astronomy attracts more adherents than astronomy—in this so called rational age of human history. Check the horoscope section of your newspaper. Incredible!

Whereas astronomy is predominantly an observational science that relies on complex techniques and time sequences that are difficult for a lecture or textbook to impart, consider class time viewing the better suited depictions available on select films, TV tapes, and computer programs. Consider the following:

NASA's films "Flight of Apollo 11" (29 min), which shows the dynamics of the solar system, star systems, and galaxies. NASA's "Space Shuttle: A Remarkable Flying Machine" (31 min) illustrates Kepler's and Newton's laws.

TV tape from the Nova series "Lives of the Stars" (60 min) presents stellar evolution in super compressed time, with characteristics of the sun, white dwarfs, neutron stars, and black holes.

A great little book with many teaching tips is *West's Great Ideas for Teaching Astronomy*, by West Publishing Company, 1989. Some of the ideas in the suggested lecture below come from this dandy book.

Martin Gardner addresses what may perk up in your class—the public fascination with *fads and fallacies in the name of science*, in his book of the same name. Exposing hoaxes perpetrated by pranksters, publicity seekers, and psychics is made difficult by what Gardner calls, semi-lies. An observer sees a balloon but is convinced it is a saucer. Others are skeptical and this irritates him. So to convince them, he adds details, or exaggerates what he has seen. He may do this without being aware of it, and later recall the episode not as he saw it, but as he "told it". This well-known human failing is likely involved in much of the pseudoscience that proliferates.

This is where you take your students to a planetarium, and where you show slides.

In the **Practice Book:**
•Stellar Parallax

In the **Next-Time Questions** book:
•Solar Black Hole

Overhead Transparency available for:
Figure 40.2.

SUGGESTED PRESENTATION

Begin by relating the statement by the philosopher Auguste Compte more than a hundred years ago; that humankind, despite advances in science, would never know much about the distant stars—certainly not their chemical compositions. Considering the information available to Compte and his contemporaries at that time, the conjecture was reasonable, for the great distance of the stars seemed certainly to put information about them out of reach. What Compte didn't realize, however, is that the light emitted by those stars, quite within reach, contained much information about their makeup. Starlight betrays the elements that emit it, as the soon-to-come science of spectroscopy showed. That we know so much about stars is incredible—and the present time is the golden age for atronomers, who are presently finding more about them each decade than was ever known previously. Gone are the eyepieces on telescopes that once viewed the visible part of the spectrum. In their places are receptors for the nonvisible parts of the spectrum—from radio waves to X-rays. The field of astronomy is aburst with excitement these days.

40.1 The Constellations
Discuss the constellations, and the Big Dipper in particular, and Polaris. Every student should be able to locate Polaris in the night sky. Explain why Polaris is directly overhead only at the pole, and how and why it is seen lower in the sky the closer one gets to the equator (the subject matter of the activity *Reckoning Latitude* in the Lab Manual).

CHECK QUESTION: Polaris is stationary above the Earth's north pole and is a guide to all in the northern hemisphere. Why are there no "stationary stars" above [your city]?

Ask your class to pretend they are on a merry-go-round in motion, viewing lamps on the stationary ceiling overhead. Further suppose they took time exposure photographs of the lamps above. Would they not see circular light patterns?

Confronting Astrology

To confront astrology, better than lecturing in an authoritarian manner, do as Stephen Pompea of the University of Arizona does and try the following experiment: Ask students NOT to consult a horoscope for three days. During this period, students keep a daily diary of their feelings and moods. They may also make note of how their financial and love lives are going, since this is a major aspect of horoscopic predictions. In class, distribute the 36 horoscopes of the three-day period, but with the sun signs removed and the order scrambled. Students must then find the three that best describe their days. Then a comparison between their answers and the "correct" horoscopes is made to see if the predictive power of astrology is significant.

Interestingly enough, due to precession of the Earth about its axis, with a period of 26,000 years, the sun is about one and a half astrological signs off those of 3000 years ago, when astrology was born. During the last 3000 years the Earth has wobbled about 1.5 constellations along the zodiac.

Astrology was an important stepping stone to science. It went beyond physical speculations and certainly emphasized observation, progressed to processes of experimentation, and to logical reasoning, which are now cornerstones of science. Interestingly, science advanced faster in western rather than eastern cultures, largely because of the different social and political climates. While early Greeks in an era of experimental democracy and freethinking were questioning their speculations about the world around them, their counterparts in eastern parts of the world were largely occupied in absorbing the knowledge of their forebears. Absorbing this knowledge was the key to personal success. So the progress in science in regions like China were without the period of questioning that accelerated the scientific advances of Europe and Euroasia.

40.2 Birth of Stars

Just as a child cannot see the aging of friends from babies to adults, the astronomer cannot see stellar evolution directly. But the child can see the various ages of other children, adults, and elderly people, even though seeing the transition for any one person is not possible. The direction of time is evident. Just as a baby in no way resembles its form as an elderly person, changes in a star throughout its lifetime are similar. Young stars do not resemble mature stars, and in no way resemble dead stars.

Stellar Distances—Parallax

How do we know the distances to stars? The only direct way is by parallax, which you'll want to explain. Begin by having students hold a finger at arm's length in front of their faces and looking with one eye at the position of the finger with respect to the background. Then have them switch eyes. Parallax! The parallax is easily seen because the finger is relatively close to the eye. The parallax of more distant objects is more difficult to see, as can be seen by judging the distance of something a few meters distant, and then something many meters distant. Cite the importance of the distance between one's eyes—the baseline. At any given moment, the largest baseline for finding parallax among the stars is the Earth's diameter. Stars viewed from one side of the Earth can be compared to the same stars viewed at the opposite side of the Earth. A still larger baseline that takes a 6-month interval to utilize is the diameter of the Earth's orbit about the sun. Have your students do page 139 in the Practice Book, about stellar parallax; at this point.

Ever wonder why a chicken or pigeon bobs its head while it walks? Ronald Stoner of Bowling Green University ties the chicken walk to stellar parallax. Here's how: While the chicken's body moves forward, the head remains momentarily fixed as if anchored in space. This is because a chicken's eyes are on the sides of its head, not suited for parallax viewing. Vision for the chicken is monocular. So the chicken gauges distances to objects in its sight by the shifts of the objects against the background with succeeding steps. Images on the retina of the chicken are compared when the head moves through a standard difference (one step). Astronomers likewise measure distances to the stars by noting shifts of images of stars on photographic plates when the telescope moves though a standard difference (one-half Earth orbit around the sun). So just as a chicken compares the image of something in the foreground with the background between steps, an astronomer does much the same with foreground and background stars between 6-month intervals.

40.3 Life and Evolution of Stars

Chris Impey at the University of Arizona points out that the composition of humans is quite different from the composition of the universe as a whole. Of every 10,000 atoms in the sun, 7400 are H, 2440 are He, only 3 are C, 2 are N, 5 are O, and 150 all other elements. But of the same 10,000 atoms in a child's body, or anyone's body, 6500 are H, 2 are He, 2000 are C, 500 are N, 900 are O, and 100 all other elements. Our bodies are cinders formed in the residue of stellar collapses in a universe that is overwhelmingly H and He. It is important to stress that the cinders came from previous generations of stars — before the sun formed.

Stellar Masses — Binary Stars

Binary stars offer the astronomer the only direct means of determining the mass of a star. About half the stars in the sky are binaries. Do as Gene Maynard of Radford University does and attach a pair of Styrofoam balls of different diameters (and masses) with plastic sticks to model binary star systems. Balance on a finger to illustrate the center of mass, and the center about which the stars circle each other. The relative sizes of orbit about the center of mass is easily seen to relate to the relative masses.

40.4 Death of Stars

Stars, like all parts of nature, eventually run their course. Even the sun will burn out in 5 million more years. In its death throes it will expand to become a red giant, swallowing the Earth. Will humans be on Earth awaiting this fate? Speculation says no—we'll have reached our end by then or be somewhere more hospitable.

40.5 The Bigger They Are, the Harder They Fall—Supernova

Supernovae are of particular interest to us because they are the source of all out atoms heavier than iron. The heavy elements consume energy when fused, so don't get manufactured in normal stellar fusion. These elements are formed when giant stars explode. These are the supernovae.

40.6 Black Holes—The Fate of the Supergiants

When you toss garbage into a garbage disposal without putting the lid on, much material goes into the drain but some pieces come flying out considerably faster than they went in. Likewise for matter that encounters a black hole. The fate of the supergiant stars is the black hole configuration. Black holes are a fascinating topic to students.

40.7 Galaxies

Invite your students to make their own model of a spiral galaxy the next time they have a cup of coffee, as Stephen Pompea at the University of Arizona does with his students. Simply stir the coffee before adding a little cream—the cream will take a shape not unlike a spiral galaxy. Fluid flow in a cup of coffee approximates the flow on a much larger scale, just as wind tunnel tests on tiny airplanes predict the behavior of larger ones in larger air flows. (There is more on this in P. Stevens' book, *Patterns in Nature*.)

40.8 The Big Bang
Most astroscientists subscribe to the Big Bang theory, called the "standard model." Point out that the model doesn't picture an explosion in space, like a giant firecracker going off, but rather an explosion of space itself—not at some time in the past, but at the beginning of time itself. This is heavy stuff—and intriguing stuff. More intriguing is recent evidence that the universe is accelerating outward in its expansion—which challenges the simple model of a universe that blows up like a firecracker in space, with remnants slowing with time. Then there is the dark matter, and the dark energy. Presently there are many more questions than answers. This is an exciting time for astrophysics folks.

The dullest lecturer has the attention of his or her class with any discussion of the beginning of the universe! An intriguing way to end your course.

Answers and Solutions to Chapter 40

Key Terms and Definitions

_18__ Big Bang
__2__ binary
__5__ black dwarf
_11__ black hole
_16__ cluster
_13__ elliptical galaxy
_12__ galaxy
_14__ irregular galaxy
__9__ neutron star
__7__ nova
__4__ planetary nebula
_19__ primeval fireball
__1__ protostar
_10__ pulsar
__3__ red giant
_15__ spiral galaxy
_17__ supercluster
__8__ supernova
__5__ white dwarf

Review Questions

1. What are constellations?
    Visible groups of stars in the nighttime sky.

2. Why does an observer at a given location see one set of constellations in the winter and a different set of constellations in the summer?
    The nighttime Earth faces in opposite directions each 6 months in its path around the sun (see Figure 40.2).

3. What process changes a protostar to a full-fledged star?
    The ignition of nuclear fuel and subsequent thermonuclear fusion.

4. What are the outward forces that act on a star?
    Outward moving radiant energy and gas due to thermonuclear fusion.

5. What are the inward forces that act on a star?
    Gravitational forces.

6. What do the outward and inward forces acting on a star have to do with its size?
    When they are equal they determine the size of the star.

7. Compare the lifetimes of high-mass and low-mass stars.
    High-mass stars are shorter lived than low-mass stars.

8. How common are binaries in the universe?
    About half the stars in the sky are binaries.

9. What is the goal of TPF programs?
    To find other planets similar to Earth.

10. What event marks the birth of a star, and what event marks its death?
    Thermonuclear fusion ignition gives birth, and burn-out of nuclear fusion is death.

11. When will our sun reach the red-giant stage?
    About 5 billion years from now.

12. What is the relationship between a planetary nebula and a white dwarf?
    A planetary nebula is a shell of interstellar material, and when shrunken becomes a white dwarf.

13. What is the relationship between a white dwarf and a black dwarf?
    A black dwarf is a burned out white dwarf—a cold black lump of matter.

14. What is the relationship between a white dwarf and a nova?
    A nova is the event of nuclear fusion ignition of a white dwarf.

15. What is the relationship between the heavy elements we find on the Earth today and supernovae?
    All elements beyond iron were once produced by supernovae.

16. What is the relationship between an ordinary star and a black hole?
    A black hole is a collapsed star.

17. How does the mass of a star before collapse compare with the mass of the black hole it becomes?
    Same.

18. Being that black holes are invisible, what is the evidence for their existence?
    Radiation patterns formed by X-ray emission from material falling into them, and binary stars with no visible companion, and other effects on neighboring stars.

19. What type of galaxy is the Milky Way galaxy?
    Spiral.

20. What are the consequences of galaxies colliding?
    Very little for most stars and some collisions that form new stars.

Solutions to Chapter 40 Exercises

1. Why do we not see stars in the daytime?
    Stars aren't seen in daytime because their relatively dim light is overwhelmed by skylight.

2. Which figure in the chapter best shows that a constellation seen in the background of a solar eclipse is one that will be seen six months later in the night sky?
    Figure 40.2, which shows that the background of a solar eclipse is the nighttime sky normally viewed 6 months earlier or later.

3. We see the constellations as distinct groups of stars. Discuss why they would look entirely different from some other location in the universe, far distant from the Earth.
    Both near and faraway stars appear as if on the inner surface of one great sphere, with us at the center. Two stars that appear very close together are on the same line of sight, but may actually be an enormous distance apart, and would not appear close together at all when viewed from the side. Astronomers distinguish between double stars and binary stars. Double stars are on the same line of sight, yet are actually far apart. Binaries are stars that are both on the same line of sight and are in close interaction.

4. The Big Dipper is sometimes right side up (can hold water), and at other times upside down (cannot hold water). What length of time is required for the Dipper to change from one position to the other?
    Twelve hours. In 24 hours it makes a complete cycle.

5. In what sense are we all made of star dust?
    The nuclei of atoms that compose our bodies were once parts of stars. All nuclei beyond iron in atomic number, were in fact manufactured in supernovae.

6. How is the gold in your mother's ring evidence of ancient stars that ran their life cycles long before the solar system came into being?
The gold in any ring was made in the death throes of stars during supernovae explosions.

7. Would you expect metals to be more abundant in old stars or new stars? Defend your answer.
Since all the heavy elements are manufactured in supernovae, the newer the star, the greater percentage of heavy elements available for its construction. Very old stars were made when heavy elements were less abundant.

8. Why is there a lower limit on the mass of a star? (What can't happen in a low-mass accumulation of hydrogen atoms and other interstellar material?)
Too low a mass, and gravitational pressure in the inner core is insufficient to provoke thermonuclear fusion. No fusion, no star.

9. What ordinarily keeps a star from collapsing?
Thermonuclear fusion reactions produce an outward pressure that counteracts the inward pressure that would lead to collapse due to gravity.

10. How does a protostar differ from a star?
A protostar is not yet a star, and is made up of an aggregation of matter many times more massive than the sun and much larger in size than the solar system.

11. How does the energy of a protostar differ from the energy that powers a star?
Thermonuclear fusion powers a star. Only nonfusion energy exists within a protostar.

12. Why do nuclear fusion reactions not occur on the outer layers of stars?
Thermonuclear fusion is caused by gravitational pressure, wherein hydrogen nuclei are squashed together. Gravitational pressures in the outer layers are insufficient to produce fusion.

13. What is meant by the statement "The bigger they are, the harder they fall" with respect to stellar evolution?
Bigger stars live faster, and collapse more energetically when they burn out.

14. Why will the sun not be able to fuse carbon nuclei in its core?
There is insufficient gravitational pressure within the sun to initiate carbon fusion, which requires greater squashing than hydrogen to fuse.

15. Some stars contain fewer heavy elements than our sun contains. What does this indicate about the age of such stars relative to the age of our sun?
Stars with fewer heavier elements formed at an earlier time than the sun.

16. Which has the highest surface temperature: red star, white star, or blue star?
Blue stars are hottest, red stars are coolest. White hot stars have surface temperatures in between.

17. In what way is a black hole blacker than black ink?
Black ink reflect *some* light. A black hole reflects none.

18. What does it mean to say that galaxies are cannibals?
Galaxies merge. Large galaxies that devour small galaxies in a merger are said to be cannibals.

19. What is meant by saying that the universe does not exist in space? Change two words around to make the statement agree with the standard model of the universe.
Space exists in the universe, not the other way around.

20. In your own opinion, do you have to be at the center of your class to be special? Does the Earth have to be at the center of the universe to be special?
Both you and the Earth don't have to occupy a central location to be special. The Earth is certainly special among planets in the solar system in that it is the only one with abundant water and an atmosphere—and us.

Appendix B Linear Motion

Computing Velocity and Distance Traveled on an Inclined Plane
Computing Distance When Acceleration is Constant

Learning Objectives
After studying this Appendix, and related sections in Chapters 2 and 3, students will be able to:
• Explain what it means to say that motion is relative.
• Define speed and give examples of units of speed.
• Distinguish between instantaneous speed and average speed.
• Distinguish between speed and velocity.
• Calculate distance traveled when average speed and time are given.
• Distinguish between velocity and acceleration.
• Calculate acceleration when change in velocity and time are given.
• Describe the motion of an object in free fall.

Possible Misconceptions to Correct
• **Not so!** Speed and velocity are two words for the same thing.
• **Not so!** Acceleration is simply a change in velocity.
• **Not so!** How fast something goes is the same as how far it goes.

Appendix B is an extension of the beginning sections in Chapters 2 and 3. Why is Appendix B tucked in the back of the book instead of being incorporated in the chapters, or as a chapter on its own? The reason is pedagogical. One of the greatest shortcomings of physics teaching is overtime in speed, velocity, and acceleration—kinematics. Teachers typically spend much more time on kinematics than any other physics concept.

Kinematics can be rich with puzzles, graphical analysis, ticker timers, photo-gates, and algebraic problems. My strong suggestion is to resist these and move quickly into the rest of mechanics, and then into the broader areas in physical science. Getting bogged down with kinematics, with so much physical science ahead, is a widespread practice. Please do your class a favor and hurry on to the next chapters. If at the end of your course you have time (ha ha), *then* bring out the kinematics toys and have a go at them.

For your students' sake, **avoid the temptation to get into the classic motion problems that involve 90% math and 10% physics!** *Just as wisdom is knowing what to overlook, good teaching is knowing what to omit.*

Here are some tidbits from Peter J. Brancazio, physics prof and sports buff from Brooklyn College in New York (*Just a Second*, March 91, Discover):

• Carl Lewis has run 100 m in 9.92 s. At this speed Carl covers 10.1 m per second. But because he starts from rest and accelerates up to speed, his top speed is more than this—about 10% over his average speed.

• Downhill skiers attain speeds of 70 to 80 mph on winding runs inclined about 10 - 15°. A speed of 70 mph is 102.7 ft/s, which means a skier covers 10.3 ft in 0.1 s. Even quicker are speed skiers, who ski slopes inclined up to 50° at speeds up to 139 mph or 204 ft/s. At this speed a skier could cover the length of a football field in 1.5 s. (This is faster than a skydiver falls in spread-eagle position.)

- Baseball pitchers such as Roger Clemens and Nolan Ryan can throw a baseball nearly 100 mph. Since the pitcher's mound is 60.5 feet from home plate, the ball takes less than 1/2 second to get to the batter. Due to the pitcher's reach, actual distance is about 55 feet. Because of air drag, a 95 mph ball slows to about 87 mph, giving a travel time of 0.41 s. On average it takes 0.2 s for a batter to get his bat from its cocked position up to speed in the hitting zone, so he must react to the pitcher's motion in a quarter-second or less, beginning his swing when the ball is only a little more than half the distance to the plate. These abilities and reflexes are rarities!

- Michael Jordan's hang time was less than 0.9 s (discussed in the Practice Book). Height jumped is less than 1.25 m (4 feet—those who insist a hang time of 2 s are way off, for 1 s up is 16 feet—clearly, no way!). A neat rule of thumb is that height jumped in feet is equal to four times hang time squared ($d = g/2 \ (T/2)^2 = g/2 \ (T^2/4) = g/8(T^2) = 4T^2$).

In the **Next-Time Questions** book:
- Two-Track Race
- Bike and the Bee

In the **Lab Manual**:
- Go! Go! Go!
- Sonic Ranger
- Graphing

SUGGESTED PRESENTATION

Your first question: What means of motion has done more to change the way cities are built than any other? Answer: The elevator!

> DEMONSTRATION: Drop a sheet of paper and note how slowly it falls because of air resistance. Crumple the paper and note it falls faster. Air resistance has been reduced. Then drop a sheet of paper and a book, side by side. Of course the book falls faster, due to its greater weight compared to air drag. (Interestingly, the air drag is greater for the faster-falling book—an idea you'll return to in the next chapter.) Now place the paper against the lower surface of the raised horizontally-held book and when you drop them, nobody is surprised to see they fall together. The book has pushed the paper with it. Now repeat with the paper on *top* of the book and ask for predictions and neighbor discussion. Then surprise your class by refusing to show it! Tell them to try it out of class! (Good teaching isn't giving answers, but raising good questions—good enough to prompt wondering. Let students discover that the book will "plow through the air" leaving an air-resistance free path for the paper to follow!)

Speed and Velocity
Define speed, writing its equation in longhand form on the board while giving examples—automobile speedometers, etc. Similarly define velocity, citing how a racecar driver is interested in his *speed*, whereas an airplane pilot is interested in her *velocity*—speed and direction. Without going too deep at this point, cite the difference between a scalar and a vector quantity, and identify speed as a scalar and velocity as a vector. Tell your class that you're not going to make a big deal about distinguishing between speed and velocity, but you are going to make a big deal of distinguishing between speed or velocity and another concept—*acceleration*.

Acceleration
Define acceleration, identifying it as a vector quantity, and cite the importance of CHANGE. That's change in speed, or change in direction. Hence both are acknowledged by defining acceleration as a rate of change in velocity rather than speed. Ask your students to identify the three controls in an automobile that make the auto *change* its state of motion—that produce *acceleration*. Ask for them (accelerator, brakes, and steering wheel). State how one lurches in a vehicle that is undergoing acceleration, especially for circular motion, and state why the

definition of velocity includes direction to make the definition of acceleration all-encompassing. Talk of how without lurching one cannot sense motion, giving examples of coin flipping in a high-speed aircraft versus doing the same when the same aircraft is at rest.

Units for Acceleration: Give numerical examples of acceleration in units of kilometers/hour per second to establish the idea of acceleration. Be sure that your students are working on the examples with you. For example, ask them to find the acceleration of a car that goes from rest to 100 km/h in 10 seconds. It is important that you not use examples involving seconds twice until they taste success with the easier kilometers/hour per second examples. Have them check their work with their neighbors as you go along. Only after they get the hang of it, introduce meters/second/second in your examples to develop a sense for the units m/s².

Falling Objects: If you round 9.8 m/s² to 10 m/s² in your lecture, you'll more easily establish the relationships between velocity and distance. Only occassionally is the more precise 9.8 m/s² needed.

CHECK QUESTION: If an object is dropped from an initial position of rest from the top of a cliff, how *fast* will it be traveling at the end of one second? [10 m/s. Two seconds? [20 m/s] Ten seconds?[100 m/s]

The answers, which your students should volunteer, is following the "rule" $v = gt$, which by now you can express in shorthand notation. After any questions, discussion, and examples, state that you are going to pose a different question—not asking for how *fast*, but for how *far*. Ask how far the object falls in one second. Ask for a written response and then ask if the students could explain to their neighbors *why* the distance is only 5 m rather than 10 m. After they've discussed this for almost a minute or so, ask "If you maintain a speed of 60 km/hr for one hour, how far do you go? "—then, "If you maintain a speed of 10 m/s for one second, how far do you go?" Important point: You'll appreciably improve your instruction if you allow some thinking time after you ask a question. Not doing so is the folly of too many instructors. Then continue, "Then why is the answer to the first question not 10 meters?" After a suitable time, stress the idea of *average* velocity and the relation $d = v_{ave}t$.

It will be your call on whether you want to teach finding distance by $d = v_{ave}t$ or by the somewhat more complicated $d = 1/2 \, gt^2$. The latter is derived in the appendix. This can be shortened to $d = 5t^2$.

(We tell our students that the derivation is a sidelight to the course—something that will be the crux of a follow-up physics course. In any event, the derivation is not something that we expect of them, but is to show that $d = 1/2 \, gt^2$ is a reasoned statement that doesn't just pop up from nowhere.)

CHECK QUESTION: How far will a freely falling object that is released from rest, fall in 2 s? [20 m] In 10 s? [500 m] (When your class is comfortable with this, then ask how far in 1/2 second. [1.25 m])

To avoid information overload, we restrict all numerical examples of free fall to cases that begin at rest. Why? Because it's simpler that way. (We prefer our students understand simple physics than be confused about not-so-simple physics!) We do go this far with them.

CHECK QUESTION: Consider a rifle fired straight downward from a high-altitude balloon. If the muzzle velocity is 100 m/s and air resistance can be neglected, what is the *acceleration* of the bullet after one second? (If most of your class say that it's g, you're on!)

We suggest *not* asking for the time of fall for a freely-falling object, given the distance. Why? Unless the distance given is the familiar 5 meters, algebraic manipulation is called for. If one of our teaching objectives were to teach algebra, this would be a nice place to do it. But we don't have time to present this stumbling block and then teach how to overcome it. We'd rather put our energy *and theirs* into straight physical science!

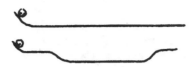

The Two-Track Demo: Be sure to fashion a pair of tracks like those here. Simple bent a pair of angle iron used as bookcase supports. The tracks are of equal length and can be bent easily with a vice. Release a pair of balls at the same time and ask which gets to the end of the track first. Be prepared for the majority of your class to say they reach the end of the track at the same time. Aha, they figure they have the same speed at the end, which throws them off base. Same *speed* does not mean same *time*. I like to quip "Which will win the race, the fast ball or the slower ball?" It will take some convincing to point out that the average speed is greater on the dipped track because the ball moves faster in the dip. Yes, it loses this speed climbing up the dip, but while doing so it still exceeds the speed of the ball on the straight track. Greater average speed means less time to make the trip.

You can return to this demo when you discuss energy in Chapter 6. There you ask a different question: Which has the greater *speed* at the ends of the tracks. Aha, since their potential energies are the same, both have the same speed.

Hang Time (Page 10 in the **Practice Book**): As strange as it first may seem, the longest time a jumper can remain in air is less than a second. It is a common illusion that jumping times are more. Even Michael Jordan's best *hang time* (the time the feet are off the ground) was 0.9 second. Then $d = 1/2\ gt^2$ predicts how high a jumper can go vertically. For a hang time of a full second, that's 1/2 s up and 1/2 s down. Substituting, $d = 5(0.5)^2 = 1.25$ m (which is about 4 feet)! So the great athletes and ballet dancers jump vertically no more than 4 feet high! Of course one can clear a higher fence or bar; but one's *center of gravity* cannot be raised more than 4 feet in free jumping. In fact very few people can jump 2 feet high! To test this, stand against a wall with arms upstretched. Mark the wall at the highest point. Then jump, and at the top, again mark the wall. For a human being, the distance between marks is at most 4 feet!

What Goes Up Must Come Down Chapter 8 covers projectile motion, and states that the slowing of a ball tossed upward equals the speeding of the ball in falling (without air drag).

Sample Problem
A ball is thrown with enough speed straight up so that it is in the air several seconds.
(a) What is the velocity of the ball when it gets to its highest point?
(b) What is its velocity 1 second before it reaches its highest point?
(c) What is the change in velocity during this 1-s interval?
(d) What is its velocity 1 second after it reaches its highest point?
(e) What is the change in velocity during this 1-s interval?
(f) What is the change in velocity during a 2-s interval?
(g) What is the acceleration of the ball during any of these time intervals and at the moment the ball has zero velocity at the top?

Answers:
(a) The velocity of the ball at the top of its vertical trajectory is instantaneously zero.
(b) One second before reaching its top, its velocity is **10 m/s.**
(c) The amount of change in velocity is **10 m/s** during this 1-second interval (or any other 1-second interval).
(d) One second after reaching its top its velocity is **-10 m/s**—equal in magnitude but oppositely directed to its value 1 second before reaching the top.
(e) The amount of change in velocity during this (or any) 1-second interval is **10 m/s.**
(f) In 2 seconds, the amount of change in velocity, from 10 m/s up to 10 m/s down, is **20 m/s** (not zero!).
(g) The acceleration of the ball is **10 m/s^2** before reaching the top, when reaching the top, and after reaching the top. In all cases acceleration is downward, toward the Earth.

Appendix C Vectors

Vectors and Scalars
Adding Vectors
Finding Components of Vectors
Sailboats

Learning Objectives
After studying Appendix C, students will be able to:
• Distinguish between a scalar and a vector quantity.
• Use the parallelogram method to find the resultant of a pair of vectors.
• Separate a vector into perpendicular components.
• Explain why a sailboat can tack into the wind.
• Explain why the intensity of light diminishes when passing though a pair of Polaroids.

Possible Misconceptions to Correct
• **Not so!** All quantities have a vector nature about them.
• **Not so!** A sailboat can sail directly into the wind.
• **Not so!** A sailboat can sail fastest when it is directed directly downwind.

Chances are pretty good that if you were sitting next to a physicist on a long bus ride, and the physicist attempting to explain some physical idea on the back of an envelope, the physicist would likely make extensive use of little arrows. These little arrows, that illustrate size and direction, are part of a physicist's language. They are *vectors*. Vectors are only lightly treated in the textbook, and are more extensive in the Practice Book and Next-Time Questions book.

In the **Practice Book:**
• Vectors and the Parallelogram Rule
• Velocity Vectors and Components
• Vectors and Sailboats
• Force-Vector Diagrams

In the **Next-Time Questions** book:
• Rotating Disk
• Motorboats
• Nellie Newton and Rope Tension
• Sailboat 1
• Sailboat 2

Consider an airplane flying in a cross wind. The resulting speed can only be found with vectors. The only vector tools the student needs is the *parallelogram rule,* and perhaps the *Pythagorean Theorem.* Avoid sines and cosines unless your students are studying to be scientists or engineers. Here we distinguish between physics and the *tools* of physics. Tools should be for preengineers and scientists only. Physics should be for everybody!

The parallelogram rule is nicely illustrated in the Nellie Newton Next-Time Question. Present variations of this figure and guide your class to solutions.

DEMONSTRATION: Have two students hold the ends of a heavy chain. Ask them to pull it horizontally to make it as straight as possible. Then ask what happens if a bird comes along and sits in the middle (as you place a 1-kg hook mass on the middle of the chain). What happens if another bird comes to join the first (as you suspend another 1-kg mass)? Ask the students to keep the chain level. Now what happens if a flock of birds join the others (as you hang additional masses). This works well!

Explain the above via the parallelogram rule (as shown in the Practice Pages). The chain must be directed slightly upward to provide the needed vertical components to offset the weight.

Force and Velocity Vectors
Have your students have a go at the vector exercises in the Practice Book. Take care to avoid force *and* velocity vectors on the same diagram. Having both on a vector diagram is an invitation to confusion—what you don't need. On the Next-Time Question about the motorboats, Boat A takes the shortest path to the opposite shore, Boat B reaches the opposite shore first, and the faster ride is provided by Boat C. Vectors giving these answers are obtained with the parallelogram rule.

Components of Vectors
For components of vectors, again, page 142 of the Practice Book is instructive.

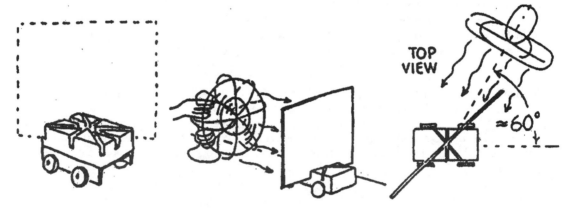

One of the most fascinating application of vectors is the sailboat tacking into the wind. This is treated quite extensively in Appendix C. An interesting demo is the model sailboat which you can easily build yourself with a small block of wood and a piece of aluminum. Cut slots in the wood and mount it on a cart (or ideally, on an air track). A ft^2 sheet of aluminum serves as a sail, and wind from a hand-held fan is directed against the sail in various directions. Most impressive is holding the fan in front, but off to the side a bit, so that the cart will sail into the wind. This is indeed an excellent vehicle for teaching vectors and their components!

You can demonstrate this on a table, holding the fan in various positions and asking your students to imagine the force vector produced by the wind. The vector points perpendicular to the sail, on the side opposite that getting the impact of wind. If there is a component of this vector in the direction in which the boat can go, then the boat is propelled. Actually, the sail "doesn't know" which direction the wind moves when making impact. If it hits the back side of the sail, then a force vector occurs on the opposite side—whether wind is from east to west or west to east. Fascinating!

The sailboat demo and the crossed Polaroids discussed in Chapter 16 are to my mind, the most intriguing illustrations of vectors and what they can do. Figure 16.20 features my daughter-in law holding crossed Polaroids with another sandwiched between. The observation that light gets through the system is quite intriguing. Second only to the sailboat sailing into the wind, it is my favorite illustration of vectors. The explanation for the passage of light through the system of three Polaroids is not given in the chapter, but is indicated in Figure C.12, Appendix C (repeated here more quantitatively).

[For an ideal polarizer, 50% of nonpolarized incident light is transmitted. That is why a Polaroid passes so little light compared to a sheet of window pane. The transmitted light is polarized. So in the above diagram, only the electric vector aligned with the polarization axis is transmitted; this is 50% of the incident light transmitted by the first sheet. The magnitude of this vector through the second sheet is 50% cos ø, where ø is the angle between the polarization axes of both sheets, and (50% cos ø) cos ß of the original vector gets through the third sheet, where ß is the angle between the polarization axes of the second and third sheet. The intensity of light is proportional to the square of the emerging vector (not treated in the textbook). In any event, the polarizers are less than ideal, so less than this actually gets through the three-sheet system.]

The force-vector diagrams on page 145 of the Practice Book are awesome. They were developed by the late Jim Court, at City College of San Francisco. They are instructive at all levels. At minimum they help students identify the forces that a body experiences. This alone is significant. Then estimating the relative magnitudes of these forces is physics at its best. Heavy and important physics.

Appendix D Fluid Physics

Density
Pressure
> **Pressure in a Liquid**

Buoyancy in a Liquid
Archimedes' Principle
Flotation
Pressure in a Gas
Boyle's Law
Atmospheric Pressure
> **Barometers**

Buoyancy in a Gas
Bernoulli's Principle

Learning Objectives
After studying Appendix D, students will be able to:
- Describe what variables determine the pressure of a liquid at any point.
- Explain what causes buoyant force on an immersed object.
- Relate the buoyant force on an object to the weight of fluid it displaces.
- Describe what detemines whether an object will sink or float in a fluid.
- Given the weight of a floating object, determine the weight of fluid it displaces.
- Describe the source of atmospheric pressure.
- Explain what determines whether an object will float in air.
- Describe the relationship between the speed of a fluid at any point and the pressure at that point when the flow is steady.
- Explain the source of lift on the wing of a bird or airplane.

Possible Misconceptions to Correct:
- **Not so!** Liquid pressure depends on the total weight of the liquid.
- **Not so!** Immersed and submerged are two words for the same thing.
- **Not so!** The buoyant force that acts on a submerged object equals the weight of the object, rather than the weight of the displaced fluid.
- **Not so!** Heavy things (rather than dense things) sink in water, whereas light things float.
- **Not so!** Air has no weight.
- **Not so!** The Earth's atmosphere extends upward for hundreds of kilometers.
- **Not so!** Things that float in air follow different rules than things that float in water.
- **Not so!** The faster a fluid flows, the greater its internal pressure.

Demonstration Equipment:
- Pascal's vases
- Overflow can, graduated cylinder or a liquid-measuring cup, and a metal or stone weight to lower into water by a string
- Pair of scales, metal block or stone, vessel filled with water, and smaller vessel to catch overflow (as shown in Figure D.9 in the text)

Treat this appendix as a chapter that you can insert almost anywhere in your course. Ideally, it can be the concluding chapter in Part 1, Mechanics. It is much more abbreviated than it would be if it were a regular chapter. The main concepts, however, are covered.

In student laboratory exercises, it is more common to work with mass density than with weight density, and floating or submerged materials are more often described in units of mass rather than weight. Displaced liquid is also described in units of mass rather than weight. This is why buoyant force in this appendix is treated as "the weight of so many kilograms," rather than "so many newtons." The expression of buoyancy in terms of mass units should be more in keeping with what goes on in lab.

An impressive buoyancy demo by John Suchocki: Place about 8 grams of dry ice in a large (several cm) uninflated balloon. Tie the balloon. Immediately set it on a digital balance reading to the nearest milligram. As the balloon inflates (over a few minutes) the balance readout plummets at a rate of about 2 mg/sec. The scale will finally read about 2.4 grams less, assuming the balloon inflates to about 2 liters (density of air is about 1.2 g/L).

Oceans tidbit: The Atlantic is getting wider, the Pacific narrower.

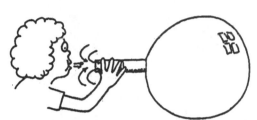

Blowing bubbles is always fun, and here's one from the Exploratorium that nicely illustrates Bernoulli's Principle. Question: Can you blow a 1-breath bubble bigger than your lungs? Answer: Yes, depending on how you do it. Here's how: Tape together two or three small juice cans that have had both ends removed. (You can use the cardboard core of a roll of paper towels, but this tube will not last through repeated uses.) Make up a soap solution that consists Joy or Dawn liquid dishwashing soap, glycerin, and water (recipe: 1 gallon of water, 2/3 cup of dishwashing soap, 3 tablespoons glycerin [available from any drug store]). Let the solution stand overnight, for better bubbles are produced by an "aged" mixture. Dip the tube to form a soap film over the end. To make a lung-sized bubble, take a deep breath and, with your mouth sealed against the nonsoapy end of the tube, exhale and blow a bubble. Don't blow too hard or else the bubble film will break. You'll note the size of this bubble is nearly the volume of your lungs (you can't exhale *all* the air from your lungs).

You can do the same with a long plastic bag. Invite students to blow up the bag, counting their breaths. After two or three students have demonstrated that many breaths of air are required, announce that you can do it with one breath. The hold the bag a few centimeters in front of

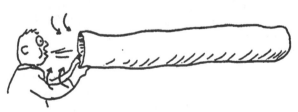

your mouth, not on it as your students likely did, and then blow. Air pressure in the air stream you produce is reduced, entrapping surrounding air to join in filling up the bag!

In the **Practice Book:**
• Archimedes' Principle I
• Archimedes' Principle II
• Gases

In the **Next-Time Questions** book:
• Styrofoam Load on a Ship

- Water Seeks its own Level
- Boat Load of Rocks Overboard
- Weighed Balloon
- Weight of Air

In the **Lab Manual**:
- Sink or Swim
- Eureka!
- Boat Float
- Tire Pressure and 18-Wheelers

SUGGESTED LECTURE PRESENTATION

Density Measure the dimensions of a large wooden cube in cm and find its mass with a pan balance. Define density = mass/volume. (Use the same cube when you discuss flotation in the next chapter.) Some of your students will unfortunately conceptualize density as massiveness or bulkiness rather than massiveness per bulkiness, even when they give a verbal definition properly. This can be helped with the following:

> CHECK QUESTIONS: Which has the greater density, a cupful of water or a lake-full of water? A kilogram of lead or a kilogram of feathers? A single uranium atom or the world?

I jokingly relate breaking a candy bar in two and giving the smaller piece to my friend who looks disturbed. "I gave you the same density of candy bar as I have."

Contrast the density of matter and the density of atomic nuclei that comprise so tiny a fraction of space within matter. From about 2 gm/cm^3 to 2×10^{14} gm/cm^3. And in a further crushed state, the interior of neutron stars, about 10^{16} gm/cm^3.

Area-Volume In this chapter we discuss volume and area, as evident in the units gm/cm^3 and N/m^2. Emphasize the relationship between area and volume as Chelcie Liu does by showing the following: Have a 500-ml spherical flask filled with colored water sitting on your lecture table. Produce a tall cylindrical flask, also of 500 ml (unknown to your students), and ask for speculations as to how high the water level will be when water is poured into it from the spherical flask. You can ask for a show of hands for those who think that the water will reach more than half the height, and those who think it will fill to less than half the height, and for those who guess it will fill to exactly half the height. Your students will be amazed when they see that the seemingly smaller spherical flask has the same volume as the tall cylinder. To explain, call attention to the fact that the *area* of the spherical flask is considerably smaller than the surface area of the cylinder. We see a greater area and we unconsciously think that the volume should be greater as well. Be sure to do this. It is more impressive than it may first seem.

Force versus Pressure Begin by distinguishing between force and pressure. Illustrate with examples: Somebody pushing on your back with a force of only 1 N—with a pin! As you're lying on the floor, a 400-N woman stands on your stomach—perched atop spike heels! Indian master lying on a bed of 1000 nails—apprentice considering starting with one nail! Why the importance of jewel bearings (remember them, old timer?) in watches, diamond stylus (still around!) in record players, rounded corners on tables, sharp blades on cutting knives, and the absurdity of standing tall while pointing your toes downward when caught in quicksand.

Have students compare in their hands the weights of a small steel ball and a large Styrofoam ball, and after agreeing that the little ball is heavier, weigh them and show the Styrofoam ball is heavier! Another example of pressure (on the nerve endings).

Liquid Pressure Liquid pressure = density × depth: After a few words about density, you may want to derive or call attention to the derivation of this relationship (footnote on page 114).

Conceptual Physical Science—Explorations **Teaching Guide**

DEMONSTRATION: Pascal's Vases (similar to Figure D.3)—rationalize your results in terms of the supporting forces exerted by the sloping sides of the vases. [That is, in the wide sloping vase, the water pushes against the glass, and the glass reacts by pushing against the water. So the glass supports the extra water without the pressure below increasing. For the narrow vase that slopes outward near the bottom, the water pushes up against the sloping glass. By reaction, the glass pushes down on the water, so the pressure at the bottom is as if water were present all the way to the surface.]

Ask why your heart gets more rest if you sleep in a prone position versus sitting up. Call attention to the fact that when swimming, the pressure one feels against the eardrums is a function of only depth—that swimming 3 meters deep in a small pool has the same effect as swimming 3 meters deep in the middle of a huge lake.

CHECK QUESTION: Would the pressure be greater swimming 3 m deep in the middle of the ocean? (Then compare the densities of fresh and salt water.)

Ask why dams are built thicker at the bottom [because pressure depends on depth. Deeper water exerts more pressure, hence the thicker part of the dam below.]

Buoyant Force Show that a consequence of pressure being depth dependent is the phenomenon of buoyancy. Sketch Figure D.6 on the board. Follow this up with a sketch of larger forces at a deeper level—but with *differences* in up and down vectors being the same.

DEMONSTRATION: Show how an overflow can enables the measure of an object's volume. Ask how one could measure a quarter of a cup of butter in a liquid measuring cup using this method.

DEMONSTRATION: Archimedes' Principle, as shown in Figure D.9.

Point out that because a liquid is incompressible (practically incompressible, as the volume of water decreases by only 50 one-millionths of its original volume for each atmosphere increase in pressure, or equivalently, for each addition 10.3 m in depth) its density is not depth dependent. The density of water near the surface is practically the same as the density far beneath the surface. You may wish to acknowledge that some variation occurs due to temperature differences. Usually a student will inquire about waterlogged objects which lie submerged yet off the bottom of the body of water. Such objects are slightly denser than the warmer surface water and not quite as dense as the cooler water at the bottom. Stress that this is unusual and that objects appreciably denser than water always sink to the bottom, regardless of the depth of the water. Scuba divers do not encounter "floating" rocks near the bottoms of deep bodies of water!

CHECK QUESTION: Two solid blocks of identical size are submerged in water. One block is lead and the other is aluminum. Upon which is the buoyant force greater?

After discussion, try this one:

CHECK QUESTION: Two solid blocks of identical size, one of lead and the other of wood, are put in the same water. Upon which is the buoyant force greater? [This time the buoyant force is greater on the lead, because it displaces more water than the wood that floats!]

CHECK QUESTION: What is the buoyant force on a ten-ton ship floating in fresh water? In salt water? In a lake of mercury? [Same buoyant force, but different *volumes* displaced.]

The unit "ton" may be taken to mean a metric tonne, the weight of 1000 kg, or the British ton, 2000 lbs. Either interpretation is sufficient in treating the idea involved.

Archimedes and the King's Crown Eureka was the solution to whether or not the king's crown was adulterated with silver. When immersed in water, a measure of the volume of water displaced gives the volume of the crown. If more water is displaced by the crown than by a mass of gold of equal weight, this indicates the presence of an alloy.

Flotation Discuss boats and rafts and the change of water lines when loaded.

CHECK QUESTIONS: What is the approximate density of a fish? Of a person? What can you say of people who can't float?

DEMONSTRATION: Cartesian diver (inverted partially filled small bottle submerged in a larger flexible plastic bottle that you squeeze to increase and decrease the weight of water in the small bottle to make it rise and fall).

Discuss the compressibility of the human body in swimming—how the density of most people a meter or two below the surface of the water is still less than the density of water, and that one need only relax and be buoyed to the surface. But that at greater depths, the greater pressure compresses one to densities greater than the density of water, and one must swim to the surface. Simply relaxing, one would sink to the bottom! Relate this to the Cartesian diver demonstration. Also state why one cannot snorkel with a tube that goes deeper than a half meter or so.

Side point: Contrary to those old Tarzan movies, you cannot sink in quicksand. Quicksand is the name given to a mass of sand particles that are supported by circulating water rather than by each other. Its density is greater than the density of human bodies, so you can float on it. If you struggle, you'll unfortunately succeed in digging yourself deeper in. So if you're ever stuck in it, keep yourself still until you stop sinking (you will), and then use slow swimming motions to get yourself into a horizontal position and then roll onto the ground.

DEMONSTRATION: (By Sean Elkins and suggested by Marshall Ellenstein.) Place a Ping-Pong ball a couple of inches below the surface of a glass container of puffed rice. Then place a golf ball on top of the puffed rice. Shake the container and say the magic words "physics." The golf ball and Ping-Pong ball soon changes places—the golf ball "sinks" and the Ping-Pong ball "floats."

Floating Mountain Box Isostacy is the concept wherein high structures like mountains are lighter and "float" on a denser substructure in the Earth—Archimedes' principle for rocks.

Weight of Air Hold out an empty drinking glass and ask what's in it. It's not really empty, for it's filled with air, and has weight. It is common to think of air as having very little mass, when the truth is air has a fairly large mass—about 1.25 kilogram for a cube one meter on a side (at sea level). The air that fills your bathtub has a mass of about 0.5 kilogram. We don't feel the weight of this mass only because we are immersed in an ocean of air. A plastic bag full of water, for example, has a significant weight, but if the bag is taken into a swimming pool it weighs nothing. Likewise for the surrounding air. A bag of air may have a fairly large mass, but as long as the bag is surrounded by air, its weight is not felt. We are as unconscious of the weight of air that surrounds us as a fish is unconscious of the weight of water that surrounds it.

CHECK QUESTION: Open the door of a refrigerator and inside is a large lonely grapefruit. Which weighs more, the air in the fridge or the grapefruit? [The inside volume of a common refrigerator is between 1/2 and 3/4 m^3, which corresponds to nearly a kilogram of cold air (about 2 pounds). So unless the grapefruit is more than a 2-pounder, the air weighs more.]

The Atmosphere Draw a circle as large as possible on the chalkboard, and then announce that it represents the Earth. State that if you were to draw another circle, indicating the thickness of the atmosphere surrounding the Earth to scale, that you would end up drawing the same line— for over 99% of the atmosphere lies within the thickness of the chalk line! Then go on to discuss the ocean of air in which we live.

DEMONSTRATION: While discussing the preceding, have a gallon metal can with a bit of water in it heating on a burner. When steam issues, cap it tightly and remove from the heat source. Continue your discussion and the collapsing can will interrupt you as it crunches. If you really want to impress your class, do the same with a 50-gallon drum! [The explanation is that pressure inside the can or drum decreases as cooling occurs and the steam condenses. Atmospheric pressure on the outside produces the crunching net force on the can or drum.]

DEMONSTRATION: Here's a goodie! Heat some aluminum soda pop cans on a burner, empty except for a small amount of water that is brought to a boil to make steam. With a pot holder or tongs, pick up a can and quickly invert it into a basin of water. Crunch! The atmospheric pressure immediately crushes the can with a resounding WHOP! Very impressive. [Condensation of the steam and vapor occur and the interior pressure is reduced. This occurs even when the temperature of the water bath into which the can is inverted is nearly boiling temperature. What happens is a "flypaper effect"—water molecules in the vapor state condense when they encounter the water into which they're placed—even hot water. You'll show this demo again if you perchance discuss the reason for the condensation cycle in a steam turbine—to decrease the back pressure on the turbine blades.]

Atmospheric Pressure While this is going on, state that if you had a 30-km tall bamboo pole of cross section 1 square cm, the mass of the air from the atmosphere in it would amount to about 1 kg. The weight of this air is the source of atmospheric pressure. The atmosphere bears down on the Earth's surface at sea level with a pressure that corresponds to the weight of 1 kg per square cm. (Remember the old days when we could talk about plain old 14.7 lb/in^2? Since the unit of force is now the newton and the unit of area is the square meter, conceptualizing atmospheric pressure is less simple than before. Nevertheless, continue with the following description.) To understand the pressure of the atmosphere in terms of newtons per square meter, ask your class to imagine a 30-km tall sewer pipe of cross section 1 square m, filled with the air of the atmosphere. How much would the enclosed air weigh? The answer is about 10^5 N. So if you draw a circle of one square meter on the lecture table, and ask what the weight is for all the air in the atmosphere above, you should elicit a chorus, silent or otherwise of "10^5 N!" If your table is above sea level, then the weight of air is correspondingly less. Then estimate the force of the air pressure that collapsed the metal can—both for a perfect vacuum and for a case where the pressure difference is about half an atmosphere.

Estimate the force of the atmosphere on a person. You can estimate the surface area by approximating different parts of the body on the board—leg by leg, arm by arm, etc. (This can be quite funny, if you want it to be!)

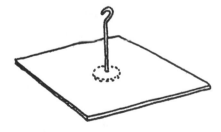

DEMONSTRATION: This great one from John McDonald of Boise State University consists of a square sheet of soft rubber with some sort of handle at its center. A 50-gram mass hanger poked through its center works well. Toss the rubber sheet on any perfectly flat surface—best on the top of a lab stool. Picking the rubber up by a corner is an easy task, because the air gets under it as it is lifted. But lifting it by the middle is another story. As the middle is raised, a low-pressure region is formed because air cannot get in. The rubber sheet behaves as a suction cup, and the entire stool is lifted when the handle is raised.

DEMONSTRATION: Whap a toilet plunger or other suction cup on the wall. (Instruct your class to inquire with their neighbors to see if there is a consensus as to the reason.)

Barometers State that a better vacuum source than sucking would remove much more air, and if all the air were removed, a very large column of water would be needed to balance the atmosphere on the other side. This would be about 10.3 m, but depends a little on today's atmospheric pressure. Such devices made up the first barometers. They are impractically large, so mercury is instead commonly used. Since mercury is 13.6 times as dense as water, the height of water needed to balance the atmosphere is 1/13.6 of 10.3 m = 76 cm. If you have the opportunity, construct a mercury barometer before the class.

CHECK QUESTION: How would the barometer level vary while ascending and descending in the elevator of a tall building? [You might quip about the student who was asked to find the height of a building with a sensitive barometer who simply dropped it from the top and measured the seconds of fall—or who exchanged it with the builder of the building for the correct information.]

Discuss ear popping in aircraft, and why cabin pressure is lower than atmospheric pressure at high altitudes.

DEMONSTRATION: As the sketch shows, try sucking a drink through a straw with two straws; one in the liquid and the other outside. It can't be done because the pressure in your mouth is not reduced because of the second straw (although with some effort a bit of liquid can be drawn). Invite your students to try this, and to share this (and other ideas!) at parties.

Boyle's Law Discuss Boyle's Law. At the risk of information overload you may or may not want to get into the differences between absolute and gauge pressures. (I avoid it in the text.)

Buoyancy of Air Hold your hands out, one a few centimeters above the other, and ask if there really is any difference in air pressure at the two places. The fact that there is can be demonstrated by the rising of a helium-filled balloon of the same size! The balloon rises only because the atmospheric pressure at its bottom is greater than the atmospheric pressure at its top. Pressure in the atmosphere really is depth dependent!

CHECK QUESTION: Which is greater, the buoyant force on the helium-filled balloon, or the buoyant force on you? [Assuming the balloon has less volume than you, there is more buoyant force on you.] Discuss why.

Interestingly enough, atmospheric pressure halves with every 6 km increase in elevation, so a freely expanding balloon becomes twice as big with each 6 km rise. Does this increase the buoyant force? No, because the displacement of twice as much half-as-dense air has the same weight!

CHECK QUESTION: A large block of Styrofoam and a small block of iron have identical weights on a weighing scale. Which has the greater mass? [Actually the Styrofoam has the greater mass. This is because it has a greater volume, displaces more air, and experiences a greater buoyant force. So it's weight on the scale is its "true weight," minus the buoyant force of the air, which is the case for all things weighed in air. The fact that it reads the same on the scale as the iron means it must have more mass than the iron. (A lobster that walks on a bathroom scale on the ocean bottom has more mass than the reading indicates.)]

CHECK QUESTION: What would happen to the bubbles in a beer mug if you dropped the mug of beer from the top of a high building? Would the bubbles rise to the top, go to the bottom, or remain motionless with respect to the mug? [First of all, you'd likely be apprehended for irresponsible behavior. As for the bubbles, they'd remain motionless relative to the mug, since the local effects of gravity on the beer would be absent. This is similar to the popular demo of dropping a cup of water with holes in the side. When held at rest the water spurts out, but drop it and the spurting stops.]

Bernoulli's Principle: Introduce Bernoulli's principle by blowing across the top surface of a sheet of paper, Figure 5.33. Follow this up with a variety of demonstrations such as making a beach ball hover in a stream of air issuing from the reverse end of a vacuum cleaner or a Ping-Pong ball in the airstream of a hair dryer.

DEMONSTRATIONS: (1) Make a beach ball hover in a stream of air issuing from the reverse end of a vacuum cleaner. (2) Do the same with a Ping-Pong ball in the airstream of a hairdryer. (3) Line a cardboard tube with sandpaper and sling the ball sidearm. The sandpaper will produce the friction to make the ball roll down the tube and emerge spinning—you'll see that the ball breaks in the correct direction. Point out that paddles have a rough surface like the sandpaper for the same reason—to spin the ball when it is properly struck—that is, to apply "English" to the ball. (4) Swing a Ping-Pong ball taped to a string into a stream of water. Follow this up with a discussion of a shower curtain that swings inward when water flows in a shower.

DEMONSTRATION: Place a pair of upright empty aluminum soft drink cans on a few parallel straws on your lecture table. Blow between the cans and they roll toward each other. Or do the same with the nearby cans suspended by strings. A puff of air between them makes them click against one another, rather than blowing them apart as might be expected. [Some people avoid Bernoulli's principle because in some cases, like plane flight, there are alternate models to account for the forces that occur. These clicking cans, however, are straight Bernoulli!]

Appendix E Exponential Growth and Doubling Time

Conceptual Physical Science—Explorations

This material, adapted from papers written by Al Bartlett, makes a fine lecture. The material is not only very important, but is fascinating—and very wide in scope. It can nicely follow Chapter 16, after global warming and continued industrial growth is discussed. Or it can be coupled to a discussion of radioactive half-life as treated in Chapter 19. Or it can be treated in any break—following an exam, perhaps, or on any day that lends itself to a departure from chapter material.

The concept of growth rate can be expressed in simple steps: Step 1: (new amount) = (old amount) + k times (old amount). Step 2: (new amount) becomes (old amount). Step 3: Keep repeating. That's it. The mathematics is just arithmetic. Use positive k for growth, and negative k for decay.

A beginning application is simple 10% annual interest on each dollar in a savings account. At the end of the 1st year, A = 1 + 0.10(1); 2nd year, A = 1.10 + 0.10(1.10); 3rd year, A = 1.21 + 0.10(1.21); and so on. Suppose your savings are silver dollars and the bank charges 10% annual storage fee.

Year	INTEREST Change	INTEREST Amount	RENTAL Change	RENTAL Amount
0		1.00		1.00
1	+0.100	1.10	-0.100	0.90
2	+0.110	1.21	-0.090	0.81
3	+0.121	1.33	-0.081	0.73
4	+0.133	1.46	-0.073	0.66
5	+0.146	1.61	-0.066	0.59
6	+0.161	1.77	-0.059	0.53
7	+0.177	1.95	-0.053	0.48
8	+0.195	2.14	-0.048	0.43
9	+0.214	2.36	-0.043	0.39
10	+0.236	2.59	-0.039	0.35
20	+0.612	6.73	-0.014	0.12

Note that in 7 years at a 10% rate the amount just about doubles for positive k and just about halves for negative k.

It is customary to use the decay halving time (half-life) of processes such as radioactive decay as a property of the decaying elements. There is nothing special about doubling-halving time. Tripling-thirding or 3/2ing-2/3ing, or any factor and its reciprocal could be used. As the number of time intervals increases, the process approaches continuity, which leads to the exponential, e^{kt}.

The formula for doubling time in the text appears without derivation, which is likely beyond the scope of a nonscience physics class. ts derivation is as follows: Exponential growth may be described by the equation

$$A = A_o e^{kt}$$

where k is the rate of increase of the quantity A_o. Re-express this for a time T when A = $2A_o$,

$$2A_o = A_o c^{kT}$$

If we take the natural logarithm of each side we get

$$\ln 2 = kT \quad \text{where T} = \frac{\ln 2}{k} = \frac{0.693}{k}$$

If k is expressed in percent, then

$$T = \frac{69.3}{\%} \sim \frac{70}{\%}$$

When percentage figures are given for things such as interest rates, population growth, or consumption of nonrenewable resources, conversion to doubling time greatly enhances the meaning of these figures.

In the **Next-Time Questions** book:
• Growing Beanstalk

ANSWERS TO APPENDIX E QUESTIONS TO PONDER

1. In an economy that has a steady inflation rate of 7% per year, in how many years does a dollar lose half its value?
   A dollar loses 1/2 its value in 1 doubling time of the inflationary economy; this is 70/7% = 10 years. It the dollar is loaned at 7% compound interest, it loses nothing.

2. At a steady inflation rate of 7%, what will be the price every 10 years for the next 50 years for a theater ticket that now costs $20? For a coat that now costs $200? For a car that now costs $20,000? For a home that now costs $200,000?
   At a steady inflation rate of 7%, the doubling time is 70/7% = 10 years; so every 10 years the prices of these items will double. This means the $20 theater ticket in 10 years will cost $40, in 20 years will cost $80, in 30 years will cost $160, in 40 years will cost $320, and in 50 years will cost $640. The $200 suit of clothes will similarly jump each decade to $400, $800, $1600, $3,200, and $6,400. For a $20,000 car the decade jumps will be $40,000, $80,000, $160,000, $320,000, and $640,000. For a $200,000 home, the decade jumps in price are $400,000, $800,000, $1600,000, $3,200,000, and $6,400,000! Inflation often increases earnings more than prices, so we'll be able to pay for these things—and more.

3. If the population of a city with one overloaded sewage treatment plant grows steadily at 5% annually, how many overloaded sewage treatment plants will be necessary 42 years later?
   For a 5% growth rate, 42 years is three doubling times (70/5% = 14 years; 42/14 = 3). Three doubling times is an eightfold increase. So in 42 years the city would have to have 8 sewerage treatment plants to remain as presently loaded; more than 8 if load per plant is to be reduced while servicing 8 times as many people.

4. If world population doubles in 40 years and world food production also doubles in 40 years, how many people then will be starving each year compared to now?
   All things being equal, doubling of food for twice the number of people simply means that twice as many people will be eating, and twice as many will be starving as are starving now!

5. Suppose you get a prospective employer to agree to hire your services for a wage of a single penny for the first day, 2 pennies the second day, and doubling each day thereafter. If the employer keeps to the agreement for a month, what will be your total wages for the month?
   Doubling one penny for 30 days yields a total of $10,737,418.23!

6. In the previous question, how will your wages for only the 30th day compare to your total wages for the previous 29 days?
   On the 30th day your wages will be $5,368,709.12, which is one penny more than the $5,368,709.11 total from all the preceding days.

Laboratory Suggestions, with Answers to Lab Manual Questions

Introduction and Part 1 Activities and Experiments

Introduction
Tuning the Senses - *Observation*
Making Cents - *Scientific Method*

Part 1: Mechanics
Go! Go! Go! - *Graphing Motion*
Sonic Ranger - *Graphing Motion*
Pulled Over - *Newton's Second Law*
Reaction Time - Free Fall
Egg Toss - *Impulse*
Bouncy Board - *Impulse*
Rolling Stop - *Energy Transformations*
The Big BB Race - *Horizontal and Vertical Motion*

Tuning the Senses [Activity]

This activity may be assigned as an "outside experience" (or homework), to be followed up later during classroom discussion.

For the second half of this activity, watching the burning candle, for a large class of 28 students or so you will probably want to use four groups of seven, (or seven groups of four), with one candle per group, as it might be impractical and unnecessary to burn 28 candles, or more, per class. Again, you may choose to assign this as an "outside experience", and avoid clean-up and potential fire problems. This activity may easily be converted into an experiment by having a student in each group measure and record the candle's length and diameter before and after burning for a recorded time. The hypothesis to be tested could be, "The change in length per minute while burning is not directly proportional to diameter."

Making Cents [Activity]

Brad Huff at The Fresno County Office of Education in Fresno, CA is credited for this activity. He discovered in 1984 that there was nearly an equal distribution of pre/post 1982 pennies in circulation. His students discovered the difference in mass as part of an exercise on how to use mass balances. So point out to your students the role of a good scientific attitude in making "accidental" discoveries—this one could have been overlooked as "human error."

The composition of the alloy in pennies was changed in 1982. Pennies since 1982 are 2.500 g; from 1944 - 1982 pennies were 3.110 g; rare 1943 pennies were 2.700 g; and prior to 1942, pennies were 3.110 g. Such differences ordinarily escape our notice.

A student can enter data on a chart written on the chalkboard. Students then plot this data as a graph. Alternatively, students can enter their data into an analysis program on a personal computer. If your students have never made a histogram, show them how to set up the values on the horizontal axis for the mass of the coins, using perhaps mass increments of 0.1 gram.

How much copper did the U.S. government save by switching to zinc filled pennies? About 2.6 grams per penny: post 1982: 0.444 g Cu and 2.13 g Zn

Density of Copper = 8.920 g/cm^3 Density of Zinc = 7.140 g/cm^3

Students see an unexpected result. Ask for more hypotheses. Is it from a change in size or from a change in composition? They can measure size based upon the displacement of water. 100 pennies displace how much water? Time permitting, they can find the density of pennies.

Answers to the Questions
1. Pennies dated before and after 1982 should show a double-humped histogram should result—indicating a change in a penny's material in 1982.
2. Worn coins have less mass than new ones. Dirty, oxidized coins may have more mass.
3. Nails, nuts, soft drink cans, blades of grass, heights of students, etc.

Go! Go! Go! [Activity]

This activity affords students an opportunity to collect data from an observable event, make measurements, and plot a graph of the results. They can then interpret the graph. The car speed and size of table should allow at least four data points.

Answers to Summing Up Questions
1. a. The marks would be farther apart.
   b. The car would reach the edge in fewer seconds.
   c. The slope would have been steeper (more vertical).
2. A steeper straight line should be added to the graph.
3. a. The marks would be closer together.
   b. The car would take more seconds to reach the edge.
   c. The slope would have been shallower (more horizontal).
4. A shallower straight line should be added to the graph.
5. a. The marks would get closer and closer together.
   b. A curved line having a decreasing slope (concave down) should be added to the graph.
6. Line A shows an object moving in the opposite ("negative") direction compared to direction of the moving car with constant speed.
   Line B shows a car moving in the "positive" direction and speeding up.

Sonic Ranger [Experiment]

To some extent, this is a high-tech version of Go! Go! Go! in which the computer plots the graph. Sonic ranging technology is revolutionizing the teaching pedagogy for graph interpretation. The computational power of the computer combined with its ability to make rapid measurements of distance and time enable your students to see the graph on the monitor in real time (where was this when *we* first learned about graphs!).
Sonic ranging kits are available from a variety of sources. Contact Pasco Scientific, 10101 Foothill Blvd, Roseville, CA 95678 (800) 772-8700, or Vernier Software, 2920 S.W. 89th St, Portland, OR 97255, (503) 297-5317 [Fax 503 297-1760].

Answers to Procedure Questions
1. Remain at rest.
2. Move away from the sensor (slowly).

3. Move away from the sensor (more quickly).
4. Move toward the sensor, slowing down as you approach it.
5.
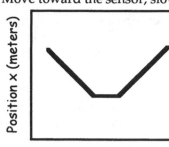

Time t (seconds)

6.
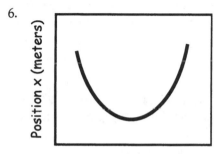

Time t (seconds)

7.
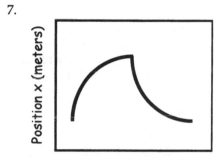

Time t (seconds)

Answers to Summing Up Questions
1. Forward motion results in an upward (positive) sloping graph. Backward motion results in a downward (negative) sloping graph.
2. Slow motion results in a line with a shallow slope, fast motion results in a line with a steep slope.
3. First segment: speeding up, second segment: moving forward with constant speed, third segment: slowing down, fourth segment: at rest, fifth segment: moving backward with constant speed.

Pulled Over [Experiment]

Students can work in groups of three or four. With small tables, a group can work at each end, and with large tables, a group can work at each corner. Understanding the role of friction is the least of the objectives of this activity, so the less the friction between the book (or other object you decide to use) the better.

Answers to the Questions

1. Greatest acceleration is the two-book drop and the one-book drag. Mid acceleration is the single-book drop and single-book drag, and least acceleration is the one book drop and the two-book drag.
2. Two books have both twice the force (gravity) and twice the mass, so acceleration is g (Figure 3.15 in the text).
3. Acceleration is less than g because the mass of the system is now twice but the gravity force of one dropping book is the same. Without friction, the acceleration would be one-half g. In terms of Newton's second law, ideally,

$$a = \frac{F_{net}}{m_{total}} = \frac{mg}{2m} = g/2.$$

4. Acceleration would increase when the force that produces the acceleration increases. When three books are dropped, and drag a single book, acceleration is predictably greater. Ideally,

$$a = \frac{F_{net}}{m_{total}} = \frac{3mg}{4m} = 3/4\,g.$$

5. The upper limit is g! Consider a dropping truck dragging a feather—the feather has negligible influence on the falling truck.
6. Friction was likely very significant, and perhaps greatly masked the idealized results above. Friction of sliding can be reduced by low-friction wheels beneath the dragged books or other objects, or even by using an air track. Friction of the twine at the table's edge can be reduced by the use of pulleys.

Reaction Time [Activity]

This activity can easily be converted into an experiment by dividing the class into three groups, and recording measurements. A hypothesis could be that there is no significant difference in reaction time for the sense of sight, hearing or touching. Group "A" would measure reaction times for several students using a sight signal—they see the holder drop the bill. In Group "B" they close their eyes, and hear the holder say "Drop!" at the instant of release. In Group "C" they close their eyes, and receive a simultaneous tap on the shoulder from the dropper's other hand.

A fourth group could explore the hypothesis that reaction times would differ between using a wooden 12 inch rule and a wooden meterstick—the meterstick is heavier, and would fall (a) faster? Or (b) slower? Or the (c) same? What if the rule were made of steel? [Same, of course!]

If you happen to have a sub-group of psychology or political science majors, suggest a hypothesis that persons who believe (a), (b), or (c) will report data that supports their expectations. You may have a future doctor who is ready to understand a "double-blind experiment"!

Answers to the Questions

1. Evidence ought to be the comparison between sound, sight, and touch on reaction time.
2. For one thing, the individual differences among people.
3. Reaction time can affect measurements that change with time. When the changes are small compared to reaction time, then the effects may be negligible. When they're not, for example in timing a falling object, then choosing the longest time interval lessens the error due to

reaction time. Just like measuring the thickness of a page is more accurate when more pages are measured at one time.

4. Reaction time plays an important role in driving. For a reaction time of 0.7 second, a car going 100 km/h (28 m/s) travels nearly 20 m (about 60 feet) in 0.7 s, which is considerable—which has too many times been fatal.

5. In many sports, a single second is a long time. Baseball is an obvious one, where top players must have extraordinary reaction times. Likewise for soccer, football, and even boxing. The winners of races of all kinds usually are discerned in fractions of a second.

Egg Toss [Activity]

This is an outdoor activity that works well as an in-class competition between lab groups. Combined with the chance to make a bit of a mess—this activity is generally a student favorite!

Answers to Summing Up Questions
1. Many groups can make it to 10 yards or meters. Some to 20; few to 30.
2. Allowing the egg to continue moving while catching it; this extends the stopping time.
3. a. The mass is the same either way.
   b. The change in velocity is the same either way.
   c. The change in momentum is the same either way.
   d. The stopping time is greater for the gradual-stop catch.
   e. The stopping force is greater in the sudden-stop catch.
4. Airbags extend the stopping time for a person moving forward in the car during a collision. It therefore reduced the stopping force compared to what it would be if they were to hit the steering wheel or dashboard.
5. Elastic cords used in bungee-jumping, nearly any kind of "shock-absorption" padding, crumple zones designed into automobile frames, bending one's knees upon landing from a jump.

Bouncy Board [Activity]

This activity comes from Earl Feltyberger, who in turn got it from rock climber Bill Berner in 1985, who taught in a Catholic high school in the Philadelphia suburbs. Bill used this idea to explain the value of stretch in safety ropes used to stop a climber in the event of a fall. It makes a nice lecture demo—nice enough to be shared with students as an activity.

Answers to the Questions
1. A sudden halt will probably either break the cord, or break the body!
2. $Ft = \Delta mv$ is central. The impulse that brings the dropped mass to a halt equals the change in momentum the mass undergoes. The breaking force of the string is greatly affected by the "give" of the stick, which lengthens time and reduces the force needed to stop the mass.
3. Less give means less time to stop; less time to stop means more stopping force—more than the string could provide.
4. Ordinarily the strength of a string has to do with its thickness, not its length. The length of the string plays an important role in that it allows the falling object to fall farther and gain more momentum. So a greater stopping force is needed when the string is long. In short, increasing string length increases Δv, which increases F.
5. The mass of the falling object is directly proportional to the momentum of the falling object; twice the mass at a given speed means twice the momentum, which in turn means twice the needed stopping force. So the greater the mass, the stronger the string required. Just as sheet music guides the musician's tune, $Ft = \Delta mv$ guides our thinking in answering this and the previous questions.
6. Bending increases the time, so decreases the force that might break the fishing string.

Rolling Stop [Experiment]

Students will enjoy this experiment. For one thing, they may notice that all balls gain the same speed in rolling down equal-angle inclines. They may not have an explanation for this, and since the textbook does not treat rotational motion, they won't get help there. The explanation for this is not unlike that of the equal accelerations of free fall for objects of different masses—which is that the ratio of weight to mass is the same for all objects—g. Similarly, the ratio of torque to rotational inertia is the same for all balls on the same incline. It is not necessary to get into this with your class, however, for it may obscure the central idea here. And that idea is the value of looking only at the beginning and end points in a problem that involves energy (almost like considering only the limits when doing integral calculus). Question 4 addresses this.

Here they should see that the PE of the raised ball is directly proportional to the work that the rug does in stopping it. In your discussion, your students may be bothered about the idea of the rug doing work on the rolling ball. Ask if the rug exerts a force on the ball. And to answer this, ask if the ball exerts a force on the rug? Then think of Newton's third law, where it was learned that when one object exerts a force on a second object, the second object exerts an equal and opposite force on the first. So we see the rug does exert a force on the ball—which is why the ball slows to a stop!

In discussing this experiment, you can emphasize that speed can be measured either as $\Delta L/\Delta t$, or as $\Delta t/\Delta L$. A marathon is usually reported as minutes per mile, as "Joe started with a five minute mile, slowed to 10 on the hill, and settled down to a smooth six". You may or may not be surprised to see how many of your students cannot translate these speed into miles per hour in less than 10 seconds.

After Step 4, you may wish to ask this follow-up question: "Would it be incorrect to reverse the axes and plot height vertically on Y, and distance horizontally on X? Why, or why not? Isn't height on Y, and distance on X, more natural?

Point out that in Summary Question 4, we have freedom to choose any level for zero potential energy, table top, or floor, or ceiling, and treat it as a relative signed quantity. Ask, "Where is the absolute level where PE cannot be negative?" [Answer.: Earth's center.] Follow-up question: "What about relative and absolute KE?", and "Does a decrease of 10 J, PE equal an increase of 10 J KE? Why or why not?" [Answer: Yes, because 10 = 10; No, because 10 is 20 more than -10."] We'll have more on "relative" or "absolute" when we get to temperature.

Answers to the Questions
1. The graphs should indicate direct proportions by their straight lines.
2. Yes, because height and ramp length are directly proportional to each other.
3. Stopping distances of different balls depended on the amount of rug friction compared to their masses. A massive ball tended to "mow down" more rug fiber than a lighter ball. The relationship between release heights and stopping distances were nonetheless directly proportional—twice the height resulted in twice the stopping distance for a particular ball.
4. One of the beauties of conserved quantities like energy, is that the beginning amount and the end amount will be the same, regardless of the details involved in the middle. Now the details may be interesting, and have a lot of good physics. But if it's the final state we're interested in, we can bypass the details and go straight to it. In this activity, the ball begins with PE, gains KE of translation and KE of rotation (not covered in the text), then spends this gain across the friction enhanced rug. Mechanical energy is completely converted to thermal energy of the rug (and ball). That is to say, the initial PE is all dissipated along the rug (if we neglect the friction of the ramp—which is reasonable, for ramp friction simply enabled rolling—there was no "dragging" across the ramp and the generation of thermal energy on the ramp). In equation form, we can describe the energy changes of the ball as

$PE_{\text{top of ramp}} = KE_{\text{bottom of ramp}} = Work_{\text{across rug}}$
Note if we are not asked for KE details, then we can simply say
$PE_{\text{top of ramp}} = Work_{\text{across rug}}$.

The Big BB Race [Activity]

The purpose of this activity is to demonstrate the independence of the horizontal and vertical motion of a projectile. This activity should inspire some lively in-class discussion prior to the demonstration. Students should be allowed to argue for an incorrect outcome. The teacher must keep a strict poker face throughout the discussion phase so as to let all lines of reasoning be explored. All this makes for a dramatic and memorable conclusion!

Answers to Procedure Questions
1. Sketches will vary; all projectile paths should start at the launch point and end at the impact point.
2. Arguments will vary.
   Student X: The dropped ball falls straight down; the launched ball travels forward, delaying its arrival on the ground.
   Student Y: The launched ball was given a high speed upon launch, so it will travel faster and reach the ground first.
   Student Z: Both will fall downward at the same rate regardless of their horizontal motion. "Gravity affects both the same way."
3. Responses will vary. Some things students might suggest::
   "No-fall distance" is increased by greater launch speed or launch force.
   "No-fall distance" is decreased by air resistance or weight of the projectile.
6. It's a tie!

Answers to Summing Up Questions
1. The horizontal motion of the launched ball has no effect on its vertical motion.
2. There is no no-fall distance! Both balls begin to fall simultaneously—right when they're launched.
3. Both would hit the ground at the same time—horizontal motion and vertical motion are independent!

Part 2 Activities and Experiments

Heat
Dance of the Molecules - *Molecular Motion*
Spiked Water - *Specific Heat Capacity*
Canned Heat I - *Thermal Absorption*
Canned Heat II - *Thermal Radiation*
I'm Melting! I'm Melting! - *Conduction and Radiation*

Dance of the Molecules [Activity]

This activity is intended to show the difference between hot and cold on a molecular level. Food coloring mixes more quickly in hot water than in cold water due to the greater motion of molecules in the hot water.

Answers to Procedure Questions
2. Predictions will vary.
3. The food coloring is more thoroughly mixed in the hot water than in the cold water. Sketches should reflect this.

Answers to Summing Up Questions
1. The fast-moving molecules in the hot water move the food coloring around and mix it more rapidly than the slow-moving molecules in the cold water. If the molecules had equal speeds in hot and cold water, the mixing would have occurred at an equal rate.
2. Both jars would look the same; the food coloring would be thoroughly mixed in both jars.
3. Air molecules moving around in the room would mix the fragrance molecules throughout the room just like the water molecules mixed the food coloring.
4. If would take longer for the fragrance to mix throughout the room if the air were colder, just like the food coloring in the cold water takes longer to mix.

Spiked Water [Activity]

This activity compares the capacity of nails and water to store thermal energy. A mass of nails and an equal mass of water will be used to heat equal volumes of cold water. The hot water will cause the temperature of the cold water to rise more than the hot nails will.

Answers to Summing Up Questions
1. The nails and hot water had the same temperature; they were in contact long enough to come to thermal equilibrium.
2. Temperature of the cold water rose more than the nails did due to the hot water.
3. Hot water: It holds more thermal energy!
4. The first student was correct. The specific heat capacity water is greater than that of iron (or steel). Any hot water clinging to the nails will aid in increasing the temperature of the cold water to a greater extent than the nails alone. (Also any water remaining on the nails also holds thermal energy "robbed" from the hot water contributes to warm the cold water.)

Canned Heat I [Experiment]

This experiment allows a comparison of the thermal absorption of different surfaces. The surfaces are black , white, and silver. Restless students will find taking data somewhat tedious and time consuming but time is a critical element in this experiment. Therefore, patience is required.

Answers to Summing Up Questions
1. Fastest: black; slowest: silver.
2. White T-shirt is better; it doesn't absorb radiant energy as quickly as black does.
3. Silver: mostly reflected, black: mostly absorbed, white: mostly reflected.

Canned Heat II [Experiment]

This experiment allows a comparison of the thermal radiation of different surfaces. The surfaces are black and silver. The data-taking is slow; the more restless students will find it somewhat tedious. But time is a critical element in this experiment, so the tedium must be endured!

Answers to Summing Up Questions
1. Faster: black, slower: silver.
2. Silvery surfaces hold thermal energy better.
3. It should be colored black (and often is!).

I'm Melting! I'm Melting! [Activity]

This activity explores the heat transfer between various surfaces and an ice cube. The surfaces vary in color and material. And the transfer rates vary dramatically!

Answers to Procedure Questions
1. Both metal surfaces feel colder than both Styrofoam surfaces.
2. Predictions will vary.
3. Predictions will vary.
4. The ice cube on the black Miracle Thaw® melts most quickly.
5. The ice cube on the white Styrofoam melts most slowly. (It may be a close call between it and the ice cube on the black Styrofoam.)

Answers to Summing Up Questions
1. Answers will vary.
2. Heat flowed from the various objects (Miracle Thaws and Styrofoam plates) to the ice cubes.
3. Miracle Thaws are metal and therefore conductors; Styrofoam plates are insulators.
4. The black Miracle Thaw can radiate better than the silvery (foil-covered) Miracle Thaw.
5. The blackened plate can radiate better than the white plate.
6. a. This is supported: Both Miracle Thaw ice cubes melt faster than either Styrofoam plate ice cubes.
   b. This conclusion is only supported when comparing surfaces made of the same material: The black Miracle Thaw ice cube melts faster than the silvery (foil-covered) Miracle Thaw.

Part 3 Activities and Experiments

Electricity and Magnetism
A Force to be Reckoned—*Electrostatic Force*
Batteries and Bulbs—*Electric Circuit Basics*
An Open and Short Case—*Faulty Circuits*
Be the Battery—*Powering a Circuit*
Magnetic Personality—*Magnetic Fields*

A Force to be Reckoned [Activity]

This is an introduction to electrostatic force. It shows students evidence of a force but demands they eliminate gravitational force and magnetic force before giving it a new name. Pith ball electroscopes may be used; or just hang a pith ball on a thread from a convenient support.

Answers to Procedure Questions
2. The brick has no effect on the pith ball; the force between the plastic and the pith ball is not gravitational.
3. Gravitational force is always attractive (as far as we know). Objects don't repel each other gravitationally.
4. The magnet has no effect on the pith ball; the force between the plastic and the pith ball is not magnetic.

Answers to Summing Up Questions
1. Negative (like charges repel).
2. The force is stronger when the objects are closer together.

Batteries and Bulbs [Activity]

This activity is includes essential experiences for students to have when learning about electric circuits.

Answers to Procedure Questions
1. Anatomy of a light bulb:

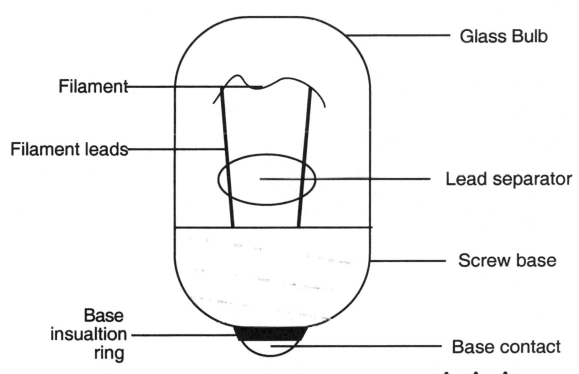

2. Conducting parts: screw base and bottom contact.
   Insulating: glass bulb and insulation ring.
   Two-Wire Circuits: connect terminals of the battery to the screw base and base contact.

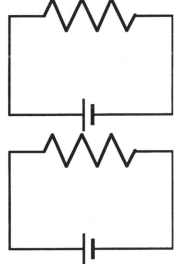

3. One-Wire Circuits: place the base contact on one terminal and connect the wire from the other terminal to the screw base. While the artistic efforts of the students may differ, the DIAGRAMS should be essentially the same (as shown here).

   No-Wire circuits are not possible: Cannot get connections from both terminals to both conducting parts of the bulb.
4. Each bulb is dimmer in the series circuit than it was in the simple circuit.
5. Both bulbs go out.
6. Each bulb is about as bright in the parallel circuit as the original bulb was in the simple circuit.
7. The unscrewed bulb goes out but the other bulb stays on.

Answers to Summing Up Questions
1. The screw base and the bottom contact.
2. They all involve connecting the two terminals of the battery to the two conducting parts of the bulb.
3. In parallel; when one item is turned off or removed, the others continue to work.
4. In parallel; when one bulb goes out, the other remains lit.

An Open and Short Case [Activity]

To understand how electric circuits work, it is important to understand how electric circuits don't work. In this activity, open circuits and short circuits are investigated. Both are considered faulty circuits, but they are very different in nature.

Answers to Procedure Questions
1. Student predictions will vary, but should address the bulb and the ammeter.
2. The bulb goes out; the ammeter drops to zero.
3. Student predictions will vary, but should address the bulb and the ammeter.
4. The bulb goes out (or dims significantly) and the ammeter shoots up to a very high (if not its maximum) reading.
5. The open circuit.
6. The short circuit.
7. a. When point c is connected to point d, bulbs 1 and 2 remain lit.
   b. When point d is connected to point e, bulb 1 remains lit and bulb 2 goes out.
   c. When point e is connected to point f, bulbs 1 and 2 remain lit.
   d. When point f is connected to point a, bulbs 1 and 2 go out.
   e. When point a is connected to point c, bulb 1 goes out and bulb 2 remains lit.
   f. When point a is connected to point d, bulb 1 goes out and bulb 2 remains lit.
   g. When point a is connected to point e, bulbs 1 and 2 go out.
   h. When point b is connected to point d, bulb 1 goes out and bulb 2 remains lit.
   i. When point b is connected to point e, bulbs 1 and 2 go out.
8. a. When point c is connected to point d, bulbs 1 and 2 go out.
   b. When point d is connected to point e, bulb 1 remains lit and bulb 2 goes out.
   c. When point e is connected to point f, bulbs 1 and 2 remain lit.
   d. When point f is connected to point a, bulbs 1 and 2 go out.
   e. When point a is connected to point c, bulbs 1 and 2 go out.
   f. When point a is connected to point d, bulbs 1 and 2 remain lit.
   g. When point a is connected to point e, bulbs 1 and 2 go out.
   h. When point b is connected to point d, bulbs 1 and 2 remain lit.
   i. When point b is connected to point e, bulbs 1 and 2 go out.

Answers to Summing Up Questions
1. The bulb doesn't light in either circuit.
2. In open circuits, no current flows; in short circuits, a large amount of current flows.
3. There is a path from one terminal of the battery to the other terminal of the battery that doesn't require current passing through a bulb.

Be the Battery [Activity]

This activity should be done only after students have completed An Open and Short Case. Material covered in this activity assumes an understanding of open and short circuits. This activity affords students an opportunity to "feel" what it is like to be a battery. Well, they feel how much effort is required to power a simple electric circuit.

Answers to Procedure Questions
1. Crank the generator more rapidly; this requires more effort.
2. It gets easy to crank; effort goes down.
3. Open circuit.
4. Low electrical resistance.
5. It gets difficult to crank; effort increases.
6. Short circuit.
7. High electrical resistance.
8. Parallel is harder to power.

Answers to Summing Up Questions
1. Low electrical circuits are harder to power.
2. Series; it's easier to power so it has more electrical resistance.
3. Low resistance circuits.
4. Series.

Magnetic Personality [Activity]

Everybody loves to play with magnets. Their actions are mysterious because the explanation of their attractions and repulsions are far removed from simpler phenomena that we do understand. Explanations involve quantum phenomena, so like the similar attractions and repulsions of electrostatics, we simply say they are fundamental.

Don't underestimate the amount of dry iron filings you may need. Students tend to use too much, and to consider used filings as trash to be thrown away. Field patterns should approximate those figures in the textbook in Chapter 12.

Answers to Procedure Questions
1.

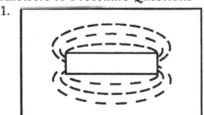

2.

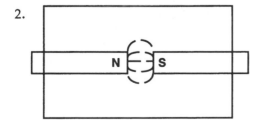

3.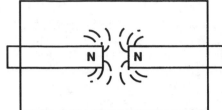

4.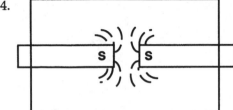

5.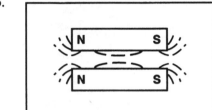

6.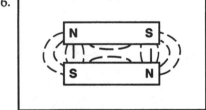

7. Possible: place three north poles or south poles together.
8. Not possible to have three mutually attracting poles.

Answers to Summing Up Questions
1. Not possible to identify the poles.
2. Not possible to identify the poles.
3. B is a south pole.
4. D is a north pole.
5. E: north, F: south; G: north, H: south; J: north, I: south; L: north, K: south
6. Figure 14a is possible; figure 14b is impossible.

Part 4 Activities and Experiments

Waves—Sound and Light

Slow-Motion Wobbler—*Vibrations*
Sound Off —*Interference*
Pinhole Image—*Light*
Pinhole Camera—*Light*
Mirror, Mirror, on the Wall—*Reflection*

Slow-Motion Wobbler [Activity]

All students know the tines of a tuning fork move when they vibrate. They can't see the motion because of the high frequency. But dip a vibrating fork in water and the motion is evidenced in the splashing water. Larger forks work best.

Best evidence is with a strobe light. Caution: Some people have unfavorable reactions to strobe lights (particularly epileptics). It is wise to casually ask if strobe lights bother anybody *before* using them.

Air near the vibrating tines is set in vibration—sound. Placing the tuning fork against a table top, or any sounding board, causes the tines to spend their energy faster. Ask your students to explain this in terms of the conservation of energy. Sound energy eventually degrades to thermal energy.

A vibrating tuning fork in outer space would vibrate longer, but its energy would eventually degrade to thermal energy.

Sound Off [Activity]

This is a great one! It is actually a demo, but so impressive that students will appreciate doing it themselves. They'll one day remember it nostalgically when anti-noise technology is commonplace.

You'll want to have your department invest in a common "boom box" and insert a DPDT switch in one of the speaker wires. This will likely become a routine demo in all courses where interference is taught.

Where does the energy go when sound is canceled? It turns out that each loudspeaker is also a microphone. When the speakers face each other they "drive" each other, inducing back voltages in each other that reduce the currents in each. Thus energy is diminished, but not canceled. So as the speakers are brought closer, and as sound is diminished, the electric bill for powering the sound source diminishes accordingly!

Answers to the Questions
1. Volume is "normal" when speakers are in phase.
2. When out of phase, cancellation of sound occurs as regions of compression from one speaker fill in regions of rarefaction from the other. If the overlap of out of phase waves is exact, then complete cancellation occurs (barring stray waves). Exact overlap cannot occur, however, because of the displacement between the speaker cones. So much of the interference is partial. For long waves, the displacement of the speaker cones is small compared to their wavelength, overlap is relatively exact, and these waves cancel well. But overlap is less exact for shorter wavelengths, producing cancellation that is more partial. For very short waves, reinforcement rather than cancellation occurs. This occurs if the

419

displacement of the cones is a half wavelength of such higher-frequency sound. Then overlap is *in* phase. So for these reasons, high frequency sound survives, giving the music that "tinny" sound.

3. Answers will vary. But interestingly enough, students were asked twenty-five years ago for the practical applications for a laser. Today we ask the same question at the outset period of a growing anti-noise technology.

Pinhole Image [Activity]

Both a prism and a lens deviate light because their faces are not parallel (only at the center of a lens are both faces parallel to each other). As a result, light passing through the center of a lens undergoes the least deviation. If a pinhole is placed at the center of the pupil of your eye, the undeviated light forms an image in focus no matter where the object is located. Pinhole vision is remarkably clear. Not magnified, but clear.

Answers to the Questions
1. Yes. Just as the image in a pinhole camera is clear near and far, likewise for this activity.
2. Yes. Just as the image in a pinhole camera is clear near and far, likewise for this activity.
3. The page is dimmer simply because less light energy gets through the pinhole.

Pinhole Camera [Experiment]

The word camera is derived from the Greek word kamara, meaning "vaulted room." Royalty in the 16th century were entertained by the "camera obscura"—a large "pinhole camera" without the film.

Answers to the Questions
1.– 4. Image is inverted in all directions; up and down as well as left and right.
5. All distances are in focus. Actually the consideration is the size of the pinhole compared to the distance to the screen. So openings of a few centimeters act as pinholes if the screen distance is in meters. Openings in the leaves of trees act as pinholes, for example, and cast images of the sun on the ground!
6. A lens gathers more light and is brighter.
7. There is much in common with the eye and a pinhole camera. Image formation is much the same for each.

Mirror, Mirror, on the Wall [Activity]

Beware of treating this activity too lightly. Nearly all your students will fail to distinguish between mirror size and image size. They all know image size is less with increased distance—which it is. But mirror size is also, in the same proportion. So a half size mirror lets you see your full size image at any distance. This is evident in a pocket mirror that you can hold near or far. You'll see a part of your face that's twice the height of the mirror.

The question often arises why a mirror inverts left and right but not up and down. Well quite simply, it doesn't reverse left and right; the hand on the east is still on the east—the reason for this misunderstanding has mainly to do with left right convention of the human body. What *is* inverted, is back and front. That person facing you in the mirror points to the east when you face east, and looks upward when you look upward. The only difference is his or her nose is pointing in a direction opposite yours. So front and back are inverted, not left and right.

Part 5 Activities and Experiments

The Atom

Thickness of a BB Pancake—*Atomic size*
Oleic Acid Pancake—*Atomic size*
Get a Half-Life—*Radioactivity*
Chain Reaction—*Fission*

Thickness of a BB Pancake [Experiment]

Consider a quick pre-lab activity and show that the diameter of a marble is the same as the thickness of a monolayer of a dozen or more marbles. The volume of the monolayer divided by its top or bottom area equals the diameter of the marble.

Note: Because of the 3-D close packing of BBs in a graduated cylinder, the volume of the same BBs spread into a monolayer is slightly greater. This produces a 5 to 10% higher value than the actual diameter. A typical BB measures about 4.5 mm using a micrometer.

Consider having your students find the density of a rectangular block of aluminum (or in the textbook). Then hand them a sheet of aluminum foil and ask them to find its thickness. From the mass they can calculate the volume, and since volume is simply surface area multiplied by thickness, they can calculate thickness. This sets the stage for this activity and the following experiment.

This experiment presents an opportunity for students to learn to use a micrometer (for those who haven't already).

Answers to the Questions

1. It was assumed that the volume occupied by the BBs in the graduated cylinder and the volume when spread in a monolayer was the same. This is not quite true; since the BBs are spheres, they pack together more compactly than cubes of the same width. Spreading them into a thin layer slightly increases the volume they occupy compared to when packed in the graduated cylinder.
2. Answers will vary; typically, BBs are about 4.3 to 4.7 mm in diameter.
3. Drop a known volume of oleic acid on water and measure the area It covers. Divide the volume of the drop by the area of the monolayer to estimate its thickness.

Oleic Acid Pancake [Experiment]

Inform your students that the oleic acid solution will be mostly alcohol with a small amount of oleic acid in it, mainly to allow portioning out less than a drop of oleic acid. When they add a drop of solution to a tray of water, the alcohol dissolves in the water, but the oleic acid floats on top, just as a drop of oil floats on water.

Caution your students not to put too much powder on the water surface, which may interrupt spreading.

The computations that follow treat the oleic acid molecules as a sphere. The conclusion of the lab is an appropriate time to relate that the molecule is actually hot-dog shaped, and they are measuring the *length* of the molecule. Still, the method and the outcome are good.

Sample Calculations
In Step 3, a typical value for the average diameter is 30 cm. The radius, *r* is then:

$$r = d/2 = 30 \text{ cm}/2 = 15 \text{ cm}$$

The area of the circle is"

$$A = \pi r^2 = (3.14)(15 \text{ cm})^2 = 706 \text{ cm}^2 = 7.06 \times 10^2 \text{ cm}^2$$

The number of drops in 1 cm^3 of 5% solution is about 38.

The volume of one drop is:

$$1 \text{ cm}^3/38 = 0.026 \text{ cm}^3 = 2.6 \times 10^{-2} \text{ cm}^3$$

In Step 4, the volume of acid in a single drop equals 0.005 multiplied by the volume of one drop:

$$(0.005)(2.6 \times 10^{-2}) \text{ cm}^3 = 1.3 \times 10^{-4} \text{ cm}^3$$

In Step 5, the diameter of an oleic acid molecule equals the volume of oleic acid in one drop divided by the area of the circle:

Diameter = (volume)/(area) = $(1.3 \times 10^{-4} \text{ cm}^3)/(7.06 \times 10^2 \text{ cm}^2)$ = 0.18×10^{-6} cm = **1.8×10^{-7} cm**

Good measurements yield values between 1.0×10^{-7} and 2.0×10^{-7} cm. If time permits a second trial, be sure students clean the trays thoroughly before making a second measurement of the diameter.

Answers to the Questions
1. A monolayer is a layer one molecule thick.
2. At full-strength, a single drop would cover a huge area.
3. Volume of one rectangular molecule assuming a rectangular shape for simplicity:
   length × one-tenth the length × one-tenth the length

   which means the volume of the long molecule is actually about one-hundredth the volume of a cube of the same thickness.

Get a Half-Life [Activity]

The simplest version of this lab is tossing coins, and using heads and tails to simulate radioactive decay. Then the half-life is each toss. The cubes add variety. Then if you have multifaceted cubes available, so much the better. You can amend the lab by equating each color with one of the facets. For example, the square facet may equal the red color, the triangular facet may equal the blue color, and a square facet with a blue dot in the center may equal the white face.

If not covered in lecture, the pre-lab meeting is a good place to introduce the concept of radioactive dating—carbon-14 dating gets most attention.

Answers to the Questions
1. Answers will vary with the data table. Red should take longest to reduce by half.
2. The unit of half-life in this experiment is the number of throws. One half-life is the number of throws required for half the cubes to leave.
3. Answers will vary with the data table. Red should take the most rolls.

4. The most radioactive is the one that decays fastest: white.
5. Re-roll the cubes that were removed. They will have new half-lives.
6. Yes, but not very accurate. Accuracy is increased with number of cubes tossed.
7. The lines should curve, corresponding to a constant rate of decay.
8. a) 10 years: 500 g; 20 years: 250 grams; 50 years: 31.25 grams; 100 years: 0.977 grams.
   b) Yes, substance X will disappear after the last atoms disintegrate. An estimate can be made from your graph in Step 8—between 500 and 1000 years.

Chain Reaction [Activity]

The standing and falling dominoes provides a visual chain-reaction model that precedes an understanding of nuclear fission. When doing this entertaining activity, link it to Figure 20.2 in the textbook.

Part 6 Activities and Experiments

Chemistry
Mystery Powders—*Qualitative Analysis*
Salt and Sand—*Separating a Mixture*
Sugar Soft—*Percent Sugar Determination*
Molecules by Acme—*Molecular Models*
Foamy Bubble Round-Up—*Collecting a Gas*
Circular Rainbows—*Chromatography*
Pure Sweetness—*Purification of Crystals*
Sensing pH—*Red Cabbage pH*
Tubular Rust—*Percent Oxygen in Air*
Upset Stomach—*Titration*
Smells Great!—*Organic Esters*
Name That Recyclable—*Recyclable Polymers*

Mystery Powders [Experiment]

The unknowns for this experiment are generally regarded as safe. Students should be advised, however, to take serious precautions against accidentally spilling these unknowns, mixing them together, or direct contact with skin. Consider drawing an analogy of what students are doing in this lab with what "real lab technicians" do in trying to identify an unknown—from the start, *anything* is possible, and so all precautions should be followed, especially wearing safety glasses.

Alert students to the hazard of working with the 0.3 M solution of sodium hydroxide (test #5). Skin will become slippery upon contact with this reagent. In such a case, the student should thoroughly rinse the affected area with water for many minutes even after the slippery sensation has disappeared. Consider also pouring some white distilled vinegar onto the affected skin.

Use parafilm to cover the test tubes to avoid contact with skin. The use of well-plates is recommended over the use of test tubes because clean up is so much easier and also force the students to minimize the quantities they use. You may wish, however, for your students to work with both. The Hot-Water test (#6), for example, works best with a test tube, while the phenolphthalein test (#3) works well with the well-plate. Because students may have a tendency to overflow their wells with reagents, you should advise them on the minimal amounts of reagents needed for each test. In general, "if you can see it, it's probably more than enough".

Perhaps, the most difficult test to discern is the Hot-Water test (#6). This test requires lots of patience and careful observation. NO TASTE TESTING ALLOWED! You might consider NOT crushing the salt in a mortar and pestle beforehand. This way the cubic shapes of the sodium chloride crystals will be of some assistance.

All unknowns are common household chemicals that can be safely washed down the drain or, preferably, disposed of in the trash can.

Answers to the Questions
2. Tests 1, 6, and 7 measure physical properties. Tests 2, 3, 4 and 5 involve chemical properties.
3. There is no contradiction in that sugar is both a food and a chemical—all foods are made of chemicals.
4. The student's answer should be the same as the number of test tubes or individual wells that they used.

Salt and Sand [Experiment]

This experiment takes most students an entire lab period. Some variations on equipment needed or procedure may include:

- A list of available equipment could be provided to the students. t is helpful for running the experiment, but also provides hints for the astute student.
- Sugar could be used in place of the salt. If this is done, it is best to ask students to determine the mass percent for the sand only. Also, if the sand is not thoroughly rinsed of the sugar, then it will remain somewhat sticky even after drying, which is a consequence worthy for the students to discover on their own.

After approving the students' procedures, it may be helpful to demonstrate some techniques to the class. In particular, consider demonstrating filtration (gravity filtration takes a long time if the paper is not fluted).

You may find it preferable for each student to work alone. Three goals include: (1) Learning the limitations of laboratory equipment; (2) Gain first hand experience on how to control variables so as to achieve reliable data; (3) Achieving a certain amount of independence.

It is most helpful to alert students of the advantages and disadvantages of using their entire sample on the first run. For example, some students completely forget that the mass of the sample is needed. They go through their procedure only to find that they cannot calculate the mass percents without it. If they use only part of their original sample, they could repeat their experiment to correct any problems encountered in the first run. If they use the entire sample, however, then they need not worry about the homogeneity of their sample.

Having drying lamps or a drying oven available will greatly decrease the time required to complete this experiment. Consider allowing students to store their samples in a safe cupboard so that they may dry thoroughly overnight before being weighed.

Consider a grading scheme where half of the credit is based solely upon the accuracy of the student's results, while the other half is credit for completing the lab and/or answering the questions. Most students are able to get within plus or minus 2.00 percentage points of the actual value. If the student wants to repeat the procedure, you might consider deducting only 2 points where 25 points is the maximum number of points possible. This is good for students whose answers are way off because of poor procedures or some mishap. Rather than saying that you are "deducting points" for repeating the procedure, tell students that they are permitted to "buy" another sample for testing, but that the sample will cost them 2 points each. This is in line with what occurs in a research laboratory where researchers need to be most careful with the samples they have, often because of financial concerns.

The following grading scheme is based upon the difference between the actual percentage of sand and the student's experimental percentage of sand, where 25 points is the maximum number of points possible.

Points awarded	Difference in % actual and experimental
25	+/- 0.10
24	+/- 0.20
23	+/- 0.30
22	+/- 0.40
21	+/- 0.50
20	+/- 0.60

19	+/- 0.70
18	+/- 0.80
17	+/- 0.90
16	+/- 1.00
15	+/- 1.20
14	+/- 1.40
13	+/- 1.60
12	+/- 1.80
11	+/- 2.00
10	+/- 2.20
9	+/- 2.40
8	+/- 2.60
7	+/- 2.80
6	+/- 3.00
5	+/- 3.20
4	+/- 3.40
3	+/- 3.60
2	+/- 3.80
1	+/- 4.00
0	> 4.00

Answers to the Questions
Student answers and responses are very dependent on the procedure used. The two most common errors encountered are:

* not rinsing the salt with sufficient quantities of water.
* not waiting for the samples to dry completely.

Sugar Soft [Experiment]

You will need to talk about calibration curves and their function during your pre-lab discussion. A typical calibration curve may look as shown below once completed. Regarding the calibration curve for this experiment, ask your students why it doesn't pass through the origin, even if the origin were shown on the graph. Also ask the students what kind of slope they might expect at sugar concentrations beyond 20%. Stress the importance of being able to relate a graph to the physical reality it represents. Lastly, you might share with students how beer and wine manufacturers measure alcohol content by way of the hydrometer. The more alcohol, the less dense the solution and the lower the hydrometer floats. Calibrated properly, the reading of the hydrometer can be translated into percent alcohol.

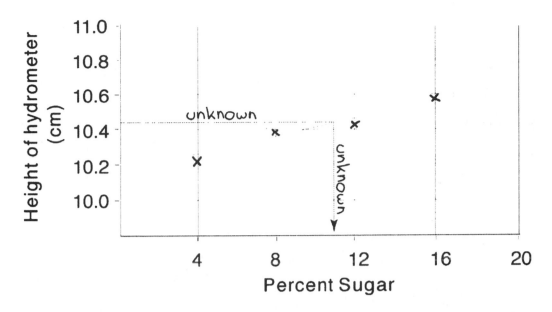

The students' data tables may show that most all soft drinks have about the same percentage of sugar. Exceptions include diet soft drinks. Also, root beer tends to be on the denser side. Consider showing students what happens when a can of diet soda and a can of root beer are thrown into a tub of water (one floats and the other sinks!).

Molecules by Acme [Experiment]

The formulas presented in Table 3 are listed in order of increasing complexity. The structures students tend to have the most difficulty with include: chloroethanol, acetylene, acetic acid, benzene, and iron (III) oxide. Note that there are a couple versions of the model for iron oxide that students might build. Have them keep trying until they arrive at one that has no double bonds and looks like a football where the two iron atoms linked together by three bridging oxygen atoms.

Here are 2 dimensional renditions of some of the more difficult-to-build models:

H H
Cl–C—C–O–H
H H

2-chloroethanol

H–C≡C–H

acetylene

H O
H–C—C
H   O–H

acetic acid

H   H
C–C
H–C   C–H
C═C
H   H

benzene

O
Fe–O–Fe
O

iron (III) oxide

Answers to the Questions
1. a) Yes. b) No, you would have hydrogen peroxide.
2. a) Both have the same shape. b) Dichloromethane is less symmetrical and more lopsided.
3. Five.
4. Hydrogen, oxygen, nitrogen, carbon dioxide, and acetylene.
5. Oxygen, nitrogen, carbon dioxide, acetylene, acetic acid, and benzene.
6. Benzene.

Foamy Bubble Round-Up [Activity]

This is the same technique used by early chemical investigators in studying the nature of gases.

In preparing the set-up, the second flask should be filled with water using water from the beaker, which has been filled close to the brim. This guarantees that water will not overflow as it is being displaced. You may either inform students of this technique or provide sponges and let them discover it on their own.

Many students will want to repeat the CO_2 collection to permit further experimentation.

Challenge students as to how many candles they can extinguish using their collected CO_2. You might direct students to use the stopper with the tubing attached to better concentrate the CO_2 over individual flames.

Students may "pour" some of the carbon dioxide into their mouths. The taste will be familiar to them.

"Going Further" with Step 5 easily changes this activity into an experiment for it requires critical thinking and careful technique. The density of carbon dioxide at 1 atm and 25°C is about 1.80 g/L. Ideally, students should measure the precise volume of the stoppered 2 liter bottle by filling it with water and then pouring that water into a graduated cylinder. This should be done after everything else as it will result in a bottle full of "heavy" water drops. This is the volume that the student should use in calculating the density of the carbon dioxide.

Answers to the Questions

1. A 2 liter plastic soda bottle does not contain exactly 2 liters of air. The best way to calculate the actual volume is to fill the bottle with water and then measure this volume of water in a graduated cylinder.
2. The flask was not initially stoppered so that the newly formed carbon dioxide would push the less dense air out. This step helps to increase the purity of the collected CO_2.
3. The displaced water filled up the beaker, which would overflow if it had been filled to capacity.

Circular Rainbows [Activity]

Chromatography is a technique often used by chemists to separate components of a mixture. In 1906, the Russian botanist Mikhail Tsvett separated color pigments in leaves by allowing a solution of these pigments to flow down a column packed with an insoluble material such as starch, alumina, or silica. Because different colored bands appeared along the column, he called the procedure chromatography. (Note: Color is not a required property to achieve separation of compounds by this procedure.) Because of its simplicity and efficiency, this technique is widely used for separating and identifying compounds such as drugs and natural products.

The basis of chromatography is the partitioning (separation due to differences in solubility) of compounds between a stationary phase and moving phase. Stationary phases such as alumina, silica, or paper (cellulose) have highly polar surface areas that attract the components (molecules) of a mixture to different extents. The components of the mixture to be separated are thought to be continuously adsorbed and then released from the stationary phase into the solvent that moves over the surface of the stationary phase. Because of differences in the attraction of each component for the stationary phase, each component travels at different speeds thus causing the separation.

In paper chromatography, where paper is the stationary phase, a small spot of a mixture is carried by solvent through the paper via capillary action. The solvent and various components of the mixture each travel at different speeds along the paper resulting in the separation of the mixture.

Technique really counts in this activity. Many students will have the tendency to add the solvent too quickly, which will cause the colors to bleed into one another. Point out to students that with a good separation they should be able to cut out individual colors using a pair of scissors. The best separations will show colors with distinct boundaries and white spaces in between colors. Have each student turn in his or her best and most spectacular separation. The name or PIN of each student should be marked on the perimeter in pencil. Base your grading or judging on the degree of separation.

Food coloring is an alternative to pen ink. Felt-tip and overhead transparency pens tend to work best.

Answers to the Questions

1. The ionic component would stick to the paper by ion-dipole interactions and not travel with the solvent.
2. A different hue of blue may be obtained by changing the proportions of a secondary or tertiary color.

Pure Sweetness [Activity]

This activity may take over a month for students to accomplish. Thus it shouldn't be started close to the end of the academic term. Students should know that in making these crystals patience is the greatest virtue. You will need to emphasize the importance of not overcooking the brown sugar. It doesn't take too much cooking time before the brown sugar simply hardens upon cooling. Students should maintain a crystal journal and tape a few of the best crystals they ultimately obtain. How well they keep their journal may be used to assess their grade for this activity. You might also grade them, in part, based upon the colorlessness of their crystals. To make your assessments less arbitrary, exhibit a set of samples along with the number of points you would have assigned to each.

Answers to the Questions
1. Make a concentrated solution of sugar in water. If any molasses is present, it should give the concentrated sugar solution a yellow color, which indeed it does.
2. White sugar is more pure than brown sugar.
3. Brown sugar is more natural than white sugar.
4. The greater the quality (colorlessness) of the sugar crystals, the less of them you have!

Sensing pH [Activity]

Have each student prepare his or her small batch of red cabbage pH indicator. A single head of red cabbage should be sufficient for a class of 30 students. Bring dry ice to the laboratory and allow students to drop pieces into test tubes of their indicator solution. After the students have become familiar with the colors that the cabbage indicator turns at various pH's have them gather around a 2 liter glass beaker containing about 300 mL of a fairly concentrated broth that is a slight shade of red from small amounts of acetic acid. Have students note the color of the broth and ask them what color the broth might turn to if you were to quickly fill the beaker with water. Some students may argue that it should stay the same color because no acid or base has been added—only water. Others may say that the color will stay the same but will become fainter because the solution is becoming more dilute. Remind the students that pH is a measure of the concentration of hydronium ions. Thus, as you dilute the solution shouldn't the concentration of hydronium ions become less and the pH rise? The color should thus turn from its slight reddish color to purple. Sure enough, if it's not too concentrated with acetic acid, this will be the case. Follow up by asking students whether adding more water will ever bring the indicator to a slightly alkaline green color. Why or why not? Try it and see.

Answers to the Questions
1. A green color forms around one of the electrodes. This occurs because of the formation of hydroxide ions at this electrode.
2. The hydroxide ions form at the positive terminal.
3. Bubble formation occurs at the negative terminal. These are bubbles of hydrogen gas.

Tubular Rust [Activity]

To take this activity a step further, have students add dilute HCl to the rusted wool. Oxygen is then released back into the atmosphere as evidenced by the bubbling.
References: "Percent Oxygen in Air" Martins, G.F. J. Chem. Ed 1987, 64 (9), 809. George F. Martins, Newton North High School, Newtonville, MA 02160.

Answers to the Questions
1. The actual percent oxygen in air is about 21%.

2. The volume of a gas is affected by the pressure exerted upon it. For this reason, it is important that the pressures inside and outside the test tube remains the same. Accomplish this by keeping the water levels even.
3. It would take longer because of less surface area.

Upset Stomach [Experiment]

Spilled acid can be neutralized with baking soda, and spilled sodium hydroxide neutralized with boric acid or vinegar. Inform students to wash and thoroughly rinse any acid or base away from their skin. The sodium hydroxide will be most apparent due to its slippery feel—slippery because it reacts with skin oils to form a layer of soap. So that students exercise proper precautions you might tell them that the sodium hydroxide *dissolves* flesh and then reacts with skin oils to form a soap-like layer.

Neutralized solutions may be poured down the drain flushed with plenty of water.

Answers to the Questions
1. The antacid that required the fewest number of drops of sodium hydroxide can be considered the "strongest".
2. The neutralizing power of an antacid, of course, also depends on the size of the tablet. The more massive the tablet, the more acid it will be able to neutralize.
3. Dividing the number of drops stomach acid relieved by the mass of the antacid tablets allows a comparison of the antacids based upon their formulation, rather than the mass of the tablet.
4. The order of strengths here may or may not be the same as that cited in question 1.
5. a) Two tablets has twice the neutralizing strength as one tablet.
   b) With less of the tablet entering the "stomach" there will be a perceived decrease in the strength of the antacid.
   c) The fewer number of drops of sodium hydroxide that is added to complete the neutralization, the stronger the antacid. Thus, if extra drops of sodium hydroxide were added, this would make the antacid appear as though it were not as effective.

Smells Great! [Activity]

In a pre-lab discussion consider addressing the receptor site model for smelling. Beforehand, however, make sure that students understand that only gaseous chemicals are detected by the nose. An odorous chemical is odorous because it has the right shape to fit within the olfactory receptors in the nose. The chemical fits into the receptor much like a key fits into a lock. Once there, it triggers a neurological signal to the brain. Receptor sites in our nose work in tandem with receptor sites on our taste buds to give distinctive flavor. This receptor site model is the same as the one addressed in Chapter 28 of the textbook.

Essential oils are often formulations of many odorous chemicals. The smell of pineapple, for example, consists of at least 10 chemicals, most of them esters. Artificial extracts reproduce these formulation only close enough to fool most people.

A special note about butyric acid: It has the smell of rancid butter and it remains with you for quite some time. Because of this, you may not wish to work with this chemical. Interestingly enough, butyric acid is a component of body odor. Animals can readily detect a human when downwind because of its strong scent. Also, bloodhounds are trained to follow remnant trails of this chemical when tracking humans.

Notes on disposal:
Have students deposit their reaction mixtures into a single waste container such as a 1 liter Erlenmeyer flask. Students may need to rinse their tubes with methanol to make cleaning easier. These rinsings may also be combined in the waste container.

Add a solution of sodium bicarbonate to neutralize the sulfuric acid (it is neutralized when addition of sodium bicarbonate ceases to cause bubbling). Decant the aqueous layer, which may be poured down the drain. The remaining oils are biodegradable and may be sealed in a jar and thrown into the trash.

Table 1.

Alcohol	Carboxylic Acid	Observed Smell
methanol	salicylic acid	Wintergreen
octanol	acetic acid	Oranges
benzyl alcohol	acetic acid	Peach
isoamyl alcohol	acetic acid	Banana
n-propanol	acetic acid	Pear
isopentenol	acetic acid	"Juicy Fruit"
methanol	butyric acid	Apple
isobutanol	propionic acid	Rum

Answers to the Questions
1. Nothing. An ester produced in the laboratory is no different from the same ester produced in nature. The plant producing this ester, however, might also produce many other esters. It is the unique combination of many of these esters that will give the plant a unique scent.
2. Molecules have a greater tendency to vaporize at higher temperatures. The assumption here of course is the understanding that a substance has odor because of the gaseous molecules it emits.

Name That Recyclable [Activity]

A main purpose of this short activity is to educate students on the meaning of recycling imprints on plastics. Cut out small pieces of plastic for the students to work with. One separation scheme is as follows:

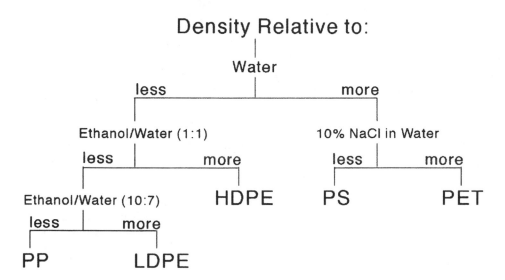

Students may also chose a scheme that separates one plastic at a time.

Students may be expecting all the unknowns to be different. To challenge their trust in their experimental observations, you might consider making two unknowns from the same plastic.

Code 3 (polyvinyl chloride) and code 7 (mixed resins) are not included in this activity because of their variable densities. For your information, since PVC contains a halogen (chlorine), it can be identified using the Beilstein test (touching the plastic with a hot copper wire and then placing the wire in a flame: A blue green flame is positive for a halogen).

Reference: "Method for Separating or Identifying Plastics" Kolb, K.E., Kolb, D.K *J. Chem. Ed.* **1991**, 68(4), 348.

Answers to the Questions
1. Melting points.
2. Discard all the pieces into a large container of water. The less dense polypropylene pieces will float to the top, while the more dense polystyrene pieces will sink to the bottom.

Part 7 Activities and Experiments

Earth Science

Crystal Growth—*Minerals*
What's that Mineral?—*Minerals*
Rock Hunt—*Rocks*
What's that Rock?—*Rocks*
Top This—*Topographical Maps*
Over and Under—*Geological Cross Sections*
Walking on Water—*Water Table*
Solar Power I—*Solar Energy*
Solar Power II—*Solar Energy*
Indoor Clouds—*Clouds*

Crystal Growth [Experiment]

This lab uses thymol which may irritate the skin. Use caution. The seed crystals speed up the process of crystallization and longer cooling promotes larger crystal size.

Answers to the Questions

1. Crystallization from a solution depends on the concentration of the solution and the rate of evaporation. Crystallization from a melt depends on temperature and the rate of cooling.

2. Yes.

3. Under ideal conditions (time, space allotment, temperature, concentration) crystal form provides a useful means for identifying minerals. Unfortunately, ideal conditions are not always possible.

4. Minerals that cool slowly develop larger crystals than minerals that cool quickly. So if you want large, well formed minerals, take your time.

What's that Mineral? [Experiment]

For the lab on mineral identification use your own collection of minerals (collections from Ward's Scientific or Miners Catalog). The number of minerals you require your students to identify depends on your time schedule and your particular collection of minerals. Please note!! Not all the minerals from the mineral identification tables are necessary for this lab. For example, in a mineral collection composed of quartz, calcite, magnetite, muscovite, and pyrite your students would use hardness to identify quartz, reaction to HCl to identify calcite, a magnet or compass to identify magnetite, cleavage and color to identify muscovite, and streak and probably color and crystal form to identify pyrite.

Answers to the Questions

1. The distinguishing characteristic for the following minerals:

    a) halite   chemical—taste
    b) pyrite   cubic form with striations, streak
    c) quartz   hexagonal form, hardness
    d) biotite   cleavage, brown color, soft
    e) fluorite   isometric form, hardness
    f) garnet   isometric form, dark color, density

2. Physical properties: a mineral's crystalline structure or chemical composition:
   a) crystal form   <u>crystalline structure</u>
   b) color   <u>chemical composition</u>
   c) cleavage   <u>crystalline structure</u>
   d) specific gravity   <u>chemical composition</u>

3. Metallic minerals exhibit streak. If there is no streak the mineral is nonmetallic.

4. Streak is the more reliable method for mineral identification. Some minerals come in a variety of different colors (Ex: quartz, fluorite, and corundum) and hence cannot be identified by a characteristic color. Weathering may also affect a mineral's color. Since streak does not change, it is more useful for mineral identification.

5. Color.

6. The physical properties that distinguish plagioclase feldspars from orthoclase feldspars are color and striations. Plagioclase is darker than orthoclase and plagioclase exhibits striations.

Rock Hunt [Activity]

This is simply an activity to encourage rock consciousness in the students' everyday environment.

What's that Rock? [Experiment]

This is a lab on rock identification where you use your own rocks or students' collection of rocks. Rock collections can also be obtained from Ward's Scientific or Miners Catalog. Once again the number of rocks you use depends on your collection. If you are using rocks collected by your students, you may find the rocks are all of one type — igneous, metamorphic, or sedimentary—depending on your area. If this is the case, you may want the students to not only identify the rock and rock type but also discuss the environment where the rock was found.

On this note, here's an interesting true story. Students in New York City find that most of the old brownstone buildings are made of Triassic sandstone quarried in Connecticut. Some, however, are built of Scottish sandstones brought across the Atlantic in the 19th century. It's hard to tell which is which. Why? Interestingly enough, both sandstones were formed at the same period under the same circumstances in the same general area. They formed during Triassic times in a northern supercontinent, before the split of the Atlantic Ocean. In the 200 million years since formation, plate tectonics has split this region onto opposite shores of the North Atlantic Ocean—part in Connecticut and part in Scotland. And now civilization has now brought them together as one city. (This tidbit from *The Practical Geologist*, by Douglas Dixon, and Raymond L. Bernor, editor.)

Answers to the Questions
1. Igneous rocks exhibit both fine and coarse grained textures. Fine grained textures occur when the rock has cooled very quickly. The texture can be so fine that individual crystals are too difficult to identify with an unaided eye. Some fine-grained textures are glassy. Coarse grained textures occur when the rock is allowed to cool slowly. Depending on the rate of cooling, most crystal grains can be easily identified.

2. Slow cooling, recrystallization, and open space. Igneous rocks that have undergone slow cooling exhibit large crystals. Metamorphic rocks subjected to increased pressures and temperatures exhibit large crystals. Sedimentary rocks precipitated

from mineral rich water or sedimentary rocks formed from the evaporation of mineral rich water may exhibit large crystals.

3. Bedding planes, fossils, ripple marks, and cross-bedding.

4. By texture and mineral composition. Metamorphic rocks generally exhibit foliation— the realignment of crystals. The process of metamorphism also forms new minerals out of old minerals.

Top This [Activity]

This is an activity in learning about topographic maps. Students draw contour lines and construct a topographical profile. Supplement this activity by giving your students topographical maps. Ask them to determine the scale of the map and the contour interval. Have them construct a topographic profile in the area that best depicts the overall landscape, and to calculate the vertical exaggeration.

Answers to the Exercises
1. Contour lines should look something like this:

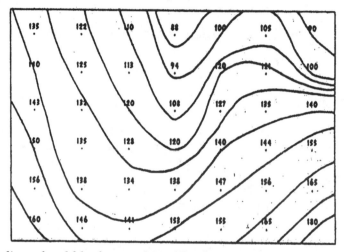

2. Contour lines should look something like this:

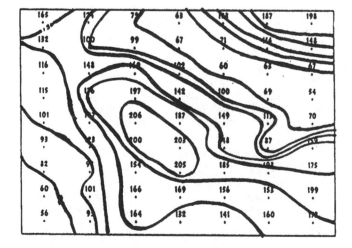

3. Elevations are as shown:

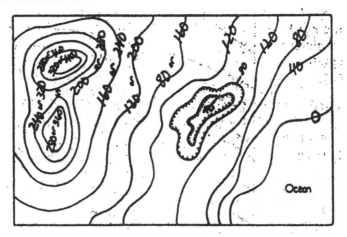

4.

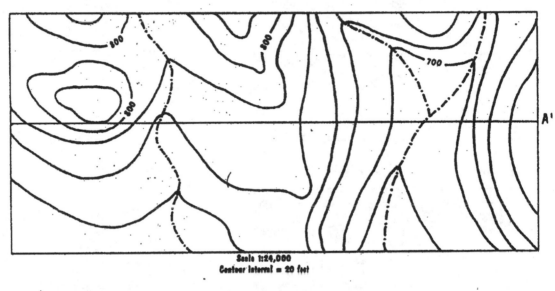

Scale 1:24,000
Contour interval = 20 feet

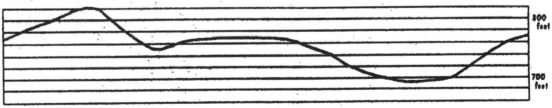

Topographical profile: Vertical scale is 1 inch = 100 feet = 1200 inches   (1:1200)

$$\frac{1/1200}{1/24000} = \frac{24000}{1200} = 20$$

Therefore the vertical exaggeration is 20 times greater than the true relief.

Over and Under [Activity]

This lab is supplemental rather than essential, so use if time permits. The lab is challenging and heightens student awareness of what lies beneath the earth's surface. Measurement of dip angles can be estimated. Students should be able to tell that a 90° reading is vertical and a 45° is between vertical and horizontal. Dip direction is more important than angle. Students may enjoy coloring in the bed layers with colored pencils.

Answers to the Exercises

1. Structure is a syncline.

2. Structure is an antiline.

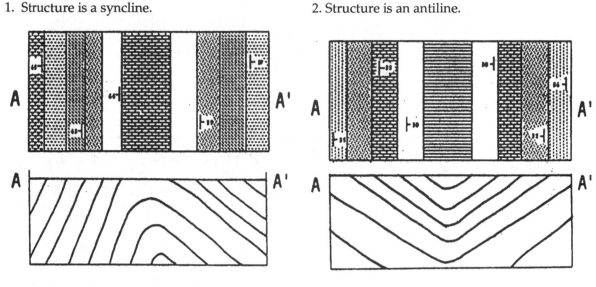

3. Structure is a plunging syncline

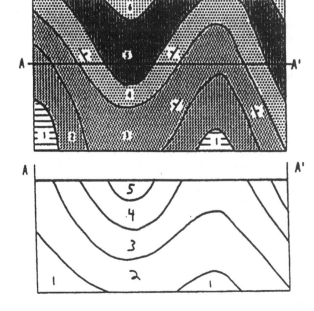

4. Structure is a basin, with youngest bed in center.

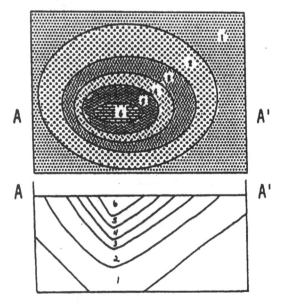

5. Structure is a dome, with oldest bed in center. 6. A syncline fold is displayed; strike slip fault; oldest structure is fold; youngest is intrusion.

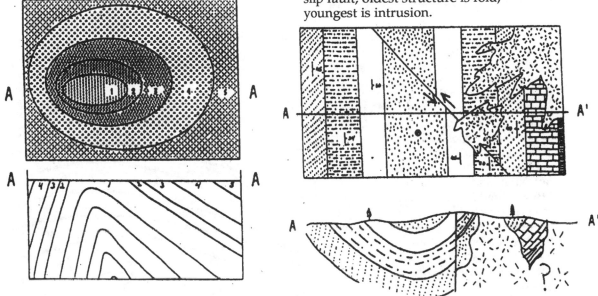

Answers to the Questions

1. A symmetrical syncline is shown in Exercise 2. The symmetry can be determined on the map view by the dip angles and by the apparent thickness of the beds.

2. An asymmetrical anticline is shown in Exercise 3. The lack of symmetry can be determined by the dip angles, which tell us that the beds are dipping in toward the fold axis.

3. A plunging inclines is shown in Exercise 3. The dip direction tells us that the beds are dipping in toward the fold axis.

4. Both Exercises 4 and 5 resemble circular structures in map view. The only way to tell the structures apart is with age sequence or dip direction. Exercise 4 represents a basin with youngest beds in the center. The dip direction would dip in toward the core of the basin. Exercise 5 represents a dome with the oldest beds in the center. The dip direction for a dome would dip outward away from the core of the dome.

5. A strike fault is shown in Exercise 6. Evidence for the fault structure is the horizontal displacement of beds. The fold structure is a syncline. The fold is the oldest structure and the intrusion is the youngest structure.

Walking On Water [Experiment]

This is meant to follow the activity on topographical maps, *Top This*. Students will then already know how to draw contour lines. Important here is that the groundwater flow is perpendicular to lines of equal hydraulic head. The lines of equal hydraulic head are *equipotential lines*, completely analogous to the lines of equal potential in an electric field. Electric field lines are perpendicular to equipotential lines, and groundwater flow is perpendicular to the equipotential lines of hydraulic head. Further study of these would lead to *diffusion equations*.

2. (shown below)

Answers to the Problems
1.

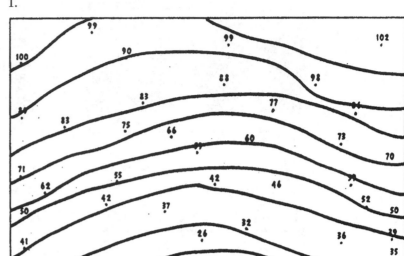

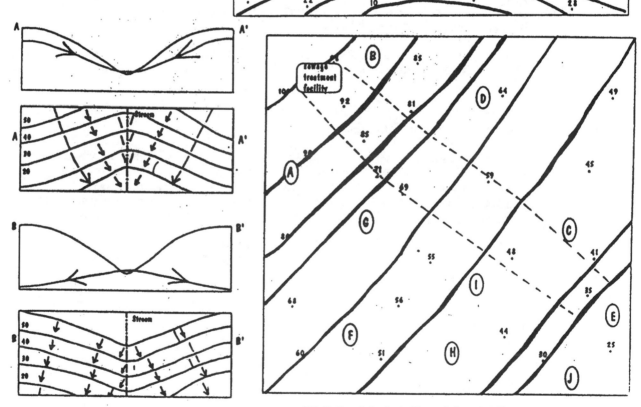

Well C might be affected, but Well E will definitely be affected.

Answers to the Questions
1. The difference between stream A and steam B is the direction of the flow lines. In stream A water flows from the ground into the stream. In stream B water flows away from the stream into the ground. Stream A represents a humid area where water is available to recharge the aquifer. In a humid area the water table slopes toward the

stream and water flows into the stream. Stream B represents a dry area where water is scarce. In dry areas precipitation is at a minimum causing no direct recharge of the aquifer. The water table slopes away from the stream bed. When water fills the stream it flows to the aquifer.

2. Yes, excessive pumping at Well H would cause a change in the flow of contamination. Well I would definitely be contaminated. Well G would most likely be affected and Well J may possibly be affected.

3. No. At point 35, however, the contamination would hit an impermeable lens and its flow path would change to go around the lens.

Solar Power I [Experiment]

Both Solar Power I and Solar Power II are included here in Part 7 to complement meteorology, but they could as well be in Part 2, Heat, or in Part 8, Astronomy. Use either or both wherever they suit your course.

This is an exercise in the inverse-square law, which requires bright sunlight. Amazingly, with some care you can obtain results reasonably close to the "ideal" data shown below. Having the foil in a jar helps to keep foil temperature closer to the inside ambient temperature. If the foil weren't enclosed, cooling by air currents would counteract its temperature rise when illuminated by the lamp or the sun.

Sample calculations:
Distance from the bulb filament to foil strip = 9.5 cm = 0.095 m and the sun's distance in meters is 1.5×10^{11} m.

So from $\dfrac{\text{sun's wattage}}{\text{bulb's wattage}} = \dfrac{\text{sun's distance}^2}{\text{bulb's distance}^2}$

We find: Sun's wattage $= \dfrac{[\text{bulb's wattage}][\text{sun's distance}]^2}{\text{bulb's distance}^2}$

$$= \frac{[100][1.5 \times 10^{11} \text{m}]^2}{[0.095 \text{ m}]^2} = 2.5 \times 10^{26} \text{W}$$

Therefore, the number of 100-W light bulbs is

$$\# \text{ bulbs} = \frac{2.5 \times 10^{26} \text{W}}{100 \text{W}/\text{bulb}} = 2.5 \times 10^{24} \text{ bulbs}$$

Not surprisingly, even if all the electric generators in the world were diverted toward just lighting the calculated number of bulbs, this would constitute only a tiny fraction of the energy radiated by the sun.

Possible sources of discrepancies include: inaccurate rating of bulb's wattage, inaccurate measurement of distance, atmospheric absorption, non-perpendicular alignment of black vanes to solar ray, absorption is only by black paint, that misses energy in other wavelengths.

Solar Power II [Experiment]

The amount of solar energy flux just above the atmosphere is 2 cal/cm^2·min—the solar constant. But only three quarters of this reaches the earth's surface after passing through the atmosphere—1.5 cal/cm^2·min. Since there are 10^4 cm^2 in 1 m^2, the solar energy flux obtained in Step 7 should be multiplied by (10^4 cm^2/m^2) for Step 8. So following the sample calculation (next page), the energy reaching each square meter of ground per minute would be 10,000 cal.

Sample Data and Calculations

Volume of water: 140 mL
Mass of water: 140 g
Initial water temperature: 23°C
Final water temperature: 26°C
Temperature difference: 3°C
Typical top diameter of Styrofoam cup: 6.9 cm

Surface area of the top of a typical Styrofoam cup is:

Area = π (diameter/2)^2 = 3.14 (3.5 cm)^2 = 38 cm^2

The energy collected by the cup is therefore:

Energy = $cm\Delta T$ = (1.0 cal/g °C) (140 g) (3°C) = 400 cal

The solar flux is therefore:

Solar energy flux = [energy/(area × time)] = 400 cal/(38 cm^2) (10 min) = 1 cal/cm^2 min

Factors that might affect the amount of solar energy reaching a location on the Earth's surface include: time of day, season of the year, latitude, cloud cover, humidity, air pollution, nearby obstructions.

Indoor Clouds [Activity]

This activity is pretty lightweight, and is probably the least exciting activity in the manual. But it does prompt attention to cloud formation. Consider assigning it as an out-of-class activity.

Answers to the Questions
1. Much the same in that air that is chilled undergoes condensation.

2. In the atmosphere there isn't the confinement that restricts air currents. Relatively little circulation occurs in the capped jar, whereas air more readily rises in the atmosphere. Then expansion rather than ice promotes cooling.

3. Warmer water undergoes more evaporation, which is why warm water was used in this activity.

4. We believe warm air rises from our observation of smoke, the warmer temperature of air near the ceiling in a room, the currents over hot roads in summer betrayed by refraction in the air, and other common occurrences.

5. Air currents are swept upward when heading toward mountains. As a result, the expanding air cools, clouds form, and precipitation follows. Further along, on the other side of the mountains, dry air remains that contributes to a desert area.

Part 7 Activities and Experiments

Astronomy
Sunballs—*Size of the Sun*
Ellipses—*Planetary Motion*
Reckoning—*Astronomy Measurements*
Tracking Mars—*Planetary Motion*

Sunballs [Experiment]

Beauty is not only seeing the world with wide open eyes, but knowing what to look for. Your students have all seen splotches of light beneath the trees. But now you can point out what nearly all haven't seen, and that is that the splotches are circular—or if the sun is low in the sky, elliptical. For they are images of the sun. They occur because the holes between the leaves above are small compared to the distance to the ground, and act as pinholes (recall the activity, Pinhole Camera). It's nice to point out the really neat things around us!

Answers to the Questions
1. The shape of the hole has no bearing as long as its size is small compared to the distance to the image.

2. Measure the short diameter, for this is the undistorted diameter needed for the calculation. The long diameter is this same diameter stretched out because of the angle of sunbeams with the ground. Or position the viewing screen perpendicular to the sunbeams and get a circle.

3. The sunball will be the same shape as the eclipsed sun. And in line with pinhole images, it will be reversed. So if the bottom half of the sun is eclipsed, the image will show the top half eclipsed.

Ellipses [Activity]

Students will enjoy this light activity. It will also very likely be one of the things they'll be sure to remember from your course.

Answers to the Questions
1. The elliptical path of the Earth about the sun is nearly circular; so the ellipse drawn with pins closest together most likely is the best representation of the Earth's orbit.

2. With pins far apart, a more eccentric ellipse results—one like the path of Halley's comet. The eccentricity of Halley's comet is 0.97, compared to Earth's eccentricity of 0.0167.

3. Evidence that the sum of the distances to the foci is constant is the constant length of string made to construct the ellipses!

Reckoning Latitude [Experiment]

This experiment has two parts: building apparatus, and viewing. The viewing segment must be carried out at nighttime. Polaris turns out to be only the 53rd brightest star in the night sky. You'll find students who will expect that it should be brighter, given its importance!

443

You might point out that Polaris is not only not exactly over the north pole—it's almost a degree away from the north celestial pole. For your friends in the Southern Hemisphere, sorry, there is no conveniently placed star above the south celestial pole. Polaris serves navigators well now, and has been in a position to do so for the last several hundred years. But because the earth precesses about its polar axis, like the wobble of a spinning top, it will remain nearly over the pole only for a few more hundred years. But that should not greatly worry us for the present.

The location of Polaris is easiest to find via the Big Dipper, as described in the text. It can also be located by using the Little Dipper. Polaris is the first star of the Little Dipper's handle. This is seen in Fig. 4 of the lab write-up. Another easily located constellation is Casseopia's Chair, the five-star big W in the sky (Fig. 5).

Answers to the Questions
1. Answers vary according to latitude.

2. Same as the altitude in Question 1.

3. Answers will vary.

4. Answers depend on latitude.

5. If the theolite shows Polaris to be lower in the sky as one moves south, and higher in the sky as one moves north, then this is evidence for a round Earth.

Tracking Mars [Activity]

This is a dandy! Students plot the orbit of Mars from measurements of the sky in Tycho Brahe's time. Data is neatly rounded off to the nearest half degree to make plotting straightforward. Corrections have been made to avoid the gap left during the transition from the Julian calendar to the Gregorian calendar now in current use. If you get into this, begin by asking your students what happened between October 5 and October 14 in 1582; the answer is *nothing*! These dates simply didn't exist when the change over in calendars was made.

The plot of this data runs nicely, and the elliptical shape of Mar's orbit is clearly evident. Once your students get the hang of it, they'll find it a pleasant and interesting experience.

Appendix D Activities and Experiments

Appendix D: Fluid Physics
Sink or Swim—*Archimedes' Principle*
Eureka!—*Archimedes' Principle*
Boat Float—*Archimedes' Principle*
Tire Pressure and 18-Wheelers—*Force and Pressure*

Sink or Swim [Activity]

In Step 3, we assume your egg is fresh. With a little planning, you can hide an egg in the back of a cupboard so that it is stale for this experiment. The next-time question is, "Can we use this procedure to separate fresh and stale eggs? Which will float? Why?". We could hard boil a few, and ask the same questions.

Although an egg is denser than tap water, it is less dense than salt water, as evidenced by its floating when salt is added to water.

Diet drinks are appreciably less dense then non-diet soft drinks, as can be evidenced by their floating. Whereas a can of Coke sinks in water, a can of Diet Coke floats. Why? Sugared water is appreciably denser than regular water.

Most people are slightly less dense than water, so most people can float in water. Muscular types, however, are often more dense than water and cannot float. Females usually have a layer of body fat beneath the skin that makes them less dense than water. Very few females are denser than water. For salt water, the difference between floating and sinking is crucial for people who are very close to the density of water. Everybody can float in the Dead Sea, with its high salt content.

Interestingly enough, the reason one can float more easily in salt water is because the volume of water that must be displaced to equal one's weight is less. Buoyant force is the same on a floating body regardless of the density of the liquid.

Eureka! [Activity]

One of the goals of Conceptual Physical Science is to help students distinguish between closely related ideas — to nurture critical thinking. The difference between volume and weight is highlighted in this activity. Also highlighted is the concept of displacement, and how it relates to the volume (not the weight) of the submerged object. A distinction between an immersed object and a submerged object can also be made. [You immerse part of your body in the bathtub; you submerge your whole body in a swimming pool when beneath the surface.]

Boat Float [Experiment]

The previous two activities and this experiment are all designed to develop a gut feel for Archimedes' Principle. You may want to combine the various elements by doing part of any one, switching to part of another, and then returning, in any pattern as grasp of the concept becomes apparent.

The questions in this experiment will tax your best students, for clear distinctions of concepts developed in the preceding activities are brought to bear. Critical thinking is central to this experiment.

Much of this material is suitable for off campus supplementation, and students should be encouraged create situations, reporting back to the class. Students often enjoy sharing experiences, and today swimming pools are often available. Interesting things can be done in a bathtub!

Answers to the Questions

1. BF equals the weight of water displaced.

2. BF (also) equals the weight of a floating body.

3, 4, and 5. Same.

6. Mass of clay is greater than mass of water displaced.

7. BF on clay less than weight; which is why it sinks.

8. When floating clay displaces more water.

9, and 10. Same.

11. Same, as evidenced by the same amount of water displaced.

12. Yes, pressure is greater with depth (not buoyant force, unless volume of object is reduced by the greater pressure).

13. Answers differ because they address different (but similar) concepts.

14. Water level goes down as boat rises. Low floating boats carry more cargo than high floating boats.

15. Water level goes down. Why? Because when floating, the cargo displaces its weight of water. When submerged it displaces only its volume of water. Since the cargo is denser than water (as evidenced by its sinking) it displaces less water submerged than floating. [Exaggeration helps: consider an enormously dense pea. It's heavy, and when placed in pie pan that floats in your kitchen sink, it displaces considerable water as the pan is pushed deeper. Now consider the amount of water the pea displaces when tossed overboard — only its size, which is very little. So the pie pan raises a lot, and the water level in the sink goes down.]

16. Same as in 15.

17. Aha! The situation is now different, because either way, the cargo floats. So the water level in the canal lock doesn't change.

18. Sea level rises (imperceptibly).

19. No change, because the rowboat displaces its weight whether on board the big ship or floating independently.

20. Simulate this in a small tub of water!

Tire Pressure and 18-Wheelers [Experiment]

The primary purpose of this experiment is to distinguish between force and pressure. The secondary purpose is understanding the application of this concept to tire pressure as a measure of a car's weight. It can be time consuming, so you may wish to schedule two lab periods for this one. Note that we ignore the role of the tire walls in supporting the load, something that is significant with modern tires.

Answers to the Questions

1. Whereas the weight stated in the owners manual may list 4 significant figures, the uncertainties in this experiment limit it to about 2 significant figures. Students will usually be within 20% of the published value.

2. Contact area goes down proportionally. In any event, for even distribution, the pressure in the tire multiplied by the area of tire contact equals one quarter the car's weight. Quite interesting!

3. Total pressure is gauge pressure plus atmospheric pressure.

4. We didn't add atmospheric pressure to our reading because atmospheric pressure does not contribute to supporting the weight of the car. When you have a flat tire, there is still 14.7 lb/in^2 of pressure *inside* the tire (as well as *outside* the tire). The result is no net force by the atmosphere.

5. The pressure in the tires (assumed the same in each tire) multiplied by the total area of tire contact equals the loaded truck's weight. For large weights, you need either great tire pressures, or more tires to provide more area. Too much tire pressure risks blowouts, so additional tires are employed. Hence the 18 wheels. Neat!